ECONOMETRICS

HARPER & ROW, PUBLISHERS

New York, Evanston, and London

ECONOMETRICS
STATISTICAL FOUNDATIONS
AND APPLICATIONS

PHOEBUS J. DHRYMES

Professor of Economics
University of Pennsylvania

PREFACE

This book was written, primarily, for the graduate student in econometrics. Its purpose is to provide a reasonably complete and rigorous exposition of the techniques frequently employed in econometric research, beyond what one is likely to encounter in an introductory mathematical statistics course. It does not aim at teaching how one can do successful original empirical research. Unfortunately, no one has yet discovered how to communicate this skill impersonally. Practicing econometricians may also find the integrated presentation of simultaneous equations estimation theory and spectral analysis a convenient reference.

I have tried, as far as possible, to begin the discussion of the various topics from an elementary stage so that little prior knowledge of the subject will be necessitated. It is assumed that the potential reader is familiar with the elementary aspects of calculus and linear algebra. Additional mathematical material is to be found in the Appendix.

Statistical competence, approximately at the level of a first-year course in elementary mathematical statistics is also assumed on the part of the reader.

The discussion, then, develops certain elementary aspects of multivariate analysis, the theory of estimation of simultaneous equations systems, elementary aspects of spectral and cross-spectral analysis, and shows how such techniques may be applied, by a number of examples.

It is often said that econometrics deals with the quantification of economic relationships, perhaps as postulated by an abstract model.

As such, it is a blend of economics and statistics, both presupposing a substantial degree of mathematical sophistication. Thus, to practice econometrics compentently, one has to be well-versed in both economic *and* statistical theory. Pursuant to this, I have attempted in all presentations to point out clearly the assumptions underlying the discussion, their role in establishing the conclusions, and hence the consequence of departures from such assumptions. Indeed, this is a most crucial aspect of the student's training and one that is rather frequently neglected. This is unfortunate since competence in econometrics entails, *inter alia*, a very clear perception of the limitations of the conclusions one may obtain from empirical analysis.

A number of specialized results from probability theory that are crucial for establishing, rigorously, the properties of simultaneous equations estimators have been collected in Chapter 3. This is included only as a convenient reference, and its detailed study is not essential in understanding the remainder of the book. It is sufficient that the reader be familiar with the salient results presented in Chapter 3, but it is not essential that he master their proof in detail. I have used various parts of the book, in the form of mimeographed notes, as the basis of discussion for graduate courses in econometrics at Harvard University and, more recently, at the University of Pennsylvania.

The material in Chapters 1 through 6 could easily constitute a one-semester course, and the remainder may be used in the second semester. The instructor who may not wish to delve into spectral analysis quite so extensively may include alternative material, e.g., the theory of forecasting.

Generally, I felt that empirical work is easily accessible in journals and similar publications, and for this reason, the number of empirical examples is small. By now, the instructor has at his disposal a number of publications on econometric models and books of readings in empirical econometric research, from which he can easily draw in illustrating the possible application of various techniques.

I have tried to write this book in a uniform style and notation and preserve maximal continuity of presentation. For this reason explicit references to individual contributions are minimized; on the other hand, the great cleavage between the Dutch and Cowles Foundation notation is bridged so that one can follow the discussion of 2SLS, 3SLS, and maximum likelihood estimation in a unified notational framework. Of course, absence of references from the discussions is not meant to ignore individual contributions, but only to insure the continuity and unity of exposition that one commonly finds in scientific, mathematical, or statistical textbooks.

Original work relevant to the subject covered appears in the references at the end of each chapter; in several instances a brief comment on the work is inserted. This is only meant to give the reader an indication of the coverage and does not pretend to be a review of the contents.

Finally, it is a pleasure for me to acknowledge my debt to a number of individuals who have contributed directly or indirectly in making this book what it is.

I wish to express my gratitude to H. Theil for first introducing me to the rigorous study of econometrics, and to I. Olkin from whose lucid lectures I first learned about multivariate analysis. T. Amemiya, L. R. Klein, J. Kmenta, B. M. Mitchell, and A. Zellner read various parts of the manuscript and offered useful suggestions. V. Pandit and A. Basu are chiefly responsible for compiling the bibliography. Margot Keith and Alix Ryckoff have lightened my burden by their expert typing.

PHOEBUS J. DHRYMES

January, 1970

CONTENTS

39843

ECONOMETRICS

ELEMENTARY
ASPECTS OF
MULTIVARIATE ANALYSIS

1

1.1 PRELIMINARIES

In elementary mathematical statistics, one studies in some detail various characteristics of the distribution of a *scalar* random variable. Thus its density and various parameters are considered and statements are made regarding this variable. For example, given the information above, we can compute the probability that the variable will exceed some value, say α, or that it will assume a value in the interval (α, β) and so on.

Still, in this elementary context the correlation of two variables was introduced and interpreted as a measure of the degree to which the two variables tend to move in the same or opposite direction.

In econometric work, however, it is often necessary to deal with a number of relations simultaneously. Thus we typically have an econometric model containing more than one equation. Such a system may be simultaneously determined in the sense that the interaction of all variables as specified by the model determines simultaneously the behavior of the entire set of (jointly) dependent variables.

Generally, the equations of an econometric model are, except for identities, stochastic ones and hence the problem arises of how to specify the (joint) stochastic character of a number of random variables simultaneously. This leads us to consider the problem of the distribution of vector random variables, that is, the characteristics of the joint distribution of a number of random variables simultaneously and not "one at a time."

When the problem is considered in this context, it is apparent that there are more complexities than in the study of the distribution of scalar random variables. Therefore, if we are dealing with the (joint) distribution of m variables, we might wish to say something about the distribution of a subset of k ($k < m$) variables given the $(m - k)$ remaining ones.

This is a problem that cannot arise in the study of univariate distributions. In the following material we shall study in some detail certain elementary aspects of multivariate distributions, confining ourselves to the special case of the *multivariate normal* distribution.

Let us now set forth the notational framework and conventions for this topic and obtain some simple but useful results.

Definition 1: Let $\{x_{ij} : i = 1, 2, \ldots, m, j = 1, 2, \ldots, n\}$ be a set of random variables. Then the matrix

$$X = (x_{ij}) \tag{1.1.1}$$

is said to be a random matrix and its expectation (mean) is defined by

$$E[X] = [E(x_{ij})] \tag{1.1.2}$$

Consider now any column, say the jth, of (1.1.1). Denote it by $x._j$. It is clear from (1.1.1) and (1.1.2) that the expectation of the *vector* $x._j$ is given by

$$E[x._j] = \begin{pmatrix} E(x_{1j}) \\ E(x_{2j}) \\ \vdots \\ E(x_{mj}) \end{pmatrix} = \mu._j \tag{1.1.3}$$

where

$$\mu._j = (\mu_{1j}, \mu_{2j}, \ldots, \mu_{mj})' \qquad \mu_{ij} = E(x_{ij}) \tag{1.1.4}$$

Definition 2: Let $z = (z_1, z_2, \ldots, z_m)'$ be a random vector; then the covariance matrix of z is defined by

$$E[(z - E(z))(z - E(z))'] = \Sigma \tag{1.1.5}$$

and as a matter of notation we write

$$\text{Cov}(z) = \Sigma \tag{1.1.6}$$

where

$$\Sigma = (\sigma_{ij}) \qquad i = 1, 2, \ldots, m, \qquad j = 1, 2, \ldots, m \tag{1.1.7}$$

Remark 1: By convention, the mean of a random vector is denoted by the lowercase Greek letter μ and its covariance matrix by the capital Greek letter Σ.

This is, of course, not a universal practice; it is, however, used quite widely. Notice, further, that in (1.1.5) $(z - E(z))(z - E(z))'$ is an $m \times m$ random matrix, and thus the meaning of the expectation operator there is given by (1.1.2) of Definition 1.

In general, we shall identify vectors and matrices by their dimensions. Thus the statement "x is $m \times 1$" will mean that x is a column vector with m elements, while "A is $m \times n$" will mean that A is a matrix with m rows and n columns.

A simple consequence of the preceding is

Lemma 1: Let x be $m \times 1$ and random; suppose that

$$E(x) = \mu \qquad \text{Cov}\,(x) = \Sigma \tag{1.1.8}$$

Define

$$y = Ax + b \tag{1.1.9}$$

where A is $m \times m$ nonsingular, b is $m \times 1$, both nonrandom. Then

$$E(y) = A\mu + b \tag{1.1.10}$$

$$\text{Cov}\,(y) = A\Sigma A' \tag{1.1.11}$$

PROOF: By definition, the ith element of y is given by

$$y_i = \sum_{j=1}^{m} a_{ij} x_j + b_i \qquad i = 1, 2, \ldots, m \tag{1.1.12}$$

Hence

$$E(y_i) = \sum_{j=1}^{m} a_{ij} E(x_j) + b_i = \sum_{j=1}^{m} a_{ij}\mu_j + b_i \qquad i = 1, 2, \ldots, m \tag{1.1.13}$$

Since

$$E(y) = \begin{pmatrix} E(y_1) \\ E(y_2) \\ \vdots \\ E(y_m) \end{pmatrix} \tag{1.1.14}$$

we conclude

$$E(y) = A\mu + b \tag{1.1.15}$$

Furthermore, we have

$$\text{Cov}\,(y) = E[(y - E(y))(y - E(y))'] = E[A(x - \mu)(x - \mu)'A'] \tag{1.1.16}$$

The (i, j) element of $(x - \mu)(x - \mu)'$ is given by

$$x_{ij}^* = (x_i - \mu_i)(x_j - \mu_j) \tag{1.1.17}$$

Notice that

$$E(x_{ij}^*) = \sigma_{ij} \tag{1.1.18}$$

The (s, t) element of the matrix whose expectation we are taking in (1.1.16) is

$$\sum_{i=1}^{m} \sum_{r=1}^{m} a_{sr} x_{ri}^* a_{it}'$$

It follows, therefore, that the (s, t) element of the covariance matrix of y is given by

$$E\left[\sum_{i=1}^{m} \sum_{r=1}^{m} a_{sr} x_{ri}^* a_{it}' \right] = \sum_{r=1}^{m} \sum_{i=1}^{m} a_{rs} \sigma_{ri} a_{it}' \tag{1.1.19}$$

From (1.1.19) we conclude

$$\text{Cov}(y) = A\Sigma A' \qquad\qquad \text{Q.E.D.} \tag{1.1.20}$$

Before considering the multivariate normal distribution in some detail, we should point out two useful facts. One, implicit in the preceding, is this: if X is a random matrix and if A, B, C are comformable nonrandom matrices, then

$$E(Y) = AE(X)B + C \tag{1.1.21}$$

where

$$Y = AXB + C \tag{1.1.22}$$

The second is given by

Lemma 2: Let x be $m \times 1$, random; then

$$\Sigma = \text{Cov}(x) \tag{1.1.23}$$

is at least a positive semidefinite, symmetric matrix.

PROOF: The symmetry of Σ is obvious; thus its (i, j) element is

$$\sigma_{ij} = E[(x_i - \mu_i)(x_j - \mu_j)] \tag{1.1.24}$$

while its (j, i) element is

$$\sigma_{ji} = E[(x_j - \mu_j)(x_i - \mu_i)] \tag{1.1.25}$$

It is clear that the right-hand sides of (1.1.24) and (1.1.25) are identical, which establishes symmetry.

To show positive semidefiniteness, let α be $m \times 1$, nonrandom and nonnull but otherwise arbitrary.

We shall establish that

$$\alpha' \Sigma \alpha \geq 0$$

Define the (scalar) random variable

$$y = \alpha' x \tag{1.1.26}$$

From elementary mathematical statistics we know that the variance of y is nonnegative. Thus

$$0 \leq \text{Var}(y) = E[\alpha'(x - \mu)(x - \mu)'\alpha] = \alpha'\Sigma\alpha \qquad \text{Q.E.D.}$$

$$(1.1.27)$$

Remark 2: Notice that if Σ is not strictly positive definite (i.e., if it is a singular matrix), then there will exist a nonnull constant vector, say γ, such that

$$\Sigma\gamma = 0 \qquad (1.1.28)$$

This means that there exists a scalar random variable, say y, which is a linear combination of the elements of x and *whose variance is zero*. The latter fact means that y is a constant. Hence a singular covariance matrix Σ in (1.1.27) implies that the elements of x are *linearly dependent* in the sense that there exists a nonnull set of constants $(\gamma_1, \gamma_2, \gamma_3, \ldots, \gamma_m)$ such that $y = \sum_{i=1}^{m} \gamma_i x_i$ is *nonrandom*.

If this is so, then the distribution of the random vector x is said to be *degenerate*.

If this is not so—that is, if Σ is strictly *positive definite, symmetric*—then the distribution of x is said to be proper. In this textbook we shall only deal with proper distributions; thus the term "proper" will be suppressed everywhere except when the context clearly requires it.

1.2 JOINT, MARGINAL, AND CONDITIONAL DISTRIBUTIONS

In this section we shall define what we mean by the joint distribution of a number of random variables, derive certain features of it, and study its associated marginal and conditional distributions. The following convention, which is often employed in mathematical statistics, will be adhered to.

Convention: We shall denote random variables by capital Roman letters.[1] We shall denote by lowercase letters *the values assumed* by the random variables. Thus $\Pr\{X \leq x\}$ indicates the probability that the random variable X will assume a value equal to or less than (the real number) x.

Definition 3: Let X be $m \times 1$, random; by its joint (cumulative) distribution function we mean a function $F(\cdot, \cdot, \ldots, \cdot)$ such that

i. $0 \leq F \leq 1$.
ii. F is monotonic nondecreasing in all its arguments.
iii. $F(-\infty, -\infty, \ldots, -\infty) = 0 \qquad F(\infty, \infty, \ldots, \infty) = 1$
iv. $\Pr\{X_1 \leq x_1, X_2 \leq x_2, \ldots, X_m \leq x_m\} = F(x_1, x_2, \ldots, x_m)$

---

[1] Recall that a random variable is a *real-valued function* defined on the relevant sample space.

In this textbook we shall always assume that $F(\cdot, \ldots)$ is absolutely continuous so that the derivative

$$\frac{\partial^m F}{\partial x_1 \, \partial x_2 \, \cdots \, \partial x_m}$$

exists almost everywhere.

Therefore we have

Definition 4: Let $F(\cdot, \cdot, \ldots)$ be the joint cumulative distribution function of the $m \times 1$ random variable X. Suppose that F is absolutely continuous; then

$$f(x_1, x_2, \ldots, x_m) = \frac{\partial^m F}{\partial x_1 \, \partial x_2 \, \cdots \, \partial x_m} \tag{1.2.1}$$

is said to be the joint density function of (the elements of) X.

In the following material we shall always assume that the density function exists.

Remark 2: It is clear from (1.2.1) and statement iv of Definition 3 that

$$F(x_1, x_2, \ldots, x_m) = \int_{-\infty}^{x_m} \int_{-\infty}^{x_{m-1}} \cdots \int_{-\infty}^{x_1} f(\xi_1, \xi_2, \ldots, \xi_m) \, d\xi_1 \, d\xi_2, \ldots, d\xi_m \tag{1.2.2}$$

and

$$\Pr \{\alpha_1 \le X_1 \le \beta_1, \alpha_2 \le X_2 \le \beta_2, \ldots, \alpha_m \le X_m \le \beta_m\}$$
$$= \int_{\alpha_m}^{\beta_m} \int_{\alpha_{m-1}}^{\beta_{m-1}} \cdots \int_{\alpha_1}^{\beta_1} f(\xi_1, \ldots, \xi_m) \, d\xi_1 \, d\xi_2, \ldots, d\xi_m \tag{1.2.3}$$

Definition 5: The marginal density of $(X_1, X_2, \ldots, X_k)$, $k < m$, is defined by

$$g(x_1, x_2, \ldots, x_k)$$
$$= \overbrace{\int_{-\infty}^{\infty} \cdots \int_{-\infty}^{\infty}}^{m-k} f(x_1, x_2, \ldots, x_k, \xi_{k+1}, \xi_{k+2}, \ldots, \xi_m) \, d\xi_{k+1} \, d\xi_{k+2}, \ldots, d\xi_m \tag{1.2.4}$$

Remark 3: It is apparent that the marginal (cumulative) distribution function of $(X_1, X_2, \ldots, X_k)$ is given by

$$G(x_1, x_2, \ldots, x_k) = F(x_1, x_2, \ldots, x_k, \overbrace{\infty, \infty, \ldots, \infty}^{m-k}) \tag{1.2.5}$$

Remark 4: It should also be clear that the marginal density of any element of X, say X_1, is given by

$$g_1(x_1) = \int_{-\infty}^{\infty} \cdots \int_{-\infty}^{\infty} f(x_1, \xi_2, \ldots, \xi_m) \, d\xi_2, \ldots, d\xi_m \qquad (1.2.6)$$

and is simply the density function of X_1 as studied in elementary mathematical statistics courses.

The marginal density of a subset of the elements of X simply characterizes their probability structure after the effects of all other variables have been allowed for ("averaged out" or "integrated out"). In particular, notice that the marginal density of $X_1, X_2, \ldots, X_k$ *does not depend* on $X_{k+1}, X_{k+2}, \ldots, X_m$.

In contradistinction to this, we have another associated density, namely, the conditional one.

Recall from elementary probability that if A and B are two events, then the conditional probability of A given B, denoted by $P(A \mid B)$, is defined as

$$P(A \mid B) = \frac{P(A \cap B)}{P(B)} \qquad (1.2.7)$$

In the multivariate context, it is often useful to ask: What is the probability structure of one group of variables given another. Thus we are led to

Definition 6: The conditional density of $(X_1, X_2, \ldots, X_k)$ given $(X_{k+1}, X_{k+2}, \ldots, X_m)$ is defined by

$$f(x^1 \mid x^2) = \frac{f(x)}{g(x^2)} \qquad (1.2.8)$$

where

$$X^1 = (X_1, X_2, \ldots, X_k)' \qquad X^2 = (X_{k+1}, X_{k+2}, \ldots, X_m)' \qquad (1.2.9)$$

$g(\cdot)$ is the marginal density of X^2 and $f(\cdot)$ is the density of $X = \begin{pmatrix} X^1 \\ X^2 \end{pmatrix}$.

Remark 5: As the notation in (1.2.8) makes clear, the conditional density of X^1 given X^2 *does depend on* X^2.

Whereas in the case of the marginal density of X^1 the effects of the variables in X^2 were "averaged" or "integrated" out, in the case of the conditional density of X^1 the effects of the variables in X^2 are allowed for explicitly by "holding them constant." The meaning of this distinction will become clearer when we study the multivariate normal distribution.

Moments are defined with respect to the densities above in the usual way. Thus let $h(\cdot)$ be a function of the random variable X. The expectation of $h(X)$ is defined by

$$E[h(X)] = \int h(x)f(x) \, dx \qquad (1.2.10)$$

where the integral sign indicates the m-fold integral with respect to $x_1, x_2, \ldots, x_m$.

If it is specified that $h(\cdot)$ depends only on X^1, then we can define two expectations for $h(X^1)$, one marginal and one conditional.

The marginal expectation of $h(X^1)$ is defined by

$$E[h(X^1)] = \int h(x_1, x_2, \ldots, x_k) f(x)\, dx = \int h(x^1) g(x^1)\, dx^1 \qquad (1.2.11)$$

The conditional expectation of X^1 given X^2 is defined by

$$E[h(X^1) \mid X^2] = \int h(x^1) f(x^1 \mid x^2)\, dx^1 \qquad (1.2.12)$$

Notice that in (1.2.11) we expect with respect to the marginal density of X^1, while in (1.2.12) we expect with respect to the conditional density of X^1 given X^2.

Example 1: Suppose that we wish to obtain the mean of one of the elements of X, say X_1. In this case, take the function $h(\cdot)$ as

$$h(X) = X_1 \qquad (1.2.13)$$

The marginal[2] mean of X_1 is thus given by

$$E(X_1) = \int x_1 f(x)\, dx = \mu_1 \qquad (1.2.14)$$

The conditional mean of X_1 is given by

$$E(X_1 \mid X_2, \ldots, X_m) = \int x_1 f(x_1 \mid x_2, \ldots, x_m)\, dx_1 = \mu_{1 \cdot 2 \ldots, m} \qquad (1.2.15)$$

The notation $\mu_{1 \cdot 2, 3, \ldots, m}$ is a very informative one; the number appearing to the left of the dot indicates the random variable being expected, while the numbers appearing to the right of the dot indicate the conditioning variables. Thus $\mu_{2 \cdot 1, 3, 4, \ldots, m}$ indicates the conditional mean of X_2 given X_1, X_3, $X_4, \ldots, X_m$. Of course, we can define quantities such as $\mu_{1 \cdot 5, 6, 7, \ldots, m}$ which would indicate the conditional mean of X_1 given $X_5, X_6, \ldots, X_m$. What we mean by this is the following: Obtain the marginal density of X_1, X_5, $X_6, \ldots, X_m$ by "integrating out" X_2, X_3, and X_4. Then, in terms of this density, determine the conditional density of X_1 given $X_5, X_6, \ldots, X_m$ as

$$f(x_1 \mid x_5, \ldots, x_m) = \frac{f(x_1, x_5, x_6, \ldots, x_m)}{g(x_5, x_6, \ldots, x_m)} \qquad (1.2.16)$$

where the numerator is the joint (marginal) density of $X_1, X_5, X_6, \ldots, X_m$ and the denominator is the joint (marginal) density of $X_5, X_6, \ldots, X_m$.

Finally, expect X_1 with respect to $f(x_1 \mid x_5, \ldots, x_m)$.

---

[2] The term "marginal" is usually omitted; one speaks only of the mean of X_1.

Example 2: Suppose that $h(\cdot)$ is such that is depends only on two variables. Thus, say,

$$h(X) = (X_1 - \mu_1)(X_2 - \mu_2) \tag{1.2.17}$$

The marginal[3] expectation of $h(X)$ is given by

$$E[h(X)] = \int (x_1 - \mu_1)(x_2 - \mu_2) f(x)\, dx = \sigma_{12} \tag{1.2.18}$$

The expectation here simply yields the covariance between the first and second elements of X.

As before, we can again define the conditional covariance between X_1 and X_2 given $X_3, X_4, \ldots, X_m$. Hence we have

$$E[(X_1 - \mu_1)(X_2 - \mu_2)\,|\,X_3, \ldots, X_m]$$
$$= \int (x_1 - \mu_1)(x_2 - \mu_2) f(x_1, x_2\,|\,x_3, \ldots, x_m)\, dx_1\, dx_2$$
$$= \sigma_{12 \cdot 3, 4, \ldots, m} \tag{1.2.19}$$

where again the numbers to the left of the dot indicate the variables whose covariance is obtained, while the numbers to the right indicate the conditioning variables.

We leave it to the reader to compute a number of different conditional variances and covariances.

The preceding discussion should be sufficient to render the meaning of the notation, say $\sigma_{55 \cdot 1, 7, 12, 13, \ldots, m}$ or $\sigma_{77 \cdot 1, 2, 19, 20, 21, \ldots, m}$, quite obvious.

Finally, let us conclude with

Definition 7: Let X be $m \times 1$ and random; then its elements are said to be mutually (statistically) independent if and only if their (joint) density can be expressed as the product of the marginal densities of the individual elements.

Remark 6: Suppose X is partitioned by X^1 and X^2 as above; then X^1 and X^2 are said to be mutually independent if and only if the joint density of X can be expressed as the product of the marginal densities of X^1 and X^2.

We shall now abandon the convention whereby random variables and the values assumed by them are distinguished by the use of capital and lowercase letters respectively. Henceforth no such distinction will be made. The meaning will usually be clear from the context.

1.3 A MATHEMATICAL DIGRESSION

Let E^n be the n-dimensional Euclidean space and let

$$h : E^n \to E^n$$

---

[3] Again the term "marginal" is suppressed; we simply speak of variances and covariances.

be a transformation of E^n into itself. Thus

$$y = h(x) \qquad x, y \in E^n \tag{1.3.1}$$

where the ith element of y is the function

$$y_i = h_i(x_1, x_2, \ldots, x_n), \qquad i = 1, 2, \ldots, n \tag{1.3.2}$$

and x and y are not necessarily random.

Suppose that the inverse transformation also exists; that is, suppose there exists a function $g(\cdot)$ such that

$$g[h(x)] = x \quad \text{or} \quad x = g(y) \tag{1.3.3}$$

Definition 8: The Jacobian of the transformation in (1.3.1), denoted by $J(x \to y)$ or simply J, is defined by

$$J(x \to y) = \left| \frac{\partial x_i}{\partial y_j} \right| \qquad i, j = 1, 2, \ldots, n \tag{1.3.4}$$

Here the determinant, written out explicitly, is

$$\left| \frac{\partial x_i}{\partial y_j} \right| = \begin{vmatrix} \dfrac{\partial x_1}{\partial y_1} & \dfrac{\partial x_1}{\partial y_2} & \cdots & \dfrac{\partial x_1}{\partial y_n} \\[2mm] \dfrac{\partial x_2}{\partial y_1} & \dfrac{\partial x_2}{\partial y_2} & \cdots & \dfrac{\partial x_2}{\partial y_n} \\[2mm] \vdots & \vdots & & \vdots \\[2mm] \dfrac{\partial x_n}{\partial y_1} & \dfrac{\partial x_n}{\partial y_2} & \cdots & \dfrac{\partial x_n}{\partial y_n} \end{vmatrix} \tag{1.3.5}$$

and thus it is expressed solely in terms of the y_i, $i = 1, 2, \ldots, n$.

Suppose now that x is random, having density $f(\cdot)$, and consider the problem of determining the density of y in terms of $f(\cdot)$ and the transformation in (1.3.1). To this effect, we prove:

Lemma 3: Let x be an $m \times 1$ random variable having the density $f(\cdot)$. Define

$$y = h(x) \tag{1.3.6}$$

such that the inverse transformation

$$x = g(y) \tag{1.3.7}$$

exists; thus, by (1.3.6), to each x corresponds a unique y and by (1.3.7) to each y corresponds a unique x.

Moreover, suppose that $h(\cdot)$ and $g(\cdot)$ are differentiable. Then the density, $\phi(\cdot)$, of y is given by

$$\phi(y) = f[g(y)] \, |J| \qquad (1.3.8)$$

where $|J|$ is the absolute value of the Jacobian of the transformation.[4]

PROOF: The cumulative distribution of x is given by

$$F(x) = \int_{-\infty}^{x_m} \cdots \int_{-\infty}^{x_1} f(\xi_1, \xi_2, \ldots, \xi_m) \, d\xi_1, \ldots, d\xi_m$$
$$= \int_A f(\xi) \, d\xi \qquad (1.3.9)$$

Notice that $F(x)$ in (1.3.9) gives the probability assigned by $f(\cdot)$ to the set

$$A = \{(-\infty, x_1) \times (-\infty, x_2) \times (-\infty, x_3), \ldots, \times (-\infty, x_n)\} \qquad (1.3.10)$$

which is the Cartesian product of the intervals $(-\infty, x_i)$ $i = 1, 2, \ldots, m$. This accounts for the notation employed in the last member of (1.3.9). Now, if in (1.3.9) we make the transformation

$$\zeta = h(\xi) \qquad (1.3.11)$$

we may, by the assumption in (1.3.7), solve it to obtain

$$\xi = g(\zeta) \qquad (1.3.12)$$

and hence the Jacobian $J(\xi \to \zeta)$. Thus (1.3.9) may now be written as[5]

$$F[g(y)] = \int_B f[g(\zeta)] \, |J(\xi \to \zeta)| \, d\zeta \qquad (1.3.13)$$

where B is the transform of A under h.

The integral in (1.3.13) gives the probability assigned to the set B by the function $f[g(\cdot)]|J|$. Moreover, the set B is of the form

$$B = \{(g_1(-\infty), g_1(y)) \times (g_2(-\infty), g_2(y)) \times \cdots \times (g_m(-\infty), g_m(y))\} \qquad (1.3.14)$$

and corresponds to the "joint event"

$$Y_1 \in B \qquad Y_2 \in B \cdots Y_m \in B$$

---

[4] We must add, of course, the restriction that J does not vanish on every (nondegenerate) subset of E^m. We should also note that in standard mathematical terminology J is the *inverse* of the Jacobian of (1.3.6). In the statistical literature, it is referred to as the Jacobian of (1.3.6). We shall adhere to this latter usage because it is more convenient for our purposes.

[5] The validity of this representation follows from the theorems dealing with change of variables in multiple integrals. See, for example, R. C. Buck, *Advanced Calculus*, p. 242, New York, McGraw-Hill, 1956.

where Y_i indicates the random variable and y_i the values assumed by it. Since the integrand of (1.3.13) is nonnegative and its integral over the entire space is unity, we conclude that

$$\phi(y) = f[g(y)]|J(x \to y)| \tag{1.3.15}$$

is the joint density of the elements of y.   Q.E.D.

1.4   THE MULTIVARIATE NORMAL DISTRIBUTION

It is assumed that the reader is familiar with the univariate normal distribution. This being the case, perhaps the simplest way of introducing the multivariate normal distribution is as follows.

Let $x_i : i = 1, 2, \ldots, m$ be random variables identically and independently distributed as $N(0, 1)$; that is, they are each normal with mean zero and unit variance. Since they are independent, the density of the vector $x = (x_1, x_2, \ldots, x_m)'$ is given by

$$f(x) = (2\pi)^{-m/2} \exp\left(-\tfrac{1}{2}x'x\right) \tag{1.4.1}$$

Consider now the transformation

$$y = Ax + b \tag{1.4.2}$$

where A is an $m \times m$ nonsingular matrix of constants and b is $m \times 1$ and nonrandom.

The Jacobian of the transformation is simply

$$J(x \to y) = |A|^{-1} \tag{1.4.3}$$

It follows, therefore, by Lemma 3 that the joint density of the elements of y is given by

$$\begin{aligned}
\phi(y) &= f[A^{-1}(y-b)]|J| \\
&= (2\pi)^{-m/2}|A|^{-1} \exp\left[-\tfrac{1}{2}(y-b)'A'^{-1}A^{-1}(y-b)\right]
\end{aligned} \tag{1.4.4}$$

For notational simplicity, we have assumed in (1.4.4) that $|A| > 0$. We know that

$$E(x) = 0 \qquad \text{Cov}(x) = I \tag{1.4.5}$$

and thus, from Lemma 1, we conclude that

$$E(y) = b \qquad \text{Cov}(y) = AA' \tag{1.4.6}$$

To conform to standard usage, put as a matter of notation

$$\mu = b \qquad \Sigma = AA' \tag{1.4.7}$$

and rewrite (1.4.4) in standard form as

$$\phi(y) = (2\pi)^{-m/2}|\Sigma|^{-\frac{1}{2}} \exp\left[-\tfrac{1}{2}(y-\mu)'\Sigma^{-1}(y-\mu)\right] \tag{1.4.8}$$

Thus we define the multivariate normal by (1.4.8). More formally,

Definition 9: Let y be $m \times 1$ random; then y is said to have the multivariate normal distribution with mean μ and covariance matrix Σ, denoted by

$$y \sim N(\mu, \Sigma)$$

if and only if the joint density of its elements is given by (1.4.8).

Before establishing certain properties of the normal distribution, let us introduce

Definition 10: *The characteristic function of a random variable x is given by*

$$\psi(t) = E[\exp(it'x)] \tag{1.4.9}$$

where i has the property $i^2 = -1$ and t is a vector of arbitrary real constants.

Remark 7: The usefulness of the characteristic function is that it is always defined for random variables possessing densities; moreover, there is one-to-one correspondence between characteristic and density functions. Thus if $f(\cdot)$ is the density of x, then explicitly we have

$$\psi(t) = \int \exp(it'x)f(x)\,dx \tag{1.4.10}$$

which is merely the Fourier transform of $f(\cdot)$.

Hence if we know the characteristic function of a random variable, we can, in principle, determine its density function by inverting (1.4.10). We have inserted "in principle" advisedly, for it is not always simple or possible to determine $f(\cdot)$ from $\psi(\cdot)$ explicitly.

Finally, note that

$$\frac{1}{i}\frac{\partial \psi}{\partial t_j} = \int x_j \exp(it'x)f(x)\,dx \tag{1.4.11}$$

and thus

$$\frac{1}{i}\frac{\partial \psi}{\partial t_j}\bigg|_{t=0} = \mu_j \qquad j = 1, 2, \ldots, m \tag{1.4.12}$$

In general,

$$\frac{1}{i^k}\frac{\partial^{(k)}\psi}{\partial t_j^k}\bigg|_{t=0} \qquad \frac{1}{i^2}\frac{\partial^2 \psi}{\partial t_j\,\partial t_s}\bigg|_{t=0}$$

denote, respectively, the kth moment of x_j and the cross moment of x_j and x_s, while

$$\frac{1}{i^k} \frac{\partial^{(k)}\psi}{\partial t_{j_1} \partial t_{j_2} \cdots \partial t_{j_k}}\bigg|_{t=0}$$

yields the cross moment of the variables $x_{j_1}, x_{j_2}, \ldots, x_{j_k}$.

We first establish

Lemma 4: The characteristic function of $x \sim N(\mu, \Sigma)$ is given by

$$\psi(t) = \exp(it'\mu - \tfrac{1}{2}t'\Sigma t) \tag{1.4.13}$$

PROOF: Let $y_1, y_2, y_3, \ldots, y_m$ be independently distributed as $N(0, 1)$. It can be shown that the characteristic function of y_j is given by

$$\psi_{y_j}(r_j) = \exp(-\tfrac{1}{2}r_j^2) \tag{1.4.14}$$

Since the $y_j, j = 1, 2, \ldots, m$, are mutually independent, their joint characteristic function is simply

$$\psi_y(r) = \exp(-\tfrac{1}{2}r'r) \tag{1.4.15}$$

where $r = (r_1, r_2, \ldots, r_m)'$.

Now define

$$x = Ay + \mu \tag{1.4.16}$$

where

$$AA' = \Sigma \tag{1.4.17}$$

Then x has what we have termed the multivariate normal distribution with mean μ and covariance matrix Σ.

Using (1.4.16) and (1.4.17), we have

$$\begin{aligned} \exp(-\tfrac{1}{2}r'r) = E[\exp(ir'y)] &= E\{\exp[ir'A^{-1}(x-\mu)]\} \\ &= E[\exp(ir'A^{-1}x) \cdot \exp(-ir'A^{-1}\mu) \end{aligned} \tag{1.4.18}$$

Put

$$t = A'^{-1}r \tag{1.4.19}$$

Since r is an arbitrary vector of constants, then so is t. Substituting (1.4.19) in (1.4.18) and rearranging terms, we obtain, as a result of (1.4.17),

$$\exp(it'\mu - \tfrac{1}{2}t'\Sigma t) = E[\exp(it'x)] = \psi_x(t) \qquad\qquad \text{Q.E.D.} \tag{1.4.20}$$

Remark 8: Notice that the characteristic function of the multivariate normal is an exponential containing a linear and a quadratic term in t, the parameter defining the characteristic function. The coefficients in the linear terms are simply the elements of the mean vector μ, while the matrix of the quadratic form in (1.4.20) is the covariance matrix of the distribution. We next prove some of the fundamental properties of the normal distribution.

Lemma 5: Let $x \sim N(\mu, \Sigma)$ and write

$$y = Bx + b \tag{1.4.21}$$

where B is $m \times m$, b is $m \times 1$, the elements of both being (nonrandom) constants. Then

$$y \sim N(B\mu + b, B\Sigma B') \tag{1.4.22}$$

PROOF: The characteristic function of y is, by definition,

$$\psi_y(t) = E[\exp(it'y)] \tag{1.4.23}$$

Let

$$s = B't \tag{1.4.24}$$

and, using (1.4.21), note that

$$E[\exp(it'y)] = E[\exp(it'Bx)] \exp(it'b) = E[\exp(is'x)] \exp(it'b)$$
$$= \exp(is'\mu - \tfrac{1}{2}s'\Sigma s + it'b) = \exp[it'(B\mu + b) - \tfrac{1}{2}t'B\Sigma B't]$$
$$\tag{1.4.25}$$

The last member here is the characteristic function of y. Therefore we conclude that $y \sim N(B\mu + b, B\Sigma B')$.   Q.E.D.

Lemma 6: Let $x \sim N(\mu, \Sigma)$ and partition x by

$$x = \begin{pmatrix} x^1 \\ x^2 \end{pmatrix} \tag{1.4.26}$$

so that x^1 and x^2 have, respectively, k and $m - k$ elements. Partition μ and Σ conformally so that

$$\mu = \begin{pmatrix} \mu^1 \\ \mu^2 \end{pmatrix} \qquad \Sigma = \begin{bmatrix} \Sigma_{11} & \Sigma_{12} \\ \Sigma_{21} & \Sigma_{22} \end{bmatrix} \tag{1.4.27}$$

Then the marginal distribution of x^1 is given by

$$x^1 \sim N(\mu^1, \Sigma_{11}) \tag{1.4.28}$$

PROOF: Since Σ is a positive definite, symmetric matrix, there exists a (nonsingular) lower triangular matrix T such that

$$\Sigma = TT' \tag{1.4.29}$$

Partition T conformally with Σ so that

$$T = \begin{bmatrix} T_1 & 0 \\ T_3 & T_2 \end{bmatrix} \tag{1.4.30}$$

where T_1, T_2 are both lower triangular. Define

$$y = T^{-1}(x - \mu) \tag{1.4.31}$$

By Lemma 4, $y \sim N(0, I_m)$, where I_m is the identity matrix of order m. Thus the $y_j : j = 1, 2, \ldots, m$ are mutually independent and each is distributed as $N(0, 1)$. It follows, therefore, that $y^1 \sim N(0, I_k)$. By (1.4.31) we have

$$x^1 = T_1 y^1 + \mu^1 \tag{1.4.32}$$

Again, by Lemma 4, we conclude

$$x^1 \sim N(\mu^1, T_1 T_1') \tag{1.4.33}$$

However,

$$T_1 T_1' = \Sigma_{11} \tag{1.4.34}$$

and we obtain

$$x^1 \sim N(\mu^1, \Sigma_{11}) \hfill \text{Q.E.D.}$$

Corollary: The marginal density of the ith element of x is normal with mean μ_i and variance σ_{ii}.

PROOF: In the proof of Lemma 5, take

$$x_i = x^{*1} \tag{1.4.35}$$

by rearranging the elements of x, μ, and Σ so that the first element of x^* is x_i, the first element of μ^* is μ_i, and the $(1, 1)$ element of Σ^* is σ_{ii}, where x^*, μ^*, and Σ^* represent the vectors and matrix after rearrangement. The conclusion of the corollary follows immediately, for

$$x^{*1} = x_i \quad \mu_i = \mu^{*1} \quad \sigma_{ii} = \Sigma_{11}^* \tag{1.4.36}$$

Lemma 7: Let $x \sim N(\mu, \Sigma)$ and partition x, μ, and Σ as in Lemma 6. Then the conditional distribution of x^1 given x^2 is

$$x^1 \mid x^2 \sim N[\mu^1 + \Sigma_{12} \Sigma_{22}^{-1}(x^2 - \mu^2) \quad \Sigma_{11} - \Sigma_{12} \Sigma_{22}^{-1} \Sigma_{21}] \tag{1.4.37}$$

PROOF: By Lemma 6, $x^2 \sim N(\mu^2, \Sigma_{22})$. By definition, the conditional density of x^1 given x^2 is the quotient of the joint density of x^1 and x^2 to the marginal density of x^2. Thus

$$h(x^1 \mid x^2) = \frac{(2\pi)^{-m/2} |\Sigma|^{-\frac{1}{2}} \exp\left[-\frac{1}{2}(x - \mu)'\Sigma^{-1}(x - \mu)\right]}{(2\pi)^{(m-k)/2} |\Sigma_{22}|^{-\frac{1}{2}} \exp\left[-\frac{1}{2}(x^2 - \mu^2)'\Sigma_{22}^{-1}(x^2 - \mu^2)\right]} \tag{1.4.38}$$

Put

$$V = \Sigma^{-1} \qquad (1.4.39)$$

and partition V conformally with Σ. Thus

$$V = \begin{bmatrix} V_{11} & V_{12} \\ V_{21} & V_{22} \end{bmatrix} \qquad (1.4.40)$$

Then notice[6]

$$|\Sigma| = |\Sigma_{22}|\,|\Sigma_{11} - \Sigma_{12}\Sigma_{22}^{-1}\Sigma_{21}| \qquad (1.4.41)$$

and

$$\Sigma_{22}^{-1} = V_{22} - V_{21}V_{11}^{-1}V_{12} \qquad (1.4.42)$$

Rearranging and developing the exponential in the right-hand member of (1.4.38), we find, in view of (1.4.40) and (1.4.42),

$$\begin{aligned}
-\tfrac{1}{2}\{&(x^1 - \mu^1)'V_{11}(x^1 - \mu^1) + 2(x^1 - \mu^1)'V_{12}(x^2 - \mu^2) \\
&+ (x^2 - \mu^2)'V_{22}(x^2 - \mu^2) - (x^2 - \mu^2)'(V_{22} - V_{21}V_{11}^{-1}V_{12})(x^2 - \mu^2) \\
&= -\tfrac{1}{2}\{[x^1 - (\mu^1 - V_{11}^{-1}V_{12}(x^2 - \mu^2)]'V_{11}[x^1 - (\mu^1 - V_{11}^{-1}V_{12}(x^2 - \mu^2)]\}
\end{aligned}$$

$$(1.4.43)$$

The determinental expressions in (1.4.38) yield, in view of (1.4.41),

$$|\Sigma_{22}|^{\frac{1}{2}}\,|\Sigma|^{-\frac{1}{2}} = |\Sigma_{11} - \Sigma_{12}\Sigma_{22}^{-1}\Sigma_{21}|^{-\frac{1}{2}} \qquad (1.4.44)$$

Moreover,[7]

$$V_{11} = (\Sigma_{11} - \Sigma_{12}\Sigma_{22}^{-1}\Sigma_{21})^{-1} \qquad V_{11}^{-1}V_{12} = -\Sigma_{12}\Sigma_{22}^{-1} \qquad (1.4.45)$$

Hence (1.4.38) may be rewritten

$$\begin{aligned}
h(x^1 \mid x^2) = (2\pi)^{-k/2}\,|V_{11}|^{-\frac{1}{2}}\,&\exp\{-\tfrac{1}{2}[x^1 - (\mu^1 + \Sigma_{12}\Sigma_{22}^{-1}(x^2 - \mu^2))]' \\
&\cdot V_{11}^{-1}[x^1 - (\mu^1 + \Sigma_{12}\Sigma_{22}^{-1}(x^2 - \mu^2))]\}
\end{aligned}$$

$$\text{Q.E.D.}$$
$$(1.4.46)$$

---

[6] This is easily established as follows. Let

$$(*) \qquad D = \begin{bmatrix} I & -\Sigma_{12}\Sigma_{22}^{-1} \\ 0 & I \end{bmatrix}$$

Then

$$(**) \qquad D\Sigma = \begin{bmatrix} \Sigma_{11} - \Sigma_{12}\Sigma_{22}^{-1}\Sigma_{21} & 0 \\ \Sigma_{21} & \Sigma_{22} \end{bmatrix}$$

Since $|D| = 1$, the result in (1.4.41) follows immediately from (**).

[7] The relations in (1.4.42) and (1.4.45) result from

$$(*) \quad \begin{bmatrix} \Sigma_{11} & \Sigma_{12} \\ \Sigma_{21} & \Sigma_{22} \end{bmatrix}^{-1} = \begin{bmatrix} (\Sigma_{11} - \Sigma_{12}\Sigma_{22}^{-1}\Sigma_{21})^{-1} & -\Sigma_{11}^{-1}\Sigma_{12}(\Sigma_{22} - \Sigma_{21}\Sigma_{11}^{-1}\Sigma_{12})^{-1} \\ -\Sigma_{22}^{-1}\Sigma_{21}(\Sigma_{11} - \Sigma_{12}\Sigma_{22}^{-1}\Sigma_{21})^{-1} & (\Sigma_{22} - \Sigma_{21}\Sigma_{11}^{-1}\Sigma_{12})^{-1} \end{bmatrix}$$

which can be verified directly and their verification is thus left as an exercise for the reader.

Remark 9: One important aspect of the preceding result is that the conditional mean of x^1 given x^2 is a *linear function* of x^2, while the covariance matrix of its conditional distribution is *independent of* x^2.

Finally, it would be desirable to have a simple test as to whether two sets of normal variables are mutually independent. Thus

Lemma 8: Let $x \sim N(\mu, \Sigma)$ and let x, μ, and Σ be partitioned as in Lemma 6.

Then x^1 and x^2 are mutually independent if and only if

$$\Sigma_{12} = 0 \tag{1.4.47}$$

PROOF: First note that since Σ is symmetric,

$$\Sigma'_{12} = \Sigma_{21} \tag{1.4.48}$$

so that the condition in (1.4.47) is equivalent to

$$\Sigma_{21} = 0 \tag{1.4.49}$$

Sufficiency:

Suppose that $\Sigma_{12} = 0$; then $\Sigma_{21} = 0$ as well and hence

$$\Sigma = \begin{bmatrix} \Sigma_{11} & 0 \\ 0 & \Sigma_{22} \end{bmatrix} \qquad |\Sigma| = |\Sigma_{11}| |\Sigma_{22}| \qquad \Sigma^{-1} = \begin{bmatrix} \Sigma_{11}^{-1} & 0 \\ 0 & \Sigma_{22}^{-1} \end{bmatrix} \tag{1.4.50}$$

Moreover,

$$(x - \mu)'\Sigma^{-1}(x - \mu) = (x^1 - \mu^1)'\Sigma_{11}^{-1}(x^1 - \mu^1) + (x^2 - \mu^2)'\Sigma_{22}^{-1}(x^2 - \mu^2) \tag{1.4.51}$$

Consequently, the joint density of the elements of x is

$$f(x) = (2\pi)^{-k/2} |\Sigma_{11}|^{-\frac{1}{2}} \exp\left[-\tfrac{1}{2}(x^1 - \mu^1)'\Sigma_{11}^{-1}(x^1 - \mu^1)\right]$$
$$\cdot (2\pi)^{-(m-k)/2} |\Sigma_{22}|^{-\frac{1}{2}} \exp\left[-\tfrac{1}{2}(x^2 - \mu^2)'\Sigma_{22}^{-1}(x^2 - \mu^2)\right] \tag{1.4.52}$$

and so by Definition 6 (and Remark 7) x^1 and x^2 are mutually independent.

Necessity:

Suppose that x^1 and x^2 are mutually independent and distributed, respectively, as $x^1 \sim N(\mu^1, \Sigma_{11})$, $x^2 \sim N(\mu^2, \Sigma_{22})$. Let x_i be an element of x^1 and x_j an element of x^2. Then

$$\sigma_{ij} = \text{Cov}(x_i, x_j) = E(x_i - \mu_i)(x_j - \mu_j)$$
$$= E(x_i - \mu_i)E(x_j - \mu_j) = 0 \tag{1.4.53}$$

Since the product of two (independent) normal densities is also normal, it follows that $x = \begin{pmatrix} x^1 \\ x^2 \end{pmatrix}$ has the multivariate normal distribution with mean $\mu = \begin{pmatrix} \mu^1 \\ \mu^2 \end{pmatrix}$ and covariance matrix

$$E\begin{pmatrix} x^1 - \mu^1 \\ x^2 - \mu^2 \end{pmatrix}\begin{pmatrix} x^1 - \mu^1 \\ x^2 - \mu^2 \end{pmatrix}' = \begin{pmatrix} \Sigma_{11} & \Sigma_{12} \\ \Sigma_{21} & \Sigma_{22} \end{pmatrix} = \Sigma \tag{1.4.54}$$

It follows by (1.4.53) that

$$\Sigma_{12} = 0 \hspace{4cm} \text{Q.E.D.}$$
$$(1.4.55)$$

These fundamental properties of the normal distribution are summarized in

Theorem 1: Let $x \sim N(\mu, \Sigma)$ and partition x by $x = \begin{pmatrix} x^1 \\ x^2 \end{pmatrix}$ such that x^1 has k elements and x^2 $(m - k)$ elements. Partition μ and Σ conformally. Then the following statements are true

i. The characteristic function of x is given by

$$\psi(t) = \exp\left(it'\mu - \tfrac{1}{2} t'\Sigma t\right)$$

ii. If

$$y = Bx + b$$

where B is an $m \times m$ nonsingular matrix, then

$$y \sim N(B\mu + b, B\Sigma B')$$

iii. The marginal distribution of x^1 is given by

$$x^1 \sim N(\mu^1, \Sigma_{11})$$

iv. The conditional distribution of x^1 given x^2 is

$$x^1 \mid x^2 \sim N[\mu^1 + \Sigma_{12}\Sigma_{22}^{-1}(x^2 - \mu^2), \Sigma_{11} - \Sigma_{12}\Sigma_{22}^{-1}\Sigma_{21}]$$

v. The subvectors x^1 and x^2 are mutually independent if and only if

$$\Sigma_{12} = 0$$

PROOF: See Lemmas 4, 5, 6, 7, and 8.

Before we leave this topic, let us establish a remarkable fact about the normal distribution.

Proposition 1: Let x be a random vector such that

$$E(x) = \mu \hspace{1cm} \text{Cov}(x) = \Sigma \hspace{3cm} (1.4.56)$$

If every (nontrivial) linear combination of the elements of x is normally distributed, then

$$x \sim N(\mu, \Sigma) \hspace{5cm} (1.4.57)$$

PROOF: Let α be an arbitrary vector of constants and define

$$y = \alpha'x \hspace{5cm} (1.4.58)$$

Then y is a scalar random variable and, by the hypothesis of the proposition, is normally distributed, say with mean v and variance σ^2. Its characteristic function is thus

$$E[\exp(isy)] = \exp(isv - \tfrac{1}{2}s^2\sigma^2) \tag{1.4.59}$$

where s is an arbitrary (real) scalar. But

$$E(y) = \alpha'\mu \qquad \text{Var}(y) = \alpha'\Sigma\alpha \tag{1.4.60}$$

Putting

$$t = s\alpha \tag{1.4.61}$$

and using (1.4.58) and (1.4.59), we conclude

$$E[\exp(it'x)] = \exp(it'\mu - \tfrac{1}{2}t'\Sigma t) \tag{1.4.62}$$

which shows that $x \sim N(\mu, \Sigma)$.   Q.E.D.

1.5 CORRELATION COEFFICIENTS AND RELATED TOPICS

In this section we shall give the definition of several types of correlation coefficients and show the similarity between some aspects of a conditional normal density and the general linear model

$$y = X\beta + u \tag{1.5.1}$$

where y is $T \times 1$, X is $T \times n$ and they refer, respectively, to the observations on the dependent and explanatory variables. The vector β consists of the unknown parameters to be estimated and u is the $T \times 1$ vector of disturbances, which is typically assumed to have mean zero and covariance matrix $\sigma^2 I$.

Definition 11: Let $x \sim N(\mu, \Sigma)$; then the (simple) correlation coefficient between two elements of x, say x_i and x_j, is defined by

$$\rho_{ij} = \frac{\sigma_{ij}}{\sqrt{\sigma_{ii}\sigma_{jj}}} \tag{1.5.2}$$

Thus it is the correlation coefficient in the (marginal) joint density of x_i and x_j.[8]

Definition 12: Let $x \sim N(\mu, \Sigma)$ and partition x by x^1 and x^2 so that x^1 has k and x^2 $(m-k)$ elements. If x_i, x_j are any two elements of x^1, then their partial correlation coefficient (for fixed $x_{k+1}, x_{k+2}, \ldots, x_m$) is defined by

$$\rho_{ij \cdot k+1, k+2, \ldots, m} = \frac{\sigma_{ij \cdot k+1, k+2, \ldots, m}}{\sqrt{\sigma_{ii \cdot k+1, k+2, \ldots, m}}\sqrt{\sigma_{jj \cdot k+1, k+2, \ldots, m}}} \tag{1.5.3}$$

---

[8] Although Definitions 11, 12, and 13 are all stated in terms of the normal distribution, they are valid for any multivariate distribution.

where $\sigma_{ij \cdot k+1, k+2, \ldots, m}$ is the (i, j) element of the covariance matrix in the conditional density of x^1 given x^2. In the present case (normal distribution), this matrix is $\Sigma_{11} - \Sigma_{12}\Sigma_{22}^{-1}\Sigma_{21}$.

Hence partial correlation coefficients are simply correlation coefficients computed with respect to the (conditional) joint density of the variables in question given another group of variables. The variables "held constant" are ennumerated after the dot, in the suggestive notation of (1.5.3).

Remark 10: The difference betwen a simple and a partial correlation coefficient is this: a simple correlation coefficient between x_i and x_j expresses the degree of relation between these variables, when the effects of all other variables have been averaged out. A partial correlation, however, expresses the degree of relation between x_i and x_j for given values of all other (relevant) variables. In the normal case, this aspect is obscured because, by iv of Theorem 1, the covariance matrix of the conditional distribution does not depend on the conditioning variables. Notice, however, that in (1.5.3) $\rho_{ij \cdot k+1, k+2, \ldots, m}$ depends on Σ_{12} and Σ_{22}, which contain the *covariance parameters* of the conditioning variables.

Finally, it should be pointed out that if x^1 and x^2 are mutually independent (in the normal case if $\Sigma_{12} = 0$), then

$$\rho_{ij} = \rho_{ij \cdot k+1, k+2, \ldots, m} \tag{1.5.4}$$

It is possible to show explicitly the relation between partial and simple correlation coefficients in the general case. When the dimension of the vector x is large, 5 or 6 or more, these relations become quite cumbersome and thus we shall not treat this aspect here. The interested reader may, however, consult Anderson [1].

Definition 13: Let $x \sim N(\mu, \Sigma)$ and partition as in Definition 12. Let $\alpha'x^2$ be a linear combination of the elements of x^2 and let x_i be an element of x^1. Then the maximum correlation[9] between x_i and the linear combination $\alpha'x^2$ is called the *multiple correlation* between x_i and the vector x^2 and is denoted by $\bar{R}_{i \cdot k+1, k+2, \ldots, m}$.

It is clear that $\bar{R}_{i \cdot k+1, \ldots, m}$ will depend on Σ. To make this dependence explicit, we first prove

Lemma 9: Let $x \sim N(\mu, \Sigma)$ and partition x, μ, and Σ as above; let x_i be an element of x^1 and consider the linear combination $\alpha'x^2$ for arbitrary (nonrandom) α. Then the variance of

$$x_i - \alpha'x^2$$

is minimized for

$$\alpha' = \sigma_i \cdot \Sigma_{22}^{-1} \tag{1.5.5}$$

where σ_i. is the ith row of Σ_{12}.

---

[9] The term maximum is needed here, for the correlation between the two *scalar* random variables x_i and $\alpha'x^2$ will depend on the arbitrary vector of constants α.

PROOF: Notice that the conditional expectation of x_i given x^2 is[10]

$$E(x_i \mid x^2) = \mu_i + \sigma_i. \, \Sigma_{22}^{-1}(x^2 - \mu^2) \qquad (1.5.6)$$

We first show that x^2 and $x_i - \alpha'x^2$ are mutually independent. Because $x_i - \alpha'x^2$ and x^2 are (jointly) normally distributed, to accomplish this we need only show that their covariance vanishes. Thus

$$E[(x_i - \mu_i - \alpha'(x^2 - \mu^2))(x^2 - \mu^2)'] = E[(x_i - \mu_i)(x^2 - \mu^2)']$$
$$- \alpha'E[(x^2 - \mu^2)(x^2 - \mu^2)'] = \sigma_i. - \alpha'\Sigma_{22} \qquad (1.5.7)$$

As a result of (1.5.5), we conclude

$$\sigma_i. - \alpha'\Sigma_{22} = 0 \qquad (1.5.8)$$

which establishes mutual independence.

Now, let γ be any vector of constants. Then

$$\text{Var}\,(x_i - \gamma'x^2) = \text{Var}\,[(x_i - \alpha'x^2) + (\alpha - \gamma)'x^2]$$
$$= \text{Var}\,(x_i - \alpha'x^2) + (\alpha - \gamma)'\Sigma_{22}(\alpha - \gamma) \qquad (1.5.9)$$

Because Σ_{22} is positive definite, it follows that the left-hand side of (1.5.9) is minimized when the second term in the right-hand side is zero. But this occurs only for

$$\gamma' = \alpha' = \sigma_i. \, \Sigma_{22}^{-1} \qquad \text{Q.E.D.}$$
$$(1.5.10)$$

To complete our task, we prove

Lemma 10: Let x, μ, and Σ be as in Lemma 9 and partition them similarly; consider linear combinations $\gamma'x^2$, with γ nonrandom. Then the correlation between x_i and $\gamma'x^2$ is maximized for

$$\gamma' = \alpha' = \sigma_i. \, \Sigma_{22}^{-1} \qquad (1.5.11)$$

PROOF: By Lemma 9, for any scalar c and vector γ we have

$$\text{Var}\,(x_i - \alpha'x^2) \le \text{Var}\,(x_i - c\gamma'x^2) \qquad (1.5.12)$$

Developing both sides, we have

$$\sigma_{ii} - 2\sigma_i.\alpha + \alpha'\Sigma_{22}\alpha \le \sigma_{ii} - 2c\sigma_i.\gamma + c^2\gamma'\Sigma_{22}\gamma \qquad (1.5.13)$$

---

[10] If x, μ, and Σ are partitioned as in the lemma, recall that

(*) $E(x^1 \mid x^2) = \mu^1 + \Sigma_{12}\Sigma_{22}^{-1}(x^2 - \mu^2)$

The matrix $\Sigma_{12}\Sigma_{22}^{-1}$ is called the *matrix of regression coefficients* of x^1 on x^2. Thus in (1.5.6) $\sigma_i.\Sigma_{22}^{-1}$ is the *vector of regression coefficients* of x_i on x^2.

Since c is arbitrary, (1.5.13) holds in particular for

$$c^2 = \frac{\alpha' \Sigma_{22} \alpha}{\gamma' \Sigma_{22} \gamma} \tag{1.5.14}$$

Substituting in (1.5.13), cancelling, rearranging terms, and multipling through by $\sigma_{ii}^{-1/2}$, we find

$$\frac{\sigma_i \cdot \alpha}{(\sigma_{ii} \alpha' \Sigma_{22} \alpha)^{\frac{1}{2}}} \geq \frac{\sigma_i \cdot \gamma}{(\sigma_{ii} \gamma' \Sigma_{22} \gamma)^{\frac{1}{2}}} \tag{1.5.15}$$

But the left-hand side of (1.5.15) is the correlation coefficient between (the scalar random variables) x_i and $\alpha' x^2$; the right-hand side is the correlation coefficient between x_i and $\gamma' x^2$, for arbitrary γ.　　Q.E.D.

Remark 11: It follows from Lemma 10 that the multiple correlation coefficient between x_i and the vector x^2 is given by

$$\bar{R}_{i \cdot k+1, k+2, \ldots, m} = \frac{\sigma_i \cdot \alpha}{(\sigma_{ii} \alpha' \Sigma_{22} \alpha)^{\frac{1}{2}}} = \left(\frac{\sigma_i \cdot \Sigma_{22}^{-1} \sigma_i'.}{\sigma_{ii}} \right)^{\frac{1}{2}} \tag{1.5.16}$$

Here it would be interesting to point out the similarity between the properties of the conditional density derived above and the classical general linear model. In the context of the latter, we are dealing with the sample

$$y = Z\beta + u \tag{1.5.17}$$

where y is $T \times 1$, Z is $T \times n$ and represent, respectively, the (T) observations on the dependent and explanatory variables; β is the vector of parameters to be estimated, and u is the vector of disturbances having the specification

$$E(u) = 0 \quad \text{Cov}(u) = \sigma^2 I \quad E[u'Z] = 0 \tag{1.5.18}$$

In what follows, let us assume for convenience that the dependent and explanatory variables are measured as deviations from their respective sample means.
    If β is estimated by least squares, then its estimator is given by

$$\hat{\beta} = (Z'Z)^{-1} Z'y \tag{1.5.19}$$

and it is such that it minimizes

$$s^2 = (y - Z\hat{\beta})'(y - Z\hat{\beta}) \tag{1.5.20}$$

Notice the similarity of this to the conclusion of Lemma 9. Note, also, the similarity between the expressions for $\hat{\beta}$ in (1.5.19) and α in (1.5.5).
    The right-hand side in (1.5.19) can be written as

$$\left(\frac{Z'Z}{T} \right)^{-1} \frac{Z'y}{T}$$

But $(Z'Z/T)^{-1}$ and $Z'y/T$ are, respectively, the sample analogs of Σ_{22}^{-1} and $\sigma_i.$ appearing in the right-hand side of (1.5.5).

Moreover,

$$(y - Z\hat{\beta})'Z = y'Z - \hat{\beta}'Z'Z = y'Z - y'Z = 0 \tag{1.5.21}$$

which is again the sample analog of the result established in (1.5.8) of Lemma 9.

Finally, the (unadjusted) coefficient of determination in multiple regression defined by

$$R^2 = \frac{y'y - (y - Z\hat{\beta})'(y - Z\hat{\beta})}{y'y} = \frac{\hat{\beta}'Z'y}{y'y} + \frac{y'Z(Z'Z)^{-1}Z'y}{y'y} \tag{1.5.22}$$

is the exact sample analog of $\bar{R}^2_{i \cdot k+1 \; k+2, \ldots, m}$ established by (1.5.16), where x_i corresponds to the dependent and x^2 corresponds to the independent or explanatory variables.

The purpose of this brief digression was to pinpoint these similarities and thus enhance the student's understanding of the general linear model in its various aspects. The discussion also indicates how the study of the multivariate normal distribution contributes to understanding of the distributional problem involved in the general linear model.

Otherwise this digression is completely extraneous to the development of this section and may be omitted without loss of continuity.

The essential conclusions of this section are summarized in

Theorem 2: Let $x \sim N(\mu, \Sigma)$; partition x by x^1, x^2, where x^1 has k and x^2 has $(m - k)$ elements. Partition μ and Σ conformally and let x_i be an element of x^1. Then the following statements are true.

i. The variance of $x_i - \alpha'x^2$ is minimized for

$$\alpha' = \sigma_i. \Sigma_{22}^{-1} \tag{1.5.23}$$

where $\sigma_i.$ is the ith row of Σ_{12}; thus α is the vector of regression coefficients of x_i on the elements of the vector x^2.

ii. $x_i - \alpha'x^2$ is independent of x^2 — and hence of any linear combination of the elements of x^2.

iii. Let γ be an arbitrary (nonrandom) vector, then the correlation between (the two *scalar* random variables) x_i and $\gamma'x^2$ is maximized for

$$\gamma = \alpha \tag{1.5.24}$$

where α is defined in (1.5.23).

iv. The multiple correlation between x_i and x^2 is given by

$$\bar{R}_{i \cdot k+1, k+2, \ldots, m} = \left[\frac{\sigma_i. \Sigma_{22}^{-1} \sigma_i.}{\sigma_{ii}} \right]^{\frac{1}{2}} \tag{1.5.25}$$

PROOF: Lemmas 9 and 10.

1.6 ESTIMATORS OF THE MEAN VECTOR AND COVARIANCE MATRIX AND THEIR DISTRIBUTION

Let $x \sim N(\mu, \Sigma)$ and consider the random sample $\{x_{.t} : t = 1, 2, \ldots, T\}$, where $x_{.t}$ indicates the column vector whose elements are the tth observation on the *random* vector x; thus $x_{.t}$ is $m \times 1$.

The problem to be examined is that of obtaining estimators for μ and Σ, the parameters of the density of x. To solve the problem, we shall employ the principle of maximum likelihood.

Now the likelihood[11] of the T observations is given by

$$L^*(x_{.1}, x_{.2}, \ldots, x_{.T}; \mu, \Sigma)$$
$$= (2\pi)^{-mT/2} |\Sigma|^{-T/2} \exp\left[-\frac{1}{2} \sum_{t=1}^{T} (x_{.t} - \mu)' \Sigma^{-1}(x_{.t} - \mu)\right] \quad (1.6.1)$$

Put

$$y_{.t} = x_{.t} - \mu \quad (1.6.2)$$

and note that (1.6.1) can be written in the more convenient form

$$L^*(x_{.1}, x_{.2}, \ldots, x_{.T}; \mu, \Sigma) = (2\pi)^{-mT/2} |\Sigma|^{-T/2} \exp\left[-\tfrac{1}{2} \operatorname{tr} (Y'\Sigma^{-1}Y)\right] \quad (1.6.3)$$

where Y is a $(m \times T)$ matrix whose tth column is $y_{.t}$. Since for any two matrices A, B, such that AB and BA are both defined, $\operatorname{tr}(AB) = \operatorname{tr}(BA)$, the exponential in (1.6.3) can be written—apart from the factor, $\tfrac{1}{2}$—as $\operatorname{tr}(\Sigma^{-1}YY')$.

Let u be the $T \times 1$ vector of units defined by

$$u = (1, 1, 1, \ldots, 1)' \quad (1.6.4)$$

and notice that

$$Y = (X - \mu u') \quad (1.6.5)$$

where X is the matrix whose tth column is $x_{.t}$. Thus

$$YY' = XX' - T\mu\bar{x}' - T\bar{x}\mu' + T\mu\mu' \quad (1.6.6)$$

where

$$\bar{x} = (\bar{x}_1, \bar{x}_2, \ldots, \bar{x}_m)' \quad (1.6.7)$$

and $\bar{x}_i$ is the sample mean of x_i defined by

$$\bar{x}_i = \frac{1}{T} \sum_{t=1}^{T} x_{it} \quad (1.6.8)$$

---

[11] Recall that the likelihood function is simply the joint density of the observations; in the present case, the function assumes the particular form given it in (1.6.1), for sampling is assumed to be random, that is, the observations are mutually independent and distributed identically.

Adding and subtracting $T\bar{x}\bar{x}'$ in the right-hand side of (1.6.6), we obtain

$$YY' = X'X - T\bar{x}\bar{x}' + T(\bar{x} - \mu)(\bar{x} - \mu)' \qquad (1.6.9)$$

Hence the (logarithm of the) likelihood function in (1.6.1) becomes

$$L(x_{.1}, x_{.2}, \ldots, x_{.T}; \mu, \Sigma) = \frac{-mT}{2} \ln(2\pi) + \frac{T}{2} \ln|V| - \frac{1}{2} \operatorname{tr}\{V(XX' - T\bar{x}\bar{x}')\}$$

$$- \frac{1}{2} T \operatorname{tr}\{V(\bar{x} - \mu)(\bar{x} - \mu)'\} \qquad (1.6.10)$$

where

$$V = \Sigma^{-1} \qquad (1.6.11)$$

To obtain maximum likelihood estimators, we maximize (1.6.10) with respect to μ and Σ. Actually, in this case it is simpler (and equivalent) to maximize with respect to μ and V.

Notice, however, that μ enters the likelihood function only through the exponential and, moreover, since

$$\operatorname{tr}\{V(\bar{x} - \mu)(\bar{x} - \mu)'\} = \operatorname{tr}\{(\bar{x} - \mu)'V(\bar{x} - \mu)\} = (\bar{x} - \mu)'V(\bar{x} - \mu)^{12} \qquad (1.6.12)$$

we conclude, by the positive definiteness of V, that the likelihood function is maximized with respect to μ if and only if $(\bar{x} - \mu)'V(\bar{x} - \mu)$ is minimized. But the smallest value this quadratic form can assume is zero and this occurs only for

$$\hat{\mu} = \bar{x} \qquad (1.6.13)$$

Thus our earlier manipulations have spared us the need of differentiating (1.6.10) with respect to μ. To complete the estimation problem, we need only differentiate with respect to V the expression resulting in (1.6.10) when we substitute therein the maximum likelihood estimator of μ given in (1.6.13). Making the substitution, we obtain

$$L(x_{.1}, x_{.2}, \ldots, x_{.T}; \Sigma) = \frac{-mT}{2} \ln(2\pi) + \frac{T}{2} \ln|V| - \frac{1}{2} \operatorname{tr} VA \qquad (1.6.14)$$

where

$$A = XX' - T\bar{x}\bar{x}' \qquad (1.6.15)$$

Differentiating L (a scalar) with respect to

$$V = (v_{ij}) \qquad i, j = 1, 2, \ldots, m \qquad (1.6.16)$$

means differentiating it with respect to the elements v_{ij}. Therefore we obtain the equations

$$\frac{\partial L}{\partial v_{ij}} = \frac{T}{2} \frac{V_{ij}}{|V|} - \frac{1}{2} a_{ji} = 0 \qquad i, j = 1, 2, \ldots, m \qquad (1.6.17)$$

---

[12] The trace operator (tr) is omitted, for $(\bar{x} - \mu)'V(\bar{x} - \mu)$ is a scalar.

where V_{ij} is the cofactor of v_{ij} and $|V|$ is the determinant of V. In matrix form, the equations (1.6.17) read

$$TV^{-1} - A = 0 \tag{1.6.18}$$

We therefore solve to obtain

$$\hat{\Sigma} = \frac{A}{T} = \frac{XX' - T\bar{x}\bar{x}'}{T} \tag{1.6.19}$$

That (1.6.19) actually respresents a maximum (and not a minimum) can be established by showing that $\ln |V| - \frac{1}{2}\operatorname{tr}(VA)$ is a concave function of (the elements of) V, which is in fact true. Indeed, then, (1.6.19) represents the global maximum of the function, and thus the estimators of μ and Σ as given in (1.6.13) and (1.6.19) are the maximum likelihood estimators of μ and Σ. Hence we established

Lemma 11: Let $x \sim N(\mu, \Sigma)$ and let $\{x_{\cdot t} : t = 1, 2, \ldots, T\}$ be a random sample on the vector x. Then the maximum likelihood estimators of μ and Σ are given, respectively, by

$$\hat{\mu} = \bar{x} \tag{1.6.20}$$

$$\hat{\Sigma} = \frac{XX' - T\bar{x}\bar{x}'}{T} \tag{1.6.21}$$

Before turning to the problem of determining the distribution of the maximum likelihood estimators just obtained, we cite, without proof, the following useful

Theorem 3: Let s be a (column) vector such that

$$s's = 1 \tag{1.6.22}$$

but is otherwise arbitrary.

Then there exists an orthogonal matrix[13] having s as its last column.

The distribution of $\hat{\mu}$ and $\hat{\Sigma}$ is established by

Lemma 12: Let $x \sim N(\mu, \Sigma)$ and consider the sample $\{x_{\cdot t} : t = 1, 2, \ldots, T\}$. Let X be the matrix having $x_{\cdot t}$ as its tth column. Let B be a $T \times T$ orthogonal matrix having for its Tth column[14]

$$b_{\cdot T} = \left(\frac{1}{T^{\frac{1}{2}}}, \frac{1}{T^{\frac{1}{2}}}, \ldots, \frac{1}{T^{\frac{1}{2}}} \right)' \tag{1.6.23}$$

and define

$$Y = XB \tag{1.6.24}$$

---

[13] A matrix B is said to be orthogonal if and only if $B'B = I$, that is, $B' = B^{-1}$.
[14] This is possible by Theorem 3; the proof of the latter is given in Proposition 10 of the Mathematical Appendix.

Then

i. $y._t, t = 1, 2, \ldots, T$ are mutually independent, where $y._t$ is the tth column of Y.

ii. $y._t \sim N(0, \Sigma)$ $\quad t = 1, 2, \ldots, (T-1)$

iii $y._T = T^{1/2}\bar{x}$ $\quad \bar{x} \sim N\left(\mu, \dfrac{\Sigma}{T}\right)$

iv. $T\hat{\Sigma}$ has the distribution of $\displaystyle\sum_{t=1}^{T-1} y._t y._t{}'$

v. $\hat{\mu}$ and $\hat{\Sigma}$ are independently distributed.

PROOF: The tth column of Y is, by definition,

$$y._t = \sum_{j=1}^{T} x._j b_{jt} \tag{1.6.25}$$

Since the vectors $x._j$ are normally distributed, then obviously so are the $y._t$; thus, to prove i, we need only show that for any two columns of Y their covariance vanishes. Now, let $y._t, y._r$ be any two columns of Y; then

$$\mathrm{Cov}\,(y._t, y._r) = E\left\{ \left[\sum_{j=1}^{T} (x._j - \mu) b_{jt} \right] \left[\sum_{s=1}^{T} (x._s - \mu) b_{sr} \right]' \right\}$$

$$= E\left\{ \sum_{j=1}^{T} \sum_{s=1}^{T} (x._j - \mu)(x._s - \mu)' b_{jt}\, b_{sr} \right\}$$

$$= \sum_{j=1}^{T} \sum_{s=1}^{T} b_{jt}\, b_{sr}\, \delta_{js} \Sigma$$

$$= \left(\sum_{j=1}^{T} b_{jt}\, b_{jr} \right) \Sigma = \delta_{tr} \Sigma \tag{1.6.26}$$

The next to the last equality sign in (1.6.26) holds because of the independence of $x._j$ and $x._s$ for $s \neq j$; the last equality is valid in view of the orthogonality of B.

The result in (1.6.26) shows that if $t \neq r$, then the covariance between $y._t$ and $y._r$ vanishes, which proves i.

To prove ii, we need only obtain the mean of $y._t$, $t = 1, 2, \ldots, (T-1)$, for we already know that they are normally distributed and, by (1.6.26), that the covariance matrix of $y._t$ is Σ for $t = 1, 2, \ldots, T$.

Now

$$E(y._t) = \sum_{j=1}^{T} E(x._j) b_{jt} = \mu \sum_{j=1}^{T} b_{jt} \tag{1.6.27}$$

and thus we must show that

$$\sum_{j=1}^{T} b_{jt} = 0 \qquad t = 1, 2, \ldots, (T-1) \tag{1.6.28}$$

Since

$$b_{jT} = \frac{1}{T^{\frac{1}{2}}} \qquad j = 1, 2, \ldots, T \tag{1.6.29}$$

it follows that

$$T^{\frac{1}{2}} b_{jt} b_{jT} = b_{jt} \tag{1.6.30}$$

Thus

$$\sum_{j=1}^{T} b_{jt} = T^{\frac{1}{2}} \sum_{j=1}^{T} b_{jt} b_{jT} = T^{\frac{1}{2}} b'_{\cdot t} b_{\cdot T} = 0 \tag{1.6.31}$$

since B is orthogonal and $t \neq T$. This establishes ii.

To establish iii, we note that

$$y_{\cdot T} = \sum_{j=1}^{T} x_{\cdot j} b_{jT} = \frac{1}{T^{\frac{1}{2}}} \sum_{j=1}^{T} x_{\cdot j} = T^{\frac{1}{2}} \bar{x} \tag{1.6.32}$$

and

$$E(y_{\cdot T}) = \mu \sum_{j=1}^{T} b_{jT} = T^{\frac{1}{2}} \mu \tag{1.6.33}$$

Since $y_{\cdot T}$ has been shown to be normal with covariance matrix Σ, then (1.6.32) and (1.6.33) imply

$$\bar{x} \sim N\left(\mu, \frac{\Sigma}{T}\right) \tag{1.6.34}$$

To establish iv, observe that from (1.6.24) and the fact that B is orthogonal, we have

$$X = YB^{-1} = YB' \tag{1.6.35}$$

Thus

$$XX' = YB'BY' = YY' = \sum_{t=1}^{T} y_{\cdot t} y_{\cdot t} \tag{1.6.36}$$

As a result of (1.6.32), we obtain

$$T\hat{\Sigma} = XX' - T\bar{x}\bar{x}' = YY' - y_{\cdot T} y'_{\cdot T} = \sum_{t=1}^{T-1} y_{\cdot t} y'_{\cdot t} \tag{1.6.37}$$

Finally, the validity of v follows from i, ii, and iv.   Q.E.D.

Corollary: The maximum likelihood estimator of μ is unbiased and consistent. The maximum likelihood estimator of Σ is biased. An unbiased[15]

---

[15] Since it can be shown that $\hat{\mu}$ and $\hat{\Sigma}$ are jointly sufficient statistics for μ and Σ, it follows that $\hat{\Sigma}$ being an unbiased sufficient statistic will also be efficient. These results will be established in Chapter 3, together with precise definitions of bias, consistency, and efficiency properties of estimators.

estimator of Σ is given by

$$\tilde{\Sigma} = \frac{XX' - T\bar{x}\bar{x}'}{T - 1} \tag{1.6.38}$$

PROOF: The unbiasedness of

$$\hat{\mu} = \bar{x} \tag{1.6.39}$$

follows immediately from iii of Lemma 12: consistency is also obvious from that result, for

$$\lim_{T \to \infty} \frac{\Sigma}{T} = 0 \tag{1.6.40}$$

That (1.6.21) is a biased estimator of Σ is obvious from

$$E[T\hat{\Sigma}] = TE(\hat{\Sigma}) = E\left[\sum_{t=1}^{T-1} y_{.t} y_{.t}'\right] = (T-1)\Sigma \tag{1.6.41}$$

Thus

$$E(\hat{\Sigma}) = \frac{T-1}{T} \Sigma \tag{1.6.42}$$

It is clear that

$$E(\tilde{\Sigma}) = \frac{T}{T-1} E(\hat{\Sigma}) = \Sigma \qquad \text{Q.E.D.} \tag{1.6.43}$$

The development of this section can be summarized in

Theorem 4: Let $x \sim N(\mu, \Sigma)$ and consider the random sample $\{x_{.t} : t = 1, 2, \ldots, T\}$. Then the following statements are true:

i. The maximum likelihood estimators of μ and Σ are given, respectively, by

$$\hat{\mu} = \bar{x} \tag{1.6.44}$$

$$\hat{\Sigma} = \frac{XX' - T\bar{x}\bar{x}'}{T} \tag{1.6.45}$$

ii. $\hat{\mu}$ and $\hat{\Sigma}$ are mutually independent.
iii. $\bar{x} \sim N(\mu, \Sigma/T)$ and $T\hat{\Sigma}$ has the distribution of $\sum_{t=1}^{T-1} y_{.t} y_{.t}'$, where the $y_{.t}$ are mutually independent and

$$y_{.t} \sim N(0, \Sigma) \qquad t = 1, 2, \ldots, (T-1) \tag{1.6.46}$$

iv. $\hat{\mu}$ is an unbiased and consistent estimator of μ.

v. $\hat{\Sigma}$ is a biased estimator of Σ; an unbiased estimator is given by

$$\tilde{\Sigma} = \frac{T}{T-1}\hat{\Sigma} = \frac{XX' - T\bar{x}\bar{x}'}{T-1} \tag{1.6.47}$$

PROOF: Lemmas 11 and 12 and their corollaries.

Before leaving this topic, let us establish the distribution of the estimator of Σ. This is known as the Wishart distribution—after John Wishart who discovered it. Its derivation is quite cumbersome and will thus be omitted. It is, however, important for the student to be acquainted with it and with some of its salient properties. The Wishart distribution is established by the following theorem, which we cite without proof.

Theorem 5: Let Z be a random matrix of dimension $m \times n$. Let $z_{\cdot t}$ be the tth column of Z and suppose that the $z_{\cdot t}$ are mutually independent, having the distribution

$$z_{\cdot t} \sim N(0, \Sigma) \qquad t = 1, 2, \ldots, n \tag{1.6.48}$$

Then the joint density of the elements of

$$S = ZZ' \tag{1.6.49}$$

is given by (the Wishart density)

$$f(S) = \frac{|S|^{\frac{1}{2}(n-m-1)}|V|^{\frac{1}{2}n} \exp\left[-\frac{1}{2}\operatorname{tr}(VS)\right]}{2^{\frac{1}{2}n \cdot m} \pi^{[m(m-1)/4]} \prod_{i=1}^{m} \Gamma[\frac{1}{2}(n+1-i)]} \tag{1.6.50}$$

where

$$V = \Sigma^{-1} \tag{1.6.51}$$

and $\Gamma(\cdot)$ is the gamma function defined by

$$\Gamma(s) = \int_0^\infty u^{s-1} \exp(-u)\, du \tag{1.6.52}$$

Remark 12: The Wishart distribution is the matrix generalization of the chi-square distribution. Just as the latter is the distribution of sums of squares of independent normal variables with mean zero (and variance σ^2), so the former is the distribution of the sums of squares and cross products of the elements of mutually independent vector random variables, each distributed as $N(0, \Sigma)$.

If S has the Wishart density, then as a matter of notation we write

$$S \sim W(\Sigma, m, n) \tag{1.6.53}$$

Notice that here m indicates the dimension of the (normal) vectors making up the columns of Z of Theorem 5; n indicates the number of columns in Z, that is, it counts the number of mutually independent normal vectors entering into

S. It is thus the analog of the degrees of freedom parameter in the chi-square distribution, for that parameter counts the number of independent normal components of the chi-square variable.

Corollary 1: If S is partitioned by

$$S = \begin{bmatrix} S_{11} & S_{12} \\ S_{21} & S_{22} \end{bmatrix} \tag{1.6.54}$$

such that S_{11} is $k \times k$, then

$$S_{11} \sim W(\Sigma_{11}, k, n) \tag{1.6.55}$$

where Σ_{11} is the upper left block submatrix in the conformal partition of Σ.

PROOF: Let Z be the matrix whose columns are mutually independent vectors, each distributed as $N(0, \Sigma)$ and such that

$$S = ZZ' \tag{1.6.56}$$

Partition Z by

$$Z = \begin{pmatrix} Z_1 \\ Z_2 \end{pmatrix} \tag{1.6.57}$$

such that Z_1 is $k \times n$. Then

$$\begin{bmatrix} S_{11} & S_{12} \\ S_{21} & S_{22} \end{bmatrix} = \begin{pmatrix} Z_1 \\ Z_2 \end{pmatrix} (Z_1', Z_2') = \begin{bmatrix} Z_1 Z_1' & Z_1 Z_2' \\ Z_2 Z_1' & Z_2 Z_2' \end{bmatrix} \tag{1.6.58}$$

Hence

$$S_{11} = Z_1 Z_1' \tag{1.6.59}$$

By iii of Theorem 1 the tth column of Z_1 has the distribution $N(0, \Sigma_{11})$; moreover, the columns are mutually independent. The conclusion of the corollary follows, then, from Theorem 5.

Corollary 2: Suppose that

$$S_1 \sim W(\Sigma, m, n_1)$$
$$S_2 \sim W(\Sigma, m, n_2) \tag{1.6.60}$$

and are mutually independent. Then

$$S_1 + S_2 = S \sim W(\Sigma, m, n_1 + n_2) \tag{1.6.61}$$

PROOF: Let X be $m \times n_1$, Y be $m \times n_2$ with mutually independent columns, each distributed as $N(0, \Sigma)$ and corresponding, respectively, to S_1 and S_2. That is,

$$S_1 = XX' \qquad S_2 = YY' \tag{1.6.62}$$

Let

$$Z = (X, Y) \tag{1.6.63}$$

Then Z is $m \times (n_1 + n_2)$, its columns are mutually independent and are each distributed as $N(0, \Sigma)$. Thus, by Theorem 5,

$$ZZ' \sim W(\Sigma, m, n_1 + n_2) \tag{1.6.64}$$

On the other hand,

$$ZZ' = (X, Y)\binom{X'}{Y'} = XX' + YY' = S_1 + S_2 = S \tag{1.6.65}$$

which establishes the corollary.

Corollary 3: Let $S \sim W(\Sigma, m, n)$ and let A be an $m \times m$ nonsingular matrix. Then

$$ASA' \sim W(A\Sigma A', m, n) \tag{1.6.66}$$

PROOF: Let X be a matrix with mutually independent columns, each distributed as $N(0, \Sigma)$ and such that

$$S = XX' \tag{1.6.67}$$

Let A be a nonsingular matrix and define

$$Y = AX \tag{1.6.68}$$

Then the tth column of Y is given by

$$y_{\cdot t} = Ax_{\cdot t} \tag{1.6.69}$$

$x_{\cdot t}$ being the tth column of X.

Thus the columns of Y are mutually independent; moreover,

$$y_{\cdot t} \sim N(0, A\Sigma A') \qquad t = 1, 2, \ldots, n \tag{1.6.70}$$

It follows from Theorem 5 that

$$ASA' = YY' \sim W(A\Sigma A', m, n) \tag{1.6.71}$$

Corollary 4: Let $x \sim N(\mu, \Sigma)$ and let $\{x_{\cdot t} : t = 1, 2, \ldots, T\}$ be a random sample on x. Let $\hat{\Sigma}$ be the maximum likelihood estimator of Σ. Then

$$T\hat{\Sigma} \sim W(\Sigma, m, T - 1) \tag{1.6.72}$$

PROOF: By iii of Theorem 4, $T\hat{\Sigma}$ has the distribution of

$$\sum_{t=1}^{T-1} y_{\cdot t} y'_{\cdot t}$$

where

$$y_{\cdot t} \sim N(0, \Sigma) \qquad t = 1, 2, \ldots, T - 1 \tag{1.6.73}$$

Now if Y is the matrix whose tth column is $y._t$, then

$$\sum_{t=1}^{T-1} y._t y._t' = YY' \tag{1.6.74}$$

and by Theorem 5 we conclude that

$$T\hat{\Sigma} \sim W(\Sigma, m, T-1) \tag{1.6.75}$$

1.7 TESTS OF SIGNIFICANCE

The problem of testing a hypothesis on the mean of a distribution often arises. Thus suppose that

$$x \sim N(\mu, \Sigma) \tag{1.7.1}$$

where Σ is known but μ is unknown and we are interested in testing the hypothesis

$$H_0 : \mu = \mu_0$$

as against

$$H_1 : \mu \neq \mu_0$$

To carry out this test, we apply the likelihood ratio principle and thus obtain the appropriate test statistic.

Let $\{x._t : t = 1, 2, \ldots, T\}$ be a random sample on x. The likelihood function can be written, in view of (1.6.10), as

$$L^*(x._1, \ldots, x._T ; \mu, \Sigma) = (2\pi)^{-mT/2} |V|^{T/2} \exp\left[-\tfrac{1}{2} \operatorname{tr}(VA)\right]$$
$$\times \exp\left[-\tfrac{1}{2} T(\bar{x} - \mu)' V(\bar{x} - \mu)\right] \tag{1.7.2}$$

where $A, V, \bar{x}$ are as defined in the discussion leading to Theorem 4.

If H_0 is in fact true, then the likelihood function under H_0 is

$$L^*(X; \mu, \Sigma \,|\, H_0) = (2\pi)^{-mT/2} |V|^{T/2} \exp\left[-\tfrac{1}{2} \operatorname{tr}(VA)\right]$$
$$\times \exp\left[-\tfrac{1}{2} T(\bar{x} - \mu_0)' V(\bar{x} - \mu_0)\right] \tag{1.7.3}$$

Maximizing (1.7.2) under H_1, we obtain the estimator

$$\tilde{\mu} = \bar{x} \tag{1.7.4}$$

Thus

$$\max_{H_1} L^*(X; \mu, \Sigma) = (2\pi)^{-mT/2} |V|^{T/2} \exp\left(-\tfrac{1}{2} \operatorname{tr} VA\right) \tag{1.7.5}$$

The likelihood ratio is defined as

$$\lambda = \frac{\max_{H_0} L^*(X; \mu, \Sigma)}{\max_{H_1} L^*(X; \mu, \Sigma)} = \exp\left[-\tfrac{1}{2} T(\bar{x} - \mu_0)' V(\bar{x} - \mu_0)\right] \tag{1.7.6}$$

Now, if H_0 were in fact correct, then λ would tend to be close to unity. If H_0 *were in fact not correct*, then λ would tend to be less than unity. Hence the hypothesis would be rejected if the sample yielded a λ such that

$$\lambda \leq \lambda_\alpha \tag{1.7.7}$$

where λ_α is some quantity defined by the desired level of significance.

Typically, however, we do not use λ as the test statistic but a simple transform whose distribution is much easier to establish. Taking logarithms in (1.7.6) and multiplying through by -2, we find

$$-2 \ln \lambda = (\bar{x} - \mu_0)'(TV)(\bar{x} - \mu_0) \tag{1.7.8}$$

Notice that if λ_α is such that, under H_0,

$$\Pr \{\lambda \leq \lambda_\alpha \,|\, H_0\} = \alpha \tag{1.7.9}$$

then, equivalently,

$$\Pr \{-2 \ln \lambda \geq -2 \ln \lambda_\alpha \,|\, H_0\} = \alpha \tag{1.7.10}$$

The distribution of $-2 \ln \lambda$, however, is established very easily. Thus let C be a nonsingular matrix such that

$$CC' = \Sigma/T \tag{1.7.11}$$

and define

$$y = C^{-1}(\bar{x} - \mu_0) \tag{1.7.12}$$

It follows, then, that

$$y \sim N(0, I) \tag{1.7.13}$$

and hence

$$y'y = \sum_{i=1}^{T} y_i^2 \tag{1.7.14}$$

is chi square with T degrees of freedom. But

$$y'y = (\bar{x} - \mu_0)'(TV)(\bar{x} - \mu_0) \tag{1.7.15}$$

which shows that the test of this hypothesis can be carried out in terms of the chi-square distribution.

In particular, if we wish to carry out the test at the α level of significance, then the rejection region is defined by

$$(\bar{x} - \mu_0)'(TV)(\bar{x} - \mu_0) \geq \chi_\alpha \tag{1.7.16}$$

where χ_α is such that

$$\Pr \{\chi_T^2 \geq \chi_\alpha\} = \alpha \tag{1.7.17}$$

and χ_T^2 is a chi-square variable with T degrees of freedom. We have therefore established

Lemma 13: Let $x \sim N(\mu, \Sigma)$ and let $\{x_{\cdot t} : t = 1, 2, \ldots, T\}$ be a random sample on x. Then, for known Σ, the likelihood ratio test statistic of the hypothesis

$$H_0 : \mu = \mu_0$$

as against

$$H_1 : \mu \neq \mu_0$$

is given by

$$\lambda = \exp\left[-\tfrac{1}{2}(\bar{x} - \mu_0)'(TV)(\bar{x} - \mu_0)\right] \tag{1.7.18}$$

An equivalent test can be carried out in terms of

$$-2 \ln \lambda = (\bar{x} - \mu_0)'(TV)(\bar{x} - \mu_0) \tag{1.7.19}$$

and, moreover, $-2 \ln \lambda$ is chi square with T degrees of freedom.

Let us turn now to the more realistic case where neither μ nor Σ is known.

In this connection, recall that in the univariate case $x_1 \sim N(\mu_1, \sigma_{11})$, neither μ_1 nor σ_{11} known, then to test

$$H_0 : \mu_1 = \mu_{10}$$

as against

$$H_1 : \mu_1 \neq \mu_{10}$$

one uses the t statistic

$$t = \sqrt{T}\, \frac{\bar{x}_1 - \mu_{10}}{s} \tag{1.7.20}$$

where T is the sample size, $\bar{x}_1$ is the sample mean, and

$$s^2 = \frac{\sum_{t=1}^{T}(x_{1t} - \bar{x}_1)^2}{T - 1} \tag{1.7.21}$$

Notice that

$$t^2 = \frac{T(\bar{x}_1 - \mu_{10})^2}{s^2} \tag{1.7.22}$$

Has the F distribution with 1 and $T - 1$ degrees of freedom. An entirely analogous situation obtains in the multivariate case. Formally, we have

Lemma 14: Let $x \sim N(\mu, \Sigma)$ and let $\{x_{\cdot t} : t = 1, 2, \ldots, T\}$ be a random sample on x. Suppose that both μ and Σ are unknown and that we wish to test

$$H_0 : \mu = \mu_0$$

as against

$H_1 : \mu \neq \mu_0$

Then the likelihood ratio test statistic is

$$\lambda = \frac{|A|^{T/2}}{|M|^{T/2}} \tag{1.7.23}$$

where

$$A = XX' - T\bar{x}\bar{x}' \quad M = Y_0 Y_0' \quad Y_0 = (x_{.1} - \mu_0, x_{.2} - \mu_0, \ldots, x_{.T} - \mu_0) \tag{1.7.24}$$

An equivalent test can be conducted in terms of

$$T^{*2} = T(\bar{x} - \mu_0)' \left(\frac{A}{T-1} \right)^{-1} (\bar{x} - \mu_0) \tag{1.7.25}$$

Furthermore,

$$\frac{T-m}{m(T-1)} T^{*2}$$

has the F distribution with m and $T - m$ degrees of freedom.

PROOF: To obtain the likelihood ratio test statistic, we first maximize the likelihood function under H_0; the function is given by

$$L^*(X; \mu_0, \Sigma) = (2\pi)^{-mT/2} |V|^{T/2} \exp \left[-\frac{1}{2} \sum_{t=1}^{T} (x_{.t} - \mu_0)' V(x_{.t} - \mu_0) \right] \tag{1.7.26}$$

For notational convenience, let

$$y_{.t} = x_{.t} - \mu_0 \tag{1.7.27}$$

and let Y_0 be the $m \times T$ matrix whose tth column is $y_{.t}$; then Y_0 is the matrix defined in (1.7.24).

In terms of this notation, the exponential in (1.7.26) becomes

$$\sum_{t=1}^{T} y_{.t}' V y_{.t} = \operatorname{tr} Y_0' V Y_0 = \operatorname{tr} V Y_0 Y_0'. \tag{1.7.28}$$

Let

$$Y_0 Y_0' = M = (m_{ij}) \quad i, j = 1, 2, \ldots, m \tag{1.7.29}$$

Maximizing the logarithm of the likelihood function in (1.7.26) with respect to the elements of V, we have, in terms of the notation in (1.7.29),

$$\frac{\partial \ln L^*}{\partial v_{ij}} = \frac{T}{2} \frac{V^{ij}}{|V|} - \frac{1}{2} m_{ji} = 0 \quad i, j = 1, 2, \ldots, m \tag{1.7.30}$$

In matrix form, the equations in (1.7.30) read

$$TV^{-1} - M = 0 \tag{1.7.31}$$

Thus the estimator of Σ under H_0 is given by

$$\hat{\Sigma}_{H_0} = \frac{M}{T} \tag{1.7.32}$$

and

$$\max_{H_0} L^*(X; \mu_0, \Sigma) = (2\pi)^{-mT/2} \left| \frac{M}{T} \right|^{-T/2} \exp\left[-\tfrac{1}{2} \operatorname{tr}(TM^{-1}M)\right]$$

$$= (2\pi)^{-mT/2} \left| \frac{M}{T} \right|^{-T/2} \exp\left(-\tfrac{1}{2}Tm\right) \tag{1.7.33}$$

Under H_1 we need to maximize the likelihood function simultaneously with respect to μ and Σ. But we have already established that the maximum is attained for

$$\hat{\mu} = \bar{x} \qquad \hat{\Sigma} = \frac{A}{T} \tag{1.7.34}$$

Hence

$$\max_{H_1} L^*(X; \mu, \Sigma) = (2\pi)^{-mT/2} \left| \frac{A}{T} \right|^{-T/2} \exp\left[-\tfrac{1}{2} \operatorname{tr}(TA^{-1}A)\right]$$

$$= (2\pi)^{-mT/2} \left| \frac{A}{T} \right|^{-T/2} \exp\left(-\tfrac{1}{2}Tm\right) \tag{1.7.35}$$

Thus the likelihood ratio is

$$\lambda = \frac{\max_{H_0} L^*(X; \mu, \Sigma)}{\max_{H_1} L^*(X; \mu, \Sigma)} = \frac{|M|^{-T/2}}{|A|^{-T/2}} = \frac{|A|^{T/2}}{|M|^{T/2}} \tag{1.7.36}$$

As before, it follows that we would reject H_0 if the sample yields a λ such that

$$\lambda \leq \lambda_\alpha \tag{1.7.37}$$

where λ_α is a quantity determined by the desired level of significance, that is, by

$$\Pr\{\lambda \leq \lambda_\alpha \mid H_0\} = \alpha \tag{1.7.38}$$

The distribution of λ, however, is very difficult to obtain. On the other hand, note that the following transformation simplifies matters considerably. Thus

$$\lambda^{2/T} = \frac{|A|}{|M|} \tag{1.7.39}$$

Recall, from (1.6.9), that

$$|M| = |Y_0 Y_0'| = |XX' - T\bar{x}\bar{x}' + T(\bar{x} - \mu_0)(\bar{x} - \mu_0)'|$$
$$= |A + T(\bar{x} - \mu_0)(\bar{x} - \mu_0)'|$$
$$= |A| |I + TA^{-1}(\bar{x} - \mu_0)(\bar{x} - \mu_0)'| \qquad (1.7.40)$$

Hence conclude that

$$\lambda^{2/T} = \frac{1}{|I + TA^{-1}(\bar{x} - \mu_0)(\bar{x} - \mu_0)'|} = \frac{1}{1 + (T^{*2}/T - 1)} \qquad (1.7.41)$$

The last equality in (1.7.41) is valid, for

$$|I + TA^{-1}(\bar{x} - \mu_0)(\bar{x} - \mu_0)'| = 1 + T(\bar{x} - \mu_0)'A^{-1}(\bar{x} - \mu_0) \qquad (1.7.42)$$

Thus

$$T^{*2} = (T - 1)[\lambda^{-2/T} - 1] \qquad (1.7.43)$$

Since T^{*2} is a one-to-one function of λ, it follows that

$$\Pr\{\lambda \le \lambda_\alpha\} = \Pr\{T^{*2} \ge T_\alpha\} \qquad (1.7.44)$$

where

$$T_\alpha = (T - 1)[\lambda_\alpha^{-2/T} - 1] \qquad (1.7.45)$$

Establishing the distribution of T^{*2} is rather cumbersome and shall be omitted here. The interested reader is referred to Anderson [1].

This, therefore, concludes the proof of the lemma.

Remark 13: It should be pointed out that the test of the hypothesis is, in practice, carried out in terms of the acceptance region

$$T^{*2} \le \frac{m(T - 1)}{T - m} F_\alpha$$

where F_α is a quantity such that

$$\Pr\{F_{m, T-m} \ge F_\alpha\} = \alpha \qquad (1.7.46)$$

α being the desired level of significance; $F_{m, T-m}$ has the F distribution with m and $T - m$ degrees of freedom. Notice that this is entirely similar to the univeriate case, where we accept the hypothesis $\mu_1 = \mu_{10}$ if the value of the t ratio

$$t^* = \sqrt{T}\, \frac{\bar{x}_1 - \mu_{10}}{s} \qquad (1.7.47)$$

and hence its square is "small."

We summarize the development in this section by

Theorem 6: Let $x \sim N(\mu, \Sigma)$ and let $\{x_{.t} : t = 1, 2, \ldots, T\}$ be a random sample on x. Suppose that it is desired to test the hypothesis

$H_0 : \mu = \mu_0$

as against

$H_1 : \mu \neq \mu_0$

Then if Σ is assumed known, the acceptance region is given by

$$(\bar{x} - \mu_0)'(TV)(\bar{x} - \mu_0) \leq \chi_\alpha \qquad (1.7.48)$$

where χ_α is a number such that

$$\Pr\{\chi_T^2 \geq \chi_\alpha\} = \alpha \qquad (1.7.49)$$

χ_T^2 being a chi-square variable with T degrees of freedom and α the desired level of significance.

If Σ is unknown, then the acceptance region of the hypothesis is given by

$$T^{*2} \leq \frac{m(T-1)}{T-m} F_\alpha \qquad (1.7.50)$$

where F_α is a quantity such that

$$\Pr\{F_{m, T-m} \geq F_\alpha\} = \alpha \qquad (1.7.51)$$

$F_{m, T-m}$ being an F-distributed variable with m and $T - m$ degrees of freedom and α the desired level of significance.

PROOF: Lemmas 13 and 14.

REFERENCES

1. Anderson, T. W., *An Introduction to Multivariate Statistical Analysis*, New York, Wiley, 1958. A comprehensive book devoted to multivariate analysis. The multivariate normal distribution, etc. covered here are discussed in Chapters 1, 2, 3, 4, 5, 7.
2. Apostol, T., *Calculus*, vol. 2, New York, Bladsdell, 1962. Like Courant's volume, this is a general reference on transformations, multiple integrals, maxima-minima, etc. It has a set theoretic approach and is a more modern reference.
3. Bellman, R., *Introduction to Matrix Analysis*, New York, McGraw-Hill, 1960. A general reference for advanced topics in matrix algebra.
4. Courant, R., *Differential and Integral Calculus*, vol. 2, New York, Interscience, 1934. This volume deals with advanced calculus of several variables. Of interest are Chapters 3, 4, 8.
5. Hotelling, H., "The Generalization of Student's Ratio," *Annals of Mathematical Statistics*, Vol. 2, 1931, pp. 360–378. The first paper to suggest the so-called "Hotelling T^2 statistic" to test the hypothesis $\mu = \mu_0$, Σ unknown.
6. Hotelling, H., "The Most Predictable Criterion," *Journal of Educational Psychology*, vol. 26, 1935, pp. 139–142.

7. Hotelling, H., "Relations Between Two Sets of Variates," *Biometrika*, vol. 28, 1936, pp. 321–377. A follow-up on the 1935 article, using the coefficients of vector correlation and vector alienation.
8. Kendall, M. G., and A. Stuart, *The Advanced Theory of Statistics*, vol. I, New York, Hafner Publishing Co., 1958. The multivariate normal distribution is discussed in Chapter 15.
9. Rao, C. R., *Linear Statistical Inference and Its Applications*, New York, Wiley; 1965. Deals with the multivariate normal distribution etc. discussed here in Chapter 8, Sections a, b, c, d.
10. Wilks, S. S., *Mathematical Statistics*, New York, Wiley; 1962. The multivariate normal distribution is discussed in Sections 10.1, 10.2.
11. Wishart, J., "The Generalized Product Moment Distribution in Samples from a Normal Multivariate Population," *Biometrika*, 1928, vol. 20A, pp. 32–52. The first derivation of the so-called "Wishart's distribution."

APPLICATIONS OF
MULTIVARIATE ANALYSIS

2

2.1 CANONICAL CORRELATIONS
AND CANONICAL VARIABLES

MOTIVATION AND THEORY

As pointed out in Section 5 of Chapter 1, the standard regression problem is related to the problem of finding the maximum correlation between a *scalar* and a *vector* random variable. Indeed, the formulation of the problem is in terms of finding a linear combination of the elements of the vector random variable exhibiting *maximum correlation* with the given scalar variable. In this section we deal with a natural generalization in which we seek to define the correlation (or set of correlations) between two *vector random variables*. Specifically, the problem dealt with is as follows:

Let $(x_1, x_2, \ldots, x_{m_1})$ and $(x_{m_1+1}, \ldots, x_{m_1+m_2})$ be two sets of variables, $(m_1 \leq m_2)$.

Define

$$z = \sum_{i=1}^{m_1} \alpha_i x_i \qquad w = \sum_{j=1}^{m_2} \beta_j x_{j+m_1} \qquad (2.1.1)$$

and determine the coefficients α_i and β_j so that the *correlation between z and w is maximized.*

We see that, for $m_1 = 1$, the problem is exactly that of ordinary regression and thus canonical correlation is a natural generalization of regression theory.

An example will help clarify the nature of the problem and illustrate some areas of potential application. Suppose that we have two (large) sets of variables, for example, a set of political or socioeconomic characteristics for a region and a set of indicators of economic performance. We may not wish to study this large set of variables without processing. We may find that a few linear combinations of the elements of the two sets completely exhaust the relationships within these two groups. Hence the problem of interaction of political, social, and economic variables may be reduced to the study of a small set (perhaps one or two) of "indicators."

Consequently, we shall now develop some elementary aspects of canonical correlation theory. Let

$$x \sim N(\mu, \Sigma) \tag{2.1.2}$$

where x is an m-component vector and partition it by

$$x = \begin{pmatrix} x^1 \\ x^2 \end{pmatrix} \tag{2.1.3}$$

x^i, $i = 1, 2$, being subvectors of m_i components, $(m_1 + m_2 = m)$. Partition conformally

$$\mu = \begin{pmatrix} \mu^1 \\ \mu^2 \end{pmatrix} \qquad \Sigma = \begin{bmatrix} \Sigma_{11} & \Sigma_{12} \\ \Sigma_{21} & \Sigma_{22} \end{bmatrix} \tag{2.1.4}$$

so that μ^i is a subvector of m_i components, Σ_{11} is $m_1 \times m_1$, Σ_{22} is $m_2 \times m_2$, and so on.

Definition 1: Let

$$z = \alpha' x^1 \qquad w = \beta' x^2 \tag{2.1.5}$$

and define

$$\rho = \frac{\text{Cov} \left[\alpha' x^1, \beta' x^2 \right]}{\left[\text{Var} \left(\alpha' x^1 \right) \text{Var} \left(\beta' x^2 \right) \right]^{1/2}} \tag{2.1.6}$$

If α and β are chosen so as to *maximize* ρ, then ρ is termed the (first) canonical correlation between x^1 and x^2, while z and w are called the (first set of) *canonical variables* associated with x^1 and x^2.

From the definition, we see that canonical correlations and variables are defined as the solution to the following (maximum) problem:

$$\underset{\alpha, \beta}{\text{Max}} \ \frac{\alpha' \Sigma_{12} \beta}{\left[(\alpha' \Sigma_{11} \alpha)(\beta' \Sigma_{22} \beta) \right]^{1/2}}$$

However, it is immediately obvious that this involves a fundamental indeterminacy. The maximand is *homogeneous of degree zero* in α and β. Thus if α_0, β_0 constitute a solution to the problem above, then so would $c_1 \alpha_0$, $c_2 \beta_0$ for arbitrary c_1 and c_2. We are faced with a scale problem; to eliminate this inter-determinacy one typically imposes the constraints

$$\alpha'\Sigma_{11}\alpha = 1 \qquad \beta'\Sigma_{22}\beta = 1 \tag{2.1.7}$$

We remind the reader that

$$\text{Var}(z) = \alpha'\Sigma_{11}\alpha \quad \text{Var}(w) = \beta'\Sigma_{22}\beta \quad \text{Cov}(z, w) = \alpha'\Sigma_{12}\beta \tag{2.1.8}$$

Strictly speaking, Definition 1 should be amended by adding at the end the phrase "provided they are so defined so as to have unit variance."

Since, however, the requirements in (2.1.7) are only one set out of many possible scale conventions we might have chosen, we shall let the definition stand, having noted the nature of the interminacy.

Thus the mathematical form of the canonical correlation problem is simply the maximization of the Lagrangean

$$L = \alpha'\Sigma_{12}\beta + \tfrac{1}{2}\lambda_1(1 - \alpha'\Sigma_{11}\alpha) + \tfrac{1}{2}\lambda_2(1 - \beta'\Sigma_{22}\beta) \tag{2.1.9}$$

The first-order conditions are

$$\frac{\partial L}{\partial \alpha} = \Sigma_{12}\beta - \lambda_1\Sigma_{11}\alpha = 0$$

$$\frac{\partial L}{\partial \beta} = \Sigma_{21}\alpha - \lambda_2\Sigma_{22}\beta = 0$$

$$\frac{\partial L}{\partial \lambda_1} = \frac{1}{2}(1 - \alpha'\Sigma_{11}\alpha) = 0 \tag{2.1.10}$$

$$\frac{\partial L}{\partial \lambda_2} = \frac{1}{2}(1 - \beta'\Sigma_{22}\beta) = 0$$

We note that the last two equations are nothing but the constraints. Premultiplying the first set of equations by α' and the second by β', we conclude, in view of the constraints, that

$$\alpha'\Sigma_{12}\beta = \beta'\Sigma_{21}\alpha = \lambda_1 = \lambda_2 = \lambda \tag{2.1.11}$$

This is so because, by the symmetry of Σ,

$$\Sigma_{12} = \Sigma'_{21} \tag{2.1.12}$$

Thus we are seeking a solution to the following system of equations:

$$\begin{bmatrix} -\lambda\Sigma_{11} & \Sigma_{12} \\ \Sigma_{21} & -\lambda\Sigma_{22} \end{bmatrix}\begin{pmatrix} \alpha \\ \beta \end{pmatrix} = 0 \tag{2.1.13}$$

But (2.1.13) will have a *nontrivial solution* if and only if

$$\begin{vmatrix} -\lambda\Sigma_{11} & \Sigma_{12} \\ \Sigma_{21} & -\lambda\Sigma_{22} \end{vmatrix} = 0 \tag{2.1.14}$$

We note that (2.1.14) is *not the characteristic equation of the matrix* Σ although it is equivalent to the characteristic equation for *some* matrix, as we shall see below. We note, further, that (2.1.14) represents a *polynomial equation* of degree m and hence it has m roots. To each of such roots, then, there corresponds a solution (in α and β) of the system in (2.1.13).

We must determine which of these m possible solutions we should choose. However, it is apparent from (2.1.11) that the *value of the maximand is equal to one of the roots of* (2.1.14). Hence we must choose the *maximal root* and the solution of (2.1.13) corresponding to it.

Indeed, this development suggests that there is an entire collection of canonical correlations and variables and not merely a unique triplet.

Solving (2.1.14) and choosing its largest root, say $\lambda^{(1)}$, and solving (2.1.13), say, for vectors $\alpha_{(1)}$, $\beta_{(1)}$ corresponding to $\lambda^{(1)}$, we may define the first set of canonical variables as

$$\zeta_1 = \alpha'_{(1)}x^1 \qquad \omega_1 = \beta'_{(1)}x^2 \tag{2.1.15}$$

We observe that

$$\text{Var}(\zeta_1) = \alpha'_{(1)}\Sigma_{11}\alpha_{(1)} = 1 \qquad \text{Var}(\omega_1) = \beta'_{(1)}\Sigma_{22}\beta_{(2)} = 1$$
$$\text{Cov}(\zeta_1, \omega_1) = \alpha'_{(1)}\Sigma_{12}\beta_{(1)} = \lambda^{(1)} \tag{2.1.16}$$

Now, suppose that we wish to define another pair of canonical variables whose elements are *uncorrelated* with corresponding elements of the first pair. Clearly the last condition or something similar is needed; otherwise it would not be possible to identify the second pair.

As before, this is equivalent to maximizing the Lagrangean

$$L = \alpha'\Sigma_{12}\beta + \tfrac{1}{2}\lambda_1(1 - \alpha'\Sigma_{11}\alpha) + \tfrac{1}{2}\lambda_2(1 - \beta'\Sigma_{22}\beta)$$
$$+ \mu_1\alpha'_{(1)}\Sigma_{11}\alpha + \mu_2\beta'_{(1)}\Sigma_{22}\beta \tag{2.1.17}$$

We observe that the last two terms of the Lagrangean equation reflect the uncorrelatedness of corresponding elements of the two pairs of canonical variables.

The first-order conditions are

$$\frac{\partial L}{\partial \alpha} = \Sigma_{12}\beta - \lambda_1\Sigma_{11}\alpha + \mu_1\Sigma_{11}\alpha_{(1)} = 0$$

$$\frac{\partial L}{\partial \beta} = \Sigma_{21}\alpha - \lambda_2\Sigma_{22}\beta + \mu_2\Sigma_{22}\beta_{(1)} = 0$$

$$\frac{\partial L}{\partial \lambda_1} = \frac{1}{2}(1 - \alpha'\Sigma_{11}\alpha) = 0 \qquad \frac{\partial L}{\partial \mu_1} = \alpha'_{(1)}\Sigma_{11}\alpha = 0 \tag{2.1.18}$$

$$\frac{\partial L}{\partial \lambda_2} = \frac{1}{2}(1 - \beta'\Sigma_{22}\beta) = 0 \qquad \frac{\partial L}{\partial \mu_2} = \beta'_{(1)}\Sigma_{22}\beta = 0$$

Premultiplying the first two sets by α' and β', respectively, we obtain

$$\alpha'\Sigma_{12}\beta = \lambda_1\alpha'\Sigma_{11}\alpha - \mu_1\alpha'\Sigma_{11}\alpha_{(1)}$$
$$\beta'\Sigma_{21}\alpha = \lambda_2\beta'\Sigma_{22}\beta - \mu_2\beta'\Sigma_{22}\beta_{(1)} \qquad (2.1.19)$$

from which we conclude, in view of the constraints, that

$$\lambda_1 = \lambda_2 = \lambda \qquad (2.1.20)$$

Furthermore, notice that from (2.1.13) we have

$$\lambda^{(1)}\Sigma_{11}\alpha_{(1)} = \Sigma_{12}\beta_{(1)} \qquad \lambda^{(1)}\Sigma_{22}\beta_{(1)} = \Sigma_{21}\alpha_{(1)} \qquad (2.1.21)$$

But (2.1.21) easily implies, by the last two equations of (2.1.18), that

$$\alpha'\Sigma_{12}\beta_{(1)} = \beta'\Sigma_{21}\alpha_{(1)} = 0 \qquad (2.1.22)$$

Hence premultiplying the first two sets of equations in (2.1.18) by $\alpha'_{(1)}$ and $\beta'_{(1)}$ respectively, we find

$$\mu_1 = \mu_2 = 0 \qquad (2.1.23)$$

so that the solutions to the problem posed by (2.1.17) are simply the solutions to

$$\begin{bmatrix} -\lambda\Sigma_{11} & \Sigma_{12} \\ \Sigma_{21} & -\lambda\Sigma_{22} \end{bmatrix}\begin{pmatrix} \alpha \\ \beta \end{pmatrix} = 0 \qquad (2.1.24)$$

However, this is exactly the system of equations we dealt with when defining the first pair of canonical variables, except that now we must choose the solution corresponding to the second largest root of (2.1.14). Thus let $\lambda^{(2)}$ be the second largest root of (2.1.14) and let $\alpha_{(2)}$, $\beta_{(2)}$ be the solution of (2.1.24) associated with that root. The second pair of canonical variables is then defined by

$$\zeta_2 = \alpha'_{(2)}x^1 \qquad \omega_2 = \beta'_{(2)}x^2 \qquad (2.1.25)$$

and it is easily verified that

$$\text{Var}(\zeta_2) = \text{Var}(\omega_2) = 1 \qquad \text{Cov}(\zeta_2, \omega_2) = \lambda^{(2)}$$
$$\text{Cov}(\zeta_1, \zeta_2) = \text{Cov}(\zeta_1, \omega_2) = \text{Cov}(\zeta_2, \omega_1) = \text{Cov}(\omega_1, \omega_2) = 0 \qquad (2.1.26)$$

We could proceed similarly to extract the third, fourth, and so on pair of canonical variables. Instead we give without proof:

Proposition 1: Let

$$x \sim N(\mu, \Sigma) \qquad (2.1.27)$$

and partition

$$x = \begin{pmatrix} x^1 \\ x^2 \end{pmatrix} \qquad (2.1.28)$$

such that x^1 and x^2 are, respectively, vectors of m_1 and m_2 elements $(m_1 \leq m_2, m_1 + m_2 = m)$. Partition μ and Σ conformally so that

$$\mu = \begin{pmatrix} \mu^1 \\ \mu^2 \end{pmatrix} \qquad \Sigma = \begin{bmatrix} \Sigma_{11} & \Sigma_{12} \\ \Sigma_{21} & \Sigma_{22} \end{bmatrix} \tag{2.1.29}$$

Then, it is possible to decompose x^1 and x^2 into mutually independent linear combinations of their elements displaying (pairwise) *maximal* correlation. Specifically, we may decompose x^1 into $\zeta_1, \zeta_2, \ldots, \zeta_{m_1}$ and x^2 into $\omega_1, \omega_2, \ldots, \omega_{m_1}$ such that

$$\operatorname{Cov}(\zeta_i, \zeta_j) = \operatorname{Cov}(\omega_i, \omega_j) = \operatorname{Cov}(\zeta_i, \omega_j) = 0 \qquad i \neq j \tag{2.1.30}$$

and the quantities

$$\rho_i = \frac{\operatorname{Cov}(\zeta_i, \omega_i)}{[\operatorname{Var}(\zeta_i) \operatorname{Var}(\omega_i)]^{\frac{1}{2}}} \qquad i = 1, 2, \ldots, m_1 \tag{2.1.31}$$

are maximized subject to the normalization

$$\operatorname{Var}(\zeta_i) = \operatorname{Var}(\omega_i) = 1 \qquad i = 1, 2, \ldots, m_1 \tag{2.1.32}$$

Such pairs (ζ_i, ω_i) are called the canonical variables (of x^1 and x^2), and the correlations in (2.1.31) are called the canonical correlations (associated with x^1 and x^2). The canonical correlations are obtained as the roots of[1]

$$\begin{vmatrix} -\lambda\Sigma_{11} & \Sigma_{12} \\ \Sigma_{21} & -\lambda\Sigma_{22} \end{vmatrix} = 0 \tag{2.1.33}$$

while the canonical variables are obtained as

$$\zeta_i = \alpha'_{(i)} x^1 \qquad \omega_i = \beta'_{(i)} x^2 \qquad i = 1, 2, \ldots, m \tag{2.1.34}$$

the vectors $\alpha_{(i)}, \beta_{(i)}$ being the solutions of

$$\begin{bmatrix} -\lambda\Sigma_{11} & \Sigma_{12} \\ \Sigma_{21} & -\lambda\Sigma_{22} \end{bmatrix} \begin{pmatrix} \alpha \\ \beta \end{pmatrix} = 0 \tag{2.1.35}$$

corresponding to the ordered roots $\lambda^{(i)}$ of (2.1.33)—ordered by $\lambda^{(1)} \geq \lambda^{(2)} \geq \lambda^{(3)} \geq \cdots \geq \lambda^{(m_1)}$—and

$$\rho_i = \lambda^{(i)} \qquad i = 1, 2, \ldots, m_1 \tag{2.1.36}$$

The reader may directly verify the truth of the proposition.

---

[1] It will become apparent to the reader, especially from (2.1.37) below, that the roots of (2.1.33) obey the following: $m_2 - m_1$ of them are zero, m_1 are nonpositive and m_1 are non-negative.

Let us now show some of the properties of canonical correlations. First, since they are defined as in (2.1.31), they "ought" to be less than unity in absolute value. Second, we can establish that their square has an interpretation as a characteristic root of a certain positive semidefinite matrix. Third, both canonical correlations *and* canonical variables are invariant with respect to the units in which the elements of x are measured.

We begin by demonstrating the second property first. Consider (2.1.33) and note that by the well-known result on the determinant of a partitioned matrix, it is equivalent to

$$(-1)^{m_1} \lambda^{m_2-m_1} |\Sigma_{22}| \, |\lambda^2 \Sigma_{11} - \Sigma_{12} \Sigma_{22}^{-1} \Sigma_{21}| = 0 \tag{2.1.37}$$

This shows that (2.1.33) has at least $m_2 - m_1$ zero roots. Thus its nonzero roots are exactly the nonzero roots of

$$|\lambda^2 \Sigma_{11} - \Sigma_{12} \Sigma_{22}^{-1} \Sigma_{21}| = 0 \tag{2.1.38}$$

Since $\Sigma_{12} \Sigma_{22}^{-1} \Sigma_{21}$ is positive semidefinite, because of the positive definiteness of Σ, the second property is proved. To show that the $\lambda^{(i)}$ are less than unity in absolute value is, of course, equivalent to showing that the quantities $(\lambda^{(i)})^2$ are less than unity. To this effect consider the roots of $\Sigma_{11} - \Sigma_{12} \Sigma_{22}^{-1} \Sigma_{21}$ in the metric of Σ_{11}. Since both matrices are *positive definite*, such roots are positive. Thus consider

$$|\mu \Sigma_{11} - (\Sigma_{11} - \Sigma_{12} \Sigma_{22}^{-1} \Sigma_{21})| = 0 \tag{2.1.39}$$

Here the roots, say μ_i, $i = 1, 2, \ldots, m_1$ obey

$$\mu_i > 0 \tag{2.1.40}$$

We note, however, that (2.1.39) is equivalent to

$$|(1 - \mu) \Sigma_{11} - \Sigma_{12} \Sigma_{22}^{-1} \Sigma_{21}| = 0 \tag{2.1.41}$$

Comparing with (2.1.38), we see that we can make the identification

$$\lambda_i^2 = 1 - \mu_i \tag{2.1.42}$$

λ_i^2 and μ_i being corresponding roots of (2.1.38) and (2.1.39)—arranged in order of magnitude. Since we have the restrictions

$$\lambda_i^2 \geq 0 \qquad \mu_i > 0 \tag{2.1.43}$$

we conclude from (2.1.42)

$$\lambda_i^2 < 1 \tag{2.1.44}$$

which proves the first assertion. We should note that no root of (2.1.38) can be unity unless some linear dependence exists amongst the elements of x. This is so because $\Sigma_{11} - \Sigma_{12} \Sigma_{22}^{-1} \Sigma_{21}$ is the *covariance matrix of the conditional distribution* of x^1 given x^2 and it cannot be singular unless Σ is also singular.

Turning now to the problem of invariance under a "units" transformation, we note that the latter is of the general form

$$x_i^* = d_i x_i \qquad i = 1, 2, \ldots, m \qquad (2.1.45)$$

where x_i is the ith element of x. If we put

$$D_1 = \text{diag}\,(d_1, d_2, \ldots, d_{m_1})$$

$$D_2 = \text{diag}\,(d_{m_1+1}, \ldots, d_{m_1+m_2}) \qquad (2.1.46)$$

$$D = \begin{bmatrix} D_1 & 0 \\ 0 & D_2 \end{bmatrix}$$

then the transformed vector is

$$x^* = \begin{pmatrix} x^{*1} \\ x^{*2} \end{pmatrix} = \begin{pmatrix} D_1 x^1 \\ D_2 x^2 \end{pmatrix} \qquad (2.1.47)$$

Furthermore,

$$x^* \sim N(D\mu, D\Sigma D')$$

$$D\Sigma D' = \begin{bmatrix} D_1 \Sigma_{11} D_1 & D_1 \Sigma_{12} D_2 \\ D_2 \Sigma_{21} D_1 & D_2 \Sigma_{22} D_2 \end{bmatrix} = \begin{bmatrix} \Sigma_{11}^* & \Sigma_{12}^* \\ \Sigma_{21}^* & \Sigma_{22}^* \end{bmatrix} \qquad (2.1.48)$$

It is clear that the canonical correlations of x^{*1} and x^{*2} are to be found as the solutions of

$$|\lambda^{*2}(D_1 \Sigma_{11} D_1) - D_1 \Sigma_{12} D_2 (D_2 \Sigma_{22} D_2)^{-1} D_2 \Sigma_{21} D_1|$$
$$= |D_1|^2 |\lambda^{*2} \Sigma_{11} - \Sigma_{12} \Sigma_{22}^{-1} \Sigma_{21}| = 0 \qquad (2.1.49)$$

Since $|D_1| \neq 0$, a comparison with (2.1.38) quite clearly shows that canonical correlations are invariant under a "units" transformation. To show the invariance of the canonical variables, we proceed as follows.

The canonical variables corresponding to x^{*1} and x^{*2} are given by

$$\zeta_i^* = \alpha_{(i)}^{*\prime} x^{*1} \qquad \omega_i = \beta_{(i)}^{*\prime} x^{*2} \qquad i = 1, 2, \ldots, m_1 \qquad (2.1.50)$$

the $\alpha_{(i)}^*$, $\beta_{(i)}^*$ being the solutions of

$$\begin{bmatrix} -\lambda^{(i)} \Sigma_{11}^* & \Sigma_{12}^* \\ \Sigma_{21}^* & -\lambda^{(i)} \Sigma_{22}^* \end{bmatrix} \begin{pmatrix} \alpha^* \\ \beta^* \end{pmatrix} = 0 \qquad (2.1.51)$$

The solutions, therefore, obey

$$\lambda^{(i)} D_1 \Sigma_{11} D_1 \alpha_{(i)}^* = D_1 \Sigma_{12} D_2 \beta_{(i)}^*$$
$$D_2 \Sigma_{21} D_1 \alpha_{(i)}^* = \lambda^{(i)} D_2 \Sigma_{22} D_2 \beta_{(i)}^* \qquad (2.1.52)$$

In addition, (2.1.52) and (2.1.24) imply

$$D_1 \alpha_{(i)}^* = \alpha_{(i)} \qquad D_2 \beta_{(i)}^* = \beta_{(i)} \qquad i = 1, 2, \ldots, m \qquad (2.1.53)$$

Thus

$$\zeta_i^* = \alpha_{(i)}^{*\prime} x^{*1} = \alpha_{(i)}^{\prime} D_1^{-1} D_1 x^1 = \zeta_i$$
$$\omega_i^* = \beta_{(i)}^{*\prime} x^{*2} = \beta_{(i)}^{\prime} D_2^{-1} x^2 = \omega_i \tag{2.1.54}$$

which is the assertion we wish to prove.

Finally, canonical correlation theory is often presented in connection with a random vector

$$x \sim N(0, \Sigma) \tag{2.1.55}$$

in which case the only units transformation that preserves the nature of the problem is that given in (2.1.45). If, however, we assume

$$x \sim N(\mu, \Sigma) \tag{2.1.56}$$

μ being an arbitrary vector, then the admissible set of transformations is

$$x_i^* = d_i x_i + c_i \tag{2.1.57}$$

If such a transformation is made, however, it is not true that equation (2.1.54) remains valid.

In the subsequent section we shall always assume, for purposes of defining canonical variables, that (2.1.55) holds.

ESTIMATION, TESTS OF SIGNIFICANCE, AND EXAMPLES OF CANONICAL CORRELATION

From the preceding discussion it is obvious that to estimate canonical variables or canonical correlations it is sufficient to estimate the covariance matrix Σ of (2.1.2), say, by maximum likelihood methods. Thus suppose we have n observations $x_{.i}$, $i = 1, 2, \ldots, n$, on the vector $x \sim N(\mu, \Sigma)$. If we let

$$X = (x_{.1}, x_{.2}, \ldots, x_{.n}) \qquad \bar{x} = \frac{1}{n} \sum_{i=1}^{n} x_{.i} \tag{2.1.58}$$

then the maximum likelihood estimator of Σ is

$$\hat{\Sigma} = \frac{XX'}{n} - \bar{x}\bar{x}' \tag{2.1.59}$$

Since the process of extracting characteristic roots and solving linear equations involves only rational operations, it follows that solving the system

$$\begin{bmatrix} -r_i \hat{\Sigma}_{11} & \hat{\Sigma}_{12} \\ \hat{\Sigma}_{21} & -r_i \hat{\Sigma}_{22} \end{bmatrix} \begin{pmatrix} a_{(i)} \\ b_{(i)} \end{pmatrix} = 0 \tag{2.1.60}$$

for r_i satisfying

$$\begin{vmatrix} -r\hat{\Sigma}_{11} & \hat{\Sigma}_{12} \\ \hat{\Sigma}_{21} & -r\hat{\Sigma}_{22} \end{vmatrix} = 0 \tag{2.1.61}$$

will yield maximum likelihood estimators for the $\lambda^{(i)}$, $\alpha_{(i)}$, and $\beta_{(i)}$ of the previous section. We would then define the estimators of canonical correlations and canonical variables by

$$\hat{\lambda}^{(i)} = r_i \qquad \hat{\zeta}_i = z_i = a'_{(i)}(x^1 - \bar{x}^1)$$
$$\hat{\omega}_i = w_i = b'_{(i)}(x^2 - \bar{x}^2) \qquad i = 1, 2, \ldots, m_1 \tag{2.1.62}$$

where $\bar{x}^1$, $\bar{x}^2$ represent an appropriate partition of the vector of sample means, $\bar{x}$.

Often it is computationally more efficient to operate not with the sample covariance matrix $\hat{\Sigma}$ but rather with the sample correlation matrix, which is given by

$$\hat{R} = S\hat{\Sigma}S \tag{2.1.63}$$

where

$$S = \text{diag}\left(\frac{1}{s_1}, \frac{1}{s_2}, \ldots, \frac{1}{s_m}\right) \qquad s_i = \sqrt{\hat{\sigma}_{ii}} \qquad i = 1, 2, \ldots, m \tag{2.1.64}$$

This ensures greater accuracy in the extraction of the roots r_i and their associated vectors $a_{(i)}$ and $b_{(i)}$. Doing so is equivalent to operating *ab initio*, with standardized deviates

$$x^*_{\tau\nu} = \frac{x_{\tau\nu} - \bar{x}_\tau}{s_\tau} \qquad \tau = 1, 2, \ldots, m, \nu = 1, 2, \ldots, n \tag{2.1.65}$$

where $\bar{x}_\tau$ is the τth element of $\bar{x}$. It is interesting that the distribution of the *squares* of the nonzero roots of (2.1.61) is known and, moreover, the distribution of the smallest and largest such roots has been tabulated[2] by K. C. Sreedharan Pillai. An indication of the type of application of canonical correlation theory to the estimation of simultaneous equations systems will be given at a later stage. An entirely different kind of application is indicated by the following

Example: Waugh [22] considers the problem of the relation between meat consumption and meat prices. For that purpose he has a sample of 20 (yearly) observations on $x_1 = $ steer prices, $x_2 = $ hog prices, $x_3 = $ beef consumption, $x_4 = $ pork consumption. The consumption data are per capita and the price data are "deflated" by per capita income—a dubious procedure at best.

The data are stated in standardized deviate units: that is, from each observation the relevant sample mean is subtracted and the difference is divided by the corresponding standard deviation. Hence the matrix $\hat{\Sigma}$ required for our purposes is, in this case, the correlation matrix, which we denote by Σ^*. We have

$$\hat{\Sigma}^* = \begin{bmatrix} 1. & .18 & -.56 & -.50 \\ & 1. & .35 & -.76 \\ & & 1. & .10 \\ & & & 1. \end{bmatrix} \tag{2.1.66}$$

---

[2] See Reference 14.

The relevant determinantal equation is

$$|r\hat{\Sigma}_{11}^* - \hat{\Sigma}_{12}^*\hat{\Sigma}_{22}^{*-1}\hat{\Sigma}_{21}^*| = 0 \qquad (2.1.67)$$

Now

$$\hat{\Sigma}_{12}^*\hat{\Sigma}_{22}^{*-1}\hat{\Sigma}_{21}^* = \frac{1}{.99}\begin{bmatrix} -.56 & -.50 \\ .35 & -.76 \end{bmatrix}\begin{bmatrix} 1. & -.1 \\ -.1 & 1. \end{bmatrix}\begin{bmatrix} -.56 & .35 \\ -.50 & -.76 \end{bmatrix}$$

$$= \begin{bmatrix} .52 & .16 \\ .16 & .73 \end{bmatrix} \qquad (2.1.68)$$

Thus (2.1.67) can be written as

$$\begin{vmatrix} r - .52 & .18r - .16 \\ .18r - .16 & r - .73 \end{vmatrix}$$

$$= r^2 - 1.25r + .38 - .03r^2 + .06r - .03 = 0 \qquad (2.1.69)$$

Hence we must solve

$$.97r^2 - 1.19r + .35 = 0 \qquad (2.1.70)$$

The roots of (2.1.70) are

$$r_1 = .70 \qquad r_2 = .48 \qquad (2.1.71)$$

It follows, therefore, that the estimators of the canonical correlations are

$$r^{(1)} = .84$$
$$r^{(2)} = .69$$
$$r^{(3)} = -.69$$
$$r^{(4)} = -.84 \qquad (2.1.72)$$

Clearly, since $m_1 = m_2 = 2$ here, there is no zero root. Waugh's choice of the canonical variables implies that he chose $r^{(4)}$ for their definition. At any rate, choosing the solution vector corresponding to $r^{(4)}$ and normalizing so that the sum of coefficients equals 100, Waugh obtains

$$z = 52.62x_1 + 47.38x_2$$
$$w = 25.38x_3 + 74.62x_4 \qquad (2.1.73)$$

The canonical correlation given by Waugh is -0.8466; he interprets his canonical variables as indices of price and quantity respectively. Thus the problem he poses is one of finding linear combinations of prices and quantities exhibiting largest "negative" correlation. His motivation for the negativity aspect is that prices and quantities "ought" to move in opposite directions. The basic motivation for this application is the construction of indices, and his criterion is that the weights selected for the components of the indices should be such that the (absolute value of their) correlation is *maximized*.

2.2 PRINCIPAL COMPONENTS

MOTIVATION AND THEORY

Related to the theory of canonical correlations is the theory of principal components. In the former, the problem was one of defining two sets of variables, all having unit variance, such that within each set variables were uncorrelated (independent), whereas corresponding elements of the two sets exhibited *maximal correlation*. In principal component theory, the problem is one of defining a number of mutually uncorrelated (independent) variables exhibiting, in some sense, maximal variance.

A few examples will clarify the nature of the problem and illustrate some possible applications.

Suppose that we have a variable y and we are interested, for forecasting or prediction purposes, in the regression of y on a number of variables $x_1, x_2, \ldots, x_m$. There are a variety of cases where it may not be feasible or desirable to use so many variables. First, the number of observations may not be large relative to the number of variables; hence we would have too few degrees of freedom. Second, it may be that the explanatory variables, the x_i, are nearly collinear, so that we may wish to represent their collective behavior in a space of dimension less than m.

Finally, there is the general problem of aggregation, or index construction. Here again the nature of the problem is the representation of m-dimensional vectors in a space of fewer dimensions—typically one.

In all the instances cited, we wish to find some linear function (or functions) of the elements of an m-dimensional vector, which in some sense captures most of their variability.

Linearity is not essential; any other functional form might do just as well, but the theory will become very tedious and complicated. With these preliminaries aside, we turn to the formal aspects of the theory.

Thus let[3]

$$x \sim N(\mu, \Sigma) \tag{2.2.1}$$

x being an m-dimensional vector and let it be desired to find a linear combination of the elements of x having maximal variance. If

$$\zeta' = \alpha'x \tag{2.2.2}$$

is such a linear combination, then

$$\text{Var}(\zeta) = \alpha'\Sigma\alpha \tag{2.2.3}$$

---

[3] Normality is not essential for the development of the theory; it is only necessary in developing the distribution characteristics of various test statistics. The same is true for canonical correlation theory and generally for all sections of this chapter.

and it quickly becomes apparent that, as posed, the problem does not admit of a solution, for if we choose

$$\alpha^* = c\alpha \qquad (2.2.4)$$

for a fixed α, then we can make the variance of ζ arbitrarily large by taking c to be large.

Hence, again we are faced with a scale problem; in this context, the problem is usually resolved by the convention

$$\alpha'\alpha = 1 \qquad (2.2.5)$$

which simply requires that the vector defining the linear combination be of unit length.

Thus the problem becomes equivalent to the maximization of the Lagrangean

$$L = \alpha'\Sigma\alpha + \lambda(1 - \alpha'\alpha) \qquad (2.2.6)$$

This yields the first-order conditions

$$\frac{\partial L}{\partial \alpha} = 2\Sigma\alpha - 2\lambda\alpha = 0$$

$$\frac{\partial L}{\partial \lambda} = 1 - \alpha'\alpha = 0 \qquad (2.2.7)$$

and it is quickly verified that the solution vector obeys

$$\alpha'\Sigma\alpha = \lambda \qquad (2.2.8)$$

On the other hand, the first set of equations in (2.2.7) implies that λ must be one of the characteristic roots of Σ. As a result of (2.2.8) and the nature of the problem, we must choose the largest characteristic root, say λ_1, and the (normalized) characteristic vector associated with it, say $\alpha_{(1)}$. Thus we define the (first) principal component of (the elements of) x by

$$\zeta_1 = \alpha'_{(1)} x \qquad (2.2.9)$$

where $\alpha_{(1)}$ obeys

$$(\lambda_1 I - \Sigma)\alpha_{(1)} = 0 \qquad \alpha'_{(1)}\alpha_{(1)} = 1 \qquad (2.2.10)$$

and λ_1 is the largest root of

$$|\lambda I - \Sigma| = 0 \qquad (2.2.11)$$

It is easy to verify that

$$E(\zeta_1) = \alpha'_{(1)}\mu \qquad \text{Var}(\zeta_1) = \lambda_1 \qquad (2.2.12)$$

Suppose, further, that we wish to define another linear combination of the elements of x having maximal variance and being uncorrelated with (independent of) ζ_1. To solve this problem, we proceed in the same fashion as before, again imposing the normalization of unit length on the vector defining the linear combination. However, in addition, we must have

$$\text{Cov}(\zeta_1, \zeta) = \alpha'_{(1)} \Sigma \alpha = 0 \qquad (2.2.13)$$

where

$$\zeta = \alpha' x \qquad (2.2.14)$$

α being the vector of the second linear combination, yet to be determined.

Thus the problem now posed is equivalent to maximizing the Lagrangean

$$L = \alpha' \Sigma \alpha + \lambda(1 - \alpha' \Sigma \alpha) + \mu_1 \alpha'_{(1)} \Sigma \alpha \qquad (2.2.15)$$

The first-order conditions are

$$\frac{\partial L}{\partial \alpha} = 2\Sigma\alpha - 2\lambda\alpha + \mu_1 \Sigma \alpha_{(1)} = 0$$

$$\frac{\partial L}{\partial \lambda} = 1 - \alpha' \Sigma \alpha = 0 \qquad (2.2.16)$$

$$\frac{\partial L}{\partial \mu_1} = \alpha'_{(1)} \Sigma \alpha = 0$$

Premultiplying the first set of equations by α', we conclude, in view of the constraints,

$$\alpha' \Sigma \alpha = \lambda \qquad (2.2.17)$$

We next note that, since by construction

$$\Sigma \alpha_{(1)} = \lambda_1 \alpha_{(1)} \qquad (2.2.18)$$

premultiplying in (2.2.18) by α', we have, in view of the constraint,

$$\alpha' \alpha_{(1)} = 0 \qquad (2.2.19)$$

Now, premultiplying the first set of equations in (2.2.16) by $\alpha'_{(1)}$, we find

$$2\alpha'_{(1)} \Sigma \alpha - 2\lambda \alpha'_{(1)} \alpha + \mu_1 \alpha'_{(1)} \Sigma \alpha_{(1)} = 0 \qquad (2.2.20)$$

But, in view of the constraints and (2.2.19), we conclude

$$\mu_1 \alpha'_{(1)} \Sigma \alpha_{(1)} = \mu_1 \lambda_1 = 0 \qquad (2.2.21)$$

Since $\lambda_1 > 0$, we conclude that

$$\mu_1 = 0 \qquad (2.2.22)$$

so that the first set of equations in (2.2.16) has the form

$$(\lambda I - \Sigma)\alpha = 0 \qquad (2.2.23)$$

By (2.2.17) we see that, to define the second linear combination, we must solve exactly the same problem as in defining the first. We need to choose the *second largest* characteristic root of Σ, say λ_2, and the (normalized) characteristic vector associated with it, say $\alpha_{(2)}$. The linear combination we are seeking is given by

$$\zeta_2 = \alpha'_{(2)} x \qquad (2.2.24)$$

and has the properties

$$E(\zeta_2) = \alpha'_{(2)} \mu \quad \text{Var}(\zeta_2) = \lambda_2 \quad \text{Cov}(\zeta_1, \zeta_2) = 0 \qquad (2.2.25)$$

The variables ζ_1 and ζ_2 are called, respectively, the first and second principal components of (the elements of) the vector x. We can proceed similarly to derive the third, fourth, and so on principal components. Instead we offer the following

Proposition 2: Let

$$x \sim N(\mu, \Sigma) \qquad (2.2.26)$$

x being $m \times 1$.

Then there exist m linear combinations of the elements of x, say

$$\zeta_i = \alpha'_{(i)} x \qquad i = 1, 2, \ldots, m \qquad (2.2.27)$$

such that

$$\text{Var}(\zeta_i) = \lambda_i \quad \text{Cov}(\zeta_i, \zeta_j) = 0 \qquad i \neq j \qquad (2.2.28)$$

where λ_i are the ordered $(\lambda_1 \geq \lambda_2 \geq \cdots \geq \lambda_m)$ characteristic roots of Σ and $\alpha_{(i)}$ their associated (orthonormal) characteristic vectors.

The ζ_i corresponding to the (ordered) set of characteristic roots of Σ have the property that they are mutually uncorrelated (independent) linear combinations of the elements of x having maximal variance.

The proof of the proposition is trivial and is left to the reader.

Definition 2: The vector

$$\zeta = (\zeta_1, \zeta_2, \ldots, \zeta_m)' \qquad (2.2.29)$$

of Proposition 2 is called the *vector of principal components of x, and ζ_i is called the ith principal component*.

Several useful properties of principal components should be mentioned before we conclude this section. Consequently, let us first introduce some terminology.

Definition 3: Let x be an m-component random vector such that

$$\text{Cov}(x) = \Sigma = (\sigma_{ij}) \qquad (2.2.30)$$

Then the *generalized variance*[4] of x is defined by

$$\text{G. Var}(x) = |\Sigma| \qquad (2.2.31)$$

---

[4] While the term *generalized variance* represents standard usage, the term *variability* does not. Indeed, no specific name commonly attaches to what we have called variability here.

and the *variability* of x is defined by

$$V(x) = \text{tr}\, \Sigma = \sum_{i=1}^{m} \sigma_{ii} \tag{2.2.32}$$

We may now prove

Theorem 1: Let[5]

$$x \sim N(0, \Sigma) \tag{2.2.33}$$

x being $m \times 1$. Then the principal components associated with x

$$\zeta = (\zeta_1, \zeta_2, \ldots, \zeta_m)' \qquad \zeta_i = \alpha'_{(i)} x \tag{2.2.34}$$

have the following properties:

i. $\zeta \sim N(0, \Lambda) \qquad \Lambda = \text{diag}\,(\lambda_1, \lambda_2, \ldots, \lambda_m)$
   the λ_i being the characteristic roots of Σ and the $\alpha_{(i)}$ their associated (ortho-normal) characteristic vectors.
ii. G. Var (x) = G. Var (ζ)
iii. $V(x) = V(\zeta)$
iv. Principal components are not independent of the units in which the elements of x are measured.

   PROOF: By definition,

$$\zeta = A^{*\prime} x \tag{2.2.35}$$

where

$$A^* = (\alpha_{(1)}, \alpha_{(2)}, \ldots, \alpha_{(m)}) \tag{2.2.36}$$

Thus

$$\zeta \sim N(0, A^{*\prime}\Sigma A^*) \tag{2.2.37}$$

Since A^* is the (orthogonal) matrix of characteristic vectors of Σ, it obeys

$$\Sigma A^* = A^* \Lambda \tag{2.2.38}$$

Premultiplying by $A^{*\prime}$, we find

$$\Lambda = A^{*\prime}\Sigma A^* \tag{2.2.39}$$

which proves property i.
   Since A^* is orthogonal,

$$|A^*| = \pm 1 \tag{2.2.40}$$

Thus, from (2.2.39),

$$|\Lambda| = |A^*|^2 |\Sigma| = |\Sigma| \tag{2.2.41}$$

which proves property ii.

---

[5] The assumption of zero mean is not essential; it is only made for notational simplicity.

Since A^* is orthogonal, it follows that

$$A^{*\prime} = A^{*-1} \tag{2.2.42}$$

Thus

$$\text{tr } \Lambda = \text{tr } A^{*\prime}\Sigma A^* = \text{tr } \Sigma A^* A^{*\prime} = \text{tr } \Sigma \tag{2.2.43}$$

which proves property iii.

To see the dependence of principal components on the units of measurement, suppose we consider the "units" transformation

$$x^* = Dx \qquad D = \text{diag}\,(d_1, d_2, \ldots, d_m) \tag{2.2.44}$$

so that the elements of x^* differ from those of x only in their scale of measurement.

Now the principal components of x^* are defined by

$$\zeta_i^* = \alpha_{(i)}^{*\prime} x^* \qquad i = 1, 2, \ldots, m \tag{2.2.45}$$

the $\alpha_{(i)}^*$ being the (orthonormal) characteristic vectors of

$$\text{Cov}\,(x^*) = D\Sigma D \tag{2.2.46}$$

Such vectors are defined by

$$D\Sigma D\alpha_{(i)}^* = \lambda_i^* \alpha_{(i)}^* \qquad i = 1, 2, \ldots, m \tag{2.2.47}$$

the λ_i^* being the roots of

$$|\lambda^* I - D\Sigma D| = 0 \tag{2.2.48}$$

If λ_i^*, $i = 1, 2, \ldots, m$, are the roots of (2.2.48), then

$$\prod_{i=1}^{m} \lambda_i^* = |D|^2 |\Sigma| \neq |\Sigma| \tag{2.2.49}$$

Since if λ_i, $i = 1, 2, \ldots, m$, are the roots of Σ

$$\prod_{i=1}^{m} \lambda_i = |\Sigma| \tag{2.2.50}$$

we conclude that, in general,

$$\lambda_i \neq \lambda_i^* \qquad i = 1, 2, \ldots, m \tag{2.2.51}$$

We next show that, in general,

$$\zeta_i \neq \zeta_i^* \qquad i = 1, 2, \ldots, m \tag{2.2.52}$$

where ζ_i are the principal components of x.

Now $\zeta_i = \zeta_i^*$ if and only if

$$\alpha_{(i)}' x = \alpha_{(i)}^{*\prime} Dx \qquad i = 1, 2, \ldots, m \tag{2.2.53}$$

which implies

$$\alpha_{(i)} = D\alpha_{(i)}^* \tag{2.2.54}$$

But this is impossible, for both $\alpha_{(i)}$ *and* $\alpha_{(i)}^*$ are by construction orthonormal sets of vectors.

This concludes the proof of the theorem.

ESTIMATION, TESTS OF SIGNIFICANCE, AND EXAMPLES OF PRINCIPAL COMPONENTS

The preceding discussion implies that maximum likelihood estimation of principal components requires only the estimation of a covariance matrix.

Suppose that we have a sample $x_{\cdot t}$, $t = 1, 2, \ldots, n$, where $x_{\cdot t}$ is the tth observation on the (m-dimensional) random vector,

$$x \sim N(\mu, \Sigma) \tag{2.2.55}$$

Define

$$X = (x_{\cdot 1}, x_{\cdot 2}, \ldots, x_{\cdot n}) \qquad n > m \tag{2.2.56}$$

and note that the maximum likelihood estimator of Σ is

$$\hat{\Sigma} = \frac{XX'}{n} - \bar{x}\bar{x}' \tag{2.2.57}$$

where

$$\bar{x} = \frac{1}{n} \sum_{i=1}^{n} x_{\cdot i} \tag{2.2.58}$$

Since the roots of a matrix are uniquely determined, it follows that the roots of

$$|rI - \hat{\Sigma}| = 0 \tag{2.2.59}$$

are the maximum likelihood estimators of the characteristic roots, λ_i, of Σ.

Furthermore, under the normalization scheme,

$$a_{(i)}' a_{(j)} = \delta_{ij} \tag{2.2.60}$$

δ_{ij} being the Kronecker delta. The characteristic vectors, $a_{(i)}$, of $\hat{\Sigma}$ are uniquely determined, except that if $a_{(i)}$ is such a vector, then so is $-a_{(i)}$. Thus, if in the definition of principal components we add the restriction, say, that in the ith principal component the coefficient of x_i is positive, then we shall have uniqueness.

In such a framework, the maximum likelihood estimators of the vectors $\alpha_{(i)}$ of the previous section are the characteristic vectors of $\hat{\Sigma}$. Thus the maximum likelihood estimators of the principal components are given by

$$z_{ij} = a_{(i)}' x_{\cdot j} \qquad i = 1, 2, \ldots, m, \, j = 1, 2, \ldots, n \tag{2.2.61}$$

where the $a_{(i)}$ are the characteristic vectors of $\hat{\Sigma}$, and z_{ij} gives the jth "observation" on the ith principal component. At the cost of being redundant, let us note that if we put

$$Z = (z_{ij}) \qquad i = 1, 2, \ldots, m, j = 1, 2, \ldots, n \tag{2.2.62}$$

then

$$Z = A'X \qquad A = (a_{(1)}, a_{(2)}, \ldots, a_{(m)}) \tag{2.2.63}$$

$$\bar{z} = A'\bar{x} \quad \bar{z} = \frac{1}{n} \sum_{j=1}^{n} z_{\cdot j} \quad z_{\cdot j} = \begin{pmatrix} z_{1j} \\ z_{2j} \\ \vdots \\ z_{mj} \end{pmatrix} \tag{2.2.64}$$

Moreover,

$$\frac{1}{n} ZZ' - \bar{z}\bar{z}' = \left[A' \frac{XX'}{n} A - A'\bar{x}\bar{x}'A \right] = A' \left[\frac{XX'}{n} - \bar{x}\bar{x}' \right] A = A'\hat{\Sigma}A \tag{2.2.65}$$

If we put

$$R^* = \text{diag} (r_1, r_2, \ldots, r_m) \tag{2.2.66}$$

the r_i being the ordered roots of (2.2.59), then we observe that

$$A'\hat{\Sigma}A = R^* \tag{2.2.67}$$

so that the principal components are uncorrelated in a *sampling sense*.

We also note that the *sample generalized variance* and the *sample variability of the original variables and their estimated principal components coincide*.

Often, in defining principal components, it is found *computationally* more convenient to operate with the (sample) *correlation* rather than the *covariance matrix*. This of course means that we operate *ab initio* with standardized deviates. Also, if the units in which the elements of x are "naturally" measured lead to large-scale differences amongst them, it would be desirable to transform to standardized deviates, in view of the sensitivity of principal components to the scale of measurement. When operating this way, we must remember that if we wish to preserve the uncorrelatedness of the estimated principal components, then we should define the latter in terms of the *standardized deviates* rather than in terms of the original variables.

One problem that frequently arises in estimation is whether there are "really" m components. This is equivalent to asking whether the matrix Σ is "really" of rank m. From a strictly statistical point of view, this question does not make much sense. For *if* Σ is nonsingular, then with probability one $\hat{\Sigma}$ will also be nonsingular and thus we can certainly extract m components. On the other hand, *if* Σ is singular, then with probability one $\hat{\Sigma}$ will be singular so that at least one of its roots will be zero and thus we can define at most $m - 1$ components.

Hence, if upon extraction of the roots of $\hat{\Sigma}$ we find that all its roots are positive, this *ipso facto* suggests that the roots of Σ are all different from zero and thus that there are "really" m components. Viewed in this light, there is no point in testing the (smallest) roots of $\hat{\Sigma}$ for significance.

There is, however, a sense in which the question of whether there are really m components can be meaningfully asked in a slightly different way.

Suppose that our objective in employing principal components is the reduction of the dimensionality of the problem at hand. Then it is perfectly appropriate to ask whether, say, the first k principal components "substantially" account for the variations of the elements of x, and thus the extraction of the $(m - k)$ remaining components is superfluous. We can employ the following test, which, in effect, tests the hypothesis that the last $m - k$ roots of Σ are indistinguishable and presumably "small."

Specifically, the null hypothesis is

$$H_0: \lambda_{k+1} = \lambda_{k+2} = \cdots = \lambda_m = \lambda \tag{2.2.68}$$

If H_0 is in fact true, then by continuing to extract components we add rather little to the power of the vector $(\zeta_1, \zeta_2, \ldots, \zeta_k)'$ to account for variations in the elements of x. It can be shown, [9], that the test can be approximately based, the order of approximation being $1/n^2$, n being the size of the sample, on a chi-square variable with

$$p = \tfrac{1}{2}(q + 2)(q - 1) \tag{2.2.69}$$

degrees of freedom, where

$$q = m - k \tag{2.2.70}$$

The relevant chi-square variable is

$$\phi = \left[n - 1 - k - \frac{1}{6}\left(2q + \frac{2}{q} + 1 \right) + \lambda^2 \sum_{r=1}^{k} \frac{1}{(\lambda_r - \lambda)^2} \right]$$

$$\cdot \left[-\ln\left(\frac{|\hat{\Sigma}|}{\prod_{i=1}^{k} \hat{\lambda}_i} \right) + q \ln\left(\frac{\operatorname{tr} \hat{\Sigma} - \sum_{r=1}^{k} \hat{\lambda}_r}{q} \right) \right] \tag{2.2.71}$$

where the $\hat{\lambda}_r$ are the characteristic roots of $\hat{\Sigma}$.

Of course, ϕ does not constitute a statistic, for it does depend on the unknown parameters λ and λ_r, $r = 1, 2, \ldots, k$, and thus to make use of the test we should replace, in (2.2.71), λ_r by $\hat{\lambda}_r$ and λ by

$$\frac{\operatorname{tr} \hat{\Sigma} - \sum_{r=1}^{k} \hat{\lambda}_r}{q}$$

In this test we are dealing with a composite hypothesis, for the value of λ is not specified. In the unlikely event that we would want to define the hypothesis more sharply by specifying that

$$\lambda = \lambda_0 \tag{2.2.72}$$

λ_0 being a prescribed constant, the appropriate test "statistic" is

$$\phi_1 = \left[n - 1 - k - \frac{1}{6}\left(2q + 1 - \frac{2}{q+1} \right) - \frac{1}{q+1}\left\{ \sum_{r=1}^{k} \left(\frac{\lambda_r}{\lambda_r - \lambda} \right) \right\}^2 \right.$$

$$\left. + \lambda^2 \sum_{r=1}^{k} \frac{1}{(\lambda_r - \lambda)^2} \right]$$

$$\cdot \left[q \ln \lambda - \ln \frac{|\hat{\Sigma}|}{\prod_{r=1}^{k} \hat{\lambda}_r} + \frac{\operatorname{tr} \hat{\Sigma} - \sum_{r=1}^{k} \hat{\lambda}_r}{\lambda} - q \right] \tag{2.2.73}$$

which is, to the same degree of approximation, chi square distributed with

$$p_1 = \tfrac{1}{2}q(q + 1) \tag{2.2.74}$$

degrees of freedom.

Finally, we should point out in this connection that even though it is desirable, in a sense, that principal components be defined with respect to the *correlation* matrix, the asymptotic distribution of the relevant characteristic roots is not nearly as well defined as in the case above and the resulting test "statistic" is considerably more complicated.

Thus let $\rho_1, \rho_2, \ldots, \rho_m$ be the roots of the correlation matrix R, and suppose we wish to test

$$H_0: \rho_{k+1} = \rho_{k+2} = \cdots = \rho_m = \rho \qquad k < m \tag{2.2.75}$$

Lawley [9] shows that the appropriate test statistic is

$$\phi^* = (n - 1)\left(-\ln \frac{|\hat{R}|}{\prod_{i=1}^{k} \hat{\rho}_i} + q \ln \frac{\operatorname{tr} \hat{R} - \sum_{i=1}^{k} \hat{\rho}_i}{q} \right) \tag{2.2.76}$$

where $\hat{R}$ is the maximum likelihood estimator of the correlation matrix given by (2.1.63) of the previous section and $\hat{\rho}_i$ are the maximum likelihood estimators of ρ_i given by the solutions of

$$|rI - \hat{R}| = 0 \tag{2.2.77}$$

The statistic in (2.2.76) is approximately (to order $1/n$) chi square distributed with degrees of freedom

$$p^* = \frac{1}{2}(q - 1)(q + 2) - \frac{1}{q}\left(2(q - 1)\rho \sum_{i=1}^{m} c_{ii}^2 - q \sum_{i=1}^{m} \sum_{j=1}^{m} c_{ij}^2 \rho_{ij}^2 + \sum_{i=1}^{m} \sum_{j=1}^{m} c_{ii} c_{jj} \rho_{ij}^2 \right) \tag{2.2.78}$$

where ρ is as defined in (2.2.75) and ρ_{ij} is the correlation between the ith and jth elements of x.

The c_{ij} are elements of

$$C = I - Q_1 Q_1' \tag{2.2.79}$$

Q_1 being the matrix of (orthonormal) characteristic vectors corresponding to the first k roots of Σ.

Obviously, even though the quantity in (2.2.76) does represent a statistic, its degrees of freedom parameter depends on several unknown parameters. Thus for the test to be operational, we need to replace ρ, c_{ij}, and ρ_{ij} in (2.2.78) by their sampling equivalents and approximate to the nearest integer.

From equations (2.2.71), (2.2.73)—and (2.2.76)—we see that the fraction of variability of the vector x accounted by its first k principal components, namely, $\sum_{r=1}^{k} \hat{\lambda}_r / \text{tr } \hat{\Sigma}$ or its analog when we operate with the correlation matrix, $\sum_{r=1}^{k} \hat{\rho}_i / \text{tr } \hat{R}$, plays a significant role in the test statistic.

In particular, the larger the fraction, the smaller the value of the relevant statistic and hence the more likely it is that the null hypothesis will be accepted.

This provides the motivation of the common practice of deciding—in a computer program context—whether additional components are to be extracted after the extraction of the kth component on the basis of the magnitude of $\sum_{i=1}^{k} \hat{\lambda}_r / \text{tr } \hat{\Sigma}$ or $\sum_{i=1}^{k} \hat{\rho}_i / \text{tr } \hat{R}$.

Finally, let us consider two examples of possible applications of principal component theory. As we shall see later, useful applications can also be made in the estimation of simultaneous equations systems.

Example 1: In his study of the relation between the price and various identifiable characteristics of automobiles, Dhrymes [3] considers *inter alia* the regression of price on the weight, length, displacement, and brake horsepower of automobiles. It should be clear from technical considerations that the information conveyed by those four variables is rather significantly dependent. In order to reduce the dimensionability of the problem and to minimize the incidence of multicollinearity, Dhrymes operates instead with (some of) the principal components of these characteristics. The sample observations considered in this example consist of 192 models produced by General Motors, Ford, and Chrysler for 1961. Such models exclude sports cars, convertibles, and station wagons.

He operates with the correlation matrix of the four characteristics noted above and obtains the relevant characteristic roots and vectors, which are given below in Table 2.1.

TABLE 2.1. Characteristic roots and vectors of the sample correlation matrix of weight, length, displacement, and brake horsepower (in that order) General Motors, Ford, and Chrysler, 1961

Characteristic roots	3.3257	.5608	.0610	0.0525
Percent of tr $\hat{R}$	83.1	97.2	98.7	100.0
Corresponding	.0068	.0052	.0045	.0090
Characteristic vectors	.0328	.0387	−0.0301	−0.0324
	.0005	−0.0003	.0006	−0.0004
	.0004	−0.0005	−0.0005	.0002

We see from the table that the four characteristics convey only two pieces of "independent information" in the sense that only the first two principal components are well defined computationally, and at any rate they appear to account for nearly all of the variability of the four characteristics. The last two roots are about one-tenth of the second and about one-fiftieth of the first. Together they amount only to 2.8 percent of tr $\hat{R}$. Due to the size of the last two roots, computational inaccuracies are likely to be severe in obtaining their associated characteristic vectors. Finally, carrying out the test of the hypothesis in (2.2.75) with $k = 2$, we find

$$\phi^* = .191 \tag{2.2.80}$$

The degrees of freedom parameter associated with this test is approximately

$$p^* \approx 1.83 \tag{2.2.81}$$

Since tabulated chi-square distributions are given for integer p^* only, we take p^* of (2.2.81) as being 2.

The upper 5 percent critical point for a chi-square variable with two degrees of freedom is 5.99. Thus we *accept* the null hypothesis that the last two roots of the correlation matrix are indistinguishable (and small). Hence, with little loss of relevance, we can operate with the first two *principal components only*.

Example 2: Richard Stone [19] deals essentially with the problem of reducing the dimensions of a transaction bloc derived from (U.S.) national income accounts over the period 1922–1938. The transactions involve employees' compensation, consumer expenditures (on durable and nondurable goods), construction, net change in inventories, interest, dividends, foreign trade balance, and the like (17 variables in all).

The data are subjected to a principal components analysis and the first three components are extracted. It turns out that the first component accounts for .8076 of the sum of the variances of the 17 variables, the second for .1059, and the third for .0609. Thus these three principal components account for .9744 of the variability of the 17 variables under study, and it would appear that the dimensionality of the problem is not 17 but rather 3.

Now, in general, one does not or cannot interpret principal components in an intuitively meaningful way. They are best regarded as the outcome of a statistical technique that handles certain types of problems efficiently. Consequently, it is rather remarkable that Stone has been able to interpret his components. Once the components were determined, he considered the correlation matrix of the three components, z_1, z_2, z_3, and of Y, ΔY, and t—the last three being national income, change in national income, and time respectively. The correlation matrix appears in Table 2.2.

From the matrix it is clear that we can identify the first component with national income, the second with change in income, and the third with time. Thus the conclusion to be derived from this analysis is that the components of the

TABLE 2.2. Correlation matrix of principal components and certain economic variables

	z_1	z_2	z_3	Y	ΔY	t
z_1	1	0	0	.995	−.056	−.369
z_2		1	0	−.041	.948	−.282
z_3			1	.057	−.124	−.836
Y				1	−.102	−.414
ΔY					1	−.112
t						1

transaction block studied by Stone can be adequately accounted for by three "factors," and these may be identified with income, change in income, and a time trend although perhaps the last identification is not quite as cogent as the first two.

2.3 DISCRIMINANT ANALYSIS

MOTIVATION AND THEORY

Frequently we are confronted with an "individual" who may have arisen from one of several, say k, *known* populations. For example, in archaeological or anthropological work a skull discovered in an excavation site might belong to a male or a female as well as to one of a number of distinct racial groups known to have inhabited the region containing the excavation site. Or again, a bank, in determining its loan policy, might wish to discriminate amongst its prospective client firms as between those who will repay loans with "various degrees of certainty" and those who will not repay at all. Clearly different terms will apply to different firms, depending on the population in which they are classified.

Now, in general, an "individual" will be characterized by a set of measurements, attributes, indicated by the vector

$$x = (x_1, x_2, \ldots, x_m)' \qquad (2.3.1)$$

and it will be known that *if* the individual belongs to the ith population, then

$$x \sim f_i(\cdot) \qquad i = 1, 2, \ldots, k \qquad (2.3.2)$$

$f_i(\cdot)$ being a well-defined density function. Customarily, $f_i(\cdot)$ is assumed to be the normal density although the normality aspect is not essential in the development of the *theory* of discriminant analysis; it is useful only in devising tests of significance.

To solve the problem of *discrimination* (or *classification* or *identification*, the terms may be used interchangeably), we need to devise some rule such that after observing a vector of attributes, x, we can decide to what population we shall classify the "individual" associated with these attributes. Let us partition the sample space—here the m-dimensional Euclidean space—into k disjoint sets E_i, $i = 1, 2, \ldots, k$, such that if an individual is characterized by a vector of attributes x and $x \in E_r$, then the individual is classified into the rth population.

Now, in this scheme we may commit the error of classifying an "individual" into the jth population, whereas he actually belongs to the ith population. It would be reasonable to attach a (positive) cost to such error. Thus let the cost of the misclassification above be denoted by c_{ij}, it being understood that

$$c_{ii} = 0 \qquad i = 1, 2, \ldots, k \tag{2.3.3}$$

The probability that an individual will be classified in population j when he belongs to population i is given by

$$p_{ij} = \int_{E_j} f_i(x)\, dx \tag{2.3.4}$$

Therefore the expected cost of classifying individuals belonging to the ith population is

$$C_i = \sum_{j=1}^{k} c_{ij}\, p_{ij} \tag{2.3.5}$$

To find the expected cost of the entire procedure, we need to weigh the quantities C_i above by the probabilities attaching to membership in the various populations; this is so since C_i may be interpreted as the cost of misclassification given that the individual belongs to the ith population. It is thus a *conditional* cost. The unconditional cost of the procedure is

$$C = \sum_{i=1}^{k} \pi_i C_i = \sum_{j=1}^{k} \int_{E_j} S_j(x)\, dx \tag{2.3.6}$$

where

$$S_j(x) = \sum_{i=1}^{k} \pi_i c_{ij}\, f_i(x) \tag{2.3.7}$$

and π_i is the probability of membership in the ith population. The problem now is to choose regions E_j so as to minimize the expected loss (or cost) as given in (2.3.6).

It can be shown that if the E_j are chosen so that

$$x \in E_j \qquad j = 1, 2, \ldots, k \tag{2.3.8}$$

implies

$$S_j(x) \le S_i(x) \qquad i = 1, 2, \ldots, k \tag{2.3.9}$$

then (2.3.6) is minimized.

The proof of this, somewhat heuristically, is as follows. Choosing any index, say j_0, we can write

$$C = \int_{E^m} S_{j_0}(x)\, dx + \sum_{j \neq j_0} \int_{E_j} [S_j(x) - S_{j_0}(x)]\, dx \qquad (2.3.10)$$

where E^m denotes the m-dimensional Euclidean space. Clearly the first term in the right-hand side of (2.3.10) is independent of the choice of regions. Thus C will be minimized if the second term is minimized. We can do this if the E_j are defined so that they *include* points x for which $S_j(x) - S_{j_0}(x) \leq 0$ and *exclude* points for which $S_j(x) - S_{j_0}(x) > 0$. But the definition of E_j in (2.3.8) and (2.3.9) shows that no matter what the choice of j_0 is, the term $S_j(x) - S_{j_0}(x)$ is *nonpositive* over E_j.

Hence this choice of regions minimizes C.

Definition 4: The quantity $-S_j(x)$ is termed the jth *discriminant score* of an individual with attribute vector x.

The classification rule implied by the procedure is as follows: *If an individual has attribute vector x, compute his discriminant scores and assign him to that population for which his discriminant score is highest.* Of course, the difficulty with this procedure is that, typically, the π_i will not be known and the c_{ij} could not be assessed with great confidence. Nonetheless, let us illustrate the procedure, for the case $k = 2$, further supposing that the densities in (2.3.2) are $N(\mu^{(i)}, \Sigma_i)$. The classification criterion can now be expressed:

Classify in E_1 if

$$\frac{S_1(x)}{S_2(x)} \leq 1 \qquad (2.3.11)$$

and classify in E_2 otherwise. But

$$\frac{S_1(x)}{S_2(x)} = \frac{\pi_2 c_{21}}{\pi_1 c_{12}} \frac{|\Sigma_1|^{\frac{1}{2}}}{|\Sigma_2|^{\frac{1}{2}}} \exp -\frac{1}{2} \{(x - \mu^{(2)})'\Sigma_2^{-1}(x - \mu^{(2)})$$

$$- (x - \mu^{(1)})'\Sigma_1^{-1}(x - \mu^{(1)})\} \qquad (2.3.12)$$

A criterion equivalent to that in (2.3.11) is

$$\frac{1}{2}\{(x - \mu^{(1)})'\Sigma_1^{-1}(x - \mu^{(1)}) - (x - \mu^{(2)})'\Sigma_2^{-1}(x - \mu^{(2)})\}$$

$$+ \frac{1}{2}\ln\frac{|\Sigma_1|}{|\Sigma_2|} \leq \ln\left(\frac{\pi_1 c_{12}}{\pi_2 c_{21}}\right) \qquad (2.3.13)$$

which in the case $\Sigma_1 = \Sigma_2$ may be reduced to

$$(\mu^{(1)} - \mu^{(2)})'\Sigma^{-1}x \geq \frac{1}{2}(\mu^{(1)} + \mu^{(2)})'\Sigma^{-1}(\mu^{(1)} - \mu^{(2)}) - \ln\left(\frac{\pi_1 c_{12}}{\pi_2 c_{21}}\right) \qquad (2.3.14)$$

Notice that the assumption of a common covariance matrix for the two populations has reduced the criteria from a *quadratic function of the attributes* in (2.3.13) to a *linear function* in (2.3.14).

The left member of the inequality in (2.3.14) is what is commonly called *the discriminant function*. It is interesting to note that in the special case considered above we arrive at the same result by a more direct approach. Indeed, this was the way in which discriminant analysis was first introduced by R. A. Fisher.

Suppose that we have an observation on a vector, say $z = (z_1, z_2, \ldots, z_m)'$, which is known to belong to one of two populations distributed, respectively, as $N(\mu^{(1)}, \Sigma)$ and $N(\mu^{(2)}, \Sigma)$. The problem is to classify z as belonging either to the first population (population 1) or to the second (population 2). One way to solve the problem is to form a *linear function* of the elements of z, say $\alpha'z$, and then, depending on the value assumed by this function, we classify the observation in population 1 or population 2.

Hence consider

$$d = \alpha'(x^{(1)} - x^{(2)}) \tag{2.3.15}$$

where

$$x^{(1)} \sim N(\mu^{(1)}, \Sigma) \qquad x^{(2)} \sim N(\mu^{(2)}, \Sigma) \tag{2.3.16}$$

In some sense (2.3.15) indicates the *distance* between the two populations so that if the expected "distance" is maximized, then the two populations will be effectively "separated" by α.

A little reflection, however, will convince us that the problem as posed above is not well formulated, for if α_0 is a solution, then $c\alpha_0$ is also a solution and thus the maximum of $E(d)$ is not bounded. Since we are again faced with a scale problem, let us introduce the convention of *maximizing the expected "distance" subject to a constraint on its variance.*

But the variance of the "distance" is given by

$$\text{Var}(d) = 2\alpha'\Sigma\alpha \tag{2.3.17}$$

for the two populations yield mutually independent observations, and thus our normalization might well be

$$\alpha'\Sigma\alpha = 1 \tag{2.3.18}$$

Now it is more convenient to maximize $[E(d)]^2$ rather than $E(d)$, subject to the constraints in (2.3.18), because if we operate with $E(d)$, we would have to take its sign into account. Thus our problem may be formulated as the maximization of the Lagrangean

$$L = \alpha'\theta\theta'\alpha + \lambda(1 - \alpha'\Sigma\alpha) \tag{2.3.19}$$

where

$$\theta = \mu^{(1)} - \mu^{(2)} \tag{2.3.20}$$

We obtain the first-order conditions

$$\frac{\partial L}{\partial \alpha} = 2\theta\theta'\alpha - 2\lambda\Sigma\alpha = 0$$

$$\frac{\partial L}{\partial \lambda} = 1 - \alpha'\Sigma\alpha = 0$$

(2.3.21)

Premultiplying the first set of equations by α', we find

$$\alpha'\theta\theta'\alpha = \lambda \qquad (2.3.22)$$

Further, the first set is equivalent to

$$(\lambda\Sigma - \theta\theta')\alpha = 0 \qquad (2.3.23)$$

Equations (2.3.22) and (2.3.23) show that λ is a characteristic root of $\theta\theta'$ in the metric of Σ and α is an associated characteristic vector; they also show that λ is the value of the maximand. Thus we must choose λ as the largest root of

$$|\lambda\Sigma - \theta\theta'| = 0 \qquad (2.3.24)$$

and α as its associated characteristic vector. If we let

$$\tau = \alpha'\theta \qquad (2.3.25)$$

then (2.3.23) can be written as

$$\lambda\Sigma\alpha = \tau\theta \quad \text{or} \quad \alpha = \frac{\tau}{\lambda}\Sigma^{-1}\theta \qquad (2.3.26)$$

and the discriminant function is obtained as

$$\alpha'z = \frac{\tau}{\lambda}(\mu^{(1)} - \mu^{(2)})'\Sigma^{-1}z \qquad (2.3.27)$$

A comparison with (2.3.14) shows that the two discriminant functions differ only by a constant of proportionality.

Of course, we should stress that such procedures are applicable only when the parameters of the populations in question are fully known. If this is not so, we may be tempted, for example, to operate with the sample analog of (2.3.14). Thus

$$D^*(x) = (\hat{\mu}^{(1)} - \hat{\mu}^{(2)})'\hat{\Sigma}^{-1}x - \frac{1}{2}(\hat{\mu}^{(1)} + \hat{\mu}^{(2)})'\hat{\Sigma}^{-1}(\hat{\mu}^{(1)} - \hat{\mu}^{(2)})$$

$$\geq -\ln\frac{\pi_1 c_{12}}{\pi_2 c_{21}} \qquad (2.3.28)$$

which reduces to the rule: Classify in population 1 if

$$D^*(x) \geq 0 \qquad (2.3.29)$$

and to population 2 otherwise in the case of equal costs of misclassification and a priori probabilities.

While this may have considerable intuitive appeal, it is not clear that it would possess the optimal properties that are known to characterize the procedure indicated by (2.3.14) when the parameters of the population are known.

Since, typically, it is seldom, if ever, that we do know the parameters of the population involved, we shall give below an alternative procedure of classification based on the likelihood ratio principle. Such procedures are characterized by certain optimal properties for the statement and proof of which the interested reader is referred to Lehman [1].

In this, as well as in all discussion to follow, we confine ourselves to the case of two (normal) populations with the *same* covariance matrix.

Thus suppose that we have n_1 observations from population 1 characterized by the density $N(\mu^{(1)}, \Sigma)$; denote the ith observation by $x_{.i}$, $i = 1, 2, \ldots, n_1$. We also have n_2 observations from population 2, whose density is $N(\mu^{(2)}, \Sigma)$; denote the jth observation by $y_{.j}$, $j = 1, 2, \ldots, n_2$. Finally, we have an observation z, whose origin is unknown except for the fact that it belongs either to population 1 or to population 2. Of course, all observations are known to be mutually independent. The problem is how to classify z. Consider the null hypothesis

$$H_0: (x_{.1}, x_{.2}, \ldots, x_{.n_1}, z) \quad \text{belong to population 1}$$
$$: (y_{.1}, y_{.2}, \ldots, y_{.n_2}) \quad \text{belong to population 2} \tag{2.3.30}$$

as against the alternative

$$H_1: (x_{.1}, x_{.2}, \ldots, x_{.n_1}) \quad \text{belong to population 1}$$
$$: (y_{.1}, y_{.2}, \ldots, y_{.n_2}, z) \quad \text{belong to population 2} \tag{2.3.31}$$

Using the assumptions already made concerning the densities of the two populations, the maximum likelihood estimators of $\mu^{(1)}$, $\mu^{(2)}$, and Σ under the null hypothesis are

$$\hat{\mu}^{(1)} = \frac{z + \sum_{i=1}^{n_1} x_{.i}}{n_1 + 1} \qquad \hat{\mu}^{(2)} = \frac{\sum_{j=1}^{n_2} y_{.j}}{n_2}$$

$$\hat{\Sigma}_{H_0} = \frac{1}{n_1 + n_2 + 1} \left[\sum_{i=1}^{n_1} (x_{.i} - \hat{\mu}^{(1)})(x_{.i} - \hat{\mu}^{(1)})' + (z - \hat{\mu}^{(1)})(z - \hat{\mu}^{(1)})' \right.$$
$$\left. + \sum_{j=1}^{n_2} (y_{.j} - \hat{\mu}^{(2)})(y_{.j} - \hat{\mu}^{(2)})' \right] \tag{2.3.32}$$

It follows, therefore, that the maximum of the *likelihood function*, $L(z, x_{.1}, \ldots, x_{.n_1}, y_{.1}, \ldots, y_{.n_2}; \mu^{(1)}, \mu^{(2)}, \Sigma)$, under the null hypothesis is given by

$$\underset{H_0}{\text{Max}} \, L(\ldots; \mu^{(1)}, \mu^{(2)}, \Sigma) = (2\pi)^{-\frac{1}{2}m(n_1 + n_2 + 1)} |\hat{\Sigma}_{H_0}|^{-\frac{1}{2}(n_1 + n_2 + 1)}$$
$$\times \exp[-\tfrac{1}{2}m(n_1 + n_2 + 1)] \tag{2.3.33}$$

Under the alternative hypothesis, the maximum likelihood estimators of $\mu^{(1)}$, $\mu^{(2)}$, Σ are given by

$$\hat{\mu}^{(1)} = \frac{\sum_{i=1}^{n_1} x_{\cdot i}}{n_1} \qquad \hat{\mu}^{(2)} = \frac{z + \sum_{j=1}^{n_2} y_{\cdot j}}{n_2 + 1}$$

$$\hat{\Sigma}_{H_1} = \frac{1}{n_1 + n_2 + 1} \left[\sum_{i=1}^{n_1} (x_{\cdot i} - \hat{\mu}^{(1)})(x_{\cdot i} - \hat{\mu}^{(1)})' \right.$$

$$\left. + \sum_{j=1}^{n_2} (y_{\cdot j} - \hat{\mu}^{(2)})(y_{\cdot j} - \hat{\mu}^{(2)})' + (z - \hat{\mu}^{(2)})(z - \hat{\mu}^{(2)})' \right] \qquad (2.3.34)$$

Thus

$$\underset{H_1}{\text{Max}}\, L(\ldots; \mu^{(1)}, \mu^{(2)}, \Sigma)$$

$$= (2\pi)^{-\frac{1}{2}m(n_1 + n_2 + 1)} |\hat{\Sigma}_{H_1}|^{-\frac{1}{2}(n_1 + n_2 + 1)} \exp\left[-\tfrac{1}{2}m(n_1 + n_2 + 1) \right] \qquad (2.3.35)$$

It follows, then, that the likelihood ratio is

$$\lambda^{2/n_1 + n_2 + 1} = \frac{\left| A + \dfrac{n_2}{n_2 + 1}(z - \bar{y})(z - \bar{y})' \right|}{\left| A + \dfrac{n_1}{n_1 + 1}(z - \bar{x})(z - \bar{x})' \right|}$$

$$= \frac{1 + \dfrac{n_2}{n_2 + 1}(z - \bar{y})'A^{-1}(z - \bar{y})}{1 + \dfrac{n_1}{n_1 + 1}(z - \bar{x})'A^{-1}(z - \bar{x})} \qquad (2.3.36)$$

where

$$A = \sum_{i=1}^{n_1} (x_{\cdot i} - \bar{x})(x_{\cdot i} - \bar{x})' + \sum_{j=1}^{n_2} (y_{\cdot j} - \bar{y})(y_{\cdot j} - \bar{y})'$$

$$\bar{x} = \frac{\sum_{i=1}^{n_1} x_{\cdot i}}{n_1} \qquad \bar{y} = \frac{\sum_{j=1}^{n_2} y_{\cdot j}}{n_2} \qquad (2.3.37)$$

Before leaving this topic, let us note that we have developed in some detail the criteria of classification in the case of two populations, for this appears to have considerable potential of application in many dichotomous types of economic problems.

ELEMENTS OF ASYMPTOTIC DISTRIBUTION THEORY OF THE CRITERIA, TESTS OF SIGNIFICANCE, AND EXAMPLES

Consider again the discriminant function of (2.3.14), which we write in the slightly different form

$$D(x) = (\mu^{(1)} - \mu^{(2)})'\Sigma^{-1}x - \frac{1}{2}(\mu^{(1)} + \mu^{(2)})'\Sigma^{-1}(\mu^{(1)} - \mu^{(2)})$$

$$\geq -\ln \frac{\pi_1 c_{12}}{\pi_2 c_{21}} \qquad (2.3.38)$$

If $\pi_1 = \pi_2$, $c_{12} = c_{21}$, then the criterion for classifying in population 1 is

$$D(x) \geq 0 \tag{2.3.39}$$

It is clear that if x belongs to population 1, then

$$E[D(x)] = \tfrac{1}{2}\theta'\Sigma^{-1}\theta = \tfrac{1}{2}\delta \tag{2.3.40}$$

while if x belongs to population 2, then

$$E[D(x)] = -\tfrac{1}{2}\theta'\Sigma^{-1}\theta = -\tfrac{1}{2}\delta \tag{2.3.41}$$

where θ is as defined in (2.3.20).

In either case,

$$\text{Var}\,[D(x)] = \delta \tag{2.3.42}$$

Thus

$$D(x) \sim N(\tfrac{1}{2}\delta, \delta) \quad \text{or} \quad D(x) \sim N(-\tfrac{1}{2}\delta, \delta) \tag{2.3.43}$$

depending on whether x belongs to population 1 or to population 2. If the parameters $\mu^{(1)}$, $\mu^{(2)}$, and Σ are not known and we considered instead the criterion in (2.3.28), which is simply the sample analog of (2.3.38), then it is clear that since $\hat{\mu}^{(1)}$, $\hat{\mu}^{(2)}$, and $\hat{\Sigma}$ are maximum likelihood (and thus consistent) estimators of $\mu^{(1)}$, $\mu^{(2)}$, and Σ, respectively, then the *asymptotic* distribution of

$$D^*(x) = (\hat{\mu}^{(1)} - \hat{\mu}^{(2)})'\,\hat{\Sigma}^{-1}x - \tfrac{1}{2}(\hat{\mu}^{(1)} + \hat{\mu}^{(2)})'\,\hat{\Sigma}^{-1}(\hat{\mu}^{(1)} - \hat{\mu}^{(2)}) \tag{2.3.44}$$

is exactly that given in (2.3.43).

We may, therefore, use that distribution to determine the boundary of E_1. If the costs of misclassification are symmetric (i.e., if $c_{12} = c_{21}$), then one admissible criterion would be to determine the boundaries of E_1 so as to make the *expected costs of misclassification the same for both populations*.[6] This, of course, entails the determination of a number, say v, such that

$$p_{12} = p_{21} \tag{2.3.45}$$

where

$$p_{12} = \frac{1}{\sqrt{2\pi\delta}} \int_{-\infty}^{v} \exp\left[-\frac{1}{2\delta}(\zeta - \tfrac{1}{2}\delta)^2\right] d\zeta = \frac{1}{\sqrt{2\pi}} \int_{-\infty}^{(v - \frac{1}{2}\delta)/\delta^{1/2}} \exp(-\tfrac{1}{2}\xi^2)\, d\xi \tag{2.3.46}$$

$$p_{21} = \frac{1}{\sqrt{2\pi\delta}} \int_{v}^{\infty} \exp\left[-\frac{1}{2\delta}(\zeta + \tfrac{1}{2}\delta)^2\right] d\zeta = \frac{1}{\sqrt{2\pi}} \int_{(v + \frac{1}{2}\delta)/\delta^{1/2}}^{\infty} \exp(-\tfrac{1}{2}\xi^2)\, d\xi \tag{2.3.47}$$

---

[6] Occasionally this procedure is referred to as the *minimax* solution of the classification problem.

Equations (2.3.45), (2.3.46), and (2.3.47) completely determine v provided we take

$$\delta = (\hat{\mu}^{(1)} - \hat{\mu}^{(2)})'\hat{\Sigma}^{-1}(\hat{\mu}^{(1)} - \hat{\mu}^{(2)}) \qquad (2.3.48)$$

The above provides a reasonably rigorous—if approximate—definition of the classification procedure in the case where *the parameters of the population are unknown (but are estimated from moderately large sample sizes) the costs of misclassification are symmetrical and the a priori probabilities attaching to the two populations are equal.*

Specifically, the procedure is as follows: Classify in population 1 if

$$D^*(x) \geq v \qquad (2.3.49)$$

and classify in population 2 otherwise.

The likelihood ratio procedure in the case of unknown population parameters yields the statistic

$$\lambda^{2/n_1 + n_2 + 1} = \frac{1 + \dfrac{n_2}{n_2 + 1}(z - \bar{y})'A^{-1}(z - \bar{y})}{1 + \dfrac{n_1}{n_1 + 1}(z - \bar{x})'A^{-1}(z - \bar{x})} \qquad (2.3.50)$$

the symbols being explained in (2.3.36) and (2.3.37). We observe that the numerator and denominator in the right member of (2.3.50) are simple transforms of Hotelling's T^{*2} variable; they are not, however, mutually independent and relatively little is known about the distribution of the quotient. It is clear that we should classify in population 1 for "large" values of the criterion. Unfortunately, since the distribution of the criterion in (2.3.50) is not well established, we have little guidance as to how large "large" is.

Finally, consider the form of the criterion obtained by solving the problem posed in (2.3.19). Neglecting the constant of proportionality and operating with the sample analog, we have the criterion

$$d^*(x) = (\hat{\mu}^{(1)} - \hat{\mu}^{(2)})'\hat{\Sigma}^{-1}x \qquad (2.3.51)$$

where $\hat{\mu}^{(1)}$, $\hat{\mu}^{(2)}$, and $\hat{\Sigma}$ are the maximum likelihood estimators of $\mu^{(1)}$, $\mu^{(2)}$, and Σ respectively.

It is, of course, apparent that the asymptotic distribution of the quantity in (2.3.51) is $N(\theta^*, \delta)$ or $N(\theta^{**}, \delta)$, depending on whether x belongs to population 1 or population 2, where

$$\theta^* = (\mu^{(1)} - \mu^{(2)})'\Sigma^{-1}\mu^{(1)} \qquad \theta^{**} = (\mu^{(1)} - \mu^{(2)})'\Sigma^{-1}\mu^{(2)} \qquad (2.3.52)$$

Frequently one is interested in estimating a discriminant function and testing its significance. What one means by that is not whether "individual coefficients are significant" (i.e., elements of $(\hat{\mu}^{(1)} - \hat{\mu}^{(2)})'\hat{\Sigma}^{-1}$) but, rather, whether *the samples at hand support the hypothesis that the two populations are distinct*; otherwise the discriminant function in (2.3.51) is merely a figment of sampling variation and only inappropriately does it "discriminate" between the two "populations."

Since the two populations under consideration differ only with respect to their *mean vectors*, testing the "significance" of the discriminant function is equivalent to testing the null hypothesis

$$H_0: \mu^{(1)} = \mu^{(2)}$$

as against the alternative

$$H_1: \mu^{(1)} \neq \mu^{(2)} \tag{2.3.53}$$

If we have the observations $x_{.i}$, $i = 1, 2, \ldots, n_1$, from population 1 and the observations $y_{.j}$, $j = 1, 2, \ldots, n_2$ from population 2 and if we estimate

$$\hat{\mu}^{(1)} = \bar{x} \quad \hat{\mu}^{(2)} = \bar{y} \quad \hat{\Sigma} = \frac{1}{n_1 + n_2} A + \frac{n_1 n_2}{n_1 + n_2} (\bar{x} - \bar{y})(\bar{x} - \bar{y})' \tag{2.3.54}$$

the quantities $\bar{x}$, $\bar{y}$, and A being as in (2.3.37), then we see that

$$d^*(\bar{x} - \bar{y}) = (\hat{\mu}^{(1)} - \hat{\mu}^{(2)})' \hat{\Sigma}^{-1} (\hat{\mu}^{(1)} - \hat{\mu}^{(2)}) \tag{2.3.55}$$

But

$$[n_1 + n_2 - 1] \, d^*(\bar{x} - \bar{y}) \sim T^{*2} \tag{2.3.56}$$

and since $[n_1 + n_2 - m/m(n_1 + n_2 - 1)]T^{*2}$ is a central F variable with m and $n_1 + n_2 - m$ degrees of freedom, it follows that a significance test for the discriminant function can be based on the F distribution, the test statistic being

$$F = \frac{n_1 + n_2 - m}{m} \, d^*(\bar{x} - \bar{y}) \tag{2.3.57}$$

There is only one slight discrepancy in the preceding. Had we followed the motivation leading to (2.3.27) of the last section, we should not have estimated Σ as in (2.3.54). Rather, we would have estimated it from the point of view of the alternative hypothesis in (2.3.53). This would mean that $\hat{\Sigma}$ of (2.3.54) should be given instead by

$$\hat{\Sigma}^* = \frac{1}{n_1 + n_2} A \tag{2.3.58}$$

But, aside from this discrepancy, we see that to "test" the discriminant function as given in (2.3.51) entails obtaining its value at the point $\bar{x} - \bar{y}$, as in (2.3.55), and using a simple transform of it as an F statistic with m and $n_1 + n_2 - m$ degrees of freedom. Clearly we accept the null hypothesis—that is, we conclude that the discriminant function is "insignificant"—if the value of the statistic in (2.3.57) is less than a suitably determined critical value, depending on the desired level of significance.

It is interesting that we can arrive at the discriminant function in (2.3.51)and the test associated with it in the following heuristic manner.

Using a slightly different notation, let us denote the tth observation on the vector x by $x_{.t}$; if x belongs to the ith population, we shall write $x_{.t}^{(i)}$.

Let us arrange the indices in such a way that if $t = 1, 2, \ldots, n_1$, then $x_{.t}$ belongs to population 1; while if $t = n_1 + 1, n_1 + 2, \ldots, n_1 + n_2$ then $x_{.t}$ belongs to population 2, and suppose we have a sample of size $n_1 + n_2$ on the vector x as above. Let

$$\bar{x}^{(1)} = \frac{1}{n_1} \sum_{t=1}^{n_1} x_{.t} \qquad \bar{x}^{(2)} = \sum_{s=1}^{n_2} x_{.n_1 + s}$$

$$\bar{x} = \frac{n_1 \bar{x}^{(1)} + n_2 \bar{x}^{(2)}}{n_1 + n_2} \tag{2.3.59}$$

In addition, define

$$y_t = \begin{cases} \dfrac{n_2}{n_1 + n_2} & t = 1, 2, \ldots, n_1 \\[2mm] -\dfrac{n_1}{n_1 + n_2} & t = n_1 + 1, n_1 + 2, \ldots, n_1 + n_2 \end{cases} \tag{2.3.60}$$

and let

$$y = (y_1, y_2, \ldots, y_{n_1 + n_2})' \qquad X = (x_{.1}, x_{.2}, \ldots, x_{.n_1 + n_2})$$
$$X^* = (e, X) \tag{2.3.61}$$

where $e = (1, 1, 1, 1, \ldots, 1)'$ is a column vector of $n_1 + n_2$ elements.

Then obtain the regression of y on X^*. The vector of regression coefficients is given by

$$b^* = (X^{*\prime} X^*)^{-1} X^{*\prime} y \tag{2.3.62}$$

We shall now show that the regression sum of squares is a multiple of the discriminant function as evaluated in (2.3.55). Note that

$$X^{*\prime} y = \begin{bmatrix} 0 \\ \dfrac{n_1 n_2}{n_1 + n_2} (\bar{x}^{(1)} - \bar{x}^{(2)}) \end{bmatrix} \tag{2.3.63}$$

and

$$b^{*\prime} X^{*\prime} X^* b^* = b^{*\prime} X^{*\prime} y = \frac{n_1 n_2}{n_1 + n_2} b'(\bar{x}^{(1)} - \bar{x}^{(2)}) \tag{2.3.64}$$

where we have written

$$b^* = \begin{pmatrix} b_0 \\ b \end{pmatrix} \tag{2.3.65}$$

so that b is the vector of the regression coefficients of the elements of x and b_0 is the constant term of the regression. To complete our task, we need an expression for b. We have

$$X^{*\prime}X^*b^* = \begin{bmatrix} e'eb_0 + e'X'b \\ Xeb_0 + XX'b \end{bmatrix} \tag{2.3.66}$$

But (2.3.63) and (2.3.66) imply

$$b_0 = -\frac{e'X'}{e'e}b \tag{2.3.67}$$

and thus

$$\hat{\Sigma}b = \frac{n_1 n_2}{(n_1 + n_2)^2}(\bar{x}^{(1)} - \bar{x}^{(2)}) \tag{2.3.68}$$

where $\hat{\Sigma}$ is as defined in (2.3.54). Hence

$$b = \frac{n_1 n_2}{(n_1 + n_2)^2}\hat{\Sigma}^{-1}(\bar{x}^{(1)} - \bar{x}^{(2)}) \tag{2.3.69}$$

and

$$b^{*\prime}X^{*\prime}X^*b^* = \frac{(n_1 n_2)^2}{(n_1 + n_2)^3}(\bar{x}^{(1)} - \bar{x}^{(2)})'\hat{\Sigma}^{-1}(\bar{x}^{(1)} - \bar{x}^{(2)}) \tag{2.3.70}$$

A comparison with (2.3.55) proves the assertion. Thus we have

$$\frac{(n_1 + n_2)^3}{(n_1 n_2)^2}\frac{n_1 + n_2 - m}{m}b^{*\prime}X^{*\prime}X^*b^* \sim F_{m,\, n_1 + n_2 - m} \tag{2.3.71}$$

We have seen, therefore, that the coefficients of the simple discriminant function in (2.3.51) can be obtained—within the factor of proportionality $n_1 n_2/(n_1 + n_2)^2$—as the regression coefficients in (2.3.69).

Often, in applications, one might be tempted to test the "significance" of individual elements of the vector b by applying the usual t test. This is a questionable procedure at best, for nothing in the development above provides a basis for a test. The only aspect of the regression that may be used for tests of significance is the *regression sum of squares*, and this is useful in testing that the discriminant function is "significant," that is, that the two populations are indeed distinct.

Example: Mansfield and Brandenburg [13] study *inter alia* the selection practices of firms in regard to their research and development activities. In deciding on whether or not to sustain the expenditures involved, the firm's managers need to know the costs and expected results as well as the probabilities of success of the relevant projects.

However, the assigned probability of success for a given project is at best a conjecture transmitted to management by the directors of their laboratories. The question then arises as to whether this conjecture (of the research directors) effectively discriminates between projects that will succeed and those that will not.

To cast this in the framework of the analysis above, we would have to assert that the conjectured probability of success, say p^*, is a random variable with mean p_1 if the project belongs to the population of successful projects and p_2 if it belongs to the population of unsuccessful projects. The variance of the two populations is assumed to be the same.

Using the scheme developed in equations (2.3.60) through (2.3.62), Mansfield and Brandenburg determine the function

$$d^*(p^*) = -0.67 + .84p^* \tag{2.3.72}$$

Since their sample consists of 25 industrial firms,

$$n_1 + n_2 = 25 \qquad m = 1 \tag{2.3.73}$$

and the test statistic for the "significance" of the discriminant function is (central) F with 1 and 24 degrees of freedom. This statistic is not given by the authors although, indirectly, a test of significance can be carried out; this is so since in regression with one "explanatory" variable a test of significance on the regression sum of squares is equivalent to the usual t test on the estimated slope. The t ratio of the coefficient of p^* in (2.3.72) is given as 1.90 and this does indicate significance. Of course, the random variable under consideration—p^*—is restricted to lie between zero and one; we can hardly then assume it to be normally distributed. Thus the "significance" referred to above can only be understood in a very approximate sense.

2.4   FACTOR ANALYSIS

GENERALITIES

Factor analysis was primarily developed by psychologists and most of its applications lie in that field. There is, however, no reason why such applications should be so restricted. On the other hand, useful applications in economics are scarce and hence treatment of this topic will be minimal.

Consider the model

$$x = \mu + Bf + u \tag{2.4.1}$$

where f and u are mutually independent p- and m-dimensional random variables, respectively, $(p < m)$, with distributions

$$f \sim N(0, I) \qquad u \sim N(0, \Sigma) \tag{2.4.2}$$

In (2.4.1), μ and B are, respectively, a vector and a matrix of constants. Thus

$$x \sim N(\mu, \Phi) \tag{2.4.3}$$

where

$$\Phi = BB' + \Sigma \tag{2.4.4}$$

The elements of f are called *factors*; B then consists of the coefficients of these factors and for that reason the elements of B are called *factor loadings*.

In factor analysis we assume that the elements of x are *observable quantities*, while the elements of f represent *nonobservable quantities*. The peculiarity of the inference problem in factor analysis arises precisely from this aspect, for we are asked to "explain" the observable elements of x in terms of the *unobservable factors*. Indeed, the usefulness of factor analysis in empirical investigations largely depends on the investigator's success in identifying these factors with intuitively interpretable entities.

The preceding assumptions and the general description of the model may appear somewhat obscure. Perhaps an interpretation will help clarify matters.

The most common interpretation of the elements of x in (2.4.1) is in terms of scores, say, by a given individual on m tests, such as e.g., reading and arithmetic.

In this context, it would not seem unreasonable to assert that such scores depend—perhaps in the form of linear combinations—on various (aptitudes) "factors" characterizing the individual, where the term "factor" has as yet no concrete assigned meaning. If a given factor, f_i, appears in all the elements of x, it is called a common factor; if only in a subset of the elements of x, a group factor.

Perhaps in addition to these group or common factors the test j calls into play a "factor" peculiar to this test alone; if that is the case, then such a factor is called a "specific factor" and it appears as an element of u.

The elements of u, however, may be interpreted in concrete applications as reflecting not merely specific factors but also any errors of observation on x as well as the collective influence of many individually insignificant factors that cannot be enumerated. Since, in (2.4.1), we have introduced a vector of constants, μ, it involves no loss of generality to specify

$$E(f) = 0 \tag{2.4.5}$$

Similarly, it involves no loss of generality to assume the *variances* of the elements of f to be all equal; this is so because the elements of B are left completely unspecified. On the other hand, it is a restriction on the generality of the model to assume that the elements of f are uncorrelated (which in view of normality means that they are mutually independent).

But perhaps in view of the interpretation made of factors, this may not be entirely unrealistic.

If the uncorrelatedness of factors is accepted as not limiting the usefulness of the model, then, as a result of the interpretation made, the assumption

$$E(fu') = 0 \tag{2.4.6}$$

does not add any further restrictions.

Now, because only x may be observed, we can at best only estimate μ and Φ of (2.4.4). It is then our task to distill, from this, information about factor loadings.

INDETERMINACIES

The problem of inference posed in the last paragraph is not uniquely soluble because there are certain fundamental indeterminacies.

First, notice the following. Suppose we do not require

$$E(ff') = I \tag{2.4.7}$$

and we postulate instead that

$$E(ff') = M \tag{2.4.8}$$

M being a general, positive definite matrix. Let A be an arbitrary, nonsingular matrix and consider

$$\bar{B} = BA \qquad \bar{f} = A^{-1}f \tag{2.4.9}$$

Now, if $f \sim N(0, M)$, then

$$\bar{f} \sim N(0, A^{-1}MA'^{-1}) \tag{2.4.10}$$

and since M is an arbitrary, positive definite matrix, we cannot distinguish f from $\bar{f}$. The model in (2.4.1) can thus also be written as

$$x = \mu + \bar{B}\bar{f} + u \tag{2.4.11}$$

and the model in (2.4.11) is statistically indistinguishable from that in (2.4.1) if (2.4.8) is valid.

Hence B is not identified, *the extent of nonidentifiability being multiplication on the right by a nonsingular matrix of suitable order.*

By imposing the uncorrelatedness of factors, that is, by assuming (2.4.7), we removed "part" of the indeterminacy, for by repeating the argument above we can only conclude that B is *not identified to the extent of multiplication on the right by an orthogonal matrix.* This, however, is an irreducible degree of indeterminacy unless we are prepared to assume something specific about B. This may be seen as follows:

Given observations on x, we can only estimate Φ, which is given by

$$\Phi = BB' + \Sigma \tag{2.4.12}$$

Even if Σ were known, identifying the elements of B in this context is equivalent to the (mathematical) problem of decomposing a positive (semi-) definite matrix. As is well known, a unique decomposition of a positive definite matrix S in the form

$$S = CC' \tag{2.4.13}$$

does not exist. If C is such a matrix and A is an orthogonal matrix, then

$$C^* = CA \qquad (2.4.14)$$

will also decompose S, for

$$C^*C^{*\prime} = CAA'C' = CC' = S \qquad (2.4.15)$$

ESTIMATION IN A SIMPLIFIED MODEL
AND REDUCTION TO PRINCIPAL COMPONENTS ANALYSIS

The special case considered here involves the model in (2.4.1), (2.4.2), and (2.4.6) with the *additional specification*

$$\Sigma = \sigma^2 I \qquad (2.4.16)$$

The import of this assumption is that "specific factors" pertaining to each "test," or errors involved in the measurement of each "test score," are not only mutually uncorrelated but have a common variance, σ^2, as well.

This simplification reduces the problem to one involving the extraction of principal components. In particular, if x_{it}, $t = 1, 2, \ldots, n$, $i = 1, 2, \ldots, m$, is a random sample of size n on the m "test scores" and if we define

$$X = (x_{it}) \qquad (2.4.17)$$

then it can be shown that the maximum likelihood estimator of the ith column, $b_{.i}$, of B and σ^2 is given by

$$\hat{\Phi}\hat{b}_{.i} = \hat{\lambda}_i \hat{b}_{.i} \qquad i = 1, 2, \ldots, p$$

$$(m - p)\hat{\sigma}^2 = \operatorname{tr} \hat{\Phi} - \sum_{i=1}^{p} \hat{\lambda}_i \qquad (2.4.18)$$

where $\hat{\Phi}$ is the maximum likelihood estimator of Φ given by

$$\hat{\Phi} = \frac{XX'}{n} - \bar{x}\bar{x}' \qquad (2.4.19)$$

$\bar{x}$ being the vector of sample means and $\hat{\lambda}_i$ being the ith characteristic root of $\hat{\Phi}$.

From (2.4.18) we recognize $\hat{b}_{.i}$ as the *characteristic vector of $\hat{\Phi}$ corresponding to its ith characteristic root, $\hat{\lambda}_i$*. Thus $\hat{B}$ is the matrix whose columns consist of the first p characteristic vectors of $\hat{\Phi}$.

Of course, characteristic vectors are not unique, but this fact may be easily corrected by imposing some normaliztaion convention. The details of the derivation, which are rather tedious and complicated, will not be given. The interested reader is, however, referred to [8] as well as to the recent book by Lawley and Maxwell [10].

Now, it is the case, perhaps typically, that we do not know the exact number of factors in a given model and thus we may wish to determine whether p factors are "sufficient" to represent the m variables $(x_1, x_2, \ldots, x_m)$.

In view of (2.4.18), this is equivalent to asking whether the $(m - p)$ smallest roots of Φ are equal to σ^2, and "small" in comparison to the remaining roots. But this is exactly the test we considered in Section 2.2, where we discussed principal components and we need not repeat this discussion now.

The connection between factor analysis, in this special case, and principal components is quite obvious; nonetheless, it bears some further elucidation.

In principal component theory, $x \sim N(\mu, \Sigma)$, x being m dimensional, is reduced to its components. Essentially this step involves an orthogonal transformation, the matrix of the transformation being the matrix of characteristic vectors of Σ. The components are therefore of maximal variance subject to the condition that they be mutually uncorrelated.

In factor analysis, the problem is somewhat different. We begin with $x \sim N(\mu, \Phi)$, but it is further asserted, due to the structural assumptions made, that

$$\Phi = BB' + \sigma^2 I \qquad (2.4.20)$$

where B is $m \times p$.

The problem is solved by estimating B as essentially the matrix consisting of the characteristic vectors corresponding to the p largest characteristic roots of $\hat{\Phi}$. Here the implication is that the residual variance of the x_i, $i = 1, 2, \ldots, m$, after the influence of the p "factors" has been removed, is minimized.

Thus, neglecting the residual variation for the moment, we have

$$x = \hat{B}f \qquad (2.4.21)$$

Premultiplying by $\hat{B}'$ and noting that $\hat{B}'\hat{B} = I$, of order p, we have

$$\hat{B}'x = f \qquad (2.4.22)$$

so that the vector f now consists essentially of the first p principal components. In this fashion, we are able to "estimate" the factors in question.

Factor analysis is often used in economics for classificatory purposes. To see the reason, consider the ith element of x as exhibited in (2.4.1), neglecting for the moment the residual errors, u_i. We have

$$x_i = \sum_{k=1}^{p} b_{ik} f_k \qquad (2.4.23)$$

If, for reasons of simplicity, we assume that $\mu = 0$, we have

$$\text{Var}(x_i) = \sum_{i=1}^{p} b_{ii}^2 \qquad (2.4.24)$$

Hence $b_{jj}^2 / \text{Var}(x_i)$ consititutes the fraction of the variance of x_i contributed, or explained, by the jth factor.

If the number of factors is reasonably small, say two for simplicity, then we could classify in one group, perhaps for the purpose of aggregation, all those variables x_i whose variance is primarily attributed to the operation of the first factor and in another group all those variables whose variance is primarily accounted for by the second factor.

An example of this application is a recent study of D. Farrar [4], where the problem is one of classifying many securities into a small number of categories for further analysis of the investment activities of mutual funds. Unfortunately, only one factor turns out to be of any consequence in Farrar's application. This hardly advances matters, for one is led back into aggregative analysis, which one sought to avoid.

REFERENCES

1. Anderson, T. W., *An Introduction to Multivariate Statistical Analysis*, New York, Wiley, 1958. A comprehensive reference for all aspects of multivariate analysis.
2. Anderson, T. W., and H. Rubin, "Statistical Inference in Factor Analysis," *Proceedings of the Third Berkeley Symposium on Mathematical Statistics and Probability*," vol. 5, Berkeley, University of California Press, 1956. Discusses statistical factor analysis in detail.
3. Dhrymes, P. J., "On the Measurement of Price and Quantity Changes in Some Consumer Capital Goods." Discussion Paper No. 67, Economic Research Unit, University of Pennsylvania, 1967.
4. Farrar, D., *The Investment Decision Under Uncertainty*, Englewood Cliffs, New Jersey, Prentice-Hall, 1962.
5. Fisher, R. A., "The Statistical Utilization of Multiple Measurements," *Annals of Engenics*, vol. 8, 1938, pp. 376–386. First paper suggesting discriminant analysis.
6. Hotelling, H., "Analysis of a Complex of Statistical Variables into Principal Components," *Journal of Educational Psychology*, vol. 24, 1933, pp. 417–441. The first paper suggesting the use of principal components.
7. Kendall, M. G., *A Course in Multivariate Analysis*, New York, Hafner Publishing Co., 1957. A concise treatment of multivariate statistical analysis.
8. Lawley, D. N., "A Modified Method of Estimation in Factor Analysis and Some Large Sample Results," Upsala Symposium on Psychological Factor Analysis, 1953.
9. Lawley, D. N., "Tests of Significance for the Latent Roots of Covariance and Correlation Matrices," *Biometrika*, vol. 43, 1956, pp. 128–136.
10. Lawley, D. N., and Maxwell, A. E., *Factor Analysis as A Statistical Method*, London, Butterworth's, 1963. A textbook on factor analysis.
11. Lehman, E. L., *Testing of Statistical Hypotheses*, New York, Wiley, 1959. An advanced reference for the principles of hypothesis testing in statistics.
12. Mahalanobis, P. C., "On the Generalized Distance in Statistics," *Proceedings of the National Inst. Sciences*, Calcutta, India, vol. 12, 1936, pp. 49–55. Suggested the D^2 statistic —an alternative to Hotelling's T^2.
13. Mansfield, E., and R. Brandenburg, "The Allocation, Characteristics, and Outcome of the Firm's Research and Development Portfolio: A Case Study," *Journal of Business*, vol. 39, 1966, pp. 447–464.
14. Pillai, K. C. S., *Multivariate Hypotheses*, The Statistical Center, Manila, University of Phillipines, 1960.
15. Rao, C. R., *Advanced Statistical Methods in Biometric Research*, New York, Wiley, 1952. Gives several anthropometric examples on the use of multivariate analysis in pp. 266–271.

16. Rao, C. R., *Linear Statistical Inference and Its Applications*, New York, Wiley, 1965. Deals concisely with all problems of inference in multivariate analysis in Chapter 8.
17. Rao, C. R., "The Use and Interpretation of Principal Component Analysis in Applied Research," *Sankhya (A)*, vol. 26, 1965, pp. 329–358.
18. Roy, S. N., *Some Aspects of Multivariate Analysis*, New York, Wiley, 1957. Deals with the relatively more difficult aspects of the subject. A pertinent reference for tests of hypotheses.
19. Stone R., "On the Interdependence of Blocks of Transactions," *Journal of the Royal Statistical Society*, Supplement, vol. 9, 1947, pp. 1–32.
20. Wald, A., "On a Statistical Problem Arising in the Classification of an Individual into One of Two Groups," *Annals of Mathematical Statistics*, vol. 15, 1944, pp. 145–162.
21. Wald, A., *Statistical Decision Functions*, New York, Wiley, 1950. Suggests a game-theoretic approach to problems of statistical inference—the minimum-maximum solutions.
22. Waugh, F. V., "Regression Between Sets of Variables," *Econometrica*, vol. 10, 1942, pp. 290–310.
23. Wilks, S. S., *Mathematical Statistics*, New York, Wiley, 1962. Chapter 18 deals briefly with all the topics discussed in this chapter.

PROBABILITY LIMITS, ASYMPTOTIC DISTRIBUTIONS, AND PROPERTIES OF MAXIMUM LIKELIHOOD ESTIMATORS

3

3.1 INTRODUCTION

The purpose of this chapter is to introduce certain basic results from probability and statistical theory. A thorough understanding of such results is quite essential to those wishing a complete grasp of econometric theory, as well as to those whose interest lies in the competent practice of econometrics.

In principle, this chapter may be detached from the remainder of the book with little loss of continuity. On the other hand, such a procedure will often leave the reader with many unanswered queries and obscurities, especially when we take up the asymptotic distribution aspects of simultaneous equations estimators. It is in anticipation of these difficulties that the material of the chapter is now presented. To fix ideas clearly, we begin by carefully defining several frequently occurring terms.

3.2 ESTIMATORS AND PROBABILITY LIMITS

PRELIMINARIES AND MOTIVATION

Definition 1: Let x_t have the density $f(x_t; \theta)$, and consider $x_t, t = 1, 2, \ldots, T$, where the x_t are identically distributed, mutually independent random variables; then the set

$$X = \{x_1, x_2, \ldots, x_T\} \tag{3.2.1}$$

is said to constitute a *random sample*.

The salient characteristic of a random sample is that its constituent random variables are *mutually independent and identically distributed*. If this condition does not hold, then the set in (3.2.1) is said to constitute a *nonrandom sample*.

Definition 2: Let $\{x_t : t = 1, 2, \ldots, T\}$ be a set of random variables, not necessarily a random sample. Then the function

$$\hat{\theta} = g(x_1, x_2, \ldots, x_T) \tag{3.2.2}$$

is said to be an *estimator*.

Remark 1: Perhaps the definition is a bit too terse and thus requires some amplification. An estimator is, by the preceding, a random variable. Indeed, if we index $\hat{\theta}$ by the size of the sample, thus $\hat{\theta}_T$, we see that we are dealing with a sequence (or family) of random variables defined on the set of positive *integers*. If the variables $\{x_t : t = 1, 2, \ldots, T\}$ have the joint density, say $H(x_1, x_2, \ldots, x_T; \theta)$, where θ is a parameter and $g(\cdot)$ gives some information on θ, then $g(\cdot)$ *is an estimator of* θ; hence the symbol $\hat{\theta}$. Finally, notice that an estimator is a function *solely of the sample* and does not depend on any of the unknown parameters of the distribution under consideration.

Example 1: Consider the *univariate* normal distribution and let $\{x_t : t = 1, 2, \ldots, T\}$ be a random sample characterized by the density $N(\mu, \sigma^2)$. Then

$$\hat{\theta} = \begin{pmatrix} \bar{x} \\ s^2 \end{pmatrix} = g(x_1, x_2, \ldots, x_T) \tag{3.2.3}$$

is an estimator of

$$\theta = \begin{pmatrix} \mu \\ \sigma^2 \end{pmatrix}$$

where

$$\bar{x} = \frac{1}{T} \sum_{t=1}^{T} x_t \qquad s^2 = \frac{1}{T} \sum_{t=1}^{T} (x_t - \bar{x})^2 \tag{3.2.4}$$

Notice that if the sample is given, then $\hat{\theta}$ is immediately determined (as a pair of numbers), for it *does not depend* on the unknown parameters μ and σ^2.

Having observed that estimators are simply families of random variables, we immediately see that various properties in which we might be interested can be studied in terms of *properties of sequences of random variables*. To use the example of (3.2.4), we observe that the sample mean we now denote by $\bar{x}_T$ has mean μ and variance σ^2/T and that it is distributed normally. Thus, as $T \to \infty$, the variance of $\bar{x}_T$ vanishes so that asymptotically $\bar{x}_T$ has a degenerate distribution, which centers all probability mass on the point μ. Unfortunately, it is not always true that inferences can be made so easily about properties of an estimator.

Often the distribution of an estimator for small samples is intractable. It may be, on the other hand, that as the sample size tends to infinity, the distribution becomes quite manageable. Then the large sample (asymptotic) distribution may be used as an approximation to the distribution of the estimator when the sample size is moderately large. Or it may be that while the moments of the small sample distribution are quite intractable, as $T \to \infty$ the estimator may, in some sense, approach a constant.

Thus it behooves us to study carefully various modes of convergence for sequences of random variables. Although the discussion will be cast in terms of sequences of random variables, following the custom of probability theory, the reader will have little difficulty in applying such results to estimators.

CONVERGENCE TO A CONSTANT

Suppose that we have a sequence of random variables $\{x_t : t = 1, 2, \ldots,\}$.[1] In the limit, this sequence may approach *a constant or a random variable*. The former is really a special case of the latter, for a constant is a degenerate form of random variable. For purposes of clarity, we shall often distinguish between these two cases.

Now, roughly speaking, convergence to a limit means that if one goes far enough in the sequence, then all elements beyond a certain point are "close" to the limit of the sequence. There are many ways of defining what we want to mean by "close." Thus we have various modes of convergence. A particularly strong convergence criterion is given in

Definition 3: Let $\{x_t : t = 1, 2, \ldots,\}$ be a sequence of random variables. The sequence is said to converge with probability one to a constant (vector) ζ if, for every component x_{ti},

$$\Pr \left\{ \lim_{t \to \infty} |x_{ti} - \zeta_i| < \varepsilon \right\} = 1 \qquad i = 1, 2, \ldots, m \tag{3.2.5}$$

where ε is *any* preassigned (small) number.

Let us make quite clear what this statement means. It means that, given any $\varepsilon, \delta > 0$, there exists an index T such that

$$\Pr \{|x_{T+1, i} - \zeta_i| < \varepsilon, |x_{T+2, i} - \zeta_i| < \varepsilon, \ldots\} > 1 - \delta \tag{3.2.6}$$

In other words, it states that the probability that all x_{ti}, $t > T$, lie *simultaneously* within ε of ζ_i is greater than $1 - \delta$. This is an exceedingly strong requirement and is typically very difficult to establish in practice. For this reason we rely on another form of convergence in econometrics. Thus

---

[1] In what follows, the symbols x and θ will always denote, respectively, m- and k-element vectors unless we indicate to the contrary.

Definition 4: Let $\{x_t : t = 1, 2, \ldots,\}$ be a sequence of random variables; then the sequence is said to *converge in probability to a* constant, ξ, if for every component x_{ti},

$$\lim_{t \to \infty} \Pr \{|x_{ti} - \xi_i| < \varepsilon\} = 1 \qquad (3.2.7)$$

where ε is any preassigned (small) number.

The constant ξ is said to be the probability limit of x_t, and one writes

$$\plim_{t \to \infty} x_t = \xi \qquad (3.2.8)$$

The distinction between this convergence and the former is seen as follows. Convergence in probability means that for any given $\varepsilon, \delta > 0$, we can find an index, say T, such that for all $t > T$ we have

$$\Pr \{|x_{ti} - \xi_i| < \varepsilon\} > 1 - \delta \qquad i = 1, 2, \ldots, m \qquad (3.2.9)$$

This, however, does not mean that it *simultaneously holds with probability* $1 - \delta$ that $|x_{ti} - \xi_i| < \varepsilon$ for all $t > T$. In (3.2.6) we are dealing with the probability of a joint event, while in (3.2.9) we are dealing with the probability of single events. It is clear, of course, that (3.2.6) implies (3.2.9); the converse, however, is not true.

Definition 5: Let $\hat\theta_T$ be an estimator of a parameter θ. If $\hat\theta_T$ converges in probability to θ, then $\hat\theta_T$ is said to be a *consistent* estimator (of θ).

Since there appears to be some confusion as to what consistency implies in terms of other properties of estimators, let us introduce

Definition 6: Let $\hat\theta_T$ be an estimator of θ; $\hat\theta_T$ is said to be an *unbiased* estimator if

$$E(\hat\theta_T) = \theta \qquad (3.2.10)$$

It is said to be *asymptotically unbiased*[2] if

$$\lim_{T \to \infty} E(\hat\theta_T) = \theta \qquad (3.2.11)$$

If an estimator is not (asymptotically) unbiased, then it is said to be (asymptotically) biased and its (asymptotic) *bias* is defined, respectively, by

$$\text{asy. } b(\hat\theta_T) = \lim_{T \to \infty} E(\hat\theta_T) - \theta \qquad b(\hat\theta_T) = E(\hat\theta_T) - \theta \qquad (3.2.12)$$

An instance of an estimator that is asymptotically unbiased but is biased for small samples is given below.

---

[2] This term is also used to denote the fact that the asymptotic distribution of $\hat\theta_T$ is centered about θ. Often, but not always, this is in agreement with the condition in (3.2.11). Such matters will be taken up in detail below.

Example 2: Consider again the estimator $\bar{x}$ of (3.2.4). We have

$$E(\bar{x}) = \mu \tag{3.2.13}$$

Hence $\bar{x}$ is unbiased and thus also asymptotically unbiased. On the other hand, the other estimator given there, s^2, yields

$$E(s_T^2) = \frac{T-1}{T}\sigma^2 \tag{3.2.14}$$

Its bias is given by

$$b(s_T^2) = -\frac{1}{T}\sigma^2 \tag{3.2.15}$$

Notice, however, that the bias vanishes asymptotically.

Now, it is occasionally thought that a consistent estimator of a parameter is necessarily an asymptotically unbiased one. Unfortunately, this is not correct, as we shall show momentarily. The misconception arises because of the intuitive interpretation one places on consistency. Thus it is said that consistency means that as $T \to \infty$ the integral of the tails of the density of a consistent estimator, say $\hat{\theta}_T$, approaches zero so that the density tends to collapse to a single point. Hence we might have asymptotic unbiasedness. This is an overly simplistic view, for what (3.2.7) implies is not that large deviations of $\hat{\theta}_T$ from θ are *impossible* but, rather, that the probability of this occurring is small. In addition, what matters for asymptotic unbiasedness is not the behavior of the tails of the density of $\hat{\theta}_T$ as $T \to \infty$ but, rather, *the behavior of the tails of $\hat{\theta}_T$ times its density.*

To make this abundantly clear, we consider

Example 3: Let $\{x_T : T = 1, 2, \ldots,\}$ be a sequence of (scalar) random variables such that

$$\Pr\{x_T = \alpha\} = 1 - \frac{1}{T}$$

$$\Pr\{x_T = T^v\} = \frac{1}{T} \tag{3.2.16}$$

We observe that

$$\plim_{T \to \infty} x_T = \alpha \tag{3.2.17}$$

so that x_T is a consistent estimator of α. Now

$$E(x_T) = \alpha\left(1 - \frac{1}{T}\right) + T^{v-1} \tag{3.2.18}$$

We see that

$$\lim_{T \to \infty} E(x_T) = \alpha + \lim_{T \to \infty} T^{\nu - 1} \qquad (3.2.19)$$

It is clear that unless $\nu < 1$, x_T is *not* an (asymptotically) unbiased estimator of α; indeed, if $\nu > 1$, the asymptotic mean of x_T does not exist.

The problem here arises because the tail of the mass function of x_T goes to zero linearly with T. However, x_T assumes values away from α which grow as a power, ν, of T. Unless T^ν increases less rapidly than the tails approach zero, it is not possible to obtain asymptotic unbiasedness.

If we wish consistency to imply asymptotic unbiasedness, then we should define the former in terms of a stronger mode of convergence. Consequently, consider

Definition 7: Let $\{x_t : t = 1, 2, \ldots,\}$ be a sequence of random variables possessing at least rth absolute moment; then x_t converges in rth moment to a constant ξ if, for every component x_{ti}, we have

$$\lim_{t \to \infty} E |x_{ti} - \xi_i|^r = 0 \qquad i = 1, 2, \ldots, m \qquad (3.2.20)$$

A special case of this, $r = 2$, is referred to as convergence in *quadratic mean*, and we denote the relation in (3.2.20) by

$$\text{l.i.m. } x_{ti} = \xi_i \qquad i = 1, 2, \ldots, m \qquad (3.2.21)$$

A simple consequence of convergence in quadratic mean is given in

Lemma 1: Let $\hat{\theta}_T$ be a (scalar) estimator that converges to θ in quadratic mean; then $\hat{\theta}_T$ is also a consistent estimator of θ. The converse, however, is not true.

PROOF: We may write the Chebyshev inequality as

$$\Pr \{|\hat{\theta}_T - \theta| > \varepsilon\} \le \frac{E |\hat{\theta}_T - \theta|^2}{\varepsilon^2} \qquad (3.2.22)$$

To prove the first part of the lemma, we must show that, given any ε, $\delta > 0$, there exists a T^* such that for all $T > T^*$,

$$\Pr \{|\hat{\theta}_T - \theta| > \varepsilon\} < \delta \qquad (3.2.23)$$

By convergence in quadratic mean, we can, for given δ, ε, choose a T^* such that for all $T > T^*$,

$$\frac{E |\hat{\theta}_T - \theta|^2}{\varepsilon^2} < \delta \qquad (3.2.24)$$

For such T^* (3.2.23) holds, which proves the first part of the lemma. To prove the second part we revert to Example 3. We see that for every ν, x_T as defined in (3.2.16) is a consistent estimator of α. On the other hand,

$$E|x_T - \alpha|^2 = 0\left(1 - \frac{1}{T}\right) + (T^\nu - \alpha)^2 \frac{1}{T} \tag{3.2.25}$$

and thus for $\nu > \frac{1}{2}$ the limit of the quantity in the right member of (3.2.25) does not exist.   Q.E.D.

Another important aspect of convergence in quadratic mean is given by

Lemma 2: $\hat{\theta}_T$ converges to θ in quadratic mean if and only if $\hat{\theta}_T$ is an asymptotically unbiased estimator of θ and its variance vanishes asymptotically.

PROOF: Necessity. Suppose convergence; then

$$E|\hat{\theta}_T - \theta|^2 = E|(\hat{\theta}_T - \theta_T) + (\theta_T - \theta)|^2 = \text{Var}\,(\hat{\theta}_T) + b^2(\hat{\theta}_T) \tag{3.2.26}$$

where

$$\theta_T = E(\hat{\theta}_T) \tag{3.2.27}$$

Since both terms of the last member of (3.2.26) are nonnegative, the hypotheses of the lemma imply

$$\lim_{T\to\infty} \text{Var}\,(\hat{\theta}_T) = 0 \qquad \lim_{T\to\infty} b^2(\hat{\theta}_T) = 0 \tag{3.2.28}$$

Sufficiency: Suppose now that (3.2.28) holds; then it is obvious from (3.2.26) that $\hat{\theta}_T$ converges to θ in quadratic mean.   Q.E.D.

Corollary 1: Let $\hat{\theta}_T$ be an estimator of θ; if (3.2.28) holds, then $\hat{\theta}_T$ is a consistent estimator of θ.

PROOF: Lemmas 1, 2.

Remark 5: Even though Lemmas 1, 2, and Corollary 1 are stated in terms of scalar estimators, it is quite clear how one would handle vector estimators; one would simply show that *such results hold with respect to each of their components.*

3.3 CONVERGENCE TO A RANDOM VARIABLE: CONVERGENCE IN DISTRIBUTION AND CONVERGENCE OF MOMENTS

A sequence of random variables, of course, need not converge to a constant; it may well have a *limit that is itself a random variable.* As may be easily surmised, this form of convergence is important in studying the asymptotic (large sample) distribution of various estimators. Perhaps no other subject in the literature of econometrics has caused as much confusion as this. The subject is rather delicate and one is led to many pitfalls if the handling of the problem is not careful.

In this section we shall develop the basic concepts and state the relevant results, often without proof. Proofs tend to be rather complex and involve a good deal of measure theory. The interested reader may consult such well-known texts as Loève [22], Chung [3], or Gnedenko and Kolmogorov [12] among others.

Before embarking systematically on this aspect, let us illustrate by an example the type of problem facing us.

Example 4: Consider the scalar random variables x, y, z, which are mutually independent, with the following probability characteristics:

$$\Pr\{x = 1\} = \alpha \quad \Pr\{x = 0\} = 1 - \alpha \quad 0 < \alpha < 1 \tag{3.3.1}$$

$$\Pr\{y = 1\} = \Pr\{y = -1\} = \frac{1}{2} \tag{3.3.2}$$

Finally, let z be uniformly distributed over $[-\frac{1}{2}, \frac{1}{2}]$ and consider the sequence of variables,

$$w_T = Txy + \frac{(1-x)z}{T} \quad T = 1, 2, \dots \tag{3.3.3}$$

The distribution of w_T is easily determined; we are particularly interested in the latter's behavior as $T \to \infty$. From (3.3.1) and (3.3.2) we see that the "event" $x = 1$ *and* $y = -1$ has probability $\alpha/2$; thus, letting $T \to \infty$, we find w_T assumes the "value" $-\infty$ with probability $\alpha/2$, because the second term vanishes when $x = 1$. Similarly, the "event" $x = 1$ *and* $y = 1$ has probability $\alpha/2$; again letting $T \to \infty$, we find that w_T assumes the "value" $+\infty$ with probability $\alpha/2$. Finally, when $x = 0$, an "event" with probability $1 - \alpha$, as $T \to \infty$, w_T assumes the value 0. Hence the distribution of the limit of the sequence in (3.3.3), say w, is

$$\Pr\{w = -\infty\} = \frac{\alpha}{2} \quad \Pr\{w = +\infty\} = \frac{\alpha}{2} \quad \Pr\{w = 0\} = 1 - \alpha \tag{3.3.4}$$

and we see that w assumes "infinite values" with positive probability.

The reader will recall from his statistical training that most of the random variables to which he has been exposed assume such infinite values with probability zero. Here we have the phenomenon that some probability mass "has wandered off to infinity." In particular, it is clear from (3.3.4) that no moments of the limiting random variable exist, and its distribution is thus not well behaved.

Although we seldom deal with discrete random variables in econometrics, nonetheless, we face the general class of problems raised by the question: What can we say about the asymptotic distribution of our estimates, and what inference problems may be solved from finite samples that are sufficiently large so that the asymptotic results may serve as useful approximations?

Let us now introduce the relevant definitions:

Definition 8: Let $\{x_t : t = 1, 2, \ldots,\}$ be a sequence of random variables; the sequence is said to converge in probability to a random variable x, if given any ε, $\delta > 0$, there exists a T^* such that for all $t > T^*$, and every component x_{ti} of the vector x_t,

$$\Pr\{|x_{ti} - x_i| < \varepsilon\} > 1 - \delta \tag{3.3.5}$$

The vector x is termed the *probability limit* of x_t, and we write

$$\operatorname*{plim}_{t \to \infty} x_t = x \tag{3.3.6}$$

Similarly, convergence of the sequence to x in rth absolute moment is defined by the condition that

$$\lim_{t \to \infty} E |x_{ti} - x_i|^r = 0 \tag{3.3.7}$$

and it would be redundant to introduce another formal definition.

Now, with every random variable there is associated its *distribution function*, (d.f.) which as we recall from Chapter 1 is a bounded monotone, nondecreasing function continuous from the left and having the value 0 at $-\infty$ and 1 at $+\infty$.

Many of the properties of random variables, and hence of sequences of random variables, can be studied in terms of their distribution functions. This is particularly convenient in view of the boundedness and monotonicity properties of the latter.

Definition 9: Let $\{x_t : t = 1, 2, \ldots,\}$ be a sequence of random variables with d.f. $\{F_t : t = 1, 2, \ldots\}$. The sequence $\{x_t : t = 1, 2, \ldots\}$ is said to *converge in distribution* to a random variable, say x, if the sequence $\{F_t\}$ converges to the distribution function $F($ of $x)$ at the continuity points of the latter.

Remark 6: Recall that every distribution function defines a random variable so that in the definition above it is superfluous to speak of the random variables x_t or x. We may just as well have dealt only with the sequence of distribution functions and its limit.

It is interesting that every sequence of distribution functions contains a convergent subsequence; however, $F_t(\pm\infty)$ may not converge to $F(\pm\infty)$ unless the sequence has the property that, for given $\varepsilon > 0$, there exists a constant A such that for $a > A$ *and* all t,

$$|F_t(\infty) - F(-\infty) - [F_t(a) - F_t(-a)]| < \varepsilon \tag{3.3.8}$$

that is, the sequence is *equicontinuous* at infinity.

Occasionally convergence of a sequence obeying (3.3.8) is said to be *strong convergence*, while convergence of a sequence not obeying (3.3.8) is said to be *weak convergence*.

It is interesting that we can prove

Lemma 3: Let $\{x_t: t = 1, 2, \ldots\}$ be a sequence of random variables corresponding to the d.f. sequence $\{F_t: t = 1, 2, \ldots\}$ and suppose x_t *converges in probability* to the random variable x. Then F_t converges to the distribution function F of x.[3]

PROOF: See Loève [22, p. 168].

The importance of this lemma is that if we are dealing with an estimator whose small sample distribution is difficult to establish, then we *could infer its asymptotic distribution if we can establish the estimator's probability limit*.[4] Often this will be easier to accomplish. In view of the weak compactness of distribution functions (d.f.) that is, the fact that every sequence of d.f. contains a convergent subsequence, we are tempted to inquire into the nature of quantities like $\int g \, dF_t$, where g is some function. Notice that if x_t is an estimator $\hat{\theta}_T$ and $g(\hat{\theta}_T) = \hat{\theta}_T$, then the integral above is the mean of the estimator. Such problems arise in connection with the convergence of moments of small sample distribution to those of the asymptotic distribution of various estimators. We have

Lemma 4: (Helly-Bray): Let the sequence of d.f. $\{F_t: t = 1, 2, \ldots\}$ converge to the distribution function F, and let $g(\cdot)$ be a *bounded continuous* function; then

$$\lim_{t \to \infty} \int g \, dF_t = \int g \, dF \qquad (3.3.9)$$

PROOF: See Loève [22, pp. 182ff].

In many instances we are interested in the asymptotic moments of an estimator, or in the moments of its asymptotic distribution (the two are *not identical*). The Helly-Bray lemma above is not, in general, sufficient to deal with such problems, for the function g of the lemma must be *bounded*. Thus we must determine by other means under what conditions, if any, small sample moments converge to the moments of the asymptotic distribution. Of course, if the random variables in question *have finite* range, then Lemma 4 is quite adequate and states that small sample moments *always* converge to the moments of the asymptotic distribution.

Before examining the question of convergence of moments, let us derive a very useful result from the lemma just stated.

---

[3] When this is true, we say that x_t *converges in distribution to x*.
[4] Notice that this essentially is what was done in Example 4.

Lemma 5: Let $\{F_t: t = 1, 2, \ldots\}$ be a sequence of distribution functions that converges strongly to F; let ϕ_t, ϕ be, respectively, the characteristic functions[5] corresponding to F_t and F; then

$$\lim_{t \to \infty} \phi_t = \phi \tag{3.3.10}$$

Conversely, if

$$\lim_{t \to \infty} \phi_t = g \tag{3.3.11}$$

where g is continuous at zero, then $\{F_t: t = 1, 2, \ldots,\}$ converges strongly to F, and

$$g = \phi \tag{3.3.12}$$

PROOF: We observe that $\exp(iux)$ is a bounded continuous function; thus, by the previous lemma,

$$\lim_{t \to \infty} \int \exp(iux)\, dF_t(t) = \int \exp(iux)\, dF(x) \tag{3.3.13}$$

which establishes (3.3.10). Now suppose that (3.3.11) holds; then for every real u,

$$h_t(u) = \int_0^u \phi_t(v)\, dv \tag{3.3.14}$$

is well defined, and, moreover,

$$\lim_{t \to \infty} h_t(u) = \int_0^u g(v)\, dv \tag{3.3.15}$$

On the other hand, by definition,

$$h_t(u) = \int_0^u \phi_t(v)\, dv = \int_0^u \int_{-\infty}^{\infty} \exp(ivx)\, dF_t(t)\, dv = \int_{-\infty}^{\infty} \frac{\exp(iux) - 1}{ix}\, dF_t(x) \tag{3.3.16}$$

Now $\exp(iux) - 1/ix$ is a bounded continuous function in x if at the origin it is defined by its limit,

$$\lim_{x \to 0} \frac{\exp(iux) - 1}{ix} = u \tag{3.3.17}$$

---

[5] We recall that if x is a (scalar) random variable with d.f. F, then its characteristic function is defined by

$$\phi(u) = \int \exp(iux)\, dF(x)$$

Also, since $\{F_t: t = 1, 2, \ldots\}$ is a sequence of distribution functions, it contains a subsequence, say $\{F_{t'}: t' = 1, 2, \ldots\}$, which converges to a bounded nondecreasing function, say F. Thus, by the previous lemma,

$$\lim_{t' \to \infty} h_{t'}(u) = \lim_{t' \to \infty} \int_{-\infty}^{\infty} \frac{\exp(iux) - 1}{ix} \, dF_{t'}(x) = \int_0^u \phi(v) \, dv \tag{3.3.18}$$

By Remark 6, to show that F is a distribution function we need only show that $F_{t'}(\infty) - F_{t'}(-\infty)$ converges to $F(\infty) - F(-\infty)$. Now, from (3.3.14) and (3.3.18), we have

$$\frac{1}{u} \int_0^u g(v) \, dv = \frac{1}{u} \int_0^u \phi(v) \, dv \tag{3.3.19}$$

Letting $u \to 0$, since $g(\cdot)$ and $\phi(\cdot)$ are continuous at the origin, we have

$$g(0) = \phi(0) \tag{3.3.20}$$

From this, the assertion follows immediately if we note that

$$\phi_{t'}(0) = \int_{-\infty}^{\infty} dF_{t'}(x) = F_{t'}(\infty) - F_{t'}(-\infty)$$

$$\phi(0) = F(\infty) - F(-\infty) \tag{3.3.21}$$

Finally, the validity of (3.3.12) follows from (3.3.15) and (3.3.18).   Q.E.D.

Remark 7: The discussion of the two lemmas above shows why it is preferable to deal with *characteristic* rather than moment-generating functions. The latter are defined by $E[\exp(ux)]$, where u is a real number. If the range of the random variable is infinite, then of course $\exp(ux)$ is not *bounded*. Moreover, the expectation $E[\exp(ux)]$ *need not* always exist. On the other hand, the characteristic function defined by $E[\exp(iux)]$ operates with a bounded function $\exp(iux)$ no matter what the range of x. Thus the Helly-Bray lemma is applicable and, moreover, *such functions always exist*. Finally, it should be apparent how the result of the lemma may be extended to the multivariate case.

Let us return now to the problem of the conditions under which the small sample moments of an estimator converge to the corresponding moments of its asymptotic distribution. Thus, we have

Lemma 6: Let $\{x_t: t = 1, 2, \ldots\}$ be a sequence of (scalar) random variables and let $\{F_t: t = 1, 2, \ldots\}$ be the sequence of their associated d.f. Suppose that for some $r_0 > 0$,

$$\int_{-\infty}^{\infty} |\xi|^{r_0} \, dF_t(\xi) < \infty \qquad \text{uniformly in } t \tag{3.3.22}$$

then the sequence $\{F_t: t = 1, 2, \ldots\}$ converges strongly, and for every subsequence $\{F_{t'} = 1, 2, \ldots\}$ which converges to the distribution function F and all $r \le r_0$,[6]

$$\lim_{t' \to \infty} \int_{-\infty}^{\infty} \xi^r \, dF_{t'}(\xi) = \int_{-\infty}^{\infty} \xi^r \, dF(\xi)$$

$$\lim_{t' \to \infty} \int_{-\infty}^{\infty} |\xi|^r \, dF_{t'}(\xi) = \int_{-\infty}^{\infty} |\xi|^r \, dF(\xi) \tag{3.3.23}$$

PROOF: We first show that (3.3.22) is valid for all $r \le r_0$. Now, for any $c > 0$,

$$\int_{|\xi| \ge c} |\xi|^r \, dF_{t'}(\xi) = c^r \int_{|\xi| \ge c} \left| \frac{\xi}{c} \right|^r \, dF_{t'}(\xi) \le c^{r-r_0} \int_{|\xi| \ge c} |\xi|^{r_0} \, dF_{t'}(\xi) \tag{3.3.24}$$

Hence, letting $c \to \infty$, we see that (3.3.22) holds for $r \le r_0$. Thus, in particular for $r = 0$, we find

$$\int_{|\xi| \ge c} dF_{t'}(\xi) \le \int_{|\xi| \ge c} \left| \frac{\xi}{c} \right|^{r_0} dF_{t'}(\xi) \le c^{-r_0} K \tag{3.3.25}$$

where K obeys, say,[7]

$$K = \sup_{t'} \int_{-\infty}^{\infty} |\xi|^{r_0} \, dF_{t'}(\xi) \tag{3.3.26}$$

But (3.3.25) can be written as

$$1 - [F_{t'}(c) - F_{t'}(-c)] \le c^{-r_0} K \tag{3.3.27}$$

uniformly in t'.

Since $F_{t'}$ is a distribution $F_{t'}(\infty) = 1$, $F_{t'}(-\infty) = 0$. Thus, subtracting $1 - [F_{t'}(\infty) - F_{t'}(-\infty)] = 0$ from both sides of (3.3.27), we have

$$[F_{t'}(\infty) - F_{t'}(-\infty)] - [F_{t'}(c) - F_{t'}(-c)] \le c^{-r_0} K \tag{3.3.28}$$

uniformly in t'. Hence the condition in (3.3.8) of Remark 6 is fulfilled and F is indeed a d.f. Moreover, it is seen from (3.3.27) that the convergence of $F_{t'}$ to F is uniform in t'. The convergence of moments is now easily obtained. Thus

$$\int |\xi|^r \, dF_{t'}(\xi) - \int |\xi|^r \, dF(\xi) = \int_{|\xi| \le c} |\xi|^r [dF_{t'}(\xi) - dF(\xi)]$$

$$+ \int_{|\xi| > c} |\xi|^r [dF_{t'}(\xi) - dF(\xi)]$$

$$\le \int_{|\xi| \le c} |\xi|^r [dF_{t'}(\xi) - dF(\xi)] + 2c^{-r_0} K \tag{3.3.29}$$

---

[6] We can prove a slightly weaker result by eliminating the uniform convergence assumption in (3.3.22). Thus if we merely assume boundedness of the r_0th absolute moment then the conclusions of the lemma will hold for $r < r_0$. This simplifies the proof somewhat, but, of course, it is a weaker result, for under the assumption of the lemma the result is valid for $r \le r_0$.

[7] If $\alpha = \{\alpha_t : t = 1, 2, \ldots\}$ is a sequence, then sup α is the smallest number, say A, such that $\alpha_t \le A$ for all elements of α; that is, it is the least upper bound of the sequence.

Now, letting $t' \to \infty$, the first term of the last member of (3.3.29) vanishes; letting $c \to \infty$, the second term vanishes as well. Hence

$$\lim_{t' \to \infty} \int_{-\infty}^{\infty} |\xi|^r \, dF_{t'}(\xi) = \int_{-\infty}^{\infty} |\xi|^r \, dF(\xi) \qquad r \le r_0 \tag{3.3.30}$$

A similar proof may be invoked for the first equation of (3.3.23).   Q.E.D.

Another variant of this lemma may be stated as

Lemma 7: Let $\{x_t : t = 1, 2, \ldots\}$ be a sequence of (scalar) random variables converging in distribution to the random variable x, whose distribution F possesses *finite absolute moments* up to order r_0. If

$$\lim_{t \to \infty} E |x_t - x|^{r_0} = 0 \tag{3.3.31}$$

then

$$E |x_t|^r < \infty \qquad r \le r_0 \tag{3.3.32}$$

and

$$\lim_{t \to \infty} E |x_t|^r = E |x|^r \qquad r \le r_0 \tag{3.3.33}$$

PROOF: The Minkowski inequality [30, p. 95] states that for two random variables, z, y, we have

$$[E|z + y|^r]^{1/r} \le \{E|z|^r\}^{1/r} + \{E|y|^r\}^{1/r} \tag{3.3.34}$$

or

$$E|z + y|^r \le [\{E|z|^r\}^{1/r} + \{E|y|^r\}^{1/r}]^r \tag{3.3.35}$$

Now for every t we have

$$x_t = x_t - x + x, \quad |x_t|^r = |z_t + x|^r \qquad z_t = x_t - x \tag{3.3.36}$$

Thus

$$E |x_t|^r = E |z_t + x|^r \le [\{E|x_t - x|^r\}^{1/r} + \{E|x|^r\}^{1/r}]^r \tag{3.3.37}$$

Taking limits, we find, in view of (3.3.31),

$$\lim_{t \to \infty} E |x_t|^r \le E |x|^r < \infty \tag{3.3.38}$$

which proves (3.3.32). But (3.3.38), together with the hypotheses of the present lemma, satisfies the hypotheses of Lemma 6, which shows convergence of moments.   Q.E.D.

An entirely analogous result can be obtained for a sequence of *vector* random variables; in addition, it is important to realize, as should be obvious from the lemma, that *unless F has finite rth absolute moment,* (3.3.31) is not sufficient to guarantee that the rth absolute moment of F_t will exist. This is illustrated by

Example 5: Let

$$x_t = \xi + v_t \tag{3.3.39}$$

where ξ is a Cauchy variable and v_t assumes the value 0 with probability $1 - 1/t$, and t^ν with probability $1/t$. It is clear that v_t converges in probability to 0, and thus x_t converges in distribution to ξ. Moreover,

$$E(x_t - \xi)^r = E(v_t^r) = t^{\nu r - 1} \tag{3.3.40}$$

Thus, if $\nu < 1/r$, then

$$\lim_{t \to \infty} E(x_t - \xi)^r = 0 \tag{3.3.41}$$

and x_t converges in rth moment to ξ; however, the rth moment of x_t does *not* exist because the Cauchy variable ξ has no finite moments of any order!

Furthermore, it should be noted that x_t might converge in distribution to a random variable, ξ, which has *finite moments of every order*, *while* x_t *itself might have no finite moments of any order*. We shall see an example of this when we deal with simultaneous equations estimators.

Finally, let us make clear the limitations of Lemma 6; it *does not say* that if the distributions F_t admit of finite (absolute) moments of order r_0 then these moments converge to the corresponding moments of the asymptotic distribution F. *It is important that* (3.3.22) *hold uniformly for* t; if that does not hold, then the conclusion of the lemma need not be valid. Hence consider

Example 6: Let $\{x_T : T = 1, 2, \ldots\}$ be the sequence of random variables defined in (3.2.16) of Example 3. The expression analogous to the left member of (3.3.22) in this case is

$$E|x_T|^{r_0} = |\alpha|^{r_0}\left(1 - \frac{1}{T}\right) + T^{r_0\nu - 1} \tag{3.3.42}$$

For every T, this is finite; however, the inequality in (3.3.22) does not hold uniformly in T. Uniformity in (3.3.22) requires that there exist a constant c such that for given $\varepsilon > 0$, and *any* t, we should have

$$\int_{|\xi| \geq c} |\xi|^{r_0}\, dF_t(\xi) < \varepsilon \tag{3.3.43}$$

It is impossible to find a c satisfying this inequality applied to the sequence of this example if $r_0\mu > 1$. To emphasize this point, consider the sequence

$$z_T = \xi + x_T \tag{3.3.44}$$

where x_T is the random variable defined in (3.2.16) with

$$\alpha = 0 \tag{3.3.45}$$

and ξ is a normal variable with finite mean μ and variance σ^2. Obviously z_T converges in probability to ξ; however,

$$E(z_T) = \mu + T^{\nu-1} \tag{3.3.46}$$

Take

$$\nu = 1 \tag{3.3.47}$$

so that z_T has a finite first-order moment for every T equal to $\mu + 1$. However,

$$\lim_{T \to \infty} E(z_T) = \mu + 1 \neq E(\xi) = \mu \tag{3.3.48}$$

Of course, some fractional[8] moments of z_T converge, but this is a result with few, if any, applications in econometrics.

To summarize the development of this section we have established the following:

i. A sequence of distribution functions always contains a subsequence that converges to a bounded nondecreasing function which is continuous from the left.
ii. If the sequence is also equicontinuous at infinity, then the limit function of the subsequence is a distribution.
iii. If a sequence $\{x_t: t = 1, 2, \ldots\}$ of random variables converges in probability to a random variable x, then the associated sequence of distribution functions converges to a distribution function—the d.f. of the limit random variable. Thus the sequence $\{x_t: t = 1, 2, \ldots\}$ *converges in distribution to x* (Lemma 3).
iv. A sequence of random variables $\{x_t: t = 1, 2, \ldots\}$ converges in distribution to a random variable x if and only if the characteristic functions asociated with x_t converge to the characteristic function associated with x (Lemma 5).
v. If a sequence $\{x_t: t = 1, 2, \ldots\}$ is such that for $r_0 > 0$ the r_0th absolute moments (of the elements x_t) converge uniformly in t, then the sequence converges in distribution to a random variable x; and, moreover,

$$\lim_{t \to \infty} E|x_t|^r = E|x|^r \qquad r \leq r_0 \qquad \text{(Lemma 6)}$$

vi. If $\{x_t: t = 1, 2, \ldots\}$ is a sequence converging in r_0th absolute moment to a random variable x, that is, if

$$\lim_{t \to \infty} E|x_t - x|^{r_0} = 0$$

---

[8] Fractional (absolute) moments of a random variable x are defined as $E|x|^r$, where r is a rational (noninteger) real number.

and *if the r_0th absolute moment of x exists*, then the rth ($\leq r_0$) absolute moments of x_t exist, and, moreover,

$$\lim_{t \to \infty} E|x_t|^r = E|x|^r \qquad r \leq r_0$$

vii. Although the results above are stated in terms of scalar random variables, *mutatis mutandis*, similar results can be established for *vector random variables*.

3.4 CENTRAL LIMIT THEOREMS AND RELATED TOPICS

INTRODUCTORY REMARKS

In the previous section we discussed conditions under which there is convergence in distribution for a sequence of random variables. Although some conditions for convergence were established, nothing in that development indicates the precise form of the asymptotic distribution. In any concrete application such results are inadequate, for it is of little use to know that a certain estimator whose small sample distribution is unknown converges in distribution as the sample size tends to infinity. It would be highly desirable if the nature of such limiting distributions were known. Many of the problems encountered in econometrics lead asymptotically to the normal distribution. In this section we shall complete our preparation for dealing with the standard problems of determining the asymptotic distribution of simultaneous equations estimators.

We shall first deal with the law of large numbers and then with various forms of the central limit theorem.

THE WEAK LAW OF LARGE NUMBERS

The general problem dealt with in this section is as follows: If $\{x_t: t = 1, 2, \ldots\}$ is a sequence of independent random variables with finite means μ_t—and often with finite variances σ_t^2—determine the limiting behavior of the sequence $\{z_T: T = 1, 2, \ldots\}$, where

$$z_T = \frac{\sum_{t=1}^{T} x_t - a_T}{b_T} \tag{3.4.1}$$

and $\{a_T: T = 1, 2, \ldots\}$, $\{b_T: T = 1, 2, \ldots\}$ are certain sequences, the latter a sequence of *positive numbers*. This is a bit vague but is perhaps useful in that it puts the various laws of large numbers and the central limit theorem under a common rubric.

Definition 10: A sequence of (scalar) random variables $\{x_t: t = 1, 2, \ldots\}$ with finite first moments μ_t, is said to obey the *weak law* of large numbers if, for any $\varepsilon, \delta > 0$, there exists a T^* such that for all $T > T^*$,

$$\Pr\left\{\frac{|w_T - m_T|}{T} < \varepsilon\right\} > 1 - \delta \tag{3.4.2}$$

where

$$m_T = \sum_{t=1}^{T} \mu_t \qquad w_T = \sum_{t=1}^{T} x_t \tag{3.4.3}$$

Remark 8: The *weak law of large numbers* is equivalent to a statement that the standardized sum $(w_T - m_T)/T$ converges in probability to zero. Notice further that here the quantity b_T of equation (3.4.1) is taken to be T.

Lemma 8: (Chebyshev): Let $\{x_t : t = 1, 2, \ldots\}$ be a sequence of mutually independent random variables with finite means μ_t and variances σ_t^2. Then if

$$\lim_{T \to \infty} \left(\frac{1}{T^2}\right) \sum_{t=1}^{T} \sigma_t^2 = 0 \tag{3.4.4}$$

the sequence obeys the weak law of large numbers.

PROOF: See Feller [6, p. 238].

Lemma 9: (Khinchine): Let $\{x_t : t = 1, 2, \ldots\}$ be a sequence of mutually independent, *identically distributed* (i.i.d) random variables with finite mean μ. Then the sequence obeys the weak law of large numbers.

PROOF: Let

$$\phi_t(u) = \int_{-\infty}^{\infty} \exp(iux)\, dF_t(x) \tag{3.4.5}$$

be the characteristic function of the element x_t of the sequence above. Defining

$$\bar{x}_T = \frac{1}{T} \sum_{t=1}^{T} x_t \tag{3.4.6}$$

we conclude, by the hypotheses of the lemma,

$$\phi_{\bar{x}_T}(u) = E[\exp(iu\bar{x}_T)] = \prod_{t=1}^{T} \phi_t\left(\frac{u}{T}\right) = \left[\phi\left(\frac{u}{T}\right)\right]^T \tag{3.4.7}$$

where, by the identical distribution (i.i.d) assumption,

$$\phi(u) = \phi_t(u) \qquad \text{all } t \tag{3.4.8}$$

Now it may be shown [33, p. 115], that if the rth moment of a random variable exists, then its characteristic function, say $\phi(\cdot)$, can be expressed as

$$\phi(u) = 1 + \sum_{s=1}^{r} \frac{(iu)^s}{s!} \mu_s + o(u^r) \tag{3.4.9}$$

where μ_s is the sth moment of the variable and the quantity $o(u^r)$ has the properties

$$\lim_{u \to \infty} \frac{o(u^r)}{u^r} = 0 \qquad o(0) = 0 \tag{3.4.10}$$

In the present case, we can thus write (3.4.7) as

$$\phi_{\bar{x}_T}(u) = \left[\phi\left(\frac{u}{T}\right)\right]^T = \left[1 + i\frac{u}{T}\mu + o\left(\frac{u}{T}\right)\right]^T \tag{3.4.11}$$

Thus

$$\lim_{T\to\infty} \phi_{\bar{x}_T}(u) = \exp(iu\mu) \tag{3.4.12}$$

which is recognized as the characteristic function of the degenerate random variable having all probability mass concentrated at μ.   Q.E.D.

Remark 9: It is important to note the difference between Lemmas 8 and 9. In the former, the existence of (finite) second moments is required; on the other hand, we allow for nonidentical distributions. In the latter, we require identical distributions but the second moment *need not exist*. In both cases, the elements of the sequence are mutually independent.

THE STRONG LAW OF LARGE NUMBERS

Definition 11: Let $\{x_t : t = 1, 2, \ldots\}$ be a sequence of mutually independent (scalar) random variables with finite means μ_t. Then the sequence is said to obey the *strong law of large numbers* if the standardized sum,

$$z_T = \frac{\sum_{t=1}^{T}(x_t - \mu_t)}{T} \tag{3.4.13}$$

converges to zero with probability one; that is, given any $\varepsilon, \delta > 0$,

$$\Pr\left\{\lim_{T\to\infty} \frac{\sum_{t=1}^{T}(x_t - \mu_t)}{T} < \varepsilon\right\} > 1 - \delta \tag{3.4.14}$$

In connection with this, we have

Lemma 10: (Kolmogorov): Let $\{x_t : t = 1, 2, \ldots\}$ be a sequence of mutually independent variables with finite means μ_t and variances σ_t^2; if

$$\lim_{T\to\infty} \sum_{t=1}^{T} \left(\frac{\sigma_t^2}{t^2}\right) < \infty \tag{3.4.15}$$

then the sequence obeys the strong law of large numbers.

PROOF: See Feller [7, p. 243].
We also have

Lemma 11: (Kolmogorov): Let $\{x_t : t = 1, 2, \ldots\}$ be a sequence of i.i.d.

random variables with finite mean μ. Then the sequence obeys the strong law of large numbers; that is, the quantity

$$\bar{x}_T = \frac{1}{T} \sum_{t=1}^{T} x_t \qquad (3.4.16)$$

converges to μ with probability one.

PROOF: See Feller [7, p. 244].

Remark 10: It should be clear from the discussion above that when we are dealing with a random sample, the sample mean converges to the population mean with probability one, hence also in probability. When not, however, convergence in probability is rather easier to establish [equation (3.4.4)] than convergence with probability one [equation (3.4.15)]. This partly explains why one popularly defines consistency in econometrics as convergence in probability. As before, the results of Lemmas 8, 9, 10, and 11 can be extended to vector random variables by having the relevant definitions (11 and 12) and the hypotheses of the lemmas apply to the individual elements of the vector random variable. We leave the verification of this statement as an exercise for the reader.

CENTRAL LIMIT THEOREMS

The problem to be examined here is the set of conditions under which the sequence whose typical element is given in (3.4.1) converges in distribution to $N(0, 1)$. For the purpose of this discussion, we take

$$a_T = \sum_{t=1}^{T} E(x_t) \qquad b_T = \left[\sum_{t=1}^{T} \text{Var}(x_t) \right]^{\frac{1}{2}} \qquad (3.4.17)$$

Occasionally z_T is then referred to as a "standardized variable."

It will be convenient, but not necessary, to assume that $E(x_t) = 0$ for all t; this will simplify the notation without detracting from the generality of our results. We see that z_T consists of the sum of random variables like x_t/b_T, where $\{b_T : T = 1, 2, \ldots\}$ is, by (3.4.17), a sequence whose elements converge to $+\infty$ with T. In addition, it ought to be apparent to the reader that the sum $\sum_{t=1}^{T} (x_t/b_T)$ cannot converge to a well-behaved variable unless, in some sense, the individual terms become negligible, at least for T large enough.

Although in a rigorous treatment of the subject this will be seen as a mathematical condition for the type of convergence we seek, historically it arose from the motivation in the physical sciences that individually infinitesimal errors accumulate to create probabilistically predictable phenomena.

The central limit theorem takes several forms. We shall begin with the simplest univariate case in which a measure of negligibility will not be explicitly required. As we progressively relax our assumptions, we shall return to a more precise definition of negligibility.

Theorem 1: Let $\{x_t: t = 1, 2, \ldots\}$ be a sequence of i.i.d. (scalar) random variables with finite mean μ and variance σ^2. Then the sequence of standardized variables,

$$z_T = \frac{\sum_{t=1}^{T}(x_t - \mu)}{s_T} \tag{3.4.18}$$

where

$$s_T^2 = \sum_{t=1}^{T} \text{Var}(x_t) = T\sigma^2 \tag{3.4.19}$$

converges in distribution to a random variable $z \sim N(0, 1)$.

PROOF: By Lemma 5, we need only prove that the sequence of characteristic functions corresponding to the variables z_T converges to $\exp(-v^2/2)$, which is the characteristic function of a $N(0, 1)$ variable.

To this effect, let $\phi(u)$ be the (common) characteristic function of the variables $(x_t - \mu)$, which have mean zero. By the result cited in (3.4.9), we may write

$$\phi(u) = 1 - \left(\frac{u^2}{2}\right)\sigma^2 + o(u^2) \tag{3.4.20}$$

Now the characteristic function of z_T is given by

$$\phi_T(v) = E(\exp(ivz_T)) = E\left\{\prod_{t=1}^{T} \exp[iv(x_t - \mu/s_T)]\right\} = \left[\phi\left(\frac{v}{s_T}\right)\right]^T \tag{3.4.21}$$

Thus, in view of (3.4.20), we have

$$\phi_T(v) = \left[1 - \frac{v^2}{2T} + o\left(\frac{v^2}{T\sigma^2}\right)\right]^T \tag{3.4.22}$$

Letting $T \to \infty$, we have

$$\lim_{T \to \infty} \phi_T(v) = \exp(-v^2/2) \qquad \text{Q.E.D.} \tag{3.4.23}$$

We next inquire: Does a similar result hold *even if* the elements of the sequence $\{x_t: t = 1, 2, \ldots\}$ are not identically distributed? This is answered by

Theorem 2 (Liapounov): Let $\{x_t: t = 1, 2, \ldots\}$ be a sequence of mutually independent (scalar) random variables such that[9]

$$E|x_t|^{2+\delta} < \infty \qquad \text{all } t, \ \delta > 0 \tag{3.4.24}$$

---

[9] We remind the reader that if $E|x|^r < \infty$, then all moments of lower order also exist and are finite.

and

$$\lim_{T \to \infty} \frac{1}{s_T^{2+\delta}} \sum_{t=1}^{T} E |x_t|^{2+\delta} = 0 \qquad (3.4.25)$$

Then the sequence of standardized variables

$$z_T = \frac{\sum_{t=1}^{T} (x_t - \mu_t)}{s_T} \qquad (3.4.26)$$

where

$$s_T^2 = \sum_{t=1}^{T} \sigma_t^2 \quad \mu_t = E(x_t) \quad \sigma_t^2 = \mathrm{Var}\,(x_t) \qquad (3.4.27)$$

converges to a random variable z having the distribution $N(0, 1)$.

For a proof of this, the reader may consult Loève [22, p. 276]. For a simpler case where the third (absolute) moment is assumed to exist, the proof in Chung [3, p. 185] is especially convenient, for it makes use of characteristic functions. The method is a rather straightforward extension of the one we employed in connection with Theorem 1.

In the case of i.i.d. variables, we have seen that existence of the second moment is sufficient for a central limit theorem. If the identical distribution assumption is dropped, then the existence of the $(2 + \delta)$th moment and condition (3.4.25), or the existence of the third (absolute) moment and a condition analogous to (3.4.25), had to be invoked. The question might then arise as to whether these are the minimum conditions for obtaining a central limit theorem for sums of independent random variables. Although a definitive answer to this question cannot be given in the brief survey of the type undertaken here,[10] the following considerations are pertinent. In the case of independent but not identically distributed (scalar) random variables, the sequence about whose convergence we are concerned consists of the sum

$$z_T = \sum_{t=1}^{T} x_{tT} \qquad x_{tT} = \frac{x_t - \mu_t}{s_T} \qquad (3.4.28)$$

As pointed out earlier, we need to say something about the order of negligibility of the individual terms, and one such condition, which turns out to be the minimum requisite if a central limit theorem is to be proved without undue complications, is that for *any* $\varepsilon > 0$,

$$\lim_{T \to \infty} \max_{1 \le t \le T} \mathrm{Pr}\,\{|x_{tT}| > \varepsilon\} = 0 \qquad (3.4.29)$$

---

[10] The interested reader may consult the excellent monograph by Gnedenko and Kolmogorov [17].

When this is so, of course, we have

$$\lim_{T \to \infty} \sum_{t=1}^{T} \Pr \{|x_{tT}| > \varepsilon\} = 0 \qquad (3.4.30)$$

If, for simplicity, we assume that all variables have mean zero, that is, if $\mu_t = 0$, all t, then in view of (3.4.28) we see that

$$\Pr \{|x_{tT}| > \varepsilon\} = \Pr \{|x_t| > \varepsilon s_T\} \qquad (3.4.31)$$

But then

$$\Pr \{|x_t| > \varepsilon s_T\} \le \frac{1}{\varepsilon^2 s_T^2} \int_{|\xi| > \varepsilon s_T} \xi^2 \, dF_t(\xi) \qquad (3.4.32)$$

$F_t(\cdot)$ being the distribution function of x_t. Thus the condition in (3.4.30) is seen to be implied by

$$\lim_{T \to \infty} \frac{1}{s_T^2} \sum_{t=1}^{T} \int_{|\xi| > \varepsilon s_T} \xi^2 \, dF_t(\xi) = 0 \qquad (3.4.33)$$

which is a condition on the original variables of the sequence.

Comparing (3.4.33) with the Liapounov condition (3.4.25), we see that the former, implied by the negligibility criterion in (3.4.21), is appreciably less restrictive than the Liapounov condition.

The following general form of the central limit theorem will be more than adequate for our purposes.

Theorem 3 (Lindeberg-Feller): Let $\{x_t : t = 1, 2, \ldots\}$ be a sequence of mutually independent (scalar) random variables that are assumed to have (for simplicity) mean zero and variance σ_t^2. A necessary and sufficient condition for the sequence,

$$z_T = \frac{\sum_{t=1}^{T} x_t}{s_T} = \sum_{t=1}^{T} x_{tT} \qquad (3.4.34)$$

to converge in distribution to a $N(0, 1)$ variable, and for all $\varepsilon > 0$,

$$\lim_{T \to \infty} \max_{1 \le t \le T} \Pr \{|x_{tT}| > \varepsilon\} = 0 \qquad (3.4.35)$$

is that for every $\eta > 0$,

$$\lim_{T \to \infty} \frac{1}{\eta^2 s_T^2} \sum_{t=1}^{T} \int_{|\xi| > \eta s_T} \xi^2 \, dF_t(\xi) = 0 \qquad (3.4.36)$$

$F_t(\cdot)$ being the distribution function of x_t.

PROOF: See Chung [3, p. 187].

Remark 11: We should emphasize to the reader that the conditions above for convergence in distribution to a $N(0, 1)$ variable pertain to sums normalized by the quantity s_T as in (3.4.34). Failure of the conditions, for example, those in (3.4.33), may lead to nonconvergence of the sequence in (3.4.34), but normalization by another sequence of constants, say $\{b_T: T = 1, 2, \ldots\}$, may lead to convergence under another set of conditions. While we shall not have occasion to deal with such cases in this book, the reader will do well to bear this in mind.

Now we turn to the multivariate problem, treating first the simplest case:

Theorem 4: Let $\{x_t: t = 1, 2, \ldots\}$ be a sequence of m-dimensional i.i.d. random vectors having finite mean μ and covariance matrix Σ. Then the sequence (of vectors)

$$z_T = \frac{\sum_{t=1}^T (x_t - \mu)}{T^{1/2}} \tag{3.4.37}$$

converges to a vector z such that

$$z \sim N(0, \Sigma) \tag{3.4.38}$$

PROOF: Let α be an arbitrary (nonrandom) vector and consider the variable

$$y_t = \alpha'(x_t - \mu) \tag{3.4.39}$$

Then the sequence of scalar *random* variables $\{y_t: t = 1, 2, \ldots\}$ consists of mutually independent, identically distributed random variables with finite mean 0 and variance $\alpha'\Sigma\alpha$. Thus by Theorem 1 (of this chapter), the sequence (of scalar random variables)

$$w_T = \frac{\sum_{t=1}^T y_t}{T^{1/2}} \tag{3.4.40}$$

converges to a random variable

$$w \sim N(0, \alpha'\Sigma\alpha) \tag{3.4.41}$$

Thus, if we denote the characteristic function of w_T by $\psi_T(u)$, we have

$$\lim_{T \to \infty} \psi_T(u) = \exp\left[-(u^2/2)(\alpha'\Sigma\alpha)\right] \tag{3.4.42}$$

On the other hand, the characteristic function of the vector quantity z_T is given by

$$\phi_T(v) = E[\exp(iv'z_T)] \tag{3.4.43}$$

In particular, this holds for the choice

$$v = \lambda\alpha, \tag{3.4.44}$$

where λ, α are, respectively, a real scalar and vector. Thus

$$\phi_T(\lambda\alpha) = E[\exp(i\lambda\alpha'z_T)] = E[\exp(i\lambda y_T)] = \psi_T(\lambda) \tag{3.4.45}$$

Hence

$$\lim_{T \to \infty} \phi_T(\lambda \alpha) = \exp\left[-(\lambda \alpha)' \Sigma (\lambda \alpha)/2\right] = \exp\left[-\lambda^2 \alpha' \Sigma \alpha/2)\right] \qquad (3.4.46)$$

But this shows that if z is the limit of the sequence defined by (3.4.37), then every linear combination of its elements is normal. Hence, by Proposition 1 of Chapter 1, we conclude

$$z \sim N(0, \Sigma) \hspace{6cm} \text{Q.E.D.}$$
$$(3.4.47)$$

A useful result for multivariate limit theorems, which, incidentally, formalizes the method of proof employed in the preceding, is

Theorem 5: Let $\{x_t: t = 1, 2, \ldots\}$ be a sequence of vector random variables and $F_t(\cdot)$ their associated distribution functions. Let $F_{\lambda t}(\cdot)$ be the distribution function of the *scalar* random variable

$$u_{\lambda t} = \lambda' x_t \hspace{7cm} (3.4.48)$$

where λ is a comformable vector of real constants. A necessary and sufficient condition that the sequence of distribution functions $\{F_t: t = 1, 2, \ldots\}$ converges to a distribution function F is that the sequence $\{F_{\lambda t}: t = 1, 2, \ldots\}$ converges to a limit for every vector λ, where $F_{\lambda t}$ is the d.f. of $u_{\lambda t}$.

PROOF: Varadarajan [31].
Notice that the import of this result is to reduce problems of multivariate convergence to those of univariate convergence.

Theorem 6: Let $\{x_t: t = 1, 2, \ldots\}$ be a sequence of independent (vector) random variables with zero means and covariance matrices Φ_t. Suppose further that

$$\lim_{T \to \infty} \frac{1}{T} \sum_{t=1}^{T} \Phi_t = \Phi \neq 0 \hspace{5cm} (3.4.49)$$

and for every $\varepsilon > 0$,

$$\lim_{T \to \infty} \frac{1}{T} \sum_{t=1}^{T} \int_{|x| > \varepsilon \sqrt{T}} |x|^2 \, dF_t(x) = 0 \hspace{3.5cm} (3.4.50)$$

where $|x|$ is the length of the vector x and $F_t(\cdot)$ is the distribution function of x_t. Then the sequence $\{z_T: T = 1, 2, \ldots\}$ converges in distribution to $N(0, \Phi)$, where

$$z_T = \frac{\sum_{t=1}^{T} x_t}{\sqrt{T}} \hspace{6cm} (3.4.51)$$

PROOF: We shall briefly sketch our argument without fully developing details. First, notice that by Theorem 5 we can reduce this to the univariate case. Thus we shall consider the sequence

$$w_T = \lambda' z_T = \sum_{t=1}^{T} \left(\frac{\lambda' x_t}{\sqrt{T}} \right) = \sum_{t=1}^{T} y_t \qquad y_t = \frac{\lambda' x_t}{\sqrt{T}} \tag{3.4.52}$$

Second, if we can show that for every real (conformable) vector λ the scalar variables y_t satisfy the analog of condition (3.4.36), then Theorem 3 implies the result we seek to establish.

To this effect, observe that if $G_t(\cdot)$ is the distribution of y_t, then for every $\varepsilon > 0$,

$$\int_{|\xi| > \varepsilon} \xi^2 \, dG_t(\xi) = \frac{1}{T} \int_{|\lambda'\zeta| > \varepsilon\sqrt{T}} |\lambda'\zeta|^2 \, dF_t(\zeta) \tag{3.4.53}$$

$F_t(\cdot)$ being the distribution of x_t.

Noting that $|\lambda'\zeta| \le |\lambda|\,|\zeta|$, we see that

$$\frac{1}{T} \int_{|\lambda'\zeta| > \varepsilon\sqrt{T}} |\lambda'\zeta|^2 \, dF_t(\zeta) \le \frac{1}{T} \int_{|\lambda'\zeta| > \varepsilon\sqrt{T}} |\lambda|^2 \, |\zeta|^2 \, dF_t(\zeta)$$

$$\le \frac{|\lambda|^2}{T} \int_{|\zeta| > (\varepsilon/|\lambda|)\sqrt{T}} |\zeta|^2 \, dF_t(\zeta) \tag{3.4.54}$$

Taking

$$\eta = \frac{\varepsilon}{|\lambda|} \tag{3.4.55}$$

we see that (3.4.54) in combination with (3.4.50) implies

$$\lim_{T \to \infty} \sum_{t=1}^{T} \int_{|\xi| > \varepsilon} \xi^2 \, dG_t(\xi) \le \lim_{T \to \infty} \frac{|\lambda|^2}{T} \sum_{t=1}^{T} \int_{|\zeta| > \eta\sqrt{T}} |\zeta|^2 \, dF_t(\zeta) = 0 \tag{3.4.56}$$

Theorem 3 then implies the validity of Theorem 6 once we note that

$$\text{Var}\,(w_T) = \lambda' \left(\frac{1}{T} \sum_{t=1}^{T} \Phi_t \right) \lambda \qquad \text{Q.E.D.} \tag{3.4.57}$$

There are many other forms for a central limit theorem, which will not be considered here; the interested reader is referred to Loève [22], especially Chapter 6, or to Rao [28], Chapter 2, or to the excellent monograph by Gnedenko and Kolmogorov [12].

3.5   MISCELLANEOUS USEFUL CONVERGENCE RESULTS

In the subsequent discussion we shall need a number of convergence results. Although such results are somewhat unrelated, nonetheless, we find it convenient to present them in this section, often without proof. We have

Proposition 1: Let $\{x_t : t = 1, 2, \ldots\}$ be a sequence of (vector) random variables converging in probability to the random variable x, and let $g(\cdot)$ be a continuous function. Then

$$\operatorname*{plim}_{T \to \infty} g(x_t) = g(x) \tag{3.5.1}$$

PROOF: See Rao [28, p. 104].

Remark 12: If the sequence above converges to a constant, say ξ, then

$$\operatorname*{plim}_{t \to \infty} g(x_t) = g(\xi) \tag{3.5.2}$$

Proposition 2: Let $\{x_t : t = 1, 2, \ldots\}$ be a sequence of (scalar) random variables converging (in distribution) to the random variable x, and let $\{y_t : t = 1, 2, \ldots\}$ be a sequence of random variables converging in probability to the constant ζ. Then the sequence $\{x_t + y_t : t = 1, 2, \ldots\}$ converges to the random variable $x + \zeta$, the sequence $\{x_t y_t : t = 1, 2, \ldots\}$ converges to the random variable ζx, and the sequence $\{x_t / y_t : t = 1, 2, \ldots\}$ converges to the random variable x/ζ.

PROOF: See Cramér [4, p. 254].

Remark 13: If F_t is the distribution function of x_t, the hypotheses of the proposition state that at all points of continuity of $F(\cdot)$,

$$\lim_{t \to \infty} F_t(x) = F(x) \tag{3.5.3}$$

where $F(\cdot)$ is the distribution function of the random variable x. Hence the conclusions of the proposition state that the sequence $\{x_t + y_t : t = 1, 2, \ldots\}$ converges in distribution to a random variable having distribution $F(x - \zeta)$, that $\{x_t y_t : t = 1, 2, \ldots\}$ converges in distribution to a random variable having distribution $F(x/\zeta)$, and that $\{x_t / y_t : t = 1, 2, \ldots\}$ converges to a random variable having distribution $F(\zeta x)$.

Corollary 1: Let $\{x_t : t = 1, 2, \ldots\}$, $\{y_t : t = 1, 2, \ldots\}$ be the sequences of Proposition 2, and suppose the expectations of $x_t y_t$ and of x exist. Then

$$\lim_{t \to \infty} E(x_t y_t) = \zeta E(x) = \operatorname*{plim}_{t \to \infty} y_t \lim_{t \to \infty} E(x_t) \tag{3.5.4}$$

PROOF: Let G_t be the distribution function of

$$z_t = x_t y_t \tag{3.5.5}$$

Thus

$$E(z_t) = \int_{-\infty}^{\infty} z \, dG_t(z) \tag{3.5.6}$$

By Lemma 6, we have

$$\lim_{t \to \infty} E(z_t) = \int_{-\infty}^{\infty} z \, dF(z/\zeta) = \zeta \int_{-\infty}^{\infty} x \, dF(x) = \zeta E(x) \qquad \text{Q.E.D.} \tag{3.5.7}$$

Remark 14: Notice that for the validity of the corollary it is *necessary* that the mean of z_t exist, at least for all $t > T^*$, for some fixed T^*.

Proposition 3 (Slutsky): Let $\{x_t : t = 1, 2, \ldots\}$ be a sequence of (vector) random variables converging in probability to the constant ζ. Let $f(\cdot)$ be a rational function of the elements of x_t and suppose that $f(\zeta)$ is well defined. Then

$$\plim_{t \to \infty} f(x_t) = f(\zeta) \tag{3.5.8}$$

PROOF: See Cramér [4, p. 254].

We shall next prove the following immediate implication of Khinchine's result (Lemma 9).

Proposition 4: Let $\{x_t : t = 1, 2, \ldots\}$ be a sequence of i.i.d. (vector) random variables and let x_{ti} be the ith element of x_t. Suppose the rth absolute moments of x_{ti}, $i = 1, 2, \ldots, m$ exist, and let $\mu_i^{(k)}$ be the kth moment of x_{ti}, $k \le r$. Then the quantities

$$s_T^{(ik)} = \frac{1}{T} \sum_{k=1}^{T} x_{ti}^k \tag{3.5.9}$$

converge in probability to $\mu_i^{(k)}$.

PROOF: The sequence $\{x_{ti}^{(k)} : t = 1, 2, \ldots\}$ is one of i.i.d. random variables having, by hypothesis, the finite mean $\mu_i^{(k)}$. The conclusion then follows immediately from Lemma 9.

Corollary 2: In Proposition 4, suppose $r \ge 2$; then the quantities

$$s_T^{(ij)} = \frac{1}{T} \sum_{t=1}^{T} x_{ti} x_{tj} \qquad i, j = 1, 2, \ldots, m \tag{3.5.10}$$

converge in probability to

$$\mu_{ij}^{(2)} = E(x_{ti} x_{tj}). \tag{3.5.11}$$

and, moreover, $1/T \sum_{t=1}^{T} (x_{ti} - \bar{x}_i)(x_{tj} - \bar{x}_j)$ converges in probability to

$$\sigma_{ij} = \text{Cov}(x_{ti}, x_{tj}) \qquad i, j = 1, 2, \ldots, m \tag{3.5.12}$$

where

$$\bar{x}_i = \frac{1}{T} \sum_{t=1}^{T} x_{ti} \qquad i = 1, 2, \ldots, m \tag{3.5.13}$$

The proof is left as an exercise for the reader.

Finally, in econometrics we often need certain approximation results regarding the moments of a function of sample moments. To this effect, we establish

Proposition 5: Let $\{x_t: t = 1, 2, \ldots\}$ be a sequence of i.i.d (scalar) random variables with finite mean μ and variance σ^2. Let $g(\cdot)$ be a function possessing continuous derivatives of order s, $s \geq 2$. Then the sequence

$$z_T = \sqrt{T}[g(\bar{x}) - g(\mu)] \tag{3.5.14}$$

converges to the random variable

$$z \sim N\{0, \sigma^2[g'(\mu)]^2\} \tag{3.5.15}$$

provided $g'(\mu) \neq 0$, where

$$\bar{x} = \frac{1}{T} \sum_{t=1}^{T} x_t \tag{3.5.16}$$

PROOF: By Taylor's theorem, we may write

$$g(\bar{x}) = g(\mu) + g'(x^*)(\bar{x} - \mu) \tag{3.5.17}$$

where

$$|x^* - \mu| \leq |\bar{x} - \mu| \tag{3.5.18}$$

Thus z_T of (3.5.14) may be expressed as

$$z_T = g'(x^*)\sqrt{T}(\bar{x} - \mu) \tag{3.5.19}$$

From Theorem 2 of this chapter we know that $\sqrt{T}(\bar{x} - \mu)$ converges to a variable distributed as $N(0, \sigma^2)$. Since the condition (3.5.18) holds, and $g'(\cdot)$ is continuous, we have that $g'(x^*)$ converges in probability to $g'(\mu)$. Hence, in view of Proposition 2, we conclude that z_T converges to a random variable z such that

$$z \sim N\{0, \sigma^2[g'(\mu)]^2\} \qquad \text{Q.E.D.}$$
$$\tag{3.5.20}$$

An analogous result for vector random variables can be established. Thus we have

Proposition 6: Let $\{x_t: t = 1, 2, \ldots\}$ be a sequence of i.i.d. (vector) random variables with finite mean (vector) μ and covariance matrix Σ. Let $g(\cdot)$

be a (scalar-valued) function defined on m-dimensional Euclidean space and possessing continuous derivatives of order s, $s \geq 2$. Then the sequence

$$z_T = \sqrt{T}[g(\bar{x}) - g(\mu)] \tag{3.5.21}$$

converges in distribution to the random variable z such that

$$z \sim N(0, \alpha'\Sigma\alpha) \tag{3.5.22}$$

where

$$\alpha = \begin{bmatrix} g_1(\mu) \\ g_2(\mu) \\ \vdots \\ g_m(\mu) \end{bmatrix} \qquad \bar{x} = \frac{1}{T}\sum_{t=1}^{T} x_t \tag{3.5.23}$$

provided that, for at least one i, $g_i(\mu) \neq 0$.[11]

PROOF: By Taylor's theorem, we can write

$$g(\bar{x}) = g(\mu) + g(x^*)(\bar{x} - \mu) \tag{3.5.24}$$

where $g(x^*)$ indicates the (row) vector of partial derivatives of $g(\cdot)$ with respect to its arguments (i.e., its gradient) evaluated and the point x^* and

$$|x^* - \mu| \leq |\bar{x} - \mu| \tag{3.5.25}$$

Thus

$$z_T = g(x^*)\sqrt{T}(\bar{x} - \mu) \tag{3.5.26}$$

By Theorem 4 of this chapter, $\sqrt{T}(\bar{x} - \mu)$ converges in distribution to a $N(0, \Sigma)$ variable. In view of (3.5.25), $g(x^*)$ converges in probability to α'. Thus, by Proposition 2 of this section, we conclude that the quantity in (3.5.21) converges in distribution to the variable z such that

$$z \sim N(0, \alpha'\Sigma\alpha) \qquad \text{Q.E.D.} \tag{3.5.27}$$

Having proved these results, a word of warning is necessary for their proper use. There is nothing in the preceding to ensure that if the results hold, then

$$\lim_{T \to \infty} E[g(\bar{x})] = g(\mu) \qquad \lim_{T \to \infty} \text{Var}\,[g(\bar{x})] = \alpha'\Sigma\alpha \tag{3.5.28}$$

Similarly for the univariate case. Indeed, the results may be perfectly valid but, for finite T, $g(\bar{x})$ *may not have finite moments of any order*. To this effect, recall the discussion relating to Lemma 7 of the previous section. One may, however,

---

[11] In (3.5.23), $g_i(\mu)$ is the partial derivative of $g(\cdot)$ with respect to its ith argument evaluated at the point μ.

obtain conditions under which the (first two) moments of $g(\bar{x})$ converge to the corresponding moments of the asymptotic distribution. A discussion of these aspects may be found in Cramér [4, pp. 354 and 366]. It is shown there that if, in addition to the hypotheses of the two propositions above, the condition

$$|g(\bar{x})| \le kT^a \tag{3.5.29}$$

holds, then

$$\lim_{T \to \infty} E[g(\bar{x})] = g(\mu) \qquad \lim_{T \to \infty} \text{Var}\,[g(\bar{x})] = \alpha'\Sigma\alpha \tag{3.5.30}$$

where k and a are nonnegative constants. From the preceding discussion, we can deduce the following useful

Corollary 3: Let $g(\cdot)$ be a scalar-valued function, as in Proposition 6. Let x be a random vector with finite mean μ, covariance matrix Σ, and density $f(\cdot)$; suppose further that $g(\cdot)$ *and its first- and second-order partial derivatives are integrable with respect to* $f(\cdot)$. Then

$$E[g(x)] \le g(\mu) \tag{3.5.31}$$

if $g(\cdot)$ *is concave, and*

$$E[g(x)] \ge g(\mu) \tag{3.5.32}$$

if $g(\cdot)$ *is convex.*

PROOF: We may expand, by Taylor's theorem (about μ), to obtain

$$g(x) = g(\mu) + \alpha'(x - \mu) + \frac{1}{2}(x - \mu)'\frac{\partial^2 g(x^*)}{\partial x\,\partial x}(x - \mu) \tag{3.5.33}$$

where α is defined in (3.5.23) and $|x^* - \mu| < |x - \mu|$. If $g(\cdot)$ is convex, then for every x, $\partial^2 g(x)/\partial x\,\partial x$ is a positive semidefinite matrix; thus

$$g(x) \ge g(\mu) + \alpha'(x - \mu) \tag{3.5.34}$$

Similarly, if $g(\cdot)$ is concave, then $\partial^2 g(x)/\partial x\,\partial x$ is negative semidefinite; thus

$$g(x) \le g(\mu) + \alpha'(x - \mu) \tag{3.5.35}$$

The conclusions then follow immediately from (3.5.34) and (3.5.35)

3.6 PROPERTIES OF MAXIMUM LIKELIHOOD (ML) ESTIMATORS

LIKELIHOOD FUNCTIONS, REGULARITY, AND ELEMENTARY PROPERTIES

In previous chapters we used extensively the method of maximum likelihood (ML) in connection with problems of estimation involving, chiefly, the multivariate normal distribution. Of course, ML estimators can, in principle, be applied to the parameters of any distribution and not only the normal. In this section we shall briefly sketch some of the salient properties of ML estimators, thus justifying and motivating ML as a highly desirable method of parameter estimation.

In what follows, unless stated to the contrary, x will be an m-dimensional vector of random variables and θ will denote a k-dimensional vector of unknown parameters to be estimated. We remind the reader of

Definition 12: Let $x_t, t = 1, 2, \ldots, T$, be a sample from a population characterized by the parameter θ; then the joint density of the observations $\{x_t: t = 1, 2, \ldots, T\}$ is said to be the *likelihood function* of the observations— or the parameter θ. If the sample is *random* and *the population is characterized by the density* $f(\cdot\,; \theta)$, then the likelihood function can be written as

$$L^*(X; \theta) = \prod_{t=1}^{T} f(x_t ; \theta) \tag{3.6.1}$$

where X is the $m \times T$ matrix whose tth column is x_t.

In what follows, we shall always deal with random samples and also assume certain properties for the underlying density functions. Consequently, we have

Definition 13: A ML estimation problem will be said to be *regular* if the following *regularity* conditions hold:

i. The range of the random variables (x_t) is independent of the parameter vector θ.

ii. The density $f(\cdot\,; \theta)$ possesses derivatives of at least the third order with respect to θ, and these (derivatives) are *bounded by integrable functions of* x.[12]

In view of the preceding, we can easily establish the following results:

Proposition 7: Let $\{x_t: t = 1, 2, \ldots, T\}$ be a random sample as in Definition 12. Then

$$\int L^*(X; \theta) \, dX = 1 \tag{3.6.2}$$

PROOF: In the above, X is a matrix whose tth column is x_t, dX is an abbreviation for $dx_{11}, dx_{12} \ldots dx_{1T}, dx_{21} \ldots dx_{2T} \ldots dx_{mT}$, and the integral sign indicates integration over mT-dimensional Euclidean space. The result is obvious, for L^* is the joint density of $x_t, t = 1, 2, \ldots, T$.

We also have

Proposition 8: Let $\{x_t: t = 1, 2, \ldots, T\}$ be a random sample from a

---

[12] This means that, for example, $|\partial^3 L/\partial\theta_i^3| \le M_i(x)$ and, moreover, $E[M_i(x)] < K$ for some constant K; the condition is assumed to hold for all derivatives up to third order.

population characterized by a density function obeying the regularity condition of Definition 13. Then

$$\int \left(\frac{\partial \ln L^*}{\partial \theta}\right) L^*(X; \theta)\, dX = 0 \tag{3.6.3}$$

and

$$\mathrm{Cov}\left(\frac{\partial \ln L^*}{\partial \theta}\right) = -E\left[\frac{\partial^2 \ln L^*}{\partial \theta\, \partial \theta}\right] \tag{3.6.4}$$

PROOF: Differentiating (3.6.2) with respect to θ, we have

$$\int \left(\frac{\partial \ln L^*}{\partial \theta}\right) L^*(X; \theta)\, dX = 0 \tag{3.6.5}$$

We note that (3.6.5) can also be written more compactly as

$$E\left[\frac{\partial \ln L^*}{\partial \theta}\right] = 0 \tag{3.6.6}$$

Now differentiating (3.6.5) with respect to θ, we find

$$\int \left\{\left[\frac{\partial^2 \ln L^*}{\partial \theta\, \partial \theta}\right] L^*(X; \theta) + \left(\frac{\partial \ln L^*}{\partial \theta}\right)\left(\frac{\partial \ln L^*}{\partial \theta}\right)' L^*(X; \theta)\right\} dX = 0 \tag{3.6.7}$$

where $[\partial^2 \ln L^*/\partial \theta\, \partial \theta]$ is the $k \times k$ matrix of second-order derivatives of $\ln L^*$ with respect to θ, and $(\partial \ln L^*/\partial \theta)$ is the (column) vector of first-order derivatives of $\ln L^*$ with respect to θ.

Since we may think of $(\partial \ln L^*/\partial \theta)$ as a vector of random variables, (3.6.6) and (3.6.7) imply

$$\mathrm{Cov}\left(\frac{\partial \ln L^*}{\partial \theta}\right) = -\int \left[\frac{\partial^2 \ln L^*}{\partial \theta\, \partial \theta}\right] L^*(X; \theta)\, dX = -E\left[\frac{\partial^2 \ln L^*}{\partial \theta\, \partial \theta}\right] \quad \text{Q.E.D.} \tag{3.6.8}$$

PROPERTIES OF ML ESTIMATORS; CONSISTENCY

Maximum likelihood (ML) estimators are obtained in practice by finding a root of the equations:

$$\frac{\partial L}{\partial \theta} = 0 \tag{3.6.9}$$

where

$$L(X; \theta) = \ln L^*(X; \theta)\, [13] \tag{3.6.10}$$

---

[13] In what follows, we shall always deal with the *logarithm of the likelihood function*. This is more convenient and involves no loss of relevance. Thus L^* will indicate the likelihood function and L its logarithm.

What is frequently overlooked, however, is that equation (3.6.9) need not have a unique root; that is, there may be more than one vector $\hat{\theta}$ satisfying (3.6.9). The following example given by Huzurbazar [14] may elucidate matters.

Let us momentarily revert to the univariate case and consider the density:

$$f(x; \theta) = 1 + \frac{2x - 1}{6} \cos \theta + \frac{3x^2 - 1}{6} \sin \theta \ (0 \le \theta \le 100\pi, 0 \le x \le 1) \quad (3.6.11)$$

This obeys all regularity conditions and in fact has bounded derivatives of all orders with respect to θ. For $T = 2$, the likelihood function is

$$L^*(X; \theta) = 1 + \cos \theta \left\{ \frac{2x_1 - 1}{6} + \frac{2x_2 - 1}{6} \right\} + \sin \theta \left(\frac{3x_1^2 - 1}{6} + \frac{3x_2^2 - 1}{6} \right)$$

$$+ \cos^2 \theta \left\{ \frac{2x_1 - 1}{6} \cdot \frac{2x_2 - 1}{6} \right\} + \cos \theta \sin \theta \left\{ \frac{2x_2 - 1}{6} \cdot \frac{3x_1^2 - 1}{6} \right.$$

$$+ \left. \frac{3x_2^3 - 1}{6} \cdot \frac{2x_1 - 1}{6} \right\} + \sin^2 \theta \left(\frac{3x_2^2 - 1}{6} \cdot \frac{3x_1^2 - 1}{6} \right) \quad (3.6.12)$$

It is clear that $L^*(X; \theta)$ is a periodic function of θ and indeed

$$\frac{\partial L^*}{\partial \theta} = 0 \quad (3.6.13)$$

has 50 roots in the permissible range of θ. The situation is, of course, unchanged if we increase the number of observations. Thus care should be exercised in stating what we mean by a maximum likelihood estimator and in ascribing to it certain optimal properties.

We shall deal first with consistency. We prove

Lemma 12: There is at most one root of (3.6.9) that is a consistent estimator of θ_0, the true value of θ.

PROOF: We shall confine our discussion to the case of a single parameter, that is, for $k = 1$; although the lemma is equally valid for the multiparameter case, its proof is then quite cumbersome and is best omitted in a book of this type.

Observe that we merely *assume* the existence of a consistent estimator; we have not yet proved that one indeed exists. We note

$$\frac{1}{T} \frac{\partial^2 L(X; \theta)}{\partial \theta^2} = \frac{1}{T} \frac{\partial^2}{\partial \theta^2} \sum_{t=1}^{T} \ln f(x_t; \theta) \quad (3.6.14)$$

The right-hand side of (3.6.14) is the sum of independent identically distributed variables, each with mean, say,

$$E\left[\frac{\partial^2}{\partial \theta^2} \ln f(x_t; \theta) \right] = M(\theta) \quad (3.6.15)$$

Thus, by Lemma 9, the right-hand side converges in probability to its mean. Noting that

$$E\left[\frac{1}{T}\frac{\partial^2 L(X;\theta)}{\partial\theta^2}\right] = M(\theta) \tag{3.6.16}$$

we conclude that the left-hand side obeys

$$\plim_{T\to\infty}\frac{1}{T}\frac{\partial^2 \ln L}{\partial\theta^2} = M(\theta)$$

In particular, this holds for $\theta = \theta_0$.

Using the boundedness—and integrability—of third-order derivatives, we can argue

$$\left|\frac{1}{T}\frac{\partial^3 L(X;\theta)}{\partial\theta^3}\right| = \left|\frac{1}{T}\sum_{t=1}^{T}\frac{\partial^3}{\partial\theta^3}\ln f(x_t;\theta)\right| \le \frac{1}{T}\sum_{t=1}^{T}g(x_t) \tag{3.6.17}$$

where

$$\left|\frac{\partial^3}{\partial\theta^3}\ln f(x_t;\theta)\right| \le g(x_t) \tag{3.6.18}$$

The quantities $g(x_t)$ for each t are independent, identically distributed random variables with finite mean; hence, by Lemma 9, the last member of (3.6.17) converges in probability to its expected value, say

$$E[g(x)] = h(\theta) \tag{3.6.19}$$

In particular, this holds for $\theta = \theta_0$.

Now let $\hat{\theta}$ be a consistent estimator of θ_0; by the mean value theorem, we have

$$\frac{1}{T}\frac{\partial^2 L(X;\hat{\theta})}{\partial\theta^2} = \frac{1}{T}\frac{\partial^2 L(X;\theta_0)}{\partial\theta^2} + \frac{1}{T}\frac{\partial^3 L(X;\bar{\theta})}{\partial\theta^3}(\hat{\theta}-\theta_0) \tag{3.6.20}$$

where $\bar{\theta}$ lies between $\hat{\theta}$ and θ_0, and the notations

$$\frac{\partial^2 L(X;\hat{\theta})}{\partial\theta^2} \quad \frac{\partial^3 L(X;\bar{\theta})}{\partial\theta^3}$$

indicate, for example, the second- and third-order partial derivatives of $L(X;\cdot)$ evaluated, respectively, at $\theta = \hat{\theta}$ and $\theta = \bar{\theta}$. We shall use this convenient notation throughout.

Because $\hat{\theta}$ is consistent and, by the previous argument, the last member of (3.6.17) converges to $h(\theta_0)$, we have that for any $\delta > 0, \varepsilon > 0$, there exists a T^* such that, for all $T > T^*$,

$$\Pr\left\{\left|\frac{1}{T}\frac{\partial^3 L(X;\bar{\theta})}{\partial\theta^3}(\hat{\theta}-\theta_0)\right| < A\varepsilon\right\} \ge 1-\delta \tag{3.6.21}$$

where A is any positive number greater than $h(\theta_0)$.

Hence, in view of (3.6.16), for sufficiently large T and any preassigned $\varepsilon_1, \delta_1 > 0$, we have

$$\Pr\left\{ M(\theta_0) - \varepsilon_1 < \frac{1}{T}\frac{\partial^2 L(X;\hat{\theta})}{\partial\theta^2} < M(\theta_0) + \varepsilon_1 \right\} \geq 1 - \delta_1 \tag{3.6.22}$$

However, by (3.6.15) and (3.6.8) $M(\theta_0) < 0$, and equation (3.6.22) implies

$$\lim_{T\to\infty} \Pr\left\{ \frac{1}{T}\frac{\partial^2 L(X;\hat{\theta})}{\partial\theta^2} < 0 \right\} = 1 \tag{3.6.23}$$

This simply states that for sufficiently large T a consistent solution to the likelihood equation (3.6.9) corresponds to a maximum with probability one.

Now, suppose that we have two distinct roots of (3.6.9), say $\hat{\theta}^1$ and $\hat{\theta}^2$, which are both consistent. Clearly, we have

$$\left.\frac{\partial L}{\partial\theta}\right|_{\theta=\hat{\theta}^1} = \left.\frac{\partial L}{\partial\theta}\right|_{\theta=\hat{\theta}^2} = 0 \tag{3.6.24}$$

It follows by Rolle's theorem[14] that the function $\partial L/\partial\theta$ must have a stationary point in the interval $(\hat{\theta}^1, \hat{\theta}^2)$; let this be at θ^3. Since $\theta^3 \in (\hat{\theta}^1, \hat{\theta}^2)$, it follows that θ^3 is consistent as well. But this implies that (3.6.23) is valid for $\theta = \theta^3$. On the other hand, from Rolle's theorem

$$\left.\frac{\partial^2 L}{\partial\theta^2}\right|_{\theta=\theta^3} = 0$$

which is a contradiction. Hence $\hat{\theta}^1$ and $\hat{\theta}^2$ cannot be distinct.   Q.E.D.

The argument of the preceding proof is instructive in that it shows that if we have a root of (3.6.9) which is a consistent estimator of θ_0, then this root corresponds to a local maximum. If we have, however, several local maxima, the development thus far does not permit us to discriminate amongst them. This is so since we have deduced only a necessary condition for a root of (3.6.9) to be a ML estimator of θ.

The discussion in the multiparameter case would be entirely parallel. One would show that if $\hat{\theta}$ is a consistent estimator of θ_0 (the true k-dimensional parameter vector), then as $T \to \infty$ the probability that

$$\left.\frac{1}{T}\frac{\partial^2 L(X;\theta)}{\partial\theta\,\partial\theta}\right|_{\theta=\hat{\theta}}$$

is negative definite approaches unity. One would then show the uniqueness of the consistent estimator of θ_0 among the roots of (3.6.9). What the lemma has shown is that the maximum likelihood equations (3.6.9) cannot have more than

---

[14] Rolle's theorem states that if a differentiable function $r(x)$ vanishes at two points x_1, x_2, then there exists a point $x_1 < x^* < x_2$ such that $r'(x^*) = 0$.

one root that is a consistent estimator of θ_0; the reader should have noticed that the *existence* of a consistent root is not asserted there. What is stated is that if a consistent estimator for θ_0 may be found among the roots of (3.6.9), then this estimator is *unique* and corresponds to a local *maximum* with probability one.

Still, the result does not allow us to discriminate among such roots. Indeed, this matter has given rise to some confusion in the literature. A definitive result asserting that if Ω is the space of admissible values for the parameter θ, then the estimator of θ_0, say $\hat{\theta}$, which satisfies

$$L(\hat{\theta}; X) \geq L(\theta; X) \qquad \theta \in \Omega \tag{3.6.25}$$

is a consistent estimator for θ_0, was given by Wald [32]. This theorem, which we shall state but not prove below, implies the following: First, there exists a consistent root of (3.6.9); second, the consistent estimator is that root of (3.6.9) which corresponds to the global maximum of the likelihood function. Notice that the result just stated does not require differentiability of L with respect to θ. Hence the statement we made regarding the roots of (3.6.9) is a specialization of Wald's result to the case treated here, namely, that derivatives of the likelihood function exist up to the third order.

We give below a statement of Wald's result under somewhat more restrictive conditions than he first employed, in keeping with the spirit of our current discussion.

Lemma 13: Let $\{x_t: t = 1, 2, \ldots, T\}$ be a random sample from a population characterized by the density $f(\cdot; \theta)$ and let Ω be the space of admissible values for the parameter θ. Suppose further that

- i. we can introduce a distance function[15], ρ, on Ω such that Ω becomes a metric space.
- ii. $f(\cdot; \theta)$ is regular in accordance with Definition 14.
- iii. if θ^* is any fixed point in Ω and $\{\theta_i: i = 1, 2, \ldots\}$ is a sequence such that

$$\lim_{\to \infty} \rho(\theta^*, \theta_i) = \infty \tag{3.6.26}$$

then

$$\lim_{i \to \infty} f(x; \theta_i) = 0 \text{ for all } x \tag{3.6.27}$$

---

[15] A linear (vector) space $\mathscr{A}$ is said to be a metric space if one can define on it a function, say ρ, having the properties: For any $a_1, a_2, a_3, \in \mathscr{A}$, $\rho(a_1, a_2) \geq 0$ with equality holding only if $a_1 = a_2$; $\rho(a_1, a_2) = \rho(a_2, a_1)$, $\rho(a_1, a_2) \leq \rho(a_1, a_3) + \rho(a_3, a_2)$. Such a function is said to be a metric. An example would be provided by the n-dimensional Euclidean space with the usual definition of distance. Thus, if x, y are the n-dimensional vectors,

$$\rho(x, y) = [\Sigma_{i=1}^n (x_i - y_i)^2]^{\frac{1}{2}}$$

iv. any closed and bounded subset of Ω is compact.
v. if θ_0 is the true parameter point, $F(\,\cdot\,;\theta)$ is the distribution function corresponding to $f(\,\cdot\,;\theta)$ and $\theta_1 \neq \theta_0$, $\theta_1 \in \Omega$, then for at least one point x,

$$F(x;\theta_0) \neq F(x;\theta_1) \tag{3.6.28}$$

vi. for m, $r > 0$, let $S = \{\theta: \rho(\theta, \theta') \leq m\}$, $S' = \{\theta: \rho(\theta, 0) > r\}$; let

$$\phi(x;r) = \sup_{\theta \in S'} f(x;\theta), \quad f(x;\theta',m) = \sup_{\theta \in S} f(x;\theta) \tag{3.6.29}$$

Define

$$\phi^*(x;r) = \phi(x;r) \quad \text{if} \quad \phi(x;r) > 1$$
$$= 1 \quad \text{otherwise} \tag{3.6.30}$$

$$f^*(x;\theta',m) = f(x;\theta',m) \quad \text{if} \quad f(x;\theta',m) > 1$$
$$= 1 \quad \text{otherwise} \tag{3.6.31}$$

and suppose that the expectations $E[\phi^*]$, $E[f^*]$ are finite;
vii. for the true parameter point, θ_0,

$$E[|\ln f(x;\theta_0)|] < \infty \tag{3.6.32}$$

viii. $f(x;\theta',m)$ is a measurable function of x for any θ' and m.

If $L(X;\theta)$ is the (log) likelihood function of the observations and $\hat\theta$ is an estimator of the true parameter point, θ_0, such that

$$L(X;\hat\theta) > L(X;\theta) \qquad \theta \in \Omega \tag{3.6.33}$$

then $\hat\theta$ is consistent for θ_0.

PROOF: See Wald [32].

Remark 15: Although Wald's result settles the question of which root of the equations (3.6.9) is consistent, still the conditions of Lemma 13 are not easy to verify in practice. Given a specific distribution, it is easy to verify conditions i through v. On the other hand, conditions vi and vii might prove quite cumbersome to verify. Condition viii, referring to the measurability of $f(x;\theta',m)$, is a relatively innocuous one, although it may not be readily intelligible to students of economics. In the more general theory of Lebesgue integration, measurability plays a role analogous to that of continuity in the theory of Riemann integration. It would be too cumbersome to explain the concept here. The reader, however, may consult the excellent textbook by Royden [30], especially Chapters 3 and 4.

ASYMPTOTIC DISTRIBUTIONS OF ML ESTIMATORS

Because the equation (3.6.9), one of whose roots (solutions) gives the ML estimator, may be quite nonlinear, it is frequently not possible to give an explicit expression for such estimators; it is also not always possible to determine their small sample distribution. Thus it is rather remarkable that, asymptotically, certain optimal properties may be shown to adhere to ML estimators. We begin first by determining their asymptotic distribution. We have

Lemma 14: Let the conditions of Lemma 13 hold and let $\hat{\theta}$ be the ML estimator of the true parameter θ_0, as determined in (3.6.33). Let

$$z_T = \sqrt{T}(\hat{\theta} - \theta_0) \tag{3.6.34}$$

Then the sequence in (3.6.34) converges in distribution to z such that

$$z \sim N[0, -M^{-1}(\theta_0)] \tag{3.6.35}$$

where

$$M(\theta_0) = E\left[\frac{\partial^2 \ln f(X; \theta_0)}{\partial \theta \, \partial \theta}\right] \tag{3.6.36}$$

PROOF: By Lemma 13, $\hat{\theta}$ is a root of $\partial L/\partial \theta = 0$. Expanding $\partial L/\partial \theta$ about θ^0, we have[16]

$$\frac{\partial L(X; \hat{\theta})}{\partial \theta} = \frac{\partial L(X; \theta^0)}{\partial \theta} + \frac{\partial^2 L(X; \theta^0)}{\partial \theta \, \partial \theta}(\hat{\theta} - \theta^0) + \text{remainder} \tag{3.6.37}$$

The ith element of the remainder vector is of the form

$$\sum_{r=1}^{k} \sum_{j=1}^{k} \frac{\partial^3 L(X; \bar{\theta})}{\partial \theta_i \, \partial \theta_j \, \partial \theta_r}(\hat{\theta}_r - \theta_r^0)(\hat{\theta}_j - \theta_j^0)$$

where $|\bar{\theta} - \theta^0| < |\hat{\theta} - \theta^0|$. In the preceding, the notation $\partial L(X; \theta^0)/\partial \theta_i$, for example, indicates the derivative of $L(X; \theta)$ with respect to the ith element of the vector θ evaluated at the true parameter point θ^0

From the regularity assumption, we have

$$\left|\frac{\partial^3 L(X; \bar{\theta})}{\partial \theta_i \, \partial \theta_j \, \partial \theta_r}\right| = \left|\sum_{t=1}^{T} \frac{\partial^3 \ln f(x_t; \bar{\theta})}{\partial \theta_i \, \partial \theta_j \, \partial \theta_r}\right| \leq \sum_{t=1}^{T} g(x_t) \tag{3.6.38}$$

where, for simplicity, we have omitted the subscripts on $g(\cdot)$. But since we are dealing with a random sample, the last member of (3.6.38) is the sum of T mutually independent, identically distributed random variables. Since by the regularity conditions the expectation $E[g(x_t)]$ exists, Lemma 11 implies that the strong law of large numbers applies to $1/T \sum_{t=1}^{T} g(x_t)$. In view of the consistency of $\hat{\theta}$ as an estimator of θ^0, we see that the ith component of the remainder vector converges to zero in probability. Hence we shall neglect it in all subsequent arguments.

---

[16] The reader should notice that, in order to avoid confusion, we denote, in this proof only, the true parameter vector by θ^0 instead of θ_0; otherwise we might confuse it with the notation relating to *elements* of the vector θ.

Returning now to (3.6.37), since $\hat{\theta}$ is a ML estimator, we can write

$$\frac{1}{\sqrt{T}} \frac{\partial L(X; \theta^0)}{\partial \theta} = -\frac{1}{T} \frac{\partial^2 L(X; \theta^0)}{\partial \theta \, \partial \theta} \sqrt{T}(\hat{\theta} - \theta^0) \qquad (3.6.39)$$

and the problem is to determine the asymptotic distribution of $\sqrt{T}(\hat{\theta} - \theta^0)$. We first observe that

$$\frac{1}{T} \frac{\partial^2 L(X; \theta^0)}{\partial \theta \, \partial \theta} = \frac{1}{T} \sum_{t=1}^{T} \frac{\partial^2 \ln f(x_t; \theta^0)}{\partial \theta \, \partial \theta} \qquad (3.6.40)$$

is the sum of T mutually independent, identically distributed random variables having finite mean

$$E\left[\frac{\partial^2 \ln f(X; \theta^0)}{\partial \theta \, \partial \theta}\right] = M(\theta^0) \qquad (3.6.41)$$

Hence, by Lemma 11, the strong law of large numbers applies, element by element, for we are dealing here with a matrix, and thus with probability one the left member of (3.6.40) converges to $M(\theta^0)$ as $T \to \infty$.

Hence, if we succeed in determining the limiting distribution of $(1/\sqrt{T}) \partial L(X; \theta^0)/\partial \theta$, a simple application of Proposition 2 will yield the limiting distribution of $\sqrt{T}(\hat{\theta} - \theta^0)$. But notice

$$\frac{1}{\sqrt{T}} \frac{\partial L(X; \theta^0)}{\partial \theta} = \frac{1}{\sqrt{T}} \sum_{t=1}^{T} \left[\frac{\partial \ln f(x_t; \theta^0)}{\partial \theta}\right] \qquad (3.6.42)$$

and the left member here is thus the sum of mutually independent, identically distributed random vectors such that

$$E\left[\frac{\partial \ln f(x_t; \theta^0)}{\partial \theta}\right] = 0 \qquad \text{Cov}\left[\frac{\partial \ln f(x_t; \theta^0)}{\partial \theta}\right] = -M(\theta^0) \qquad (3.6.43)$$

Thus, by Theorem 4, the asymptotic distribution of $(1/\sqrt{T}) \partial L(X; \theta^0)/\partial \theta$ is $N[0, -M(\theta^0)]$.

In view of the convergence of $(1/T) \partial^2 L(X; \theta^0)/\partial \theta \, \partial \theta$ to $M(\theta^0)$, we conclude that, asymptotically,

$$\sqrt{T}(\hat{\theta} - \theta^0) \sim N[0, -M^{-1}(\theta^0)] \qquad \qquad \text{Q.E.D.}$$
$$(3.6.44)$$

EFFICIENCY OF ESTIMATORS; THE CRAMÉR-RAO INEQUALITY

Given any estimation problem, it is certainly possible to produce several other estimators besides the ML one. It is thus important that we have at our disposal some way of discriminating among such estimators. A customary criterion of desirability is that of efficiency, a concept we shall develop below.

In this connection, we remind the reader that if we have two estimators having distributions belonging to the same family—for example, if both are normally distributed and both *unbiased*—then the estimator having the smallest variance is to be preferred. This is so since its distribution is more "tight" about the true value of the parameter, and inferences made with respect to that parameter will be much sharper if based on the distribution having the smallest variance. It is from these intuitive considerations that we build up the notion of efficiency of estimators.

It is quite remarkable that (for a scalar parameter) the variance of estimators is subject to a *lower bound*, irrespective of the method of estimation. The lower bound depends, of course, on the underlying probability structure of the process under consideration. This is the celebrated Cramér-Rao inequality, to which we now turn. For pedagogical reasons, we develop first the scalar case.

Lemma 15 (Cramér-Rao inequality): Let $\{x_t : t = 1, 2, \ldots, T\}$ be a random sample from a population characterized by the regular density $f(\cdot\,; \theta)$, where θ is a scalar. If b is any estimator having finite mean and variance and such that

$$E(b) = \psi(\theta) \tag{3.6.45}$$

then

$$\text{Var}\,(b) \geq \frac{[\psi'(\theta)]^2}{E(\partial L/\partial\theta)^2} \tag{3.6.46}$$

$L(X; \theta)$ being the (log) likelihood function of the observations.

PROOF: In view of (3.6.45), we can write

$$\int b L^*(X; \theta)\, dX = \psi(\theta) \tag{3.6.47}$$

Differentiating with respect to θ, in view of the regularity assumption, we find

$$\int \left(b\,\frac{\partial L}{\partial\theta} \right) L^*(X; \theta)\, dX = \psi'(\theta) \tag{3.6.48}$$

Using the Schwarz inequality for integrals [3, p. 45], we have

$$\text{Var}\,(b)\,\text{Var}\left(\frac{\partial L}{\partial\theta}\right) \leq [\psi'(\theta)]^2 \qquad\qquad \text{Q.E.D.} \tag{3.6.49}$$

Remark 16: The validity of (3.6.49) is verified as follows: Since $E(\partial L/\partial\theta) = 0$, in view of the regularity assumption, (3.6.48) can also be written as

$$\int [b - \psi(\theta)]\,\frac{\partial L}{\partial\theta}\,L^*(X; \theta)\, dX = \psi'(\theta) \tag{3.6.50}$$

Schwarz's inequality then implies

$$[\psi'(\theta)]^2 \geq \left\{ \int [b - \psi(\theta)]^2 L^*(X;\theta)\, dX \right\} \cdot \left\{ \int \left(\frac{\partial L}{\partial \theta}\right)^2 L^*(X;\theta)\, dX \right\}$$

$$= \text{Var}\,(b) \cdot \text{Var}\left(\frac{\partial L}{\partial \theta}\right) \quad (3.6.51)$$

The multiparameter case is similar in its result although the method of proof is slightly different.

Lemma 16: Let $\{x_t: t = 1, 2, \ldots, T\}$ be a random sample from a population characterized by the density $f(\cdot\,; \theta)$. Let $b = (b_1, b_2, \ldots, b_n)'$ be a set of n functionally independent estimators such that

$$E(b) = \psi(\theta) \qquad E(b_i) = \psi_i(\theta) \qquad\qquad\qquad (3.6.52)$$

and

$$\text{Cov}\,(b) = V \qquad\qquad\qquad (3.6.53)$$

Then the matrix

$$V^* = V + \frac{1}{T}\frac{\partial \psi(\theta)}{\partial \theta}[M(\theta)]^{-1}\left(\frac{\partial \psi(\theta)}{\partial \theta}\right)' \qquad\qquad\qquad (3.6.54)$$

is positive semidefinite.

PROOF: Let $L(X;\theta)$ be the (log) likelihood function of the observations; we remind the reader that

$$L(X;\theta) = \sum_{t=1}^{T} \ln f(x_t\,; \theta) \qquad M(\theta) = E\left[\frac{\partial^2 \ln f(x_t\,; \theta)}{\partial \theta\, \partial \theta}\right] \qquad (3.6.55)$$

Now, by definition,

$$\int b L^*(X;\theta)\, dX = \psi(\theta) \qquad\qquad\qquad (3.6.56)$$

Differentiating with respect to θ, we find

$$\frac{\partial \psi(\theta)}{\partial \theta} = \int b\left(\frac{\partial L}{\partial \theta}\right)' L^*(X;\theta)\, dX \qquad\qquad\qquad (3.6.57)$$

where

$$\frac{\partial \psi(\theta)}{\partial \theta} = \left[\frac{\partial \psi_i(\theta)}{\partial \theta_j}\right] \qquad i = 1, 2, \ldots, n, j = 1, 2, \ldots, k \qquad (3.6.58)$$

Since $E(\partial L/\partial\theta) = 0$, by regularity, we conclude that the cross covariance between the vectors b and $\partial L/\partial\theta$ is given by $\partial\psi(\theta)/\partial\theta$. Defining the vector

$$\phi = \begin{pmatrix} b \\ \dfrac{\partial L}{\partial\theta} \end{pmatrix} \tag{3.6.59}$$

we see that

$$\text{Cov}\,(\phi) = \begin{bmatrix} V & \left(\dfrac{\partial\psi(\theta)}{\partial\theta}\right) \\ \left(\dfrac{\partial\psi(\theta)}{\partial\theta}\right)' & -TM(\theta) \end{bmatrix} = \Phi \tag{3.6.60}$$

is a positive semidefinite matrix.

Letting

$$D = \begin{bmatrix} I & \left(\dfrac{\partial\psi(\theta)}{\partial\theta}\right)[TM(\theta)]^{-1} \\ 0 & I \end{bmatrix} \tag{3.6.61}$$

we conclude that

$$\Phi^* = D\Phi D' = \begin{bmatrix} V + \left(\dfrac{\partial\psi(\theta)}{\partial\theta}\right)'[TM(\theta)]^{-1}\left(\dfrac{\partial\psi(\theta)}{\partial\theta}\right) & 0 \\ 0 & I \end{bmatrix} \tag{3.6.62}$$

is also a positive semidefinite matrix. But this implies that

$$V^* = V - \left[\dfrac{\partial\psi(\theta)}{\partial\theta}\right]'[-TM(\theta)]^{-1}\dfrac{\partial\psi(\theta)}{\partial\theta} \tag{3.6.63}$$

is positive semidefinite.   Q.E.D.

Remark 17: In the case of scalar estimators, it is relatively easy to compare their respective variances, and thus the bound given in Lemma 15 is unambiguously understood. The situation is a bit more complicated in Lemma 16 because there is no single measure of the variance of a vector estimator. On the other hand, we may introduce a measure of magnitude over the collection of $k \times k$ positive semidefinite matrices. Thus, if A, B are two such matrices, we may say that A is at least as large as B and denote that by $A \geq B$ if and only if $A - B$ is positive semidefinite. Notice also that if A, B are, respectively, the covariance matrices of the estimators a and b, then $A \geq B$ implies that the variances of the individual elements of a are no smaller than those of corresponding elements of

b and the generalized variance, $|A|$, of the former is no less than the generalized variance of the latter, $|B|$.

When viewed in this light, Lemma 16 states that no matter what the technique of estimation, the covariance matrix of an estimator b has a lower bound given by

$$-\left[\frac{\partial\psi(\theta)}{\partial\theta}\right]'[TM(\theta)]^{-1}\left[\frac{\partial\psi(\theta)}{\partial\theta}\right]$$

In particular, if b is an *unbiased* estimator of θ and $n = k$, then

$$\frac{\partial\psi(\theta)}{\partial\theta} = I \tag{3.6.64}$$

Thus the bound in (3.6.63) simplifies to

$$V \geq -[TM(\theta)]^{-1} \tag{3.6.65}$$

Notice that if $k = 1$, (3.6.63) [or (3.6.65) as the case might be] implies the conclusion of Lemma 15, for in that case

$$E\left(\frac{\partial L}{\partial\theta}\right)^2 = -TE\left[\frac{\partial^2 \ln f(x;\theta)}{\partial\theta^2}\right] \tag{3.6.66}$$

The development in the preceding two lemmas has motivated certain definitions of efficiency. Intuitively, and in addition to the relevant remarks made at the beginning of this section, the notion of efficiency of estimators is meant to convey some information regarding the efficacy of the use by the latter of the information conveyed by the sample. Indeed, such considerations are intimately connected with the notion of the information conveyed by an observation as first formulated by R. A. Fisher. Without going into the history of the concept, let us formulate several versions currently employed in the literature of econometrics.

Definition 14: Let $\{x_t: t = 1, 2, \ldots, T\}$ be a random sample from a population characterized by the *regular* density $f(\cdot\,;\theta)$. The estimator $\hat{\theta}$ is said to be a minimum variance bound (MVB) estimator of θ if $\hat{\theta}$ is unbiased and its covariance matrix, say V, obeys

$$V = -[TM(\theta)]^{-1} \tag{3.6.67}$$

where $M(\theta)$ is as in (3.6.55).

Remark 18: It should be stressed that MVB estimators need not always exist; thus it would not be expedient to define efficiency of estimators in terms of the bounds determined in Lemmas 15 and 16. Moreover, these bounds are not the sharpest possible.

A more useful definition of efficiency is in terms of the following consideration.

Definition 15: Let $\{x_t : t = 1, 2, \ldots, T\}$ be a random sample from a population characterized by the density $f(\cdot\,; \theta)$, and let C be the class of all unbiased estimators of θ. If $\hat{\theta} \in C$ and is such that, for *any other* estimator $\tilde{\theta} \in C$, $\mathrm{Cov}\,(\tilde{\theta}) - \mathrm{Cov}\,(\hat{\theta})$ is a positive semidefinite matrix, then $\hat{\theta}$ is said to be a minimum variance (MV) estimator.

Remark 19: Often the class C is restricted to those unbiased estimators that are *linear* functions of the data, in which case $\hat{\theta}$ is said to be a best linear unbiased estimator (BLUE). This definition of efficiency is used frequently in econometrics.

Finally, we introduce the concept of relative efficiency:

Definition 16: Let $\{x_t : t = 1, 2, \ldots, T\}$ be a random sample from a population characterized by the density $f(\cdot\,; \theta)$. Let C be the class of unbiased estimators of θ. An estimator $\tilde{\theta}^1 \in C$ *is said to be efficient relative to another estimator*, say $\tilde{\theta}^2 \in C$, if $\mathrm{Cov}\,(\tilde{\theta}^2) - \mathrm{Cov}\,(\tilde{\theta}^1)$ is a positive semidefinite matrix.

The perceptive reader should have noticed that all definitions above require the existence of first and second moments of the proposed estimators for all sample sizes T. Frequently, in econometrics, we are confronted with estimators whose first two moments may not exist but for which a simple transform possesses a well-defined asymptotic distribution. In many instances, simultaneous equations estimators are consistent, but the moments of their small sample distributions either do not exist or, if they do, are not known.

In such situations, the notion of asymptotic efficiency is relevant. One way of formalizing this concept is to note that in the sampling context above it frequently happens that $\sqrt{T}(\hat{\theta} - \theta)$ has a well-defined asymptotic distribution. If we restrict our attention to the class of estimators for which this quantity is *asymptotically normally distributed*, then we are dealing with what in the statistical literature is called the class of consistent asymptotically normal (CAN) estimators. In this context, one then defines efficiency of an estimator in terms of attainment of the bounds of Lemmas 15 and 16 *with respect to the asymptotic distribution of the estimator*. Efficient estimators in the foregoing sense are called best asymptotic normal (BAN). Unfortunately, however, this approach is rather ambiguous, as the following illustration will make clear.

Example 9: Let $\hat{\theta}$ be an estimator of the *scalar* parameter θ such that $\sqrt{T}(\hat{\theta} - \theta)$ is asymptotically normal with mean zero and variance $m(\theta)$, and consider now the alternative estimator,

$$\hat{\theta}^* = \gamma\hat{\theta} \quad \text{if} \quad |\hat{\theta}| \leqslant T^{-1/4}$$
$$= \hat{\theta} \quad \text{if} \quad |\hat{\theta}| > T^{-1/4} \tag{3.6.68}$$

It is clear that $\sqrt{T}(\hat{\theta}^* - \theta)$ is also asymptotically normal, with mean zero and variance $\gamma^2 m(0)$ *if* $\theta = 0$; if $\theta \neq 0$, then its variance is $m(\theta)$. Thus, given an asymptotically normal estimator, we can always construct another whose variance is smaller in at least one point of the admissible parameter space, and the same elsewhere. This difficulty will be avoided if we impose on the class of admissible estimators the condition that in *compact subsets of the admissible parameter space* the convergence to normality be *uniform*. Such estimators are called consistent uniformly asymptotically normal (CUAN) estimators. We shall not belabor this point, which is only of peripheral interest in econometrics. The interested reader may refer to the excellent paper by Rao [29] and the bibliography it contains.

In subsequent discussion we shall have need of the following asymptotic concept of relative efficiency, which we therefore formalize in

Definition 17: Let $\{x_t: t = 1, 2, \ldots, T\}$ be a random sample from a population characterized by the density $f(\,\cdot\,; \theta)$. Let $\tilde{\theta}^1, \tilde{\theta}^2$ be two estimators of θ such that, asymptotically,

$$\sqrt{T}(\tilde{\theta}^1 - \theta) \sim N(0, \Sigma_1), \ \sqrt{T}(\tilde{\theta}^2 - \theta) \sim N(0, \Sigma_2) \tag{3.6.69}$$

Then $\tilde{\theta}^1$ is said to be asymptotically efficient relative to $\tilde{\theta}^2$ if

$$\Sigma = \Sigma_2 - \Sigma_1 \tag{3.6.70}$$

is positive semidefinite.

An obvious byproduct of the preceding development is

Lemma 17: Let $\{x_t: t = 1, 2, \ldots, T\}$ be a random sample from a population characterized by the regular density $f(\,\cdot\,; 0)$ and let $\hat{0}$ be the ML estimator of θ. Let C be the class of estimators $\tilde{0}$ such that $\sqrt{T}(\tilde{0} - \theta)$ converges asymptotically to a normal distribution with mean zero and finite covariance matrix and the convergence to normality is uniform over compact subsets of the admissible parameter space. Then the maximum likelihood estimator is efficient in the sense that it attains the Cramér-Rao bound.

The discussion of this section may be summarized in

Theorem 7: Let $\{x_t: t = 1, 2, \ldots, T\}$ be a random sample characterized by the density $f(\,\cdot\,; \theta)$, which, together with the admissible parameter space Ω, obeys the conditions of Lemma 13. Let $L(X; \theta)$ be the (log) likelihood function of the observations and $\hat{\theta}$ that root of

$$\frac{\partial L}{\partial \theta} = 0 \tag{3.6.71}$$

satisfying

$$L(X; \hat{\theta}) \geq L(X; \theta) \qquad \theta \in \Omega \tag{3.6.72}$$

Then the following are true:

i. There is at most one root of (3.6.71) that is a consistent estimator of θ_0, the true parameter vector.

ii. The consistent root, if it exists, corresponds to a maximum of the likelihood function with probability one.
iii. The root, $\hat{\theta}$, which obeys (3.6.72), is the consistent root.
iv. The sequence $z_T = \sqrt{T}(\hat{\theta} - \theta_0)$ converges to the random variable z having the distribution $z \sim N(0, -M^{-1}(\theta_0))$, where

$$M(\theta_0) = E\left(\frac{\partial^2 f(x; \theta_0)}{\partial\theta\,\partial\theta}\right)$$

v. Within the class of consistent, uniformly asymptotically normal (CUAN) estimators, $\hat{\theta}$ is efficient in the sense that (asymptotically) it attains the Cramér-Rao bound; that is, it is asymptotically MVB.

PROOF: Lemma 12 (i, ii), Lemma 13 (iii), Lemma 14 (iv), Lemma 17 (v).

3.7 ESTIMATION FOR DISTRIBUTIONS ADMITTING OF SUFFICIENT STATISTICS

CHARACTERIZATION OF A CLASS

In previous sections we studied various properties of ML estimators; in particular, we attempted to devise a measure of desirability of estimators based on their variance properties (efficiency). We may, however, be interested in the following question: In a given estimation context, can we find estimators that, in some sense, "exhaust the information" conveyed by the sample?[17] This leads to the concept of sufficiency first suggested by R. A. Fisher. More precisely, we have

Definition 18: Let $\{x_t : t = 1, 2, \ldots, T\}$ be a random sample from a population characterized by the density $f(\cdot\,; \theta)$ and let

$$s = (s_1, s_2, \ldots, s_k)' \tag{3.7.1}$$

be an estimator of the (k-element) vector θ. Further, let

$$\{s^i : i = 1, 2, \ldots, r\} \qquad r \leq T - 1 \tag{3.7.2}$$

be any other set of statistics for θ, where, of course,

$$s^i = (s^i_1, s^i_2, \ldots, s^i_k)' \tag{3.7.3}$$

---

[17] This sentence may appear cryptic to the reader. However, he may consider the following obvious problem: Let $\{x_t : t = 1, 2, \ldots, T\}$ be a sample from a population having finite mean μ and covariance matrix Σ. Let T^* be the largest integer equal to or less than $T/2$ and consider the estimator $\tilde{\mu} = 1/T^* \sum_{t=1}^{T^*} x_t$. Clearly, this is a consistent estimator but one that obviously neglects a great deal of the information conveyed by the sample. Although this is not precisely what we had in mind in connection with the property of sufficiency, nonetheless, the reader will gain from it some intuitive grasp of the type of property we are after.

Then s is said to be sufficient relative to the s^i, $i = 1, 2, \ldots, r$, if the conditional distribution of the latter, *given s*, does not depend on θ.

Occasionally the elements of s are said to be a set of jointly sufficient statistics (for the elements of θ). It is interesting that we can obtain a characterization of the class of densities admitting of sufficient statistics for its parameter. Hence, we have

Lemma 18: (Koopman-Pittman): A necessary and sufficient condition for the density $f(x; \theta)$ to admit of a set of jointly sufficient statistics for its parameter (vector) θ is that f be of the form

$$f(x; \theta) = \exp \left\{ \sum_{i=1}^{k} A_{0i}(\theta) B_{0i}(x) + B_1(x) + A_1(\theta) \right\} \tag{3.7.4}$$

PROOF: See Koopman [18] and Pittman [26].

Example 7: The multivariate normal density is

$$f(x; \theta) = (2\pi)^{-m/2} |\Sigma|^{-\frac{1}{2}} \exp \left\{ -\frac{1}{2} (x - \mu)' \Sigma^{-1} (x - \mu) \right\} \tag{3.7.5}$$

Here

$$\theta = (\mu_1, \mu_2, \ldots, \mu_m, \sigma_{11}, \sigma_{12} \ldots \sigma_{1m}, \sigma_{22}, \ldots, \sigma_{mm})' \tag{3.7.6}$$

and we may write

$$f(x, 0) = \exp \left\{ \left[\left(-\frac{m}{2} \right) \ln (2\pi) - \left(\frac{1}{2} \right) \operatorname{tr} (\Sigma^{-1} xx' - 2\Sigma^{-1} \mu x') \right] - \left(\frac{1}{2} \right) \ln |\Sigma| \right.$$

$$\left. - \operatorname{tr} \Sigma^{-1} \tfrac{1}{2} \mu\mu' \right\} \tag{3.7.7}$$

Here the term in square brackets corresponds to $\sum_{i=1}^{k} A_{0i}(\theta) B_{0i}(x)$ in (3.7.4), while the remaining terms in the braces correspond to $A_1(\theta)$. Thus the multivariate normal density does admit of sufficient statistics for its parameters. Actually, we can show that the estimators

$$\hat{\mu} = \bar{x}, \quad \hat{\Sigma} = \frac{XX' - T\bar{x}\bar{x}'}{T} \tag{3.7.8}$$

of the parameters of the multivariate normal are jointly sufficient.

Although Definition 18 makes the meaning of sufficiency quite clear, the criterion it proposes is not easily applicable in practice. On the other hand, the following relatively simple result is available:

Lemma 19 (Fisher-Neyman criterion): Let $\{x_t : t = 1, 2, \ldots, T\}$ be a random sample from a population characterized by the density $f(\cdot; \theta)$. Then

$$s = s(x_1, x_2, \ldots, x_T) \tag{3.7.9}$$

is a sufficient statistic for θ if and only if the likelihood function of the observations, $L^*(X; \theta)$, can be decomposed as

$$L^*(X; \theta) = g(s; \theta)K(X) \tag{3.7.10}$$

where $g(s; \theta)$ is the density function of s and $K(\cdot)$ is a function depending solely on the data *and not on* θ.

PROOF: Suppose (3.7.10) is valid; we shall show that s is sufficient according to Definition 18. To this effect, let

$$r_1 = r_1(x_1, x_2, \ldots, x_T) = s$$
$$r_i = r_i(x_1, x_2, \ldots, x_T) \qquad i = 2, 3, \ldots, T \tag{3.7.11}$$

We shall show that the conditional distribution of r_i, $i = 2, \ldots, T$, given r_1, does not involve θ. With little loss of generality, we shall suppose that the transformations in (3.7.11) are invertible so that we can uniquely express

$$x_t = x_t(r_1, r_2, \ldots, r_T) \qquad t = 1, 2, \ldots, T \tag{3.7.12}$$

and that the Jacobian of the transformation, J, does not vanish. By Lemma 3 of Chapter 1, the joint density of the r_i, $i = 1, 2, \ldots, T$, is given by

$$\prod_{t=1}^{T} f[x_t(r_1, \ldots, r_T); \theta] |J| = h(r_1, r_2, \ldots, r_T; \theta) \tag{3.7.13}$$

where $|J|$ is the absolute value of the Jacobian of the transformation.
    From (3.7.10), we have

$$h(r_1, r_2, \ldots, r_T; \theta) = g(s; \theta)K[x_1(r_1, r_2, \ldots, r_T), \ldots, x_T(r_1, r_2, \ldots, r_T)] |J| \tag{3.7.14}$$

Since $g(s; \theta)$ is the (marginal) density of r_1 and h is the joint density of $r_1, r_2, \ldots, r_T$, we see that h/g is the conditional density of $r_2, r_3, \ldots, r_T$, given r_1; in view of the fact that K does not depend on θ, we conclude that $s(=r_1)$ is a sufficient estimator.
    Next, suppose that s is sufficient; we shall show that the decomposition is valid. Since s is sufficient, the joint density of r_i, $i = 1, 2, \ldots, T$, can be written as

$$h(r_1, r_2, \ldots, r_T; \theta) = g(s; \theta)H(r_2, r_3, \ldots, r_T | r_1) \tag{3.7.15}$$

where $H(r_2, r_3, \ldots, r_T | r_1)$ is the conditional density of r_i, $i = 2, \ldots, T$, given r_1, which by assumption does not depend on θ.
    Consider now the transformation from the r's to the x's, and let J^* be the Jacobian of that transformation [in (3.7.12)]. The joint density of the $\{x_t: t = 1, 2, \ldots, T\}$ again, in view of Lemma 3 of Chapter 1, is

$$L^*(X; \theta) = h[r_1(x_1, x_2, \ldots, x_T), \ldots, r_T(x_1, x_2, \ldots, x_T)]|J^*| \tag{3.7.16}$$

Taking (3.7.15) into account and expressing the r's in terms of the x's, we have

$$L^*(X; \theta) = g(s; \theta)H(r_2, \ldots, r_T | r_1)|J^*| = g(s; \theta)K(X) \tag{3.7.17}$$

where K depends only on the x's *and not on* θ.   Q.E.D.

An illustration of the usefulness of Lemma 19 is given by

Example 8: Let $\{x_t : t = 1, 2, \ldots, T\}$ be a random sample from a population characterized by the multivariate normal distribution $N(\mu, \Sigma)$. From (1.6.10) of Chapter 1, we see that the likelihood function of the sample can be written as

$$L^*(X; \theta) = (2\pi)^{-(Tm/2)} |\Sigma|^{-T/2} \exp\left[-T/2 \operatorname{tr} (\Sigma^{-1}A)\right]$$
$$\times \exp\{-T/2 \operatorname{tr} [\Sigma^{-1}(\bar{x} - \mu)(\bar{x} - \mu)']\} \tag{3.7.18}$$

The right-hand side, apart from constants not depending on μ or Σ, is recognized as the joint density of $T\hat{\Sigma}$ (Wishart) and $\bar{x}$ (normal), for the two estimators are mutually independent. By Lemma 19, this implies that $\hat{\Sigma}$ and $\bar{x}$ are jointly sufficient for the parameters Σ and μ.

MAXIMUM LIKELIHOOD ESTIMATION AND SUFFICIENCY

Maximum likelihood estimation is an attractive procedure not only in terms of the asymptotic results derived in Section 3.6 but also, and perhaps chiefly, because if the underlying density admits of sufficient statistics, the maximum likelihood estimator is sufficient. As made clear in Definition 18, sufficiency is an important property in that it is not possible to extract information from the sample concerning the parameters under consideration beyond that captured by the sufficient estimator.

The following simple but important result makes the sufficiency of maximum likelihood estimators quite clear.

Lemma 20: Let $\{x_t : t = 1, 2, \ldots, T\}$ be a random sample from a population characterized by the density $f(\cdot; \theta)$ and suppose that the latter admits of a sufficient statistic, s, for the parameter θ. Then the ML estimator of θ is a function of the sufficient statistic.

PROOF: By virtue of the Fisher-Neyman criterion (Lemma 19), the (log) likelihood function of the observations may be written as

$$L(X; \theta) = \ln g(s; \theta) + \ln K(X) \tag{3.7.19}$$

where $K(\cdot)$ does not contain θ. The maximum likelihood estimator of θ, say $\hat{\theta}$, is a root of

$$\frac{\partial L}{\partial \theta} = 0 \tag{3.7.20}$$

But (3.7.19) implies that

$$\frac{\partial L}{\partial \theta} = \frac{1}{g(s; \theta)} \frac{\partial g(s; \theta)}{\partial \theta} = 0 \tag{3.7.21}$$

Thus the roots of (3.7.20) are exactly those of

$$\frac{\partial g(s; \theta)}{\partial \theta} = 0 \tag{3.7.22}$$

and we see that the ML estimator $\hat{\theta}$ must be a function of s.   Q.E.D.

The significance of this result will perhaps be brought out more clearly if the reader realizes that sufficient statistics are not unique. In fact, the following is true; the proof is left as an exercise.

Lemma 21: Let $\{x_t: t = 1, 2, \ldots, T\}$ be a random sample from a population characterized by the density $f(\cdot; \theta)$. If s is a sufficient statistic for θ, then so is $h(s)$ provided $h(\cdot)$ is a differentiable and invertible function (i.e., it is one to one).

Lemmas 20 and 21 imply that if a sufficient statistic exists for θ, then the ML estimator is sufficient. It is natural then to ask whether this makes any difference in the process of ML estimation.

It turns out that in the presence of sufficiency the estimation of the covariance matrix of the asymptotic distribution of the ML estimator is greatly simplified. We remind the reader that this matrix is consistently estimated by

$$\left[-E\left(\frac{1}{T} \frac{\partial^2 L}{\partial \theta \, \partial \theta} \right) \right]^{-1}$$

its elements evaluated at the point $\theta = \hat{\theta}$. In the presence of sufficiency, we may dispense with the expectation above, as the following makes clear:

Lemma 22: Let $\{x_t: t = 1, 2, \ldots, T\}$ be a random sample from a population characterized by the regular density $f(\cdot; \theta)$; suppose further that the density admits of a sufficient statistic, and let $\hat{\theta}$ be the ML estimator of θ. Then the consistent estimator of the asymptotic covariance matrix of $\hat{\theta}$ can be computed as the inverse of

$$-M(\hat{\theta}) = -\left[\frac{1}{T} \frac{\partial^2 L(X; \hat{\theta})}{\partial \theta \, \partial \theta} \right] \tag{3.7.23}$$

PROOF: In view of Lemma 18, the logarithm of the likelihood function may be written as

$$L(X; \theta) = \sum_{t=1}^{T} \sum_{i=1}^{k} A_{0i}(\theta) B_{0i}(x_t) + \sum_{t=1}^{T} B_1(x_t) + T A_1(\theta) \tag{3.7.24}$$

If $\hat{\theta}$ is the maximum likelihood estimator of θ, then it obeys

$$\frac{\partial L(X;\hat{\theta})}{\partial \theta} = \sum_{i=1}^{k} \frac{\partial A_{0i}(\hat{\theta})}{\partial \theta} V_i + T \frac{\partial A_1(\hat{\theta})}{\partial \theta} = 0 \qquad (3.7.25)$$

where the notation, for example, $\partial A_1(\hat{\theta})/\partial \theta$ means the derivative (gradient) $\partial A_1/\partial \theta$ evaluated at $\theta = \hat{\theta}$, and

$$V_i = \sum_{t=1}^{T} B_{0i}(x_t) \qquad (3.7.26)$$

We also have

$$E\left[\frac{\partial \ln L(X;\theta)}{\partial \theta}\right] = \sum_{i=1}^{k} \frac{\partial A_{0i}}{\partial \theta} \bar{V}_i + T \frac{\partial A_1}{\partial \theta} = 0 \qquad (3.7.27)$$

where

$$E(V_i) = \bar{V}_i \qquad (3.7.28)$$

Let

$$V = (V_1, V_2, \ldots, V_k)' \qquad \bar{V} = E(V) \qquad \frac{\partial A_0}{\partial \theta} = \left[\frac{\partial A_{0i}}{\partial \theta}\right] \qquad (3.7.29)$$

Then (3.7.25) and (3.7.27) imply, respectively,

$$V = -T\left[\frac{\partial A_0(\hat{\theta})}{\partial \theta}\right]^{-1} \frac{\partial A_1(\hat{\theta})}{\partial \theta} \qquad (3.7.30)$$

$$\bar{V} = -T\left(\frac{\partial A_0}{\partial \theta}\right)^{-1} \frac{\partial A_1}{\partial \theta} \qquad (3.7.31)$$

In particular, for $\theta = \hat{\theta}$, (3.7.31) implies

$$\bar{V} = V \qquad (3.7.32)$$

Moreover, operating with the elements of the Hessian of the likelihood function, we find

$$\frac{\partial^2 L(X;\hat{\theta})}{\partial \theta_r \, \partial \theta_s} = \sum_{i=1}^{k} \frac{\partial^2 A_{0i}(\hat{\theta})}{\partial \theta_r \, \partial \theta_s} V_i + T \frac{\partial^2 A_1(\hat{\theta})}{\partial \theta_r \, \partial \theta_s} \qquad (3.7.33)$$

$$E\left[\frac{\partial^2 \ln L}{\partial \theta_r \, \partial \theta_s}\right] = \sum_{i=1}^{k} \frac{\partial^2 A_{0i}}{\partial \theta_r \, \partial \theta_s} \bar{V}_i + T \frac{\partial^2 A_1}{\partial \theta_r \, \partial \theta_s} \qquad \text{any } \theta \in \Omega \qquad (3.7.34)$$

In particular, evaluating the relation (3.7.34) for $\theta = \hat{\theta}$, we conclude, in view of (3.7.32),

$$\frac{1}{T}\frac{\partial^2 \ln L}{\partial \theta \, \partial \theta}\bigg|_{\theta=\hat{\theta}} = \frac{1}{T} E\left[\frac{\partial^2 \ln L}{\partial \theta \, \partial \theta}\right]_{\theta=\hat{\theta}} = M(\hat{\theta}) \qquad \text{Q.E.D.} \qquad (3.7.35)$$

Remark 20: Since the covariance matrix of the asymptotic distribution of the ML estimator $\hat{\theta}$ is given by the inverse of

$$-M(\theta_0) = -E\left[\frac{1}{T}\frac{\partial^2 L}{\partial\theta\,\partial\theta}\right] \tag{3.7.36}$$

where θ_0 is the true value of the parameter vector, it follows that a consistent estimator of it can always be obtained by substituting $\hat{\theta}$ for θ_0 in the matrix appearing in the right-hand side of (3.7.36). The operation of taking expectations may, however, be complex. The import of the preceding lemma is that when *the underlying density of the problem admits of a sufficient statistic,* a consistent estimator for $-M(\theta_0)$ can be obtained by substituting $\hat{\theta}$ for θ_0 in the *Hessian of the likelihood function.* Thus no expectation is entailed.

The results pertinent to ML estimation in the case where the underlying density admits of sufficient statistics are summarized in

Theorem 8: Let $\{x_t : t = 1, 2, \ldots, T\}$ be a random sample from a population characterized by the regular density $f(\cdot\,; \theta)$; suppose further that the latter admits of sufficient statistics. Then the maximum likelihood estimator of θ, say $\hat{\theta}$, is sufficient. Moreover, the covariance matrix of its asymptotic distribution may be consistently estimated by the inverse of

$$-\left[\frac{1}{T}\frac{\partial^2 L}{\partial\theta\,\partial\theta}\right]_{\theta=\hat{\theta}}$$

PROOF: Lemmas 20, 21, and 22.

3.8 MINIMUM VARIANCE ESTIMATION AND SUFFICIENT STATISTICS

In the previous sections we introduced the concept of a minimum variance bound (MVB) estimator and established that the ML estimator of the parameters of the regular density $f(x; \theta)$ is *asymptotically* MVB.

One may then be tempted to ask whether in the case where $f(x; \theta)$ admits of sufficient statistics we can *always* (i.e., for every sample size) find MVB estimators for θ. The answer, unfortunately, is No. We can prove, however, the assertion in reverse. We do that for illustrative purposes in the case where θ is a scalar. Thus we have

Lemma 23: Let $\{x_t : t = 1, 2, \ldots, T\}$ be a random sample from a population characterized by the regular density of $f(\cdot\,; \theta)$, and suppose that an unbiased MVB estimator for θ, say b, exists. Then $f(\cdot\,; \theta)$ admits of a sufficient statistic.

PROOF: Under the hypotheses of the lemma, the relation (3.6.48) encountered in the proof of Lemma 15 becomes

$$\int\left(\frac{\partial L}{\partial\theta}\,b\right)L^*(X; \theta)\,dX = 1 \tag{3.8.1}$$

Applying Schwarz's ineqality to (3.8.1), we have

$$\left[\int \left(\frac{\partial L}{\partial \theta}\right)^2 L^*(X;\theta)\, dX \right] \cdot \left[\int (b-\theta)^2 L^*(X;\theta)\, dX \right] \geq 1 \qquad (3.8.2)$$

But the MVB property of b requires the strict equality to hold in (3.8.2). This, however, can be so if and only if

$$\frac{\partial L}{\partial \theta} = a(\theta)(b-\theta) \qquad (3.8.3)$$

Integrating with respect to θ, we find

$$L(X;\theta) = A_0(\theta)b - A_1(\theta) + B_1(X) \qquad (3.8.4)$$

where $A_0(\theta)$, $A_1(\theta)$ are, respectively, the indefinite integrals $\int a(\theta)\, d\theta$, $\int \theta a(\theta)\, d\theta$. From Lemma 18, we then conclude that $f(\cdot\,;\theta)$ admits of a sufficient statistic. Q.E.D.

Remark 21: Perhaps one can see from (3.8.4) why it is not enough for a density to admit of sufficient statistics in order that an MVB estimator for its parameters exist. The logarithm of the likelihood function of a random sample with a density admitting of a sufficient statistic for its parameter is, according to Lemma 18, of the form

$$L(X;\theta) = \sum_{t=1}^{T}\sum_{i=1}^{k} A_{0i}^*(\theta)B_{0i}(x_t) + TA_1^*(\theta) + \sum_{t=1}^{T} B_1(x_t) \qquad (3.8.5)$$

However, no specific relation is required between $A_{0i}^*(\cdot)$ and $A_1^*(\cdot)$. From the lemma above, we see that the existence of an MVB estimstor for θ requires the relation, say,

$$A_{01}^*(\theta) = \int a(\theta)\, d\theta \qquad A_1^*(\theta) = -\int \theta a(\theta)\, d\theta \qquad A_{0i}^*(\cdot) \equiv 0,\ i \geqslant 2 \qquad (3.8.6)$$

for some function $a(\theta)$.

It is interesting that if a density function $f(\cdot\,;\theta)$ admits of a sufficient statistic for its parameters, then, even though we are not guaranteed the existence of MVB estimators for θ, we are still guaranteed estimators possesing the property of minimum variance. To this effect, we give the following two lemmas due (independently) to C. R. Rao (1945) and D. Blackwell (1947).

Lemma 24: Let $\{x_t : t = 1, 2, \ldots, T\}$ be a sample from a population characterized by the density $f(\cdot\,;\theta)$. Suppose that f admits of a set of sufficient statistics s; let

$$b = (b_1, b_2, \ldots, b_n)' \qquad (3.8.7)$$

where n may be greater, smaller, or equal to k,[18] be an estimator such that

$$E(b) = b(\theta) \qquad \text{Cov } (b) = V \tag{3.8.8}$$

Then there exist functions of the set of sufficient statistics s, say

$$\psi = \psi(s) = (\psi_1(s), \psi_2(s), \ldots, \psi_n(s))' \tag{3.8.9}$$

such that

$$E[\psi] = b(\theta) \tag{3.8.10}$$

PROOF: Let $h(b, s; \theta)$ be the joint density of b and s, $h(b \mid s)$ the conditional on b, given s and $h_1(s; \theta)$ the marginal on s. The densities are as indicated, for f admits of a set of sufficient statistics for its parameters. Thus for the ith element of b, b_i, we have

$$E(b_i) = \iint b_i h(b, s; \theta) \, db \, ds$$

$$= \iint [b_i h(b \mid s) \, db] h_1(s; \theta) \, ds$$

$$= \int \psi_i(s) h_1(s; \theta) \, ds = b_i(\theta) \tag{3.8.11}$$

where

$$\psi_i(s) = \int b_i h(b \mid s) \, db \qquad\qquad \text{Q.E.D.} \tag{3.8.12}$$

Remark 22: Notice that $\psi_i(s)$ is indeed a statistic, for it does not depend on θ. This is so because neither b_i nor $h(b \mid s)$ depend on θ, the latter being true since f admits of, and s is, a set of sufficient statistics for θ.

Remark 23: It is also important to understand the limitations of this result. It does *not* say that there exists a set of unbiased estimators for the parameters of a density admitting of sufficient statistics. What it does state is this: If $\{b_i(\theta): i = 1, 2, \ldots, n\}$ is a set of functions of the parameters θ for which there exist unbiased estimators, then one can find functions of the sufficient statistics, say $\{\psi_i(s): i = 1, 2, \ldots, n\}$ (which under some mild restrictions would themselves be sufficient) such that the ψ_i are unbiased estimators of the $b_i(\theta)$. The significance of this result will become evident from the following lemma. For the moment, it should be understood that the lemma above does not imply that one can always find unbiased (and sufficient) estimators for $\{\theta_j: j = 1, 2, \ldots, k\}$.

We next provide an answer to the question: Why should one wish to obtain unbiased estimators of parametric functions, the estimators being functions of the set of sufficient statistics?

---

[18] We remind the reader of our convention that θ is a k-element vector.

Lemma 25: Let $\{x_t : t = 1, 2, \ldots, T\}$, $f(x; \theta)$, b, s, $\psi(s)$, and V be as in Lemma 24. Let

$$\Phi = \text{Cov}(\psi) \tag{3.8.13}$$

Then

$$\Phi^* = V - \Phi \tag{3.8.14}$$

is at least positive semidefinite.

PROOF: Let

$$\alpha = (\alpha_1, \alpha_2, \ldots, \alpha_n)' \tag{3.8.15}$$

be an arbitrary constant vector not all of whose elements are zero. Then

$$E(\alpha'b) = \alpha'b(\theta) = E[\alpha'\psi(s)] \tag{3.8.16}$$

Further,

$$
\begin{aligned}
\text{Var}(\alpha'b) &= E\{\alpha'[b - b(\theta)][b - b(\theta)]'\alpha\} \\
&= E\{\alpha'[b - \psi(s) + \psi(s) - b(\theta)][b - \psi(s) + \psi(s) - b(\theta)]'\alpha\} \\
&= E\{\alpha'[b - \psi(s)][b - \psi(s)]'\alpha\} \\
&\quad + E\{\alpha'[\psi(s) - b(\theta)][\psi(s) - b(\theta)]'\alpha\} \\
&\quad + E\{\alpha'[b - \psi(s)][\psi(s) - b(\theta)]'\alpha\} \\
&\quad + E\{\alpha'[\psi(s) - b(\theta)][b - \psi(s)]'\alpha\}
\end{aligned}
\tag{3.8.17}
$$

Consider now the last two terms following the third equality sign in (3.8.17) and, in particular, the (i, j) element of the matrix involved. It is given by

$$E\{[b_i - \psi_i(s)][\psi_j(s) - b_j(\theta)]\} = \iint (b_i - \psi_i)[\psi_j - b_j(\theta)]h(b, s; \theta)\, db\, ds \tag{3.8.18}$$

where the first integral sign indicates the multiple integration with respect to the elements of the vector b, the second integral sign indicates the multiple integration with respect to the elements of the vector s, and $h(b, s; \theta)$ is the joint density of b and s. Following the notation established in the proof of Lemma 24, we can write the integral in (3.8.18) as

$$
\begin{aligned}
\iint (b_i - \psi_i)[\psi_j - b_j(\theta)]h(b \mid s)h_1(s; \theta)\, db\, ds \\
= \int \left[\int (b_i - \psi_i)h(b \mid s)\, db \right][\psi_j - b_j(\theta)]h_1(s; \theta)\, ds = 0
\end{aligned}
\tag{3.8.19}
$$

The last equality above is valid, for by definition [see (3.8.12)],

$$\psi_i(s) = \int b_i h(b \mid s) \, db \qquad (3.8.20)$$

Thus we may write

$$\text{Var} \, (\alpha'b) = \alpha' E[b - \psi(s)][b - \psi(s)]'\alpha + \alpha'\Phi\alpha \geq \alpha'\Phi\alpha \qquad (3.8.21)$$

The inequality holds in view of the fact that the first component of the variance of $\alpha'b$ is a positive semidefinite quadratic form. Notice, also, that

$$\text{Var} \, (\alpha'b) = \alpha'V\alpha \qquad (3.8.22)$$

Hence (3.8.21) implies

$$\alpha'(V - \Phi)\alpha \geq 0 \qquad (3.8.23)$$

for any nonnull arbitrary real vector α. Thus

$$\Phi^* = V - \Phi \qquad (3.8.24)$$

is positive semidefinite.   Q.E.D.

Corollary 4: Under the hypotheses of Lemma 25, if an unbiased MVB estimator exists, it is a function of the sufficient statistic.

PROOF: Let b be any unbiased estimator of θ and V its covariance matrix. Since b is unbiased, then by Lemma 16 (Cramér-Rao inequality) we conclude that $V + [\text{TM}]^{-1}$ is positive semidefinite, where M is as defined in (3.6.55). If b is also MVB, then

$$V = -[\text{TM}]^{-1} \qquad (3.8.25)$$

On the other hand, defining $\psi(s)$ as in Lemma 24, we conclude that $V - \Phi$ is positive semidefinite, where

$$\Phi = \text{Cov} \, [\psi(s)] \qquad (3.8.26)$$

Since by construction $\Phi + [TM]^{-1}$ must be positive semidefinite, we conclude that[19]

$$\psi(s) = b \qquad \text{Q.E.D.}$$
$$(3.8.27)$$

Remark 24: The lemma just proved indicates that if $\psi(s)$ obeys (3.8.12), then it is an efficient estimator of $b(\theta)$ in the sense of Definition 16 and within the class of *unbiased* estimators of $b(\theta)$. In particular, if

$$b(\theta) = \theta \qquad (3.8.28)$$

---

[19] Actually, for (3.8.27) to be valid we must assert some sort of uniqueness for $\psi(s)$. Indeed, this can be shown to hold if certain conditions are imposed on $\psi(\cdot)$—continuity, for example.

and thus if an unbiased estimator of θ exists, then the efficient estimator is that function of the (jointly) sufficient statistics which is an unbiased estimator of θ. Therefore we have, by this lemma, a relatively simple way of constructing efficient (MV) estimators. We must stress that this is an important advance. If it is not known that the underlying density admits of a sufficient statistic, and we have an estimator of θ, say $\tilde{\theta}$, it is not easy to establish its efficiency. On the other hand, the lemma above provides a relatively simple procedure for doing just that in the special case when the density admits of sufficient statistics.

Finally, the specialization of the lemma to the uniparameter case is trivial and is left to the reader as an exercise.

The main results of this section are summarized in

Theorem 9: Let $\{x_t : t = 1, 2, \ldots, T\}$ be a random sample from a population characterized by the regular density $f(\cdot\,; \theta)$. Then

i. if an unbiased MVB estimator of θ exists, f admits of a set of (jointly) sufficient statistics for its parameters.

ii. if f admits of sufficient statistics and an unbiased estimator for θ exists, there exists a minimum variance estimator of θ and it (the estimator) is that function of the set of (jointly) sufficient statistics, which is an unbiased estimator of θ.

iii. if f admits of sufficient statistics and an unbiased MVB estimator exists, the latter is a function of the sufficient statistics.

PROOF: Lemmas 23, 24, 25, and Corollary 4.

We conclude this section by giving an example of some applications of these results.

Example 9: An application of some of the preceding concepts is as follows Dhrymes [6]:

Consider an economic unit characterized by the production process

$$Q(t) = A L^\alpha K^\beta \exp[u(t)] \qquad \alpha + \beta = 1 \tag{3.8.29}$$

where Q, K, L, u are, respectively, output, labor, capital, and a random variable. If the economic unit operates as if it were a perfect competitor, then one can show that

$$\ln \alpha(t) = \ln \alpha + u(t) \tag{3.8.30}$$

We need not be concerned with β for we may write $\beta = 1 - \alpha$. In (3.8.30), $\alpha(t)$ is the observed share of labor. If we have a sample of size T, we may assume that

$$u \sim N(0, \sigma^2 I) \qquad u = [u(1), u(2), \ldots, u(T)]' \tag{3.8.31}$$

The maximum likelihood estimator of $\ln \alpha$ is given by

$$\widehat{\ln \alpha} = \frac{1}{T} \sum_{t=1}^{T} \ln \alpha(t) \tag{3.8.32}$$

If we wish to estimate not $\ln \alpha$ but α, we may take as our estimator

$$\tilde{\alpha} = \exp \widehat{\ln \alpha} \tag{3.8.33}$$

It may be shown, however, that $\tilde{\alpha}$ is a biased estimator of α. In fact,

$$E(\tilde{\alpha}) = \exp \left[\ln \alpha + \left(\frac{\sigma^2}{2T} \right) \right] = \alpha \exp \left\{ \left(\frac{\sigma^2}{2T} \right) \right\} \tag{3.8.34}$$

From (3.8.30) it is clear that $\ln \alpha(t)$ is normal, with mean $\ln \alpha$ and variance σ^2. By the previous discussion, its density admits of a set of jointly sufficient statistics for its parameters. It follows, therefore, from Lemmas 24 and 25 that if we can find an unbiased estimator for α, then it would be efficient as well.

It may be verified that the estimator

$$\hat{\alpha} = \tilde{\alpha} K(\hat{\sigma}^2) \tag{3.8.35}$$

where

$$K(\hat{\sigma}^2) = \sum_{j=0}^{\infty} \left(-\frac{1}{4} \right)^j \frac{B\left(\frac{T-1}{2}, j \right)}{\Gamma(j)j!} \hat{\sigma}^{2j} \tag{3.8.36}$$

is an unbiased estimator of α.

In (3.8.35), $\hat{\sigma}^2$ is the sample variance of $\ln \alpha(t)$—the estimator of σ^2—$B(a, b)$ is the beta function defined by

$$B(a, b) = \frac{\Gamma(a + b)}{\Gamma(a)\Gamma(b)} \tag{3.8.37}$$

and $\Gamma(a)$ is the gamma function defined by

$$\Gamma(a) = \int_0^{\infty} u^{a-1} \exp(-u)\, du \tag{3.8.38}$$

Since $\hat{\alpha}$ is a function of $\widehat{\ln \alpha}$ and $\hat{\sigma}^2$, the set of jointly sufficient statistics, it is itself sufficient. Since it may be further verified that it is unbiased, and indeed unique, we conclude that it is an efficient estimator as well.

REFERENCES

1. Bahadur, R. R., "Examples of Inconsistency of Maximum Likelihood Estimators," *Sankhya*, vo. 20, 1958, pp. 207–210.
2. Blackwell, D., "Conditional Expectation and Unbiased Sequential Estimation," *Annals of Mathematical Statistics*, vol. 18, 1947, pp. 105–110. Gives a general method for obtaining an unbiased sequential estimator for a parameter admitting a sufficient statistic.

3. Chung, K. L., *A Course In Probability Theory*, New York, Harcourt, Brace and World, 1968.
4. Cramér, H., *Mathematical Methods of Statistics*, Princeton, N.J., Princeton University Press, 1946. A good discussion of the probability measure in Chapters 13, 14, 15. Also, in Chapters 32 and 33 gives the Cramér-Rao inequality and properties of the maximum likelihood estimator.
5. Cramér, H., *Random Variables and Probability Distributions*, 2nd ed., Cambridge, Cambridge University Press: 1962.
6. Dhrymes, P. J., "On Devising Unbiased Estimators for the Parameters of a Cobb-Douglas Production Function," *Econometrica*, vol. 30, 1962, pp. 297–304.
7. Feller, W., *An Introduction to Probability Theory and Its Applications*, 2nd ed., New York, Wiley, 1957. A good reference for central limit theorems and related topics.
8. Fisher, R. A., "On the Mathematical Foundations of Theoretical Statistics," *Transactions Royal Philosophical Society, London*, vol. 222 (A), 1922, pp. 309–368. First of the series of papers that suggested the maximum likelihood estimates and discussed some of their properties.
9. Fisher, R. A., "Theory of Statistical Estimation," *Proceedings Cambridge Philosophical Society*, vol. 22, 1925, pp. 700–725. Introduces the notion of sufficiency and necessity of factorization for sufficiency.
10. Frechet, M., *Recherches Theoretiques Modernes: Trait du Calcul des Probabilities*, par E. Borel: tome I, fasc. 3, Paris, 1937. Discusses several modes of convergence in probability.
11. Geary, R. C., "The Estimation of Many Parameters," *Journal of the Royal Statistical Society*, Series A, vol. 105, 1942, pp. 213–217. Proves that maximum likelihood estimators minimize the generalized variance in large samples.
12. Gnedenko, B. V., and A. N. Kolmogorov, *Limit Distributions for Sums of Independent Random Variables*, Reading, Mass., Addison-Wesley, 1954. Reference for the central limit theorems.
13. Halmos, P. R., and L. J. Savage, "Application of the Radon-Nikodym Theorem to the Theory of Sufficient Statistics," *Annals of Mathematical Statistics*, vol. 20, 1949, pp. 225–241. A rigorous measure-theoretic proof for the necessity and sufficiency of factorization for sufficiency.
14. Huzurbazar, V. S., "The Likelihood Equation, Consistency and the Maxima of the Likelihood Function," *Annals of Engenics*, vol. 14, 1948, pp. 185–200. Shows that as *n* increases, there is a unique consistent maximum likelihood estimator under regularity conditions.
15. Kendall, M. G., and A. Stuart, *The Advanced Theory of Statistics*, vol. 2, New York, Hafner Publishing Co., 1961. General problems of point estimation treated in Chapter 17. Chapter 18 discusses in detail the method and properties of maximum likelihood estimation.
16. Khinchine, A., "Sur la Loi des Grands Nombres," *Comptes Rendus Academie des Sciences*, vol. 188, 1929, pp. 477–479.
17. Kolmogoroff, A. N., *Grandbegriffe der Wahrscheinlichkeitsrechnung*, Ergeb. Math. no. 3, Berlin, 1950. English translation: *Foundations of the Theory of Probability*, New York, Chelsea. Pioneering work on axiomatic probability theory.
18. Koopman, B. O., "On Distributions Admitting Sufficient Statistics," *Transactions American Mathematical Society*, vol. 39, 1936, pp. 399–409. Introduced the Koopman-Pitman family.
19. Le Cam, L., "On the Asymptotic Theory of Estimation and Testing of Hypotheses," *Proceedings of the Third Berkeley Symposium on Mathematical Statistics and Probability*, vol. 1, Berkeley, University of California Press, 1957, pp. 129–156.
20. Levy, P., "Proprietes Asymptotiques des Sommes des Variables Aleatoires Independants ou Enchainees," *Journal de Mathematiques Pures et Appliquees*, vol. 14, 1935, p. 347. A study on the conditions under which the central limit theorem holds.
21. Lindeberg, M. W., "Eine neue Herlutung des Exponentialgesetz in der Wahrscheinlichkeitsrechnung," *Mathematische Zeitschrift*, vol. 15, 1922, pp. 211–225. Determines certain sufficient conditions under which the sum of random variables with different means and variances is distributed normally.
22. Loève, M., *Probability Theory*, Princeton, N.J., D. Von Nostrand, 1955. Topics discussed here are dealt with in Chapter 6; in particular, Sections 10–12.

23. Lukacs, E., *Characteristic Functions*, New York, Hafner Publishing Co., 1960.
24. Lyapunov, A., "Nouvelle forme de Theoreme sur la Limite de Probabilite," *Mem. Acadm. Sci. of St. Petersbourg*, vol. 12, 1901, pp. 1–24.
25. Neyman, J., "Su un teorema concernente le Considdetti Statistiche Sufficienti," *Giornale dell Istituto Italiano degli Attuari*, vol. 6, 1935, pp. 320–334. Proves the sufficiency of factorization for sufficiency.
26. Pitman, E. J. G., "Sufficient Statistics and Intrinsic Accuracy," *Proceedings of the Cambridge Philosophical Society*, vol. 32, 1936 pp. 567–579. Introduces the Pitman-Koopman family and works out some other properties of sufficient statistics.
27. Rao, C. R., "Information and Accuracy Attainable in the Estimation of Statistical Parameters," *Bulletin of the Calcutta Mathematical Society*, vol. 37, 1945, pp. 81–91. Proves the so-called Cramer-Rao inequality and the Rao-Blackwell theorem on MVUE.
28. Rao, C. R., *Linear Statistical Inference and Its Applications*, New York, Wiley, 1965. Probability theory and related issues are discussed in Chapter 2, estimation problems in Chapter 5.
29. Rao, C. R., "Criteria of Estimation in Large Samples," *Sankhya* (A), vol. 25, 1963, pp. 189–206.
30. Royden, H. L.: *Real Analysis*, New York, MacMillan, 1963.
31. Varadarajan, V. S., "A Useful Convergence Theorem," *Sankhya*, vol. 20, 1958, pp. 221–222.
32. Wald, A., "Note on the Consistency of Maximum Likelihood Estimates," *Annals of Mathematical Statistics*, vol. 20, 1949, pp. 595–601. Proves the consistency of maximum likelihood estimates.
33. Wilks, S. S., *Mathematical Statistics*, New York, Wiley, 1962. Of relevance are Chapters 4 and 5.

ESTIMATION OF SIMULTANEOUS EQUATIONS SYSTEMS

4

4.1 REVIEW OF CLASSICAL METHODS

A certain class of estimators for the parameters of a simultaneous equations (S.E.) system can be shown to have an interpretation as an ordinary least squares (OLS) estimator. In view of this fundamental unity of estimation procedures, it would be desirable at this stage to review carefully the estimation problem in the context of the general linear model and some of its (straightforward) extensions.

THE GENERAL LINEAR MODEL; PARAMETER ESTIMATION

Let y be a variable of interest and suppose that observations on it, at time t, are generated by

$$y_t = \sum_{i=1}^{k} \beta_i x_{ti} + u_t \qquad t = 1, 2, \ldots, T \tag{4.1.1}$$

Here y is said to the *dependent* and the x_i, $i = 1, 2, \ldots, k$, the independent or explanatory variables; the latter are usually assumed nonstochastic. The β_i are unknown parameters to be estimated. In matric form, (4.1.1) reads

$$y = X\beta + u \tag{4.1.2}$$

where y is a $T \times 1$ vector of observations on the dependent variable,

$$X = (x_{ti}) \qquad t = 1, 2, \ldots, T, \, i = 1, 2, \ldots, k \tag{4.1.3}$$

is the matrix of observations on the explanatory variables, and

$$\beta = (\beta_1, \beta_2, \ldots, \beta_k)' \qquad u = (u_1, u_2, \ldots, u_T)' \tag{4.1.4}$$

In connection with (4.1.2), the following assumptions are made:

$$|x_{ti}| < \chi \quad E(u) = 0 \quad \text{Cov}(u) = \sigma^2 I \quad E(X'u) = 0$$
$$\text{rank}(X) = k \qquad k < T \tag{4.1.5}$$

These assumptions, in order of appearance, mean:

i. The explanatory variables are uniformly bounded by the finite (but perhaps very large) constant χ.
ii. The disturbances, u_t, have mean zero, are uncorrelated, and have common variance σ^2.
iii. The explanatory variables are *uncorrelated* with the disturbances.
iv. There are *no linear dependencies* among the explanatory variables.

The technique of ordinary least squares (OLS) obtains an estimator for β, say b, by minimizing the sum of squared errors committed when we replace β by b—and thus "predict" y by Xb.

Thus the minimand is[1]

$$S = (y - Xb)'(y - Xb) = y'y - b'X'y - y'Xb + b'X'Xb \tag{4.1.6}$$

The first-order conditions are

$$\frac{\partial S}{\partial b} = -2X'y + 2X'Xb = 0 \tag{4.1.7}$$

Solving, we obtain

$$b = (X'X)^{-1}X'y \tag{4.1.8}$$

The expression for b exists and is unique in view of the assumption that the rank of X is k. In fact, $X'X$ is a *positive definite matrix*. To show that (4.1.8) gives the global minimum of S, as desired, we note that we may also write (4.1.6) as

$$S = [b - (X'X)^{-1}X'y]'(X'X)[b - (X'X)^{-1}X'y] + y'[I - X(X'X)^{-1}X']y \tag{4.1.9}$$

Since the second term in the right-hand side does not involve b, it is clear that to minimize S we must make the first term as small as possible. But since $X'X$ is a

---

[1] Here we are careful to distinguish between the parameter vector β and its estimator b; we do this for conceptual clarity at this early stage. Subsequently we shall not make this distinction. Thus we could also write $S = (y - X\beta)'(y - X\beta)$ and minimize with respect to β, although β is a fixed vector (of unknown parameters) it being understood that we merely seek an estimator of β which minimizes S.

positive definite matrix, the smallest value that term may assume is zero and this occurs if and only if we choose b according to (4.1.8). This shows that (4.1.8) indeed represents the global minimum of S.

The properties of the OLS estimator in the context of the present model are established by

Theorem 1 (Markov Theorem): Let the sample on the model in (4.1.1) be given by (4.1.2) and suppose the assumptions in (4.1.5) are valid. Then the OLS estimator of β as determined by (4.1.8) is

  i. unbiased,
 ii. consistent,
iii. efficient (within the class of linear unbiased estimators).

PROOF: Substituting (4.1.2) in (4.1.8), we have

$$b = \beta + (X'X)^{-1}X'u \qquad (4.1.10)$$

and thus

$$E(b) = \beta + (X'X)^{-1}X'E(u) = \beta \qquad (4.1.11)$$

which proves i.

From Chapter 3 (Corollary 1, Lemma 2), we know that if an estimator is asymptotically unbiased and its variance tends to zero, then it is consistent. Thus, in view of (4.1.11), we shall show consistency for b if we show that its covariance matrix vanishes asymptotically.[2] We have

$$\text{Cov}(b) = E[(X'X)^{-1}X'uu'X(X'X)^{-1}]$$
$$= (X'X)^{-1}X'E(uu')X(X'X)^{-1} = \sigma^2(X'X)^{-1} \qquad (4.1.12)$$

Now define

$$M = \frac{X'X}{T} \qquad (4.1.13)$$

and note that the (i, j) element of M obeys

$$|m_{ij}| = \left| \frac{\sum_{t=1}^{T} x_{ti} x_{tj}}{T} \right| \leq \chi^2 \qquad (4.1.14)$$

and that the inequality holds for all T.

Hence, for all T, the matrix M has finite elements and is nonsingular. But

$$(X'X)^{-1} = \frac{M^{-1}}{T} \qquad (4.1.15)$$

---

[2] The boundedness assumption on the explanatory variables may be removed and consistency may be shown directly. As an exercise, the reader should carefully carry out a direct proof using the results of Chapter 3.

and, moreover, M^{-1} is also a matrix with finite elements for all T. Thus we conclude

$$\lim_{T \to \infty} \text{Cov}(b) = \sigma^2 \lim_{T \to \infty} \frac{M^{-1}}{T} = 0 \qquad (4.1.16)$$

which proves ii.

To show efficiency, we proceed as follows. Let $\tilde{b}$ be another estimator of β. Since we require linearity, we must have

$$\tilde{b} = Hy \qquad (4.1.17)$$

where H is a matrix whose elements depend only on the elements of X. Since we require unbiasedness, we must have

$$\beta = E(\tilde{b}) = HE(y) = HX\beta \qquad (4.1.18)$$

and thus we conclude

$$HX = I \qquad (4.1.19)$$

Now define a matrix C by

$$H = (X'X)^{-1}X' + C \qquad (4.1.20)$$

that is, write H as the matrix defining the OLS estimator plus a remainder.

From (4.1.19) we conclude that C has the property

$$CX = 0 \qquad (4.1.21)$$

However, in view of (4.1.20) and (4.1.21), the covariance matrix of $\tilde{b}$ is given by

$$\text{Cov}(\tilde{b}) = \sigma^2 [(X'X)^{-1} + CC'] = \text{Cov}(b) + \sigma^2 CC' \qquad (4.1.22)$$

From (4.1.22) we conclude that

$$\text{Cov}(\tilde{b}) - \text{Cov}(b) = \sigma^2 CC' \qquad (4.1.23)$$

is a *positive semidefinite* matrix and thus b is efficient. Q.E.D.

Remark 1: Estimators that are efficient with respect to the class of linear unbiased estimators are said to be "best linear unbiased estimators" (BLUE).

To complete the estimation problem, we must derive an estimator for the remaining parameter, namely, σ^2. Thus consider

$$\hat{\sigma}^2 = \frac{\hat{u}'\hat{u}}{T - k} \qquad (4.1.24)$$

where

$$\hat{u} = y - Xb \qquad (4.1.25)$$

But

$$\hat{u}'\hat{u} = y'[I - X(X'X)^{-1}X']y = u'[I - X(X'X)^{-1}X']u \qquad (4.1.26)$$

Hence

$$E(\hat{u}'\hat{u}) = \sigma^2 \operatorname{tr} [I - X(X'X)^{-1}X']$$
$$= \sigma^2[\operatorname{tr} I - \operatorname{tr} (X'X)^{-1} X'X)] = (T - k)\sigma^2 \tag{4.1.27}$$

The last equality holds, for I is $T \times T$, while $(X'X)^{-1}X'X$ is *the identity matrix of order k*.

The estimator in (4.1.24) is thus unbiased. It can also be shown to be consistent; we leave this as an exercise for the reader.

The distributional aspects of b and $\hat{\sigma}^2$ are easily established when the disturbances in (4.1.1) are assumed normal. We have

Theorem 2: Let the conditions of Theorem 1 hold and assume in addition that $u \sim N(0, \sigma^2 I)$. Then

  i. the OLS and maximum likelihood estimators of β are identical.
  ii. $b \sim N[\beta, \sigma^2(X'X)^{-1}]$
  iii. b and $\hat{\sigma}^2$ are mutually independent and $(T - k)\hat{\sigma}^2/\sigma^2$ is chi square with $T - k$ degrees of freedom.

PROOF: If $u \sim N(0, \sigma^2 I)$, then the (log) likelihood function of the observations is

$$L(\beta, \sigma^2; y, X) = -\frac{T}{2} \ln (2\pi) - \frac{T}{2} \ln \sigma^2 - \frac{1}{2\sigma^2} (y - X\beta)'(y - X\beta) \tag{4.1.28}$$

Maximizing L with respect to β and σ^2, we find

$$\frac{\partial L}{\partial \beta} = -\frac{1}{\sigma^2}(-X'y + X'X\beta) = 0 \tag{4.1.29}$$

$$\frac{\partial L}{\partial \sigma^2} = -\frac{T}{2}\frac{1}{\sigma^2} + \frac{1}{2\sigma^4}(y - X\beta)'(y - X\beta) = 0 \tag{4.1.30}$$

Solving (4.1.29), we obtain

$$\hat{\beta} = (X'X)^{-1}X'y \tag{4.1.31}$$

which is identical with b of (4.1.8), thus proving i. Substituting this in (4.1.30), we find

$$\tilde{\sigma}^2 = \frac{\hat{u}'\hat{u}}{T} = \frac{T - k}{T}\hat{\sigma}^2 \tag{4.1.32}$$

This differs from $\hat{\sigma}^2$ by a factor of proportionality that tends to unity as $T \to \infty$.

Now to prove ii, we note that

$$\hat{\beta} = \beta + (X'X)^{-1}X'u \tag{4.1.33}$$

From Theorem 1 of Chapter 1, we immediately conclude

$$\hat{\beta} \sim N[\beta, \sigma^2(X'X)^{-1}]$$ (4.1.34)

which proves ii. To prove iii, we proceed as follows.
   Note that

$$u'u = u'[I - X(X'X)^{-1}X']u + u'[X(X'X)^{-1}X']u$$
$$= u'A_1 u + u'A_2 u.$$ (4.1.35)

Notice, also, that

$$A_1'A_2 = 0$$ (4.1.36)

and, moreover, that A_1 and A_2 are both idempotent matrices.[3] Thus

$$\text{rank } A_1 = T - k \qquad \text{rank } A_2 = k$$ (4.1.37)

From Cochran's theorem [45, p. 420], we conclude that

$$\frac{u'A_1 u}{\sigma^2} \qquad \frac{u'A_2 u}{\sigma^2}$$

are independently chi square with $(T - k)$ and k degrees of freedom respectively.
   But from (4.1.10), (4.1.26), (4.1.31), and (4.1.32), we see that

$$u'A_1 u = (T - k)\hat{\sigma}^2$$
$$u'A_2 u = (b - \beta)'X'X(b - \beta)$$ (4.1.38)

Since $X'X$ is by assumption positive definite, there exists a nonsingular matrix P such that

$$X'X = PP'$$ (4.1.39)

Thus (4.1.38) may be written as

$$[P'(b - \beta)]'[P'(b - \beta)] = u'A_2 u$$ (4.1.40)

which shows $P'(b - \beta)$, and hence $(b - \beta)$, to be independent of $\hat{\sigma}^2$.   Q.E.D.

AITKEN ESTIMATION FOR A SINGLE EQUATION

The model discussed above, often referred to as the classical form of the general linear model, imposes a highly simplified structure on the covariance matrix of the error terms. Suppose, instead, that in the model of (4.1.2) we assume

$$E(u) = 0 \qquad \text{Cov } (u) = \Sigma$$ (4.1.41)

---

[3] A matrix A is said to be *idempotent* if $AA = A$. As an exercise, show that for an idempotent matrix A, rank $(A) = \text{tr } A$. (*Hint*: First show that the roots of A, say λ_i, obey $\lambda_i = 1$ or $\lambda_i = 0$.)

where Σ is a general positive definite matrix. In this context, how can we efficiently estimate β? This problem was first investigated by Aitken [1] and thus efficient estimators of β in this model are said to be *Aitken estimators*. The procedure is given by

Theorem 3: Let the conditions of Theorem 1 hold except as indicated by (4.1.41). Then the efficient estimator of β is given by

$$\tilde{\beta} = (X'\Sigma^{-1}X)^{-1}X'\Sigma^{-1}y \qquad (4.1.42)$$

and its covariance matrix is

$$\text{Cov}(\tilde{\beta}) = (X'\Sigma^{-1}X)^{-1} \qquad (4.1.43)$$

PROOF: Since Σ is a positive definite matrix, there exists a nonsingular matrix R such that

$$\Sigma = RR' \qquad (4.1.44)$$

Transform the system in (4.1.2) by R^{-1} to obtain

$$R^{-1}y = R^{-1}X\beta + R^{-1}u \qquad (4.1.45)$$

Putting $w = R^{-1}y$, $Z = R^{-1}X$, and $v = R^{-1}u$, we write

$$w = Z\beta + v \qquad (4.1.46)$$

Observe now that

$$E(v) = 0 \quad \text{Cov}(v) = I \quad E(Z'v) = 0 \qquad (4.1.47)$$

and thus the system (4.1.46) obeys all the assumptions stated in Theorem 1. Hence the ordinary least squares estimator of β *in the context of the model as given in* (4.1.46) is best linear unbiased. But this estimator is

$$\tilde{\beta} = (Z'Z)^{-1}Z'w \qquad (4.1.48)$$

Expressing Z and w in terms of X, Σ, and y, we obtain

$$\tilde{\beta} = (X'\Sigma^{-1}X)^{-1}X'\Sigma^{-1}y \qquad (4.1.49)$$

To obtain the covariance matrix of $\tilde{\beta}$, we note that by substituting for w in (4.1.48) we find

$$\tilde{\beta} = \beta + (Z'Z)^{-1}Z'v \qquad (4.1.50)$$

and thus

$$\text{Cov}(\tilde{\beta}) = (Z'Z)^{-1} = (X'R'^{-1}R^{-1}X)^{-1} = (X'\Sigma^{-1}X)^{-1} \qquad \text{Q.E.D.}$$
$$(4.1.51)$$

Corollary 1: Suppose that the conditions of Theorem 3 hold. Then the OLS estimator of β is unbiased and consistent but inefficient.

PROOF: The OLS estimator is given by

$$\hat{\beta} = (X'X)^{-1}X'y = \beta + (X'X)^{-1}X'u \tag{4.1.52}$$

Evaluating its expectation, we find

$$E(\hat{\beta}) = \beta + (X'X)^{-1}X'E(u) = \beta \tag{4.1.53}$$

Evaluating its probability limit, we find

$$\plim_{T \to \infty} (\hat{\beta} - \beta) = \plim_{T \to \infty} \left[\left(\frac{X'X}{T} \right)^{-1} \left(\frac{X'u}{T} \right) \right] \tag{4.1.54}$$

If, as we assume, the elements of X are nonrandom, then the right-hand side becomes

$$\plim_{T \to \infty} \left[\left(\frac{X'X}{T} \right)^{-1} \frac{X'u}{T} \right] = \lim_{T \to \infty} \left(\frac{X'X}{T} \right)^{-1} \plim_{T \to \infty} \frac{X'u}{T} \tag{4.1.55}$$

By the arguments given in the proof of Theorem 1, $\lim_{T \to \infty} (X'X/T)^{-1}$ exists and thus we need only evaluate $\plim_{T \to \infty} X'u/T$. But this is a vector whose elements are the probability limits of the cross moments between the independent variables and the error terms. Since by assumption these two sets of variables are uncorrelated, we conclude

$$\plim_{T \to \infty} \frac{X'u}{T} = 0 \tag{4.1.56}$$

Hence, from (4.1.54), we conclude

$$\plim_{T \to \infty} \hat{\beta} = \beta \tag{4.1.57}$$

This completes the proof of the corollary, for the efficient estimator was derived in (4.1.49).

Remark 2: Notice that, strictly speaking, $\tilde{\beta}$ of (4.1.49) is not an *estimator unless Σ is known*. This is so because, according to our definition (in Section 3.2 of Chapter 3), an estimator cannot depend on the unknown parameters of the problem.

The remark above motivates

Definition 1: The estimator $\tilde{\beta}$ in (4.1.42) is said to be the *Aitken estimator of β* under the hypotheses of Theorem 3. *If Σ is unknown but a consistent estimator, say $\hat{\Sigma}$, is available*, then

$$\tilde{\beta} = (X'\hat{\Sigma}^{-1}X)^{-1}X'\hat{\Sigma}^{-1}y \tag{4.1.58}$$

is said to be the *feasible Aitken estimator of β*.

Remark 3: While the distinction made above is conceptually useful, we shall not always observe it; for simplicity we shall typically be referring to the estimator in (4.1.58) as the Aitken estimator. We should also point out in this connection that a consistent estimator of Σ cannot always be obtained. This is so because if Σ is a general positive definite matrix, it will have $T(T + 1)/2$ distinct elements which *cannot be consistently estimated on the basis of T observations.* In special cases, however, it will be possible to obtain a consistent estimator of Σ if, for every sample size, its elements are well-defined functions of a *fixed finite number* of parameters.

ESTIMATION OF PARAMETERS IN MULTIPLE EQUATION (REGRESSION) MODELS

Let us generalize the preceding problem so that we consider not a single equation but rather a system of equations of the form

$$y_{ti} = \sum_{j=1}^{k} x_{tj}\beta_{ji} + u_{ti} \qquad t = 1, 2, \ldots, T, i = 1, 2, \ldots, m \qquad (4.1.59)$$

The system here contains k independent (or exogenous) variables $x_1, x_2, \ldots, x_k$ and m dependent variables $y_1, y_2, \ldots, y_m$. It might appear that all independent variables appear in *each equation* of (4.1.59) but this need not be so, for some of the β_{ji} may be known to be zero. In general, we will assume that only $k_i \le k$ independent variables appear in the ith equation.

Let us denote by $y_{.i}$ the vector of observations on the dependent variable y_i and by X_i the matrix of observations on the (k_i) independent variables *actually appearing in the ith equation.* Then the system in (4.1.59) may be written more conveniently as

$$y_{.i} = X_i\beta_{.i} + u_{.i} \qquad i = 1, 2, \ldots, m \qquad (4.1.60)$$

The vector $\beta_{.i}$ differs from $(\beta_{1i}, \beta_{2i}, \ldots, \beta_{ki})'$ in that it is the subvector of the latter resulting after deletion of elements β_{ji} *known to be zero.* Thus, in (4.1.60), $y_{.i}$ is $T \times 1$, X_i is $T \times k_i$, $\beta_{.i}$ is $k_i \times 1$, and $u_{.i}$ is $T \times 1$. Now each equation in (4.1.60) represents a general linear model of the type examined earlier. However, if all the classical assumptions of Equation (4.1.5) are made here as well, even then the stochastic specification of the system is incomplete. In particular, the classical assumptions do not specify anything concerning the correlation, if any, between random terms appearing in any two equations. Thus although we may, by analogy, specify that

$$\text{Cov}(u_{.i}) = \sigma_{ii}I \qquad (4.1.61)$$

we still need to say something about the covariance matrix of $u_{.i}$ and $u_{.j}$, $i \ne j$. The two vectors need not be uncorrelated.[4] Clearly, if

$$\text{Cov}(u_{.i}, u_{.j}) \ne 0 \qquad (4.1.62)$$

then the ith equation conveys some information about the jth equation. Thus, to treat each equation in isolation from the rest of the system means, we would conjecture, that we are not using our sample efficiently due to our disregard of information possibly conveyed by the remaining equations of the system.

---

[4] It is because of such considerations that Zellner [54] terms systems of the type exhibited in (4.1.60) "systems of seemingly unrelated regressions."

In general, since the error terms of the system may be interpreted as reflecting, in part, the impact of many relevant influences that are not individually accounted for (because presumably they are individually infinitesimal), it would be reasonable to assume that u_{ti} is *correlated* with u_{tj}. Finally, if the observations are interpreted as being a *random sample* on the *multivariate* vector $(y_1, y_2, \ldots, y_m)$, then, of course, u_{ti} is uncorrelated with, indeed independent of, $u_{t'j}$ for $t \neq t'$. Hence let us solve the estimation problem posed by the system in (4.1.60) under these assumptions. Specifically, we assume

$$\text{Cov}(u_{\cdot i}, u_{\cdot j}) = \sigma_{ij} I \qquad E(X'_j u_{\cdot i}) = 0, \qquad E(u_{\cdot i}) = 0 \qquad i, j = 1, 2, \ldots, m$$

$$(4.1.63)$$

Now there is one immediately obvious susggestion concerning the estimation of parameters in this system, namely, estimate each $\beta_{\cdot i}$ from the relevant equation by applying OLS techniques. One might ask, however: Is this an efficient procedure?

To answer this question, we shall reformulate the problem so that it becomes a special case of the problems already considered. Thus define

$$y = \begin{pmatrix} y_{\cdot 1} \\ y_{\cdot 2} \\ \vdots \\ y_{\cdot m} \end{pmatrix} \qquad X = \begin{bmatrix} X_1 & & & \\ & X_2 & & 0 \\ & 0 & & \cdot \\ & & & X_m \end{bmatrix}$$

$$\beta = \begin{pmatrix} \beta_{\cdot 1} \\ \beta_{\cdot 2} \\ \vdots \\ \beta_{\cdot m} \end{pmatrix} \qquad u = \begin{pmatrix} u_{\cdot 1} \\ u_{\cdot 2} \\ \vdots \\ u_{\cdot m} \end{pmatrix} \qquad (4.1.64)$$

Then the entire system in (4.1.60) can be written more compactly (and revealingly) as

$$y = X\beta + u \qquad (4.1.65)$$

The problem of efficient estimation of the parameter vector in (4.1.65) has already been solved in the preceding discussion; the solution hinges on the form of the covariance matrix of the error vector u. So our first task is to establish this on the basis of our assumptions in (4.1.63).

Thus

$$\text{Cov}(u) = E(uu') = E \begin{bmatrix} u_{\cdot 1} u'_{\cdot 1} & u_{\cdot 1} u'_{\cdot 2} & \cdots & u_{\cdot 1} u'_{\cdot m} \\ u_{\cdot 2} u'_{\cdot 1} & u_{\cdot 2} u'_{\cdot 2} & \cdots & u_{\cdot 2} u'_{\cdot m} \\ \vdots & \vdots & & \vdots \\ u_{\cdot m} u'_{\cdot 1} & u_{\cdot m} u'_{\cdot 2} & \cdots & u_{\cdot m} u'_{\cdot m} \end{bmatrix}$$

$$= \begin{bmatrix} \sigma_{11} I & \sigma_{12} I & \cdots & \sigma_{1m} I \\ \sigma_{21} I & \sigma_{22} I & \cdots & \sigma_{2m} I \\ \vdots & \vdots & & \vdots \\ \sigma_{m1} I & \sigma_{m2} I & \cdots & \sigma_{mm} I \end{bmatrix} \qquad (4.1.66)$$

Since each block $u._iu'._j$ is a $T \times T$ matrix, we conclude that Cov (u) is a $(Tm) \times (Tm)$ matrix.

Matrices of the type appearing in the last member of (4.1.66) will recur repeatedly in this and subsequent discussions and so we digress momentarily to discuss some of their relevant properties.

Definition 2: Let A be $m \times n$, B be $p \times q$. Then the $(mp) \times (nq)$ matrix

$$C = \begin{bmatrix} a_{11}B & a_{12}B & \cdots & a_{1m}B \\ a_{21}B & a_{22}B & \cdots & a_{2m}B \\ \vdots & \vdots & & \vdots \\ a_{m1}B & aa2_mB & \cdots & a_{mm}B \end{bmatrix} \tag{4.1.67}$$

is said to be the *Kronecker product* of the matrices A and B and is denoted by[5]

$$C = A \otimes B \tag{4.1.68}$$

First, note that by direct verification we can establish

$$(A \otimes C) \cdot (B \otimes D) = (A \cdot B) \otimes (C \cdot D) \tag{4.1.69}$$

where A is $m \times n$, B is $n \times q$, C is $p \times r$, and D is $r \times s$.

Second, if P and Q are two nonsingular matrices of order m and n, respectively, then

$$(P \otimes Q)^{-1} = P^{-1} \otimes Q^{-1} \tag{4.1.70}$$

and, finally, if M and N are two rectangular matrices, then

$$(M \otimes N)' = M' \otimes N' \tag{4.1.71}$$

The following result will also be found occasionally useful.

Lemma 1: Let A, B be two (nonsingular) square matrices of order m and n, respectively. Then

i. the characteristic roots of $A \otimes B$ are given by

$$\{v_{ij} : v_{ij} = \lambda_i \mu_j \quad i = 1, 2, \ldots, m, j = 1, 2, \ldots, n\}$$

where the λ_i are the roots of A and μ_j are the roots of B.

ii. $|A \otimes B| = |A|^n |B|^m$

iii $\text{tr}(A \otimes B) = (\text{tr } A)(\text{tr } B)$

iv. if A and B are both positive definite, then so is $A \otimes B$.

PROOF: Let x^i be the characteristic vector of A corresponding to the root λ_i

---

[5] It is important to observe that $A \otimes B \neq B \otimes A$. As an exercise, the reader may write the Kronecker product of B and A, that is, $B \otimes A$.

and y^j the characteristic vector of B corresponding to the root μ_j. Consider the vectors

$$w_{ij} = \begin{pmatrix} x_1^i y^j \\ x_2^i y^j \\ \vdots \\ x_m^j y^j \end{pmatrix} \tag{4.1.72}$$

where x_s^i is the sth element of the vector x^i.

We shall show that

$$(A \otimes B)w_{ij} = \lambda_i \mu_j w_{ij} \tag{4.1.73}$$

thus establishing that w_{ij} is the characteristic vector of $A \otimes B$ corresponding to its characteristic root $\lambda_i \mu_j$.

Now the rth (block) element of (the vector) $(A \otimes B)w_{ij}$ is given by

$$\sum_{s=1}^{m} a_{rs} x_s^i By^j = \mu_j \left(\sum_{s=1}^{m} a_{rs} x_s^i y^j \right) = \mu_j \lambda_i (x_r^i y^j) \tag{4.1.74}$$

The first equality follows, for μ_j is the characteristic root of B corresponding to the characteristic vector y^j; the second equality follows, for λ_i is the characteristic root of A corresponding to the characteristic vector x^i. Finally, the last member of (4.1.74) shows that

$$(A \otimes B)w_{ij} = \lambda_i \mu_j w_{ij} \tag{4.1.75}$$

which establishes i.

To establish ii, we note that the determinant of a matrix is equal to the product of its roots. Thus

$$|A \otimes B| = \prod_{i=1}^{m} \prod_{j=1}^{n} \lambda_i \mu_j = \prod_{i=1}^{m} \lambda_i^n \prod_{j=1}^{n} \mu_j$$

$$= \left(\prod_{i=1}^{m} \lambda_i^n \right) \left(\prod_{j=1}^{n} \mu_j \right)^m = |A|^n |B|^m \tag{4.1.76}$$

To prove iii, we note that the trace of a matrix is equal to the sum of its roots. Thus

$$\operatorname{tr}(A \otimes B) = \sum_{i=1}^{m} \sum_{j=1}^{n} \lambda_i \mu_j = \left(\sum_{i=1}^{m} \lambda_i \right) \left(\sum_{j=1}^{n} \mu_j \right) = (\operatorname{tr} A) \cdot (\operatorname{tr} B) \tag{4.1.77}$$

To establish iv, we note that a matrix is positive definite[6] if and only if all its roots are positive. Since A and B are both positive definite, we have $\lambda_i > 0$, $\mu_j > 0$ all i and j. Thus

$$v_{ij} = \lambda_i \mu_j > 0 \qquad\qquad \text{Q.E.D.} \tag{4.1.78}$$

---

[6] When we say a matrix is positive definite, it is to be understood in addition that the matrix is symmetric.

Let us return now to our estimation problem and observe that the covariance matrix of the error vector in (4.1.65) can be written as

$$\text{Cov}(u) = \Sigma \otimes I = \Phi \tag{4.1.79}$$

where

$$\Sigma = (\sigma_{ij}) \tag{4.1.80}$$

is the covariance matrix of the vector $(u_{t1}, u_{t2}, \ldots, u_{tm})'$; the elements of this vector are the error terms attaching to the individual equations of the system in (4.1.59) at time t. Since Σ is thus a positive definite matrix, so is Φ because the $T \times T$ identity matrix appearing in (4.1.79) is also positive definite. Thus our manipulations in getting from (4.1.59) to (4.1.65) have certainly produced no contradition, and we see that the system in (4.1.59) is exactly equivalent to the model we considered in connection with Theorem 3, above.

But then it is apparent that the efficient estimator of the parameters of the system in (4.1.59) is given by

$$\hat{\beta} = (X'\Phi^{-1}X)^{-1}X'\Phi^{-1}y \tag{4.1.81}$$

and, moreover, its covariance matrix is

$$\text{Cov}(\hat{\beta}) = (X'\Phi^{-1}X)^{-1} \tag{4.1.82}$$

We observe that $\hat{\beta}$ of (4.1.81) is not an estimator in the usual sense, for it contains the (generally) unknown parameters $\Sigma = (\sigma_{ij})$.

However, in contrast to the situation described in Remark 3, we now have the means of consistently estimating these unknown parameters. A feasible estimator, which is also asymptotically equivalent to that in (4.1.81), is obtained if we replace Φ there by its (consistent) estimator

$$\hat{\Phi}^{-1} = \hat{\Sigma}^{-1} \otimes I \tag{4.1.83}$$

The covariance matrix in (4.1.82) can, similarly, be consistently estimated. This is so since Φ depends only on the $m(m + 1)/2$ distinct elements of Σ even though Φ is a matrix of order Tm.

We must now produce a consistent estimator of Σ. But this is easy. Consider again the equations in (4.1.60). Each equation represents a general linear model in which the classical assumptions hold, and thus we can obtain the OLS estimator of $\beta_{\cdot i}$ as

$$\tilde{\beta}_{\cdot i} = (X_i'X_i)^{-1}X_i'y_{\cdot i} \qquad i = 1, 2, \ldots, m \tag{4.1.84}$$

Consider the least squares residuals

$$\tilde{u}_{\cdot i} = y_{\cdot i} - X_i\tilde{\beta}_{\cdot i} = [I - X_i(X_i'X_i)^{-1}X_i']u_{\cdot i} \tag{4.1.85}$$

Thus

$$\frac{\tilde{u}'_{\cdot i}\tilde{u}_{\cdot j}}{T} = \frac{u'_{\cdot i}u_{\cdot j}}{T} - \frac{u'_{\cdot i}X_i}{T}\left(\frac{X'_iX_i}{T}\right)^{-1}\frac{X'_iu_{\cdot j}}{T}$$

$$-\frac{u'_{\cdot i}X_j}{T}\left(\frac{X'_jX_j}{T}\right)^{-1}\frac{X'_ju_{\cdot j}}{T}$$

$$+\frac{u'_{\cdot i}X_i}{T}\left(\frac{X'_iX_i}{T}\right)^{-1}\frac{X'_iX_j}{T}\left(\frac{X'_jX_j}{T}\right)^{-1}\frac{X'_ju_{\cdot j}}{T} \tag{4.1.86}$$

and since we assume $\text{plim}_{T\to\infty}X'X/T$ (or $\lim_{T\to\infty}X'X/T$ as the case may be) exists as a nonsingular matrix with finite elements, we conclude that

$$\underset{T\to\infty}{\text{plim}}\frac{\tilde{u}'_{\cdot i}\tilde{u}_{\cdot j}}{T} = \sigma_{ij} \qquad i,j = 1,2,\ldots,m \tag{4.1.87}$$

This is so since the error terms are uncorrelated with the explanatory variables and thus $\text{plim}_{T\to\infty}X'_ju_{\cdot i}/T = 0$; further, $u'_{\cdot i}u_{\cdot j}/T$ is simply the "sample covariance" between the error terms in the ith and jth equations and thus converges in probability to the covariance between these two random variables, that is, σ_{ij}. Thus if we put

$$s_{ij} = \frac{\tilde{u}'_{\cdot i}\tilde{u}_{\cdot j}}{T} \qquad S = (s_{ij}) \tag{4.1.88}$$

we can take

$$\hat{\Phi} = S^{-1}\otimes I \tag{4.1.89}$$

and the estimation problem is completely solved.

Clearly, this entire (two-stage) estimation procedure is cumbersome and we are entitled to ask: Do we necessarily gain by it? Under what circumstances, if any, do we fail to materialize any gain in efficiency?

First, let us establish the nature of the gain of this procedure over the alternative of applying OLS to each equation *seriatim*. The estimator obtained by the latter procedure is equivalent to that obtained by applying OLS to the system in (4.1.65).

The OLS estimator of β in (4.1.65) is simply

$$\tilde{\beta} = (X'X)^{-1}X'y = \begin{bmatrix}(X'_1X_1)^{-1} & & & 0 \\ & (X'_2X_2)^{-1} & & \\ & & \cdot & \\ & & & \cdot \\ 0 & & & (X'_mX_m)^{-1}\end{bmatrix}\begin{pmatrix}X'_1y_{\cdot 1} \\ X'_2y_{\cdot 2} \\ \vdots \\ X'_my_{\cdot m}\end{pmatrix}$$

$$= \begin{pmatrix}\tilde{\beta}_{\cdot 1} \\ \tilde{\beta}_{\cdot 2} \\ \vdots \\ \tilde{\beta}_{\cdot m}\end{pmatrix} \tag{4.1.90}$$

This being the case, the efficiency of $\hat{\beta}$ in (4.1.81) relative to $\tilde{\beta}$ of (4.1.90) can be appraised as follows.

Write

$$(X'X)^{-1}X' = (X'\Phi^{-1}X)^{-1}X'\Phi^{-1} + B = A^{-1}X'\Phi^{-1} + B \qquad (4.1.91)$$

where $A = X'\Phi^{-1}X$, and note that (4.1.91) implies

$$BX = 0 \qquad (4.1.92)$$

Substituting for y in (4.1.90), we have

$$\begin{aligned}
\text{Cov}\,(\tilde{\beta}) &= E[(X'X)^{-1}X'uu'X(X'X)^{-1}] \\
&= E[A^{-1}X'\Phi^{-1}uu'\Phi^{-1}XA^{-1} + Buu'B + Buu'\Phi^{-1}XA^{-1} \\
&\quad + A^{-1}X'\Phi^{-1}uu'B] \\
&= A^{-1} + B\Phi B' = \text{Cov}\,(\hat{\beta}) + B\Phi B' \qquad (4.1.93)
\end{aligned}$$

The next to the last equality in (4.1.93) is valid because the expectation of the last two terms in square brackets is zero in virtue of (4.1.92).

Now (4.1.93) shows that

$$\text{Cov}\,(\tilde{\beta}) - \text{Cov}\,(\hat{\beta}) = B\Phi B' \qquad (4.1.94)$$

But $B\Phi B'$ is at least a positive semidefinite matrix. Thus, we conclude that $\hat{\beta}$ is efficient relative to $\tilde{\beta}$. Indeed by Corollary 7 of the Mathematical Appendix and Equation (4.1.94) above, we know that *unless* B is of rank zero $\hat{\beta}$ is strictly efficient relative to $\tilde{\beta}$ in the sense that the generalized variance of the former is *strictly* less than that of the latter and in the sense that at least one element of $\hat{\beta}$ has variance which is strictly less than that of the corresponding element of $\tilde{\beta}$.

Now that we have established the formal conditions under which a gain in efficiency will materialize, we are encouraged to put forth the conjecture that as an empirical matter we are unlikely to encounter situations in which the rank of B is zero unless also B is the zero matrix. In terms of (4.1.91) this means that

$$(X'X)^{-1}X' = (X'\Phi^{-1}X)^{-1}X'\Phi^{-1} \qquad (4.1.95)$$

This occurs if

$$\sigma_{ij} = 0 \qquad \text{for } i \neq j \qquad (4.1.96)$$

and thus in this case we do not gain anything by applying Aitken estimation to (4.1.65). Still, however, we ought to estimate the σ_{ii} from the OLS *residuals of each equation*, unless we can also assert that

$$\sigma_{ii} = \sigma^2 \qquad i = 1, 2, \ldots, m \qquad (4.1.97)$$

Another instance where no gain in efficiency materializes is when all m equations contain the *same (relevant) independent variables*. In such a case,

$$X_i = X^* \qquad i = 1, 2, \ldots, m \qquad (4.1.98)$$

and thus the matrix X of (4.1.64) may be written as

$$X = I \otimes X^* \qquad (4.1.99)$$

But notice

$$X'\Phi^{-1}X = (I \otimes X^*)'(\Sigma^{-1} \otimes I)(I \otimes X^*) = \Sigma^{-1} \otimes X^{*'}X^* \qquad (4.1.100)$$

Hence

$$\begin{aligned}
(X'\Phi^{-1}X)^{-1}X'\Phi^{-1} &= [\Sigma \otimes (X^{*'}X^*)^{-1}][\Sigma^{-1} \otimes X^*] \\
&= [I \otimes (X^{*'}X^*)^{-1}X^*] = (X'X)^{-1}X'
\end{aligned} \qquad (4.1.101)$$

We thus conclude that when (4.1.98) holds, no gain is obtained by the use of the Aitken estimator.

Finally, let us observe that when Σ is not known and thus we must use the estimator

$$b = (X'(S^{-1} \otimes I)X)^{-1}X'(S^{-1} \otimes I)y \qquad (4.1.102)$$

the results determined above apply asymptotically since S converges in probability to Σ.

We have therefore proved

Theorem 4: Consider the sample

$$y_{\cdot i} = X_i \beta_{\cdot i} + u_{\cdot i} \qquad i = 1, 2, \ldots, m \qquad (4.1.103)$$

on m ordinary regression models and assume the conditions in (4.1.63) to hold. Then the efficient estimator of the parameters of the model is given by

$$\hat{\beta} = (X'\Phi^{-1}X)^{-1}X'\Phi^{-1}y \qquad (4.1.104)$$

where X, y, and Φ are defined, respectively, by (4.1.64) and (4.1.79).

Its covariance matrix is given by

$$\text{Cov}\,(\hat{\beta}) = (X'\Phi^{-1}X)^{-1} \qquad (4.1.105)$$

If

$$\tilde{\beta} = (X'X)^{-1}X'y \qquad (4.1.106)$$

is the OLS estimator of the parameters, then

$$\text{Cov}\,(\tilde{\beta}) - \text{Cov}\,(\hat{\beta}) = B\Phi B' \qquad (4.1.107)$$

where B is the matrix defined in (4.1.91). Hence,[7]

$$\frac{|\text{Cov}\,(\tilde{\beta})|}{|\text{Cov}\,(\hat{\beta})|} = \prod_{i=1}^{n}(1 + \lambda_i) \qquad (4.1.108)$$

---

[7] This follows immediately from Corollary 5 of the Mathematical Appendix.

where λ_i are the roots of $B\Phi B'$ in the metric of $(X'\Phi^{-1}X)^{-1}$, and $n = \sum_{i=1}^{m} k_i$. Thus no gain in efficiency will result from the use of (4.1.104) (in the sense of Equation (4.1.107)) if and only if the rank of B is zero. In particular, if $\sigma_{ij} = 0$, $i \neq j$, or if $X_i = X^*$, all i, then $B = 0$ and the two estimators will coincide.

4.2 ASYMPTOTIC DISTRIBUTION OF AITKEN ESTIMATORS

In this section we shall consider in some detail the distribution and efficiency characteristics of the estimators derived in the preceding section.

The probability theoretic results requisite for this discussion have already been established in Chapter 3 so that this section is essentially an illustration of the use to which we can put the propositions of that chapter.

It will be useful to begin with the simplest case of the general linear model

$$y = X\beta + u \tag{4.2.1}$$

obeying the assumptions of Theorem 1 in Section 4.1. While this problem is rather trivial, nonetheless it constitutes a worthwhile exercise in determining asymptotic distributions of estimators. It will thus serve as a prelude to the more difficult problems we shall encounter subsequently. We have already established the distribution of the OLS estimator of β, say $\hat{\beta}$, when

$$u \sim N(0, \sigma^2 I) \tag{4.2.2}$$

However, if the normality assumption in (4.2.2) is dropped, then the distribution of $\hat{\beta}$ has not been established. The following theorem provides a solution to this problem.

Theorem 5: Consider the model in (4.2.1) and suppose that the elements of X are uniformly bounded and nonstochastic; suppose further that the error vector u has the property

$$E(u) = 0 \quad \mathrm{Cov}\,(u) = \sigma^2 I \quad \lim_{T \to \infty} \frac{1}{T} \sum_{t=1}^{T} \int_{|\phi| > \varepsilon\sqrt{T}} \phi^2\, dF_t(\phi) = 0 \tag{4.2.3}$$

where $F_t(\cdot)$ is the distribution function of the tth element of u and the u_t are mutually independent. Then, asymptotically,

$$\sqrt{T}(\hat{\beta} - \beta) \sim N\left[0,\ \lim_{T \to \infty} \sigma^2 \left(\frac{X'X}{T}\right)^{-1}\right] \tag{4.2.4}$$

where $\hat{\beta}$ is the OLS estimator of β.

PROOF: We observe that

$$\sqrt{T}(\hat{\beta} - \beta) = \left(\frac{X'X}{T}\right)^{-1} \frac{X'u}{\sqrt{T}} \tag{4.2.5}$$

and also that

$$\frac{X'u}{\sqrt{T}} = \frac{1}{\sqrt{T}} \sum_{t=1}^{T} x'_t \cdot u_t \tag{4.2.6}$$

We remind the reader that by our notational convention x_t. is the tth row of X and thus it is *a row vector with k elements*. Now

$$E(x'_t \cdot u_t) = 0 \qquad \mathrm{Cov}\,(x'_t \cdot u_t) = \sigma^2 x'_t \cdot x_t \cdot = \Phi_t \tag{4.2.7}$$

By the uniform boundedness of the explanatory variables and the third condition in (4.2.3), we have

$$\lim_{T \to \infty} \frac{\sum_{t=1}^{T} |x_t \cdot|^2}{T} \int_{|x_t \cdot| \, |\phi| > \varepsilon \sqrt{T}} \phi^2 \, dF_t(\phi) = 0 \tag{4.2.8}$$

Hence the conditions of Theorem 6 (Chapter 3) are fulfilled; we thus conclude that, asymptotically,

$$\frac{X'u}{\sqrt{T}} \sim N\left(0, \lim_{T \to \infty} \frac{1}{T} \sum_{t=1}^{T} \Phi_t\right) \tag{4.2.9}$$

But

$$\frac{1}{T} \sum_{t=1}^{T} \Phi_t = \sigma^2 \frac{1}{T} \sum_{t=1}^{T} x'_t \cdot x_t \cdot = \sigma^2 \left(\frac{X'X}{T}\right) \tag{4.2.10}$$

From (4.2.5), we have

$$\sqrt{T}(\hat{\beta} - \beta) \sim N\left[0, \sigma^2 \lim_{T \to \infty} \left(\frac{X'X}{T}\right)^{-1}\right] \qquad \text{Q.E.D.} \tag{4.2.11}$$

Remark 4: The third condition in (4.2.3) really refers to the *uniform* convergence of the variance integral of the error terms. If the $\{u_t : t = 1, 2, \ldots\}$ are identically distributed, this is obviously satisfied. If not, this condition is needed in the proof of the appropriate central limit theorem. Since no identical distribution assumption has been made in (4.2.3), the theorem we have just proved applies to a slightly more general class of problems. Notice that if the normality assumption is made, then the elements of the sequence $\{u_t : t = 1, 2, \ldots\}$ are identically distributed so that the third condition in (4.2.3) holds automatically. Actually, more is true in that case, as the following theorem shows.

Theorem 6: Consider the general linear model of (4.2.1) and suppose all assumptions in Theorem 5 hold except that the conditions in (4.2.3) are replaced by

$$u \sim N(0, \sigma^2 I) \tag{4.2.12}$$

Then the OLS estimator of β, say $\hat{\beta}$, is asymptotically an MVB (minimum variance bound) estimator.

PROOF: Under the hypotheses of the theorem, $\hat{\beta}$ is an ML estimator of β. Moreover, if we put

$$\theta = \begin{pmatrix} \beta \\ \sigma^2 \end{pmatrix} \tag{4.2.13}$$

and if θ^1 is *any* (CUAN)[8] estimator of θ, then the multivariate Cramer-Rao inequality—Lemma 16 of Chapter 3—implies that

$$V^* = V - M \tag{4.2.14}$$

is a positive semidefinite matrix, where V is the (asymptotic) covariance matrix of θ^1. Thus M forms a lower bound for the covariance matrix of all *possible* (*and not merely linear*) *estimators* of β. In this case, M is given by

$$M = \sigma^2 \lim_{T \to \infty} \begin{bmatrix} \dfrac{X'X}{T} & 0 \\ 0 & \dfrac{T+2}{2T} \end{bmatrix}^{-1} \tag{4.2.15}$$

Thus the lowest bound for *any* estimator of β is given by

$$\sigma^2 \lim_{T \to \infty} \left(\frac{X'X}{T} \right)^{-1}$$

But this is precisely the asymptotic covariance matrix of $\sqrt{T}(\hat{\beta} - \beta)$ Q.E.D.

Remark 5: The result above indicates that when the error terms of a general linear model obey (4.2.12), then the OLS estimator of β, is not only BLUE, but in fact attains the bound of the multivariate Cramer-Rao inequality.

Let us now examine the asymptotic distribution of Aitken estimators. We shall not consider the model dealt with in Theorem 3, for typically in such a case a consistent estimator for the $(T \times T)$ covariance matrix will not exist.

Theorem 7: Consider the model of (4.1.65), (4.1.64), and (4.1.66); assume further that the elements of the matrices $X_i, i = 1, 2, \ldots, m$ are uniformly bounded and nonstochastic.

Define the matrix

$$U = (u_{\cdot 1}, u_{\cdot 2}, \ldots, u_{\cdot m}) \tag{4.2.16}$$

and let $u_{t \cdot}$ be its tth row. If for every $\varepsilon > 0$,

$$\lim_{T \to \infty} \frac{1}{T} \sum_{t=1}^{T} \int_{|\phi| > \varepsilon \sqrt{T}} |\phi|^2 \, dF_t(\phi) = 0 \tag{4.2.17}$$

---

[8] For an explanation of this term the reader should refer to Definition 17 of Chapter 3 and the discussion following.

and the u_t. are mutually independent, then, asymptotically,

$$\sqrt{T}(\hat{\beta} - \beta) \sim N\left[0, \lim_{T \to \infty} \left(\frac{X'\Phi^{-1}X}{T}\right)^{-1}\right] \qquad (4.2.18)$$

where $F_t(\cdot)$ is the distribution function of u_t.

$$\hat{\beta} = (X'\Phi^{-1}X)^{-1}X'\Phi^{-1}y \qquad (4.2.19)$$

and

$$\Phi = \Sigma \otimes I_T \quad \Sigma = \text{Cov}(u'_t.) \qquad \text{for all } t \qquad (4.2.20)$$

PROOF: From (4.1.65) and (4.2.19), we find

$$\sqrt{T}(\hat{\beta} - \beta) = \left(\frac{X'\Phi^{-1}X}{T}\right)^{-1} \frac{X'\Phi^{-1}u}{\sqrt{T}} \qquad (4.2.21)$$

Since by assumption

$$\lim_{T \to \infty} \left(\frac{X'\Phi^{-1}X}{T}\right)^{-1}$$

exists as a finite nonsingular matrix, we need only be concerned with $X'\Phi^{-1}u/\sqrt{T}$. We observe that this is a $(\sum_{i=1}^{m} k_i)$-dimensional column vector.

Let $c_s^{(i)}$ be the sth *column* of X'_i, $\sigma^{k\cdot}$ the kth *row* of Σ^{-1}, and define the $(k_i \times m)$ matrices

$$V_s^{(i)} = c_s^{(i)}\sigma^{i\cdot} \qquad i = 1, 2, \ldots, m \qquad (4.2.22)$$

Let

$$V_s = \begin{pmatrix} V_s^{(1)} \\ V_s^{(2)} \\ \vdots \\ V_s^{(m)} \end{pmatrix} \qquad (4.2.23)$$

and notice that

$$\frac{X'\Phi^{-1}u}{\sqrt{T}} = \frac{1}{\sqrt{T}} \sum_{s=1}^{T} V_s u'_s. \qquad (4.2.24)$$

Since, by hypothesis, the random vectors $u'_s.$, $s = 1, 2, \ldots, T$, are mutually independent, the column vectors $V_s u'_s.$ are also mutually independent and have the properties

$$E(V_s u'_s.) = 0 \qquad \text{Cov}(V_s u'_s.) = V_s \Sigma V'_s \qquad (4.2.25)$$

It is also easily verified that $1/\sqrt{T}V_s u'_s.$ satisfies a condition similar to that in (4.2.17).

Now we need to determine what is $\lim_{T\to\infty} \sum_{s=1}^{T} V_s \Sigma V_s'/T$. But it is a simple matter to verify directly that

$$\frac{1}{T} \sum_{s=1}^{T} V_s \Sigma V_s' = \frac{1}{T}(X'\Phi^{-1}X) \qquad (4.2.26)$$

Hence by the multivariate central limit theorem (Theorem 6 of Chapter 3), we conclude that asymptotically

$$\frac{X'\Phi^{-1}u}{\sqrt{T}} \sim N\left(0, \lim_{T\to\infty} \frac{X'\Phi^{-1}X}{T}\right) \qquad (4.2.27)$$

In view of (4.2.21), we thus conclude that asymptotically

$$\sqrt{T}(\hat{\beta} - \beta) \sim N\left[0, \lim_{T\to\infty} \left(\frac{X'\Phi^{-1}X}{T}\right)^{-1}\right] \qquad \text{Q.E.D.}$$
$$(4.2.28)$$

We now turn to the more interesting case of the feasible Aitken estimator of the parameters of the model. Hence we prove

Lemma 2: Consider the model of the previous theorem and the estimator

$$\tilde{\beta} = (X'\hat{\Phi}^{-1}X)^{-1}X'\hat{\Phi}^{-1}y \qquad (4.2.29)$$

where

$$\hat{\Phi}^{-1} = S^{-1} \otimes I \qquad (4.2.30)$$

and S is as defined in (4.1.88).

The asymptotic distribution of $\sqrt{T}(\tilde{\beta} - \beta)$ is identical with that of $\sqrt{T}(\hat{\beta} - \beta)$.

PROOF: By definition, the asymptotic distribution of $\sqrt{T}(\tilde{\beta} - \beta)$ is the distribution of the random variable to which the sequence converges. Further, if $\sqrt{T}(\tilde{\beta} - \beta)$ converges in probability to a random variable, say z, then it also converges to z in distribution, (see Lemma 3 of Chapter 3). Thus we shall show that

$$\plim_{T\to\infty} \sqrt{T}(\tilde{\beta} - \beta) = \plim_{T\to\infty} \sqrt{T}(\hat{\beta} - \beta) \qquad (4.2.31)$$

where $\hat{\beta}$ is the estimator studied in the previous theorem. Now

$$\sqrt{T}(\tilde{\beta} - \beta) = \left(\frac{X'\hat{\Phi}^{-1}X}{T}\right)^{-1} \frac{X'\hat{\Phi}^{-1}y}{\sqrt{T}} \qquad (4.2.32)$$

Since $\hat{\Phi}$ is a consistent estimator of Φ, we have

$$\plim_{T\to\infty} \sqrt{T}(\tilde{\beta} - \beta) = \lim_{T\to\infty} \left(\frac{X'\Phi^{-1}X}{T}\right)^{-1} \plim_{T\to\infty} \frac{X'\Phi^{-1}y}{\sqrt{T}} \qquad (4.2.33)$$

$$= \plim_{T\to\infty} \sqrt{T}(\hat{\beta} - \beta)$$

By Theorem 7, we thus conclude that, asymptotically

$$\sqrt{T}(\tilde{\beta} - \beta) \sim N\left[0, \lim_{T \to \infty} \left(\frac{X'\Phi^{-1}X}{T}\right)^{-1}\right]$$

Q.E.D.

(4.2.34)

Remark 6: It should be pointed out that if in the above it is assumed that the joint distribution of the error terms in all equations is normal, that is, if

$$u_t'. \sim N(0, \Sigma) \qquad \text{all } t \tag{4.2.35}$$

then the condition (4.2.17) is *not* needed to establish the asymptotic normality of $\sqrt{T}(\hat{\beta} - \beta)$. Indeed, under these assumptions we have that, for *every sample size T*,

$$\hat{\beta} \sim N[\beta, (X'\Phi^{-1}X)^{-1}] \tag{4.2.36}$$

Hence, asymptotically,

$$\sqrt{T}(\hat{\beta} - \beta) \sim N\left[0, \lim_{T \to \infty} \left(\frac{X'\Phi^{-1}X}{T}\right)^{-1}\right] \tag{4.2.37}$$

It would then follow by Lemma 2 that, asymptotically,

$$\sqrt{T}(\tilde{\beta} - \beta) \sim N\left[0, \lim_{T \to \infty} \left(\frac{X'\Phi^{-1}X}{T}\right)^{-1}\right] \tag{4.2.38}$$

Of course, the small sample distribution of $\tilde{\beta}$ is not easily established.

Remark 7: Before concluding this section, we ought to point out two obvious consequences of the preceding. First, a consistent estimator of the covariance matrix of the asymptotic distribution of $\sqrt{T}(\tilde{\beta} - \beta)$ is easily obtained as $(X'\hat{\Phi}^{-1}X/T)^{-1}$.

Second, if tests of significance are to be conducted on elements of the estimated parameter vector β, then such tests are to be based on the *normal* or *chi-square* distribution as the case may be, *not* on the t distribution. This is so since the distribution results obtained are asymptotic ones. Hence we have no other basis for conducting tests of significance *except that provided by asymptotic results*. Thus, for example, if $\beta^{(s)}$ is the sth element of β and q_{ss} is the sth diagonal element of $(X'\hat{\Phi}^{-1}X/T)^{-1}$, then, asymptotically,

$$\frac{\sqrt{T}(\tilde{\beta}^{(s)} - \beta^{(s)})}{q_{ss}} \sim N(0, 1) \tag{4.2.39}$$

If we cannot invoke asymptotic results, then it is not clear what the distribution of the quantity in (4.2.39) is. There is no justification whatsoever for using the t distribution. Further, if one did, one would have little indication as to what degrees of freedom to attach to that distribution. Fortunately, for moderately large degrees of freedom parameter, the t distribution is well approximated by the normal distribution. Nonetheless, one ought to be very clearly aware of this aspect of large sample inference theory in such models.

4.3 TWO-STAGE LEAST SQUARES (2SLS)

MOTIVATION AND NOTATIONAL CONVENTIONS

In the general linear model, one deals with a situation in which the explanatory variables of the relation are either nonstochastic or at least independent of the error term. Frequently (perhaps typically) in econometrics we are interested in the parameters of a relation in which, by the nature of the economic process we describe, that assumption cannot hold. What sort of problems does this entail and how can we cope with them? These are essentially the issues we shall consider in this and subsequent sections. Perhaps an example will elucidate the nature of the problems involved. Thus suppose we have the simplest possible model of any economy, namely, the simplified Keynesian system

$$C_t = \alpha + \beta Y_t + u_t \tag{4.3.1}$$

$$Y_t = C_t + A_t \tag{4.3.2}$$

The first equation gives the consumption function, while the second states the national income identity. In the model C_t, Y_t, A_t are, respectively, consumption, income, and investment at time t; u_t is an error term having, say, the standard specification

$$E(u_t) = 0 \quad E(u_t u_{t'}) = \delta_{tt'}\sigma^2 \qquad \text{all } t, t' \tag{4.3.3}$$

where $\delta_{tt'}$ is the Kronecker delta.

In (4.3.1), β is the marginal propensity to consume parameter. Thus β is a crucial parameter, and we are particularly concerned with the problem of estimating it as efficiently as the data permit.

In this simplified model, we may take investment, A_t, as exogenously determined and thus independent of the error term u_t.

Now it may be thought that, since (4.3.2) does not contain any parameters, we may disregard it and thus obtain estimators of the parameters of (4.3.1) by OLS. This certainly appears to be very straightforward. Before we begin using such estimated coefficients for policy (or other) purposes, we ought to at least ask ourselves. If we apply OLS to (4.3.1), what are the properties of the resulting estimators?

If we have a sample of size T, then the OLS estimators of α and β are given by

$$\hat{\beta} = \beta + \frac{\sum_{t=1}^{T} y_t(u_t - \bar{u})}{\sum_{t=1}^{T} y_t^2}, \qquad \hat{\alpha} = \bar{C} - \hat{\beta}\bar{Y} \tag{4.3.4}$$

where $\bar{Y}$, $\bar{C}$ are respectively the sample means of income and consumption and $y_t = Y_t - \bar{Y}$, $c_t = C_t - \bar{C}$.

Thus

$$\text{plim}_{T \to \infty} \hat{\beta} = \beta + \frac{\text{plim}_{T \to \infty} \dfrac{\sum_{t=1}^{T} y_t(u_t - \bar{u})}{T}}{\text{plim}_{T \to \infty} \dfrac{\sum_{t=1}^{T} y_t^2}{T}} \tag{4.3.5}$$

The numerator probability limit is that of the *sample covariance* between Y_t and u_t; the denominator probability limit is that of the *sample variance of Y_t*. Since sample moments converge in probability to the corresponding population moments, we need to determine the variance of Y_t and the covariance between Y_t and u_t.

In order to do that, we need to say something about investment. Thus suppose that

$$\lim_{T \to \infty} \frac{1}{T} \sum_{t=1}^{T} (A_t - \bar{A})^2 = \sigma_A^2 \tag{4.3.6}$$

where

$$\bar{A} = \frac{1}{T} \sum_{t=1}^{T} A_t \tag{4.3.7}$$

The quantity σ_A^2 may be thought of as the "variance" of investment; if A_t is random and the operator $\lim_{T \to \infty}$ is replaced by $\text{plim}_{T \to \infty}$, then σ_A^2 will, indeed, be the variance of investment. Now, solving (4.3.1) and (4.3.2) for Y_t, we obtain

$$Y_t = \frac{\alpha}{1 - \beta} + \frac{1}{1 - \beta} A_t + \frac{u_t}{1 - \beta} \tag{4.3.8}$$

Thus

$$\text{Var}(Y_t) = \frac{\sigma_A^2 + \sigma^2}{(1 - \beta)^2} \qquad \text{Cov}(Y_t u_t) = \frac{\sigma^2}{1 - \beta} \tag{4.3.9}$$

From (4.3.5) we find

$$\text{plim}_{T \to \infty} \hat{\beta} = \beta + \frac{\sigma^2/1 - \beta}{(\sigma_A^2 + \sigma^2)/(1 - \beta)^2} = \beta + \frac{1 - \beta}{1 + (\sigma_A^2/\sigma^2)} \tag{4.3.10}$$

Since

$$\frac{1 - \beta}{1 + (\sigma_A^2/\sigma^2)} > 0$$

we see that the probability limit of $\hat{\beta}$ exceeds β, thus showing the *inconsistency* of the OLS estimator of the marginal propensity to consume. This estimator will be consistent only if $\sigma_A^2 = \infty$, which is, of course, a rather peculiar and unacceptable requirement.

How is it that such a serious problem arises? A look at the system (4.3.1) and (4.3.2) will disclose the source of the difficulty. Notice that Y_t explicitly depends on C_t, and hence on u_t, and that in fact Y_t and C_t are *mutually determined* in terms of the exogenous investment A_t and the error term u_t. But if Y_t and C_t are subject to the same disturbance, we can hardly expect to obtain estimators of α and β having desirable properties by simply regressing C_t on Y_t. In no way can we consider $\alpha + \beta Y_t$ as the "systematic part" of C_t in the context of the model. In fact, Y_t is itself determined in another part of the system—equation (4.3.2)—in which C_t enters as a determining variable.

It is problems of this type that we consider in the theory of simultaneous equations estimation. In any general equilibrium (or even a sectoral equilibrium) model, a number of explanatory variables in one equation are themselves "determined" by another equation (or equations) of the system. In such a system, ordinary least squares techniques fail and we need to establish alternative techniques that yield at least consistent and possibly efficient estimators. Indeed, equations (4.3.1) and (4.3.2) represent a particularly simple simultaneous equations model, that is, one in which a number of variables of interest, here C_t and Y_t, are mutually and simultaneously determined. In (4.3.1) and (4.3.2), we have three types of variables. First, u_t, which is a random variable and concerning which nothing more can be said except to specify some of the moments and perhaps the form of its distribution. Second, we have variables such as A_t (investment), which is by assumption *not* determined within the system; such variables are called *exogenous*; that is, the "explanation" for their behavior resides outside the system and thus insofar as the latter is concerned they may be taken as *given*.

The statistical counterpart of the preceding (economic theory) argument is that exogenous variables are independent of the random terms of the system or minimally uncorrelated with them. Thus we (minimally) assert with respect to exogenous variables

$$E(A_t u_t) = 0 \qquad t = 1, 2, \ldots, T \tag{4.3.11}$$

Finally, there are variables such as C_t and Y_t (consumption and income), whose behavior is "explained" or determined by the operation of the system. These are termed *jointly dependent* or *endogenous* variables. The statistical property that characterizes an endogenous variable is that it is (at least contemporaneously) correlated with the error terms of the system. Thus, in the present system, if we solve completely we shall obtain

$$C_t = \frac{\alpha}{1-\beta} + \frac{\beta}{1-\beta} A_t + \frac{1}{1-\beta} u_t$$

$$Y_t = \frac{\alpha}{1-\beta} + \frac{1}{1-\beta} A_t + \frac{1}{1-\beta} u_t \tag{4.3.12}$$

and so

$$E(C_t u_t) = \frac{\sigma^2}{1-\beta} \qquad E(Y_t u_t) = \frac{\sigma^2}{1-\beta} \tag{4.3.13}$$

Now, suppose that we slightly revise the model to read

$$C_t = \alpha + \gamma Y_{t-1} + u_t$$
$$Y_t = C_t + A_t \tag{4.3.14}$$

This differs from (4.3.1) in the way in which the jointly dependent variables interact with each other. Notice that although C_t and Y_t are *still simultaneously determined by the system*, we have the special situation in which C_t *serves to determine* Y_t *but* Y_t *does not serve to determine* C_t. By the fundamental definition of endogeneity given above, both C_t and Y_t are endogenous. Still, there is a logical distinction between them in the sense that we can determine C_t without reference to Y_t, and having done so we can then determine Y_t. Such systems are called *recursive*. We shall return to them at a later stage and study them in somewhat greater detail.

But beyond that we have in (4.3.14) another novel aspect. In its first equation, we have Y_{t-1} as an explanatory variable. At first it might appear that this is merely an insignificant detail insofar as the estimation problem is concerned. This is, however, not so at all. To appreciate the significance of this, recall that one of the assumptions involved in the proof of consistency for OLS estimators was that *explanatory variables are uncorrelated with the* error terms. In the present case, this would read

$$E(u_t Y_{t-1}) = 0 \tag{4.3.15}$$

Is (4.3.15) in fact valid? Well, this depends on what we assume (or is in fact true) about the error terms. If we make the customary assumption

$$E(u_t u_{t'}) = \delta_{tt'} \sigma^2 \tag{4.3.16}$$

then (4.3.15) will indeed be a valid equation. This is so because if we solve the system in (4.3.14), we shall obtain

$$C_t = \frac{\gamma}{1-\gamma} + \sum_{i=1}^{\infty} \gamma^i A_{t-i} + \sum_{i=0}^{\infty} \gamma^i u_{t-i}$$

$$Y_t = \frac{\alpha}{1-\gamma} + \sum_{i=0}^{\infty} \gamma^i A_{t-i} + \sum_{i=0}^{\infty} \gamma^i u_{t-i} \tag{4.3.17}$$

We see, therefore, that Y_{t-1} depends on $u_{t-1}, u_{t-2}, u_{t-3}, \ldots$, but *not on* u_t. By (4.3.16), we conclude that (4.3.15) is indeed valid.

The import of the preceding discussion is that, in this simple recursive model, we can apply OLS and still obtain consistent estimators for α and γ.

We must caution the reader, however, that this is not generally true; it is crucially dependent on the assumptions we make about the error terms—or more precisely on their true stochastic structure. For example, if the error terms u_t obey

$$u_t = \varepsilon_t + \rho\varepsilon_{t-1} \tag{4.3.18}$$

where the ε_t are mutually uncorrelated, then u_t would be correlated with u_{t-1} and *hence* with Y_{t-1}. Thus OLS *would not produce consistent estimators* for α and γ. On the other hand, if Y_{t-2} were to be substituted for Y_{t-1} in (4.3.14), then OLS *would produce consistent estimators*.

In general, if u_t is correlated with $u_{t-i} \, i = 1, 2, \ldots, k$ but is uncorrelated with u_{t-i} for $i > k$, then if in (4.3.14) we enter, for example, Y_{t-k-1} as the explanatory variable, we could still obtain consistent estimators for α and γ. Variables such as Y_{t-i}, for $i \geq 1$, are determined by the system but at a time *prior to time t*; they are termed *lagged endogenous variables*. The class of *lagged endogenous and exogenous variables* is termed that of the *predetermined variables* in that the value assumed by such variables is *not determined by the system at time t*.

In general, the equations of a structural system are of three types.

i. Identities: these are equations that express essentially definitions. Thus in a simple aggregative model, income is defined as the sum of consumption and saving. Or the wage bill is equal to employment times the wage rate and so on.
ii. Technical or institutional equations: these originate in the technology or the legal framework of the economy. Thus, for example, the production function connects inputs and outputs in a manner specified by the current technology. Or gasoline tax proceeds are equal to the unit tax times the gallons sold. This is a relation that originates in the legal framework of the economy, which determines the *tax rate*.
iii. Behavioral equations: these purport to describe the manner in which certain individuals in the economy behave. Thus the consumption function or the various marginal productivity conditions purport to describe the manner in which individuals and firms behave, respectively, in relation to their consumption and factor employment policies.

Typically, equations of types ii and iii are written as *stochastic*, while those of type i are written as *nonstochastic*.

The preceding discussion had the purpose of establishing a terminology formalized in

Definition 3: Let the operation of an economic system be (at least approximately) characterized at time t by

$$y_{ti} = \sum_{j=1}^{m} y_{tj}\beta_{ji}^{*} + \sum_{s=1}^{G} x_{ts}\gamma_{si}^{*} + u_{ti} \qquad i = 1, 2, \ldots, m \tag{4.3.19}$$

it being understood that some of the β_{ji}^*, γ_{si}^* may be known to be zero; in particular, β_{ii}^*, $i = 1, 2, \ldots, m$, are known to be zero.

Suppose that the following conditions are satisfied:

$$E(u_{ti}) = 0 \quad E(u_{ti}u_{t'j}) = \delta_{tt'}\sigma_{ij} \quad E(x_{ti}u_{tj}) = 0 \qquad \text{all } i, j, t, \text{ and } t' \qquad (4.3.20)$$

and that the system (4.3.19) *uniquely determines* the y_{ti}, $i = 1, 2, \ldots, m$, in terms of the x_{ts}, $s = 1, 2, \ldots, G$ and the disturbances u_{ti}, $i = 1, 2, \ldots, m$. Then the variables $y_i : i = 1, 2, \ldots, m$ (y_{ti} is the tth observation on y_i) are referred to as the *jointly dependent* or *endogenous* variables, and, in general, have the property

$$E(y_{ti}u_{tj}) \neq 0 \qquad i, j = 1, 2, \ldots, m \tag{4.3.21}$$

Further, the $x_s : s = 1, 2, \ldots, G$ (x_{ts} is the tth observation on x_s) are said to be the *predetermined* variables and have the property

$$E(x_{ts}u_{tj}) = 0 \qquad s = 1, 2, \ldots, G, j = 1, 2, \ldots, m \tag{4.3.22}$$

Some of the x_s may be *lagged endogenous* variables. For example, suppose $x_{t2} = y_{t-r, 5}$; that is, it is y_5 lagged r periods; others may be *exogenous in the sense that no matter what the stochastic specification of the error terms, (4.3.22) holds.*

Remark 8: In a statistical sense, it would appear more economical of terminology to term *exogenous* the variables for which (4.3.22) holds, given the specification of the error term probability structure. Surely this is the only relevant consideration in an estimation context. We shall, however, preserve the distinction between *endogenous*, *lagged endogenous*, and *exogenous* variables.

Let us return now to the system in (4.3.19) and consider the problem of estimating its parameters from a sample of size T. In any concrete model of interest, we will typically know that some of the β_{ji}^* and the γ_{si}^* will be zero; for the moment, let us focus our attention on only one equation in (4.3.19), say the first. In general, that equation will contain as explanatory variables, some current endogenous variables, say m_1, and some predetermined ones, say G_1 where $m_1 < m$, $G_1 \leq G$. To keep our notation simple, let us agree to number current endogenous variables in such a way that those appearing as *explanatory variables in the first equation* are numbered $y_2, y_3, \ldots, y_{m_1+1}$; the dependent variable is, of course, numbered y_1. Similarly, we shall number the predetermined variables in such a way that those appearing as *explanatory variables in the first equation* are numbered $x_1, x_2, \ldots, x_{G_1}$.

With this convention in mind, we can write the T observations on the first equation as

$$y_{\cdot 1} = Y_1 \beta_{\cdot 1} + X_1 \gamma_{\cdot 1} + u_{\cdot 1} \tag{4.3.23}$$

where the notation $y_{.i}$ refers to the $T \times 1$ vector of observations on the current endogenous variable y_i. Thus the columns of Y_1 are $y_{.2}, y_{.3}, \ldots, y_{.m_1+1}$. Similarly, the columns of X_1 are $x_{.1}, x_{.2}, \ldots, x_{.G_1}$, where $x_{.j}$ is the $T \times 1$ column of observations on the predetermined variable x_j. Evidently $u_{.1}$ is the $T \times 1$ column of disturbances appearing in the first equation. The vector $\beta_{.1}$ is the subvector of

$$\beta_{.1}^* = (\beta_{11}^*, \beta_{21}^*, \ldots, \beta_{m1}^*)' \tag{4.3.24}$$

which results after we *delete* from the latter the *elements known to be zero*.

Similarly, $\gamma_{.1}$ is the subvector of

$$\gamma_{.1}^* = (\gamma_{11}^*, \gamma_{21}^*, \ldots, \gamma_{G1}^*)' \tag{4.3.25}$$

which results after we *delete* from the latter the *elements known to be zero*.

As a result of our convention, we may write all T observations on the model appearing in (4.3.19) as

$$Y = YB^* + XC^* + U \tag{4.3.26}$$

where

$$
\begin{aligned}
Y &= (y_{.1}, y_{.2}, \ldots, y_{.m_1+1}, \ldots, y_{.m}) = (y_{.1}, Y_1, y_{.m_1+2}, \ldots, y_{.m}) \\
X &= (X_1, x_{.G_1+1}, \ldots, x_{.G}) \\
B^* &= (\beta_{ji}^*) \qquad C^* = (\gamma_{si}^*) \\
U &= (u_{.1}, u_{.2}, \ldots, u_{.m_1+1}, \ldots, u_{.m})
\end{aligned} \tag{4.3.27}
$$

If the system in (4.3.26) does, according to Definition 3, determine uniquely the values of the current endogenous variables in terms of the predetermined and random variables of the system, then the matrix $I - B^*$ must be nonsingular.

Thus the system may be solved to yield

$$Y = XC^*(I - B^*)^{-1} + U(I - B^*)^{-1} \tag{4.3.28}$$

If we put

$$C^*(I - B^*)^{-1} = \Pi \quad (I - B^*)^{-1} = D \quad UD = V \tag{4.3.29}$$

we may write (4.3.28) in the compact notation

$$Y = X\Pi + V \tag{4.3.30}$$

In terms of the above, we have

Definition 4: Let the operation of an economic system be described by the equations in (4.3.19). Such a system is said to be a system of *structural equations*. If the system is such that the predetermined variables (together with the errors) *uniquely determine the current endogenous variables*, then the system may be solved as in (4.3.30). The latter set of equations is said to be a *reduced form system*.

Remark 9: The statistical difference between a *reduced form* and a *structural system* is that in the former only *predetermined* variables appear as explanatory variables, whereas in the latter *current endogenous variables* may (and typically do) appear as explanatory ones.

In a fundamental economic sense, the property that characterizes a *structural system* is the (truth of the) assertion that it describes accurately (or adequately) the precise fashion in which all the current endogenous and predetermined variables mutually interact within the specified economic system. Thus, as of a given moment of time, observations on the system represent the result of such interaction. A reduced form system, on the other hand, gives only a partial view of that interaction, for it merely describes the way in which the *predetermined* variables serve to influence the behavior of the *current endogenous* variables, after all interactions amongst jointly dependent variables have been allowed for. For an extended discussion of this matter the interested reader may consult Koopmans and Hood [30], especially Section 6.1.

INCONSISTENCY OF ORDINARY LEAST SQUARES (OLS) ESTIMATORS FOR STRUCTURAL PARAMETERS

With notational matters aside, let us consider the problem of estimating the parameters of one of the equations of the system in (4.3.26), say the first, subject to the stochastic specifications made on the columns of U.

We may write the first equation in the somewhat more convenient form

$$y_{.1} = Z_1 \delta_{.1} + u_{.1} \tag{4.3.31}$$

where

$$Z_1 = (Y_1, X_1) \qquad \delta_{.1} = \begin{pmatrix} \beta_{.1} \\ \gamma_{.1} \end{pmatrix} \tag{4.3.32}$$

The OLS estimator of $\delta_{.1}$ is given by

$$\tilde{\delta}_{.1} = (Z_1' Z_1)^{-1} Z_1' y_{.1} = \delta_{.1} + (Z_1' Z_1)^{-1} Z_1' u_{.1} \tag{4.3.33}$$

Since Y_1 is not uncorrelated with $u_{.1}$, we *cannot* assert that $E(\tilde{\delta}_{.1}) = \delta_{.1}$; indeed, the expected value of $\tilde{\delta}_{.1}$ may not even exist. Hence the OLS estimator of the parameters of a structural equation is, in general, a *biased* one.

Is it at least consistent?[9] To answer this question, we examine the probability limit of the second term in the last member of (4.3.33). Thus we wish to evaluate

$$\operatorname*{plim}_{T \to \infty} \left[\left(\frac{Z_1' Z_1}{T} \right)^{-1} \frac{Z_1' u_{.1}}{T} \right] = \operatorname*{plim}_{T \to \infty} \begin{bmatrix} \dfrac{Y_1' Y_1}{T} & \dfrac{Y_1' X_1}{T} \\ \dfrac{X_1' Y_1}{T} & \dfrac{X_1' X_1}{T} \end{bmatrix}^{-1} \operatorname*{plim}_{T \to \infty} \begin{pmatrix} \dfrac{Y_1' u_{.1}}{T} \\ \dfrac{X_1' u_{.1}}{T} \end{pmatrix} \tag{4.3.34}$$

---

[9] In the preceding discussion we had actually answered the question in the negative in the simple Keynesian model considered there. It will, however, be pedagogically useful to examine this question in the context of a general model.

Consider the first matrix first. From the reduced form in (4.3.30) we conclude that

$$Y_1 = X\Pi_1 + V_1 \tag{4.3.35}$$

where Π_1 consists of the second, third, $\ldots$, $(m_1 + 1)$st columns of Π. Similarly,

$$V_1 = UD_1 \tag{4.3.36}$$

where D_1 consists of the second, third, $\ldots$, $(m_1 + 1)$st columns of $D = (I - B^*)^{-1}$ as defined in (4.3.29). Now

$$\frac{Y_1'Y_1}{T} = \frac{\Pi_1'X'X\Pi_1}{T} + \frac{V_1'X}{T}\Pi_1 + \Pi_1'\frac{X'V_1}{T} + D_1'\frac{U'U}{T}D_1 \tag{4.3.37}$$

But since the predetermined variables are uncorrelated with the error terms in the reduced form, we conclude

$$\operatorname*{plim}_{T \to \infty} \frac{Y_1'Y_1}{T} = \Pi_1'M_1\Pi + D_1'\Sigma D_1 \tag{4.3.38}$$

where

$$M = \operatorname*{plim}_{T \to \infty} \frac{X'X}{T} \qquad \Sigma = (\sigma_{ij}) \tag{4.3.39}$$

Moreover, if we write $X = (X_1, X_2)$, then

$$\operatorname*{plim}_{T \to \infty} \frac{X'X}{T} = \operatorname*{plim}_{T \to \infty} \begin{bmatrix} \dfrac{X_1'X_1}{T} & \dfrac{X_1'X_2}{T} \\ \dfrac{X_2'X_1}{T} & \dfrac{X_2'X_2}{T} \end{bmatrix} = \begin{bmatrix} M_{11} & M_{12} \\ M_{21} & M_{22} \end{bmatrix} = M \tag{4.3.40}$$

Employing a similar argument, we conclude

$$\operatorname*{plim}_{T \to \infty} \frac{Y_1'X_1}{T} = \Pi_1'\begin{pmatrix} M_{11} \\ M_{21} \end{pmatrix} \qquad \operatorname*{plim}_{T \to \infty} \frac{X_1'Y_1}{T} = (M_{11}, M_{12})\Pi_1 \tag{4.3.41}$$

Furthermore,

$$\operatorname*{plim}_{T \to \infty} \frac{Y_1'u_{.1}}{T} = \operatorname*{plim}_{T \to \infty} \Pi_1'\frac{X'u_{.1}}{T} + \operatorname*{plim}_{T \to \infty} D_1'\frac{U'u_{.1}}{T} = D_1'\sigma_{.1} \tag{4.3.42}$$

where $\sigma_{.1}$ is the first column of Σ. This is so because

$$\operatorname*{plim}_{T \to \infty} \frac{X'u_{.1}}{T} = 0 \tag{4.3.43}$$

in view of the uncorrelatedness of the predetermined variables and the error terms. Assuming that

$$\operatorname*{plim}_{T \to \infty} \frac{Z_1'Z_1}{T}$$

exists as a *nonsingular matrix*, we can write

$$\operatorname*{plim}_{T \to \infty} \tilde{\delta}_{\cdot 1} = \delta_{\cdot 1} + \left[\begin{array}{cc} \Pi_1' M \Pi_1 + D_1' \Sigma D_1 & \Pi_1 \begin{pmatrix} M_{11} \\ M_{21} \end{pmatrix} \\ (M_{11}, M_{12}) \Pi_1 & M_{11} \end{array} \right]^{-1} \begin{pmatrix} D_1' \sigma_{\cdot 1} \\ 0 \end{pmatrix}$$

$$= \delta_{\cdot 1} + \alpha \qquad\qquad (4.3.44)$$

Sometimes the result in (4.3.44) is referred to as demonstrating the "least squares bias" of the estimator $\tilde{\delta}_{\cdot 1}$. This is a most unfortunate term, for the result there does not refer to the bias properties of the estimator—the expectation of $\tilde{\delta}_{\cdot 1}$ may not even exist—but rather to its lack of consistency. If we want to give α in (4.3.44) a name, it seems more appropriate to do so by

Definition 5: Let $\tilde{\theta}_T$ be an estimator of a relevant parameter θ (θ may be either a vector or a scalar), where T is the sample size. Suppose that

$$\operatorname*{plim}_{T = \infty} \tilde{\theta}_T = \theta^* \qquad\qquad (4.3.45)$$

Then the difference

$$i(\tilde{\theta}_T) = \theta^* - \theta \qquad\qquad (4.3.46)$$

is said to be the inconsistency of $\tilde{\theta}_T$.

In terms of Definition 5, α of (4.3.44) is the inconsistency of the OLS estimator of the parameters of a structural equation.

The preceding discussion has established

Theorem 8: Let it be desired to estimate the parameters of (4.3.31), which is one of a system of m structural equations as defined in (4.3.19) and (4.3.20). Then the OLS estimator of its parameters is generally *biased* and *inconsistent and its inconsistency is given by*

$$i(\tilde{\delta}_{\cdot 1}) = \alpha$$

where α is defined in (4.3.44).

DERIVATION OF TWO-STAGE LEAST SQUARES (2SLS) ESTIMATORS AND THEIR CONSISTENCY

We shall give here the intuitive derivation of the estimator as originally presented by one of its discoverers,[10] H. Theil [49]. We saw, in the discussion above that the essential difficulty in the failure of the OLS estimator to be consistent lies in the fact that *some* of the explanatory variables in (4.3.31) *are not uncorrelated* with the error term appearing there. This is quite obvious from (4.3.42).

---

[10] The other is R. Basmann [2].

Notice that this difficulty will *not* disappear if we assume the error terms in the various equations to be mutually uncorrelated. Even in that case

$$\operatorname*{plim}_{T \to \infty} \frac{Y_1' u._1}{T} = D_1' \begin{pmatrix} \sigma_{11} \\ 0 \\ 0 \\ \vdots \\ 0 \end{pmatrix} \tag{4.3.47}$$

which is certainly not the zero vector unless the first column of D_1' is identically zero. This *cannot* be so, however, for the latter is simply the second column of $(I - B^*)^{-1}$; this must be a *nonsingular matrix*, if, as we require, the system in (4.3.19) uniquely determines the current endogenous variables as explicit functions of the predetermined variables and the error terms of the structural system.

Since, however, this is the source of trouble, we could perhaps eliminate it as follows. From the reduced form, we note that Y_1 is the sum of two components, one random, V_1, and another nonrandom or at least independent of or uncorrelated with $u._1$, namely, $X\Pi_1$.

If we knew the matrix Π_1, then we could simply substitute in (4.3.23) $X\Pi_1$ for Y_1. Thus by using only the systematic part of Y_1, we ensure that no correlation exists between the error term and *any* of the explanatory variables appearing in that equation. This will guarantee *at least consistency*.

Unfortunately, we do not know Π_1; we *can*, however, *estimate it consistently*. Thus from the reduced form we note that we deal with a system of m_1 regression equations *all containing the same explanatory variables* and hence, by the results of Section 4.1, we conclude that the OLS estimator of Π_1 is best linear unbiased. It is also consistent. So instead of Y_1 we might use $X\tilde{\Pi}_1$, where $\tilde{\Pi}_1$ is the OLS estimator of Π_1. Thus as the sample size increases, $\tilde{\Pi}_1$ converges to Π_1 in probability and thus, it is hoped, estimators of the structural parameters will be consistent.

Let us now formalize this intuitive argument and indeed show that the resulting estimators *are* consistent.

We are dealing with the problem of estimating the vector $\begin{pmatrix} \beta._1 \\ \gamma._1 \end{pmatrix}$ in

$$y._1 = Y_1 \beta._1 + X_1 \gamma._1 + u._1 \tag{4.3.48}$$

where the meaning of symbols was defined in (4.3.23) and the ensuing discussion.

The reduced form expression of the *current endogenous variables* appearing as *explanatory variables* in (4.3.48) is

$$Y_1 = X\Pi_1 + V_1 \tag{4.3.49}$$

Now the OLS estimator of Π_1 is simply

$$\tilde{\Pi}_1 = (X'X)^{-1} X' Y_1 \tag{4.3.50}$$

Define $\tilde{V}_1$ by

$$Y_1 = X\tilde{\Pi}_1 + \tilde{V}_1 \tag{4.3.51}$$

so that $\tilde{V}_1$ is the matrix of OLS residuals in the regression of Y_1 on X. Notice that

$$X'\tilde{V}_1 = X'Y_1 - X'X(X'X)^{-1}X'Y_1 = 0 \tag{4.3.52}$$

Further,

$$\tilde{V}_1'\tilde{V}_1 = (Y_1' - \tilde{\Pi}_1' X')\tilde{V}_1 = Y_1' \tilde{V}_1 \tag{4.3.53}$$

and in view of (4.3.53),

$$(Y_1 - \tilde{V}_1)'(Y_1 - \tilde{V}_1) = Y_1'Y_1 - \tilde{V}_1'\tilde{V}_1 \tag{4.3.54}$$

Now, the equation to be estimated may be written as

$$y_{.1} = (Y_1 - \tilde{V}_1)\beta_{.1} + X_1\gamma_{.1} + u_{.1} + \tilde{V}_1 \beta_{.1} \tag{4.3.55}$$

and thus expresses $y_{.1}$ in terms of Y_1, approximately "purged" of its stochastic component V_1.

If we let

$$\tilde{Z}_1 = (Y_1 - \tilde{V}_1, X_1) \tag{4.3.56}$$

we can write (4.3.48) or (4.3.55) more compactly as

$$y_{.1} = \tilde{Z}_1 \delta_{.1} + u_{.1} + \tilde{V}_1 \beta_{.1} \tag{4.3.57}$$

The 2SLS estimator of $\delta_{.1}$ is then *the OLS estimator of $\delta_{.1}$ applied to equation* (4.3.57). Hence the term two-stage least squares; the first stage consists, so to speak, in removing $\tilde{V}_1$ from Y_1 and the second stage consists in estimating the structural parameters from (4.3.57). Thus the 2SLS estimator of $\delta_{.1}$ is

$$\hat{\delta}_{.1} = (\tilde{Z}_1'\tilde{Z}_1)^{-1}\tilde{Z}_1'y_{.1} \tag{4.3.58}$$

Substituting for $y_{.1}$ from (4.3.57), we find

$$\hat{\delta}_{.1} = \delta_{.1} + (\tilde{Z}_1'\tilde{Z}_1)^{-1}\tilde{Z}_1'u_{.1} \tag{4.3.59}$$

The term $\tilde{V}_1 \beta_{.1}$ is missing, for

$$\tilde{Z}_1'\tilde{V}_1\beta_{.1} = \begin{pmatrix} \tilde{\Pi}_1' X' \tilde{V}_1 \beta_{.1} \\ X_1' \tilde{V}_1 \beta_{.1} \end{pmatrix} = 0 \tag{4.3.60}$$

by (4.3.52).

To examine the consistency aspects of $\hat{\delta}_{.1}$, we need only evaluate the probability limit of $(\tilde{Z}_1'\tilde{Z}_1)^{-1}\tilde{Z}_1' u_{.1}$. Hence note that

$$\operatorname*{plim}_{T\to\infty} (\tilde{Z}_1'\tilde{Z}_1)^{-1}\tilde{Z}_1'u_{.1} = \operatorname*{plim}_{T\to\infty} \left(\frac{\tilde{Z}_1'\tilde{Z}_1}{T}\right)^{-1} \operatorname*{plim}_{T\to\infty} \frac{\tilde{Z}_1'u_{.1}}{T} \tag{4.3.61}$$

Thus, by (4.3.52), (4.3.53), and (4.3.54),

$$\frac{\tilde{Z}_1'\tilde{Z}_1}{T} = \begin{bmatrix} \dfrac{Y_1'Y_1}{T} - \dfrac{\tilde{V}_1'\tilde{V}_1}{T} & \dfrac{Y_1'X_1}{T} \\[3mm] \dfrac{X_1'Y_1}{T} & \dfrac{X_1'X_1}{T} \end{bmatrix} \tag{4.3.62}$$

But the probability limit of this matrix was evaluated in (4.3.44) except for the term $\tilde{V}_1'\tilde{V}_1/T$.

Now, from (4.3.53), we note that

$$\frac{\tilde{V}_1'\tilde{V}_1}{T} = \frac{Y_1'\tilde{V}_1}{T} = \frac{Y_1'Y_1}{T} - \frac{Y_1'X}{T}\left(\frac{X'X}{T}\right)^{-1}\frac{X'Y_1}{T} \tag{4.3.63}$$

But we have, in fact, already evaluated these probability limits in (4.3.38), (4.3.39), and (4.3.41). We conclude, therefore,

$$\operatorname*{plim}_{T\to\infty} \frac{\tilde{V}_1'\tilde{V}_1}{T} = \Pi_1'M\Pi_1 + D_1'\Sigma D_1 - \Pi_1'MM^{-1}M\Pi_1 = D_1'\Sigma D_1 \tag{4.3.64}$$

Hence

$$\operatorname*{plim}_{T\to\infty} \frac{\tilde{Z}_1'\tilde{Z}_1}{T} = \begin{bmatrix} \Pi_1'M\Pi_1 & \Pi_1'\begin{pmatrix} M_{11} \\ M_{21} \end{pmatrix} \\[3mm] (M_{11}, M_{12})\Pi_1 & M_{11} \end{bmatrix} \tag{4.3.65}$$

which we shall assume to be a nonsingular matrix. We next note that

$$\frac{\tilde{Z}_1'u_{.1}}{T} = \begin{bmatrix} \tilde{\Pi}_1'\dfrac{X'u_{.1}}{T} \\[3mm] \dfrac{X_1'u_{.1}}{T} \end{bmatrix} \tag{4.3.66}$$

Since

$$\operatorname*{plim}_{T\to\infty}\left(\tilde{\Pi}_1'\frac{X'u_{.1}}{T}\right) = \operatorname*{plim}_{T\to\infty} \tilde{\Pi}_1' \operatorname*{plim}_{T\to\infty}\frac{X'u_{.1}}{T}$$

we conclude from the consistency of $\tilde{\Pi}_1$ as an estimator of Π_1, and (4.3.43)

$$\operatorname*{plim}_{T\to\infty} \frac{\tilde{Z}_1'u_{.1}}{T} = 0 \tag{4.3.67}$$

Hence we obtain

$$\operatorname*{plim}_{T\to\infty} \tilde{\delta}_{.1} = \delta_{.1} \tag{4.3.68}$$

which shows the consistency of the 2SLS estimator.

The bias characteristics of the estimator are difficult to establish precisely. In general, however, it will be biased because

$$E(\check{\delta}_{.1}) = \delta_{.1} + E[(\tilde{Z}_1'\tilde{Z}_1)^{-1}\tilde{Z}_1'u_{.1}] \tag{4.3.69}$$

and $\tilde{Z}_1$ is, for finite samples, correlated with $u_{.1}$. Indeed, the expectation in (4.3.69) may not exist. Perhaps the simplest way to make this point perfectly clear is through the following

Example 1: Consider again the simple national income model

$$C_t = \alpha + \beta Y_t + u_t$$
$$Y_t = C_t + A_t \tag{4.3.70}$$

where C, Y, A are, respectively, consumption, income, and investment. The last is considered exogenous. The reduced form is given by

$$C_t = \frac{\alpha}{1-\beta} + \frac{\beta}{1-\beta} A_t + \frac{u_t}{1-\beta}$$

$$Y_t = \frac{\alpha}{1-\beta} + \frac{1}{1-\beta} A_t + \frac{u_t}{1-\beta} \tag{4.3.71}$$

Let us now estimate β by 2SLS following exactly the procedure we have outlined above.

To make things simpler, we shall deal with deviations from sample means. Thus we have

$$c_t = \beta y_t + u_t - \bar{u} \tag{4.3.72}$$

The reduced form expression for y_t is given by

$$y_t = \frac{1}{1-\beta} a_t + \frac{u_t - \bar{u}}{1-\beta} \tag{4.3.73}$$

where $c_t = C_t - \bar{C}$, $y_t = Y_t - \bar{Y}$, $a_t = A_t - \bar{A}$, $\bar{C}$, $\bar{Y}$, $\bar{A}$ being the sample means of the respective variables.

Now we must estimate first $1/(1 - \beta)$ from (4.3.73) by ordinary least squares. Its estimator, say d, is

$$d = \frac{\sum_{t=1}^{T} y_t a_t}{\sum_{t=1}^{T} a_t^2} \tag{4.3.74}$$

Then we write

$$y_t = da_t + \tilde{v}_t \tag{4.3.75}$$

and rewrite (4.3.72) as

$$c_t = \beta(y_t - \tilde{v}_t) + (u_t - \bar{u}) + \beta\tilde{v}_t \tag{4.3.76}$$

The 2SLS estimator of β is

$$\hat{\beta} = \frac{\sum_{t=1}^{T} c_t(y_t - \tilde{v}_t)}{\sum_{t=1}^{T} (y_t - \tilde{v}_t)^2} = \beta + \frac{\sum_{t=1}^{T} (y_t - \tilde{v}_t)(u_t - \bar{u})}{\sum_{t=1}^{T} (y_t - \tilde{v}_t)^2} \tag{4.3.77}$$

But from (4.3.75) we conclude

$$\sum_{t=1}^{T} (y_t - \tilde{v}_t)(u_t - \bar{u}) = d \sum_{t=1}^{T} a_t(u_t - \bar{u}) = d \sum_{t=1}^{T} a_t u_t \tag{4.3.78}$$

$$\sum_{t=1}^{T} (y_t - \tilde{v}_t)^2 = d^2 \sum_{t=1}^{T} a_t^2 \tag{4.3.79}$$

Thus, by (4.3.77), (4.3.78), (4.3.79), and (4.3.74), we find

$$\hat{\beta} - \beta = \frac{\sum_{t=1}^{T} a_t u_t}{d \sum_{t=1}^{T} a_t^2} = \frac{\sum_{t=1}^{T} a_t u_t}{\sum_{t=1}^{T} y_t a_t} \tag{4.3.80}$$

But referring to the reduced form, we see that

$$\sum_{t=1}^{T} y_t a_t = \frac{1}{1-\beta} \sum_{t=1}^{T} a_t^2 + \frac{1}{1-\beta} \sum_{t=1}^{T} a_t u_t \tag{4.3.81}$$

Hence we conclude that

$$\frac{\hat{\beta} - \beta}{1 - \beta} = \frac{r}{1 + r} \tag{4.3.82}$$

where

$$r = \frac{\sum_{t=1}^{T} a_t u_t}{\sum_{t=1}^{T} a_t^2} \tag{4.3.83}$$

Now if we put $u = (u_1, u_2, \ldots, u_T)'$, $a = (a_1, a_2, \ldots, a_T)'$, we can write

$$r = \frac{a'u}{a'a} \qquad a'a = \sum_{t=1}^{T} a_t^2 \tag{4.3.84}$$

If we assume

$$u \sim N(0, \sigma^2 I) \tag{4.3.85}$$

then

$$r \sim N\left(0, \frac{\sigma^2}{a'a}\right) \tag{4.3.86}$$

Since A_t is not constant over time but is bounded, we may well assume that

$$\lim_{T \to \infty} \frac{a'a}{T} = \alpha < \infty \qquad \lim_{T=\infty} a'a = \infty \tag{4.3.87}$$

We see that r converges in probability to zero and thus $\hat{\beta}$ is a consistent estimator of β. On the other hand, consider the expectation of $\hat{\beta} - \beta/1 - \beta$. We have

$$E\left(\frac{\hat{\beta} - \beta}{1 - \beta}\right) = \frac{1}{\sqrt{2\pi\phi}} \int_{-\infty}^{\infty} \frac{r}{r+1} \exp\left(-\frac{1}{2\phi} r^2\right) dr \qquad (4.3.88)$$

where $\phi = \sigma^2/a'a$.

The integral, however, *is not defined for any finite sample*. This is so since, for $r = -1$, the exponential is finite while the fraction $r/(1+r)$ becomes infinite. Indeed, $\hat{\beta} - \beta/1 - \beta$ has no finite moments of any order!

Thus we have a consistest estimator here whose moments are infinite for any finite sample, however large.

What is the relevance of this to our discussion? Well, it is the following. An estimator can be thought of as a family of random variables indexed by the sample size, say T. The property of consistency implies that this family of random variables tends in probability to a constant—the parameter being estimated. From *this alone we cannot infer that the estimator is also asymptotically unbiased in the sense that its expectation tends to that parameter*. If this is indeed so, then it must be established by a separate argument.

In this section we have established

Theorem 9: Let it be desired to estimate the parameters of (4.3.48), which is one of a system of m structural equations as defined in (4.3.19) and (4.3.20). Then the 2SLS estimator of these parameters is given by

$$\tilde{\delta}_{.1} = \begin{bmatrix} Y_1'Y_1 - \tilde{V}_1'\tilde{V}_1 & Y_1'X_1 \\ X_1'Y_1 & X_1'X_1 \end{bmatrix}^{-1} \begin{bmatrix} Y_1' - \tilde{V}_1' \\ X_1' \end{bmatrix} y_{.1} \qquad (4.3.89)$$

The estimator is consistent; it is, however, generally biased and its expectation (for finite samples) need not exist.

Remark 10: In the preceding material, there is a crucial assumption that can easily escape notice, for its significance is not immediately obvious. The assumption is that

$$G \geq m_1 + G_1 \qquad (4.3.90)$$

This is related to the identification problem in econometrics, which we shall study at a later stage. Formally, the assumption in (4.3.90) refers to the existence of the inverse in (4.3.89). Intuitively one can regard it as follows. In the relevant equation we have to estimate $m_1 + G_1$ parameters—the elements of $\beta_{.1}$ and $\gamma_{.1}$. At our disposal we only have G pieces of information, which are uncorrelated with the error term, namely, the predetermined variables of the system. It would be reasonable to suppose that unless we had at least as many pieces of information as there are parameters to be estimated, that is, unless (4.3.90) is valid, the latter could not be identified.

Remark 11: It should be pointed out that the fact that we discuss the problem of estimating *the first equation* of the system in no way affects the applicability of the results (or the techniques developed) to the problem of estimating the parameters of any specified equation of the system. Thus suppose we are interested in the *k*th equation; simply renumber the current endogenous and predetermined variables so that in the notation of this section Y_1 and X_1 contain, respectively, the observations on the current endogenous and predetermined variables *appearing in the right-hand side of the *k*th equation.*

4.4   2SLS AS AITKEN AND AS OLS ESTIMATOR

In the preceding section we gave the (historically) original derivation of the 2SLS estimator. While that derivation has great intuitive appeal, it gives the impression of an immense computational burden, an impression that is, in fact, incorrect. We do not really need to compute two sets of regressions. But beyond that, the approach obscures the essential unity of the estimation techniques considered in this chapter. For this reason we shall employ an alternative formulation, which will considerably elucidate this aspect.

Thus let us examine again the problem of estimating the parameters of

$$y_{.1} = Y_1\beta_{.1} + X_1\gamma_{.1} + u_{.1} \tag{4.4.1}$$

which is the first equation in a system of *m*-structural equations as discussed in the previous section. As before, let X (of rank G) be the $T \times G$ matrix of observations on all the predetermined variables appearing in the entire system and consider the transformed equation

$$X'y_{.1} = X'Y_1\beta_{.1} + X'X_1\gamma_{.1} + X'u_{.1} \tag{4.4.2}$$

Why should we wish to consider the equation as exhibited in (4.4.2)? Well, notice that the new explanatory variables consist essentially of sample cross moments between the current endogenous and the predetermined variables— the former as they appear in the first equation, the latter as they appear in the entire system. Certainly this would be precisely so if we divided through by T, which will not change anything at all. Hence, as the sample size increases, the new explanatory variables converge (in probability) to a nonstochastic limit and thus are uncorrelated with the error term appearing in (4.4.2). Thus, if we were to apply an "efficient" estimation technique to that equation, we would expect to obtain at least consistent estimators of the vectors $\beta_{.1}$ and $\gamma_{.1}$. Here we should caution the reader that, in general, it is *not true* that

$$\text{Cov}(X'u_{.1}) = E(X'u_{.1}u'_{.1}X) = \sigma_{11}X'X \tag{4.4.3}$$

This is so since the matrix X need not be nonstochastic; but worse, some of its columns may represent the observations on some lagged endogenous variables and unless we assert that u_{ti} is *independent* (and not merely uncorrelated) with $u_{t'j}$ for $t \neq t'$ the expectation in (4.4.3) cannot be obtained on the basis of the assumptions customarily made in such models. Thus, for example, suppose that the second column of X represents the T observations on the sth endogenous variable lagged one period. Then the $(2, 2)$ element of $X'u_{.1} u'_{.1} X$ is given by

$$\sum_{t'=1}^{T} \sum_{t=1}^{T} y_{t-1, s} u_{t1} u_{t'1} y_{t'-1, s}$$

where we assume that y_{0s} is available. Now for $t = t'$, the sum above contains terms of the form $\sum_{t=1}^{T} y_{t-1, s}^2 u_{t1}^2$. However, in (4.3.20) we merely made the assumption that u_{ti} is *uncorrelated* with $u_{t'j}$, $t \neq t'$. This assumption alone does not permit us to write

$$E\left(\sum_{t=1}^{T} y_{t-1, s}^2 u_{t1}^2 \right) = E\left(\sum_{t=1}^{T} y_{t-1, s}^2 \right) E(u_{t1}^2) \tag{4.4.4}$$

For (4.4.4) to be valid we need to make an additional assumption beyond those listed in (4.3.20). This would be either that the errors in the system are jointly normally distributed or that the errors at time t are independent of errors at time t', for $t \neq t'$. Of course, normality in conjunction with the assumptions in (4.3.20) *implies independence* for errors at distinct times. If we do make the normality or independence assumptions, then

$$E\left(\sum_{t'=1}^{T} \sum_{t=1}^{T} y_{t-1, s} u_{t1} u_{t'1} y_{t'-1, s} \right) = \sigma_{11} \sum_{t=1}^{T} E(y_{t-1, s}^2) \tag{4.4.5}$$

and thus for large samples we would have approximately

$$\text{Cov} (X'u_{.1}) = \sigma_{11} X'X \tag{4.4.6}$$

in the sense that $X'X/T$ has as its probability limit $E(X'X/T)$. In view of these heuristic arguments, it would appear that an "efficient" procedure for estimating $\beta_{.1}$ and $\gamma_{.1}$ from (4.4.2) would be the application of Aitken techniques, where the covariance matrix of the error vector $X'u_{.1}$ is taken as $\sigma_{11}(X'X)$. It may be verified that the Aitken estimator of the parameters in (4.4.2) computed as just indicated is precisely the 2SLS estimator obtained in the previous section. Since Aitken estimation has some optimal properties, it is reasonable to conjecture that 2SLS is optimal in some sense within the class of consistent estimators of the parameters $\beta_{.1}$, $\gamma_{.1}$, which use only information conveyed by the equation containing $\beta_{.1}$ and $\gamma_{.1}$ and thus disregard information conveyed by the rest of the system.

As shown by Basmann [2], 2SLS estimators are "best linear consistent." We shall not discuss this property here. The interested reader, however, may consult Basmann's paper just cited.

The derivation of 2SLS as Aitken estimators of the parameters of a single structural equation considered in isolation is, as we have seen above, rather weakly motivated, and, moreover, it does not make sufficiently transparent the connection between 2SLS and three-stage least squares to be considered below. In order to make this connection clear, as well as to simplify matters, we shall consider an alternative derivation.

By assumption, rank $(X) = G$ and thus $X'X$ is a *positive definite* matrix; hence there exists a nonsingular matrix R such that

$$X'X = RR' \tag{4.4.7}$$

Now transform the equation in (4.4.2) by R^{-1} to obtain

$$R^{-1}X'y_{.1} = R^{-1}X'Y_1\beta_{.1} + R^{-1}X'X_1\gamma_{.1} + R^{-1}X'u_{.1} \tag{4.4.8}$$

For notational simplicity, let

$$w_{.1} = R^{-1}X'y_{.1} \qquad Q_1 = (R^{-1}X'Y_1, \ R^{-1}X'X_1)$$

$$\delta_{.1} = \binom{\beta_{.1}}{\gamma_{.1}} \qquad r_{.1} = R^{-1}X'u_{.1} \tag{4.4.9}$$

and write (4.4.8) as

$$w_{.1} = Q_1\delta_{.1} + r_{.1} \tag{4.4.10}$$

What have we accomplished by this? Two things. First, *the 2SLS is simply the OLS estimator applied to* (4.4.10), a fact we shall show explicitly below. Second, one can show that asymptotically the covariance matrix of $r_{.1}$ is that of $u_{.1}$, except for the obvious difference in dimension. Let us now prove the validity of our first claim; verification of the second claim will be postponed to a later section. The OLS estimator of $\delta_{.1}$ in (4.4.10) is simply

$$d_{.1} = (Q_1'Q_1)^{-1}Q_1'w_{.1} \tag{4.4.11}$$

But

$$Q_1'Q_1 = \binom{Y_1'XR'^{-1}}{X_1'XR'^{-1}}(R^{-1}X'Y_1, R^{-1}X'X_1)$$

$$= \begin{bmatrix} Y_1'X(X'X)^{-1}X'Y_1 & Y_1'X(X'X)^{-1}X'X_1 \\ X_1'X(X'X)^{-1}X'Y_1 & X_1'X(X'X)^{-1}X'X_1 \end{bmatrix} \tag{4.4.12}$$

Notice that if we partition X by $X = (X_1, X^*)$, then

$$X_1 = X\binom{I_{G_1}}{0} = (X_1, X^*)\binom{I_{G_1}}{0} \tag{4.4.13}$$

where the symbol I_k indicates the identity matrix of order k; obviously, the zero matrix in (4.4.13) is $(G - G_1 \times G_1)$.

Using the relation in (4.4.13), we conclude

$$X_1'X(X'X)^{-1}X'Y_1 = X_1'Y_1 \qquad X_1'X(X'X)^{-1}X'X_1 = X_1'X_1 \tag{4.4.14}$$

But from (4.3.50) and (4.3.51), we see

$$X(X'X)^{-1}X'Y_1 = X\tilde{\Pi}_1 = Y_1 - \tilde{V}_1 \tag{4.4.15}$$

Finally, from (4.4.15), we obtain

$$Y_1'X(X'X)^{-1}X'Y_1 = Y_1'(Y_1 - \tilde{V}_1) = Y_1'Y_1 - \tilde{V}_1'\tilde{V}_1 \tag{4.4.16}$$

and thus we conclude

$$Q_1'Q_1 = \tilde{Z}_1'\tilde{Z}_1 \tag{4.4.17}$$

where $\tilde{Z}_1$ is as defined in (4.3.56) and $\tilde{Z}_1'\tilde{Z}_1$ is the matrix to be inverted in obtaining the 2SLS estimator of (4.3.58).

Next we see that by (4.4.15) and (4.4.16)

$$Q_1'w_{\cdot 1} = \begin{pmatrix} Y_1'X(X'X)^{-1}X'y_{\cdot 1} \\ X_1'(X('X)^{-1}X'y_{\cdot 1}) \end{pmatrix} = \begin{pmatrix} Y_1' - \tilde{V}_1' \\ X_1' \end{pmatrix} y_{\cdot 1} = \tilde{Z}_1'y_{\cdot 1} \tag{4.4.18}$$

We therefore conclude

$$d_{\cdot 1} = (Q_1'Q_1)^{-1}Q_1'w_{\cdot 1} = (\tilde{Z}_1'\tilde{Z}_1)^{-1}\tilde{Z}_1'y_{\cdot 1} \tag{4.4.19}$$

Thus we have demonstrated that the OLS *estimator of* $\delta_{\cdot 1}$ *from* (4.4.10) is exactly the 2SLS estimator as obtained in the previous section.

But this particular formulation of the problem opens the way to a routine derivation of the 2SLS estimator of all the parameters of the entire system of m-structural equations. To see this, we proceed as follows. Evidently every equation of the system may be put in the form exhibited in (4.4.10). Thus we can write

$$w_{\cdot i} = Q_i\delta_{\cdot i} + r_{\cdot i} \qquad i = 1, 2, \ldots, m \tag{4.4.20}$$

where

$$w_{\cdot i} = R^{-1}X'y_{\cdot i} \qquad Q_i = (R^{-1}X'Y_i, R^{-1}X'X_i)$$

$$\delta_{\cdot i} = \begin{pmatrix} \beta_{\cdot i} \\ \gamma_{\cdot i} \end{pmatrix} \qquad r_{\cdot i} = R^{-1}X'u_{\cdot i} \tag{4.4.21}$$

and Y_i and X_i are, respectively, the matrices of observations on the explanatory current endogenous and predetermined variables appearing in the ith equation.

Define

$$w = \begin{pmatrix} w_{\cdot 1} \\ w_{\cdot 2} \\ \vdots \\ w_{\cdot m} \end{pmatrix} \qquad \delta = \begin{pmatrix} \delta_{\cdot 1} \\ \delta_{\cdot 2} \\ \vdots \\ \delta_{\cdot m} \end{pmatrix}$$

$$Q = \text{diag}(Q_1, Q_2, \ldots, Q_m) \qquad r = \begin{pmatrix} r_{\cdot 1} \\ r_{\cdot 2} \\ \vdots \\ r_{\cdot m} \end{pmatrix} \tag{4.4.22}$$

and thus write the entire system in (4.4.20) as

$$w = Q\delta + r \tag{4.4.23}$$

The 2SLS estimator of all the parameters of the system is therefore[11]

$$\tilde{\delta} = (Q'Q)^{-1}Q'w = \delta + (Q'Q)^{-1}Q'r \tag{4.4.24}$$

In the preceding section we have in fact shown that

$$\operatorname*{plim}_{T\to\infty} \left(\frac{Q'Q}{T}\right)^{-1}$$

exists as a matrix with finite nonstochastic elements and, furthermore, that

$$\operatorname*{plim}_{T\to\infty} \frac{Q'r}{T} = 0 \tag{4.4.25}$$

Hence that

$$\operatorname*{plim}_{T\to\infty} \tilde{\delta} = \delta \tag{4.4.26}$$

Since, in general, the covariance matrix of $r._i$ with $r._j$, $i \neq j$ will not vanish, we would suspect that $\tilde{\delta}$ is an asymptotically inefficient estimator of δ. We shall return to this problem later when we consider three-stage least squares estimators. Let us now examine the precise nature of the estimator exhibited in (4.4.24). We have

$$Q'Q = \begin{bmatrix} Q_1'Q_1 & & 0 \\ & Q_2'Q_2 & \\ & & \ddots \\ 0 & & Q_m'Q_m \end{bmatrix} \qquad Q'w = \begin{bmatrix} Q_1'w._1 \\ Q_2'w._2 \\ \vdots \\ Q_m'w._m \end{bmatrix} \tag{4.4.27}$$

Hence the ith subvector of $\tilde{\delta}$ is given by

$$\tilde{\delta}._i = (Q_i'Q_i)^{-1}Q_i'w._i$$

$$= \begin{bmatrix} Y_i'X(X'X)^{-1}X'Y_i & Y_i'X_i \\ X_i'Y_i & X_i'X_i \end{bmatrix}^{-1} \begin{bmatrix} Y_i'X(X'X)^{-1}X_i'y._i \\ X_i'y._i \end{bmatrix} \tag{4.4.28}$$

which is exactly the 2SLS estimator and, incidentally, *is also the computationally efficient method for obtaining it.*

Thus 2SLS estimators for the parameters of *an entire system* can be obtained by applying *seriatim* to the (m) equations of (4.4.20) *ordinary least squares.* In this framework, it becomes possible to justify the need for the assumption made in (4.3.90) of the previous section. At that time we merely stated the need for it (Remark 9) and indicated that it was related to the identification problem in econometrics. Let us now see, in a formal sense, precisely why it is needed. In

---

[11] Here it is to be understood that identities have been substituted out of the system.

order for the estimator in (4.4.24) to be uniquely defined, it is necessary and sufficient that $(Q'Q)^{-1}$ exist. But from (4.4.27) we see that the existence of $(Q'Q)^{-1}$ *entails the existence* of $(Q_i'Q_i)^{-1}$ for $i = 1, 2, \ldots, m$.

What minimal conditions does this impose on the system? To examine this question, recall first that if A is a matrix of rank n and B is a matrix of rank m, and $A'BA$ is defined, then

$$\text{rank } (A'BA) \le \min \, [\text{rank } (A), \text{rank } (B)] \tag{4.4.29}$$

The weak inequality sign in (4.4.29) is essential; thus take

$$A = \begin{bmatrix} 1 & 0 \\ 0 & 0 \end{bmatrix} \qquad B = \begin{bmatrix} 0 & 1 \\ 1 & 0 \end{bmatrix} \tag{4.4.30}$$

Note that rank $(A) = 1$, rank $(B) = 2$, and

$$A'BA = 0 \tag{4.4.31}$$

Hence

$$0 = \text{rank } (A'BA) < \min \, (1, 2) \tag{4.4.32}$$

What is the bearing of the above on the existence of $\tilde{\delta}$? It is this. Letting

$$Z_i^* = (X'Y_i, X'X_i) \tag{4.4.33}$$

we note that

$$Q_i'Q_i = Z_i^{*'}(X'X)^{-1}Z_i^* \tag{4.4.34}$$

Thus

$$\text{rank } (Q_i'Q_i) \le \min \, [\text{rank } (Z_i^*), \text{rank } (X'X)] \tag{4.4.35}$$

Now $Q_i'Q_i$ is $(G_i + m_i) \times (G_i + m_i)$, Z_i^* is $G \times (G_i + m_i)$, and $X'X$ is $G \times G$ and nonsingular, that is, of rank G. For $Q_i'Q_i$ to be invertible, we must have

$$\text{rank } (Q_i'Q_i) = G_i + m_i \tag{4.4.36}$$

and hence a *necessary condition* for its invertibility is that

$$G_i + m_i \le G \tag{4.4.37}$$

We must emphasize that this is not sufficient as the example in (4.4.30) and (4.4.31) indicates.

An equation for which

$$G = G_i + m_i \tag{4.4.38}$$

is said to be *just identified*.

An equation for which

$$G > G_i + m_i \tag{4.4.39}$$

is said to be overidentified.

An equation for which

$$G < G_i + m_i \qquad (4.4.40)$$

is said to be underidentified.

This terminology is introduced only for convenience of exposition and will not be elaborated upon at this time. We shall discuss it extensively at a later stage.

We have therefore proved

Theorem 10: Let the conditions of Theorem 9 hold and consider the problem of estimating the parameters of

$$y_{.1} = Y_1\beta_{.1} + X_1\gamma_{.1} + u_{.1} \qquad (4.4.41)$$

Then the 2SLS estimator of $\begin{pmatrix} \beta_{.1} \\ \gamma_{.1} \end{pmatrix}$ defined in (4.3.89) is identical with the "Aitken estimator" of the parameters in

$$X'y_{.1} = X'Y_1\beta_{.1} + X'X_1\gamma_{.1} + X'u_{.1} \qquad (4.4.42)$$

provided we take the covariance matrix of the error term in (4.4.42) to be (approximately)

$$\text{Cov}(X'u_{.1}) = \sigma_{11}X'X \qquad (4.4.43)$$

assuming that X is of rank G.

Moreover, if we define a nonsingular matrix R such that

$$RR' = X'X \qquad (4.4.44)$$

then the 2SLS estimator of the parameters in (4.4.41) is the *OLS estimator* of the parameters in

$$R^{-1}X'y_{.1} = R^{-1}X'Y_1\beta_{.1} + R^{-1}X'X_1\gamma_{.1} + R^{-1}X'u_{.1} \qquad (4.4.45)$$

provided (4.4.42) is just- or overidentified.

Moreover, if *every equation* of the system

$$y_{.i} = Y_i\beta_{.i} + X_1\gamma_{.i} + u_{.i} \qquad i = 1, 2, \ldots, m \qquad (4.4.46)$$

is *just- or overidentified*, then the 2SLS estimator of the vectors $\begin{pmatrix} \beta_{.i} \\ \gamma_{.i} \end{pmatrix}$, $i = 1, 2, \ldots, m$ is given by

$$\tilde{\delta} = (Q'Q)^{-1}Q'w \qquad (4.4.47)$$

where $\tilde{\delta}$, Q, and w are as defined in (4.4.9) and (4.4.22).

If the system contains underidentified equations, then the parameters of such equations cannot be estimated. [Of course, the parameters of other equations can be estimated from (4.4.45) even though $\tilde{\delta}$ of (4.4.47) is not defined.] It is interesting to observe, further, that if all equations of the system are just identified, then the Q_i are square matrices of dimension $m_i + G_i$ and thus generally invertible. Hence Q^{-1} will exist and thus the 2SLS estimator of δ reduces to

$$\tilde{\delta} = (Q'Q)^{-1}Q'w = Q^{-1}Q'^{-1}Q'w = Q^{-1}w \tag{4.4.48}$$

4.5 ASYMPTOTIC PROPERTIES OF 2SLS ESTIMATORS

In Sections 4.3 and 4.4 we had established that the 2SLS estimator is a consistent one. However, in any applied problem we need to perform tests of significance, and thus it is not enough to know that a given estimator is consistent. For that purpose we need to know something about its distribution or, failing that, at least its asymptotic distribution.

Unfortunately, the small sample distribution of the *general* 2SLS estimator is not known. Indeed, we have shown in Example 1 that its mean *need not* exist (in small samples). In certain special cases it is shown by Basmann [4], [6] that small sample distributions with finite moments exist. Thus the problem of significance of empirical results in the context of a general system of structural equations is very difficult indeed for small samples. For large samples, however, the situation is considerably simpler and it is in fact possible to establish certain useful results.

Let us begin by establishing the asymptotic distribution of the 2SLS estimator of the parameters of a single structural equation, say the first. For clarity of exposition, we shall consider in detail the case where the predetermined variables of the system are entirely *exogenous* so that they may be taken to be either as *nonstochastic* or (minimally) *independent of the error terms of the system*. We shall then indicate how the argument may be modified to allow for lagged endogenous variables. Now, in the notation of Theorem 10, the 2SLS estimator of the parameters of the first structural equation is given by

$$\tilde{\delta}_{.1} = (Q_1'Q_1)^{-1}Q_1'w_{.1} = \delta_{.1} + (Q_1'Q_1)^{-1}Q_1'r_{.1} \tag{4.5.1}$$

The problem is to determine the limiting distribution of the sequence $\sqrt{T}(\tilde{\delta}_{.1} - \delta_{.1})$ (as $T \to \infty$). This is precisely what one means when one speaks of the asymptotic distribution of the 2SLS estimator. We are not speaking of the distribution of $\tilde{\delta}_{.1}$, for the latter, being a consistent estimator, will generally have, asymptotically, a degenerate distribution. What can be done in this context would be to approximate the distribution of $\tilde{\delta}_{.1}$, for moderately large samples, by the appropriate transform of the asymptotic distribution of

$$\sqrt{T}(\tilde{\delta}_{.1} - \delta_{.1}).$$

From (4.5.1) we have

$$\sqrt{T}(\tilde{\delta}_{.1} - \delta_{.1}) = \left(\frac{Q_1'Q_1}{T}\right)^{-1} \frac{Z_1'X}{T} \left(\frac{X'X}{T}\right)^{-1} \frac{X'u_{.1}}{\sqrt{T}} \tag{4.5.2}$$

In Section 4.3 we established the existence of the probability limits of all quantities in the right-hand side of (4.5.2) except for $X'u_{.1}/\sqrt{T}$. In fact, such probability limits were shown to be *nonstochastic*. Thus, the only remaining problem is to establish the limiting distribution of the sequence of random vectors $X'u_{.1}/\sqrt{T}$. Let C_s be the sth *column of X'* and notice that

$$\frac{X'u_{.1}}{\sqrt{T}} = \frac{1}{\sqrt{T}} \sum_{s=1}^{T} C_s u_{s1} \tag{4.5.3}$$

Moreover, observe that C_s is a (G-dimensional) column vector whose elements are, by assumption, either nonstochastic or, if stochastic, then independent of u_{s1}. Now the vectors $C_s u_{s1}$ are mutually independent with covariance matrix.[12]

$$\text{Cov}(C_s u_{s1}) = \sigma_{11} C_s C_s' \tag{4.5.4}$$

If, in addition, a condition similar to (4.2.17) is assumed to hold, then, by Theorem 6 of Chapter 3, we conclude that $X'u_{.1}/\sqrt{T}$ is asymptotically normal with mean zero and covariance matrix

$$\Phi_1 = \sigma_{11} \lim_{T \to \infty} \frac{1}{T} C_s C_s' = \sigma_{11} \lim_{T \to \infty} \left(\frac{X'X}{T}\right) \tag{4.5.5}$$

Thus from (4.5.2) we see that, asymptotically,

$$\sqrt{T}(\tilde{\delta}_{.1} - \delta_{.1}) \sim N\left[0, \sigma_{11} \plim_{T \to \infty} \left(\frac{Q_1'Q_1}{T}\right)^{-1}\right] \tag{4.5.6}$$

The argument is simplified somewhat if the error terms of the system are assumed to be jointly normal. In that case, the condition in (4.2.17) is not needed. We can argue more directly as follows: $X'u_{.1}/\sqrt{T}$ is normal with mean zero and covariance matrix $\sigma_{11}(X'X/T)$; letting $T \to \infty$, we conclude that, asymptotically it is normal with mean zero and covariance matrix $\sigma_{11} \lim_{T \to \infty} (X'X/T)$. Since the asymptotic distribution of $\sqrt{T}(\tilde{\delta}_{.1} - \delta_{.1})$ is that of

$$\left\{\plim_{T \to \infty} \left(\frac{Q_1'Q_1}{T}\right)^{-1} \frac{Z_1'X}{T} \left(\frac{X'X}{T}\right)^{-1}\right\} \frac{X'u_{.1}}{\sqrt{T}}$$

we conclude that (4.5.6) is fully valid.

Remark 12: In the foregoing discussion we confined ourselves to the case where the system does not contain lagged endogenous variables. We have done

---

[12] If the elements of C_s are stochastic, then $C_s C_s'$ should be replaced by $E(C_s C_s')$. We will conduct the argument as if C_s were a nonstochastic vector.

so because then we can obtain the asymptotic distribution of the 2SLS estimator by rather simple and straightforward arguments based on the central limit theorems given in Chapter 3. If, however, we admit *lagged endogenous variables* into the system, the situation becomes considerably more complicated. To see the nature of this complexity, suppose that the second column of X consists, say, of observations on the lagged endogenous variable $y_{t-2,3}$. Thus we have

$$x_{t'2} = y_{t-2,3} \qquad t = 3, 4, \ldots, T \tag{4.5.7}$$

Now the sth column of X' consists of

$$C_s = \begin{pmatrix} x_{s1} \\ x_{s2} \\ \vdots \\ x_{sG} \end{pmatrix} \tag{4.5.8}$$

In general, however, the x_{s2} will be *correlated for different values of the index s* so that in (4.5.3) it is no longer true that we are dealing with mutually independent random vectors. Hence we cannot invoke the same central limit theorem in order to establish the normality of the asymptotic distribution of 2SLS estimators. One may, however, obtain essentially the same results by employing certain central limit theorems for dependent random variables. This aspect will not be developed here.

Remark 13: One often encounters statements in the literature concerning the "asymptotic covariance" matrix of 2SLS estimators; such "results" are established by the following type of argument. From (4.5.1) one defines the *sampling error* of the 2SLS estimator by

$$e_{.1} = \tilde{\delta}_{.1} - \delta_{.1} \tag{4.5.9}$$

Then one considers the quantity

$$\lim_{T \to \infty} TE(e_{.1}e'_{.1}) = \lim_{T \to \infty} E\left[\left(\frac{Q'_1 Q_1}{T} \right)^{-1} \frac{Q'_1 r_{.1} r'_{.1} Q_1}{T} \left(\frac{Q'_1 Q_1}{T} \right)^{-1} \right] \tag{4.5.10}$$

and argues that since

$$\plim_{T \to \infty} \left(\frac{Q'_1 Q_1}{T} \right)^{-1}$$

exists as a matrix with finite nonstochastic elements and

$$\lim_{T \to \infty} \frac{1}{T} E[Q'_1 r_{.1} r'_{.1} Q_1] = \sigma_{11} \plim \left(\frac{Q'_1 Q_1}{T} \right)^{-1} \tag{4.5.11}$$

therefore

$$\lim_{T \to \infty} TE(e_{.1}e'_{.1}) = \sigma_{11} \plim_{T \to \infty} \left(\frac{Q'_1 Q_1}{T} \right)^{-1} \tag{4.5.12}$$

Unfortunately, although this argument has heuristic merit and, indeed, obtains the *correct expression for the covariance matrix of the asymptotic distribution of the 2SLS estimator*, it is rather specious, for the expectation $E(e_{.1}e'_{.1})$ may *not* exist for any finite T. Thus it is not clear what meaning is to be ascribed to the limit operations of (4.5.10). As was pointed out in Chapter 3, convergence in distribution of a sequence of random variables does not imply that the moments of the elements of the sequence necessarily converge to the corresponding moments of the asymptotic distribution, although in some circumstances this may be so. To make such considerations, as well as the earlier discussion, perfectly clear, we return to the case considered in Example 1.

Example 2: Consider again the simple Keynesian model of (4.3.70). The 2SLS estimator of the marginal propensity to consume parameter, $\hat{\beta}$, may be expressed as

$$\frac{\hat{\beta} - \beta}{1 - \beta} = \frac{r}{1 + r} \qquad (4.5.13)$$

where

$$r = \frac{a'u}{a'a} \qquad (4.5.14)$$

Under the assumptions of that example,

$$u \sim N(0, \sigma^2 I) \qquad (4.5.15)$$

and thus

$$r \sim N\left(0, \frac{\sigma^2}{a'a}\right) \qquad (4.5.16)$$

We have verified in that example that *no* (finite sample) *moments of any order exist* for the estimator $\hat{\beta}$. On the other hand,

$$\sqrt{T}(\hat{\beta} - \beta) = (1 - \beta)\frac{a'u/\sqrt{T}}{a'a/T + a'u/T} \qquad (4.5.17)$$

Clearly the random variable in the right-hand side converges in distribution to the variable

$$\left[\frac{1 - \beta}{\plim_{T\to\infty} (a'a/T + a'u/T)}\right]\frac{a'u}{\sqrt{T}}$$

The first term yields

$$\frac{1 - \beta}{\plim_{T\to\infty} (a'a/T + a'u/T)} = \frac{1 - \beta}{\alpha} \qquad (4.5.18)$$

where α was defined in (4.3.87) as $\lim_{T \to \infty} (a'a/T)$. In addition,

$$\frac{a'u}{\sqrt{T}} \sim N\left(0, \sigma^2 \frac{a'a}{T}\right) \tag{4.5.19}$$

so that its asymptotic distribution is $N(0, \sigma^2\alpha)$. Thus, asymptotically,

$$\frac{\sqrt{T}(\hat{\beta} - \beta)}{1 - \beta} \sim N(0, \sigma^2 \alpha) \tag{4.5.20}$$

and has finite moments of every order. On the other hand, there is no meaning to the expression

$$\lim_{T \to \infty} \frac{T}{(1 - \beta)^2} E(\hat{\beta} - \beta)^2$$

which, in the context of this example, corresponds to (4.5.10) of Remark 13.

Consider now the asymptotic distribution of the 2SLS estimator of the parameters of the *entire system*. In the notation of (4.4.22) and (4.4.23), the entire system may be written as

$$w = Q\delta + r \tag{4.5.21}$$

and the 2SLS estimator of its parameters as

$$\tilde{\delta} = (Q'Q)^{-1}Q'w = \delta + (Q'Q)^{-1}Q'r \tag{4.5.22}$$

Hence

$$\sqrt{T}(\tilde{\delta} - \delta) = \left(\frac{Q'Q}{T}\right)^{-1} \frac{Q'r}{\sqrt{T}} \tag{4.5.23}$$

and the asymptotic distribution of $\sqrt{T}(\tilde{\delta} - \delta)$ is that of

$$\left[\underset{T \to \infty}{\text{plim}} \left(\frac{Q'Q}{T}\right)^{-1}\right]\left(\frac{Q'r}{\sqrt{T}}\right)$$

Since the first term exists as a nonstochastic matrix with finite elements, we need only be concerned with the second term. Thus

$$\frac{Q'r}{\sqrt{T}} - \frac{1}{\sqrt{T}} \begin{bmatrix} Q_1'r_{\cdot 1} \\ Q_1'r_{\cdot 1} \\ \vdots \\ Q_m'r_{\cdot m} \end{bmatrix}$$

$$= \text{diag}\left[\frac{Z_1'X}{T}\left(\frac{X'X}{T}\right)^{-1} \quad \frac{Z_2'X}{T}\left(\frac{X'X}{T}\right)^{-1}, \ldots, \frac{Z_m'X}{T}\left(\frac{X'X}{T}\right)^{-1}\right]$$

$$\times \left\{\frac{1}{\sqrt{T}}\begin{bmatrix} X' & & 0 \\ & X' & \\ & & \ddots \\ 0 & & X' \end{bmatrix} u\right\} \tag{4.5.24}$$

Now the first term of the last member of (4.5.24) has a well-defined nonstochastic probability limit; hence the asymptotic distribution of $\sqrt{T}(\tilde{\delta} - \delta)$ is essentially determined by the asymptotic distribution of the last term. This is so by Proposition 2 of Chapter 3.

Let C_s be the sth column of X' and notice that C_s is a column vector of G elements. Denote by

$$u_{s \cdot} = (u_{s1}, u_{s2}, \ldots, u_{sm}) \tag{4.5.25}$$

the (row) vector of all error terms in the system at "time" s. We note that, by hypothesis, the $u_{s \cdot}$, $s = 1, 2, \ldots, T$, are mutually independent random variables. Further, define[13]

$$V_s = \mathrm{diag}\,(C_s, C_s, \ldots, C_s) \tag{4.5.26}$$

and note that V_s is a matrix of dimension $mG \times m$. It is easy to verify that in this notation we can write

$$\frac{1}{\sqrt{T}} \begin{bmatrix} X' & & 0 \\ & X' & \\ & & \ddots & \\ 0 & & & X' \end{bmatrix} u = \frac{1}{\sqrt{T}} \sum_{s=1}^{T} V_s u'_{s \cdot}. \tag{4.5.27}$$

We see then that the quantity of interest in establishing the asymptotic distribution of the 2SLS estimators of all the parameters of the system is the sum of mutually independent random vectors with the properties

$$E(V_s u'_{s \cdot}) = 0 \qquad \mathrm{Cov}\,(V_s u'_{s \cdot}) = V_s \Sigma V'_s \tag{4.5.28}$$

Furthermore, we see that

$$\lim_{T \to \infty} \frac{1}{T} \sum_{s=1}^{T} V_s \Sigma V'_s = \Sigma \otimes \lim_{T \to \infty} \left(\frac{X'X}{T}\right)^{-1} \tag{4.5.29}$$

Since by assumption, this is a nonzero matrix with finite elements, then by Theorem 6 of Chapter 3 we conclude that if the disturbance vectors $u_{s \cdot}$ obey, for every $\varepsilon > 0$,

$$\lim_{T \to \infty} \frac{1}{T} \sum_{s=1}^{T} \int_{|\phi| > \varepsilon \sqrt{T}} |\phi|^2 \, dF_s(\phi) = 0 \tag{4.5.30}$$

the quantity in (4.5.27) obeys a multivariate central limit theorem. In (4.5.30), $F_s(\cdot)$ is the distribution function of the disturbance vector $u_{s \cdot}$.

---

[13] For purposes of clarity, let us note that V_s consists of

$$V_s = \begin{bmatrix} V_s^{(1)} \\ V_s^{(2)} \\ \vdots \\ V_s^{(m)} \end{bmatrix}$$

where *each* $V_s^{(i)}$, $i = 1, 2, \ldots, m$, is a $G \times m$ matrix whose ith column consists of C_s, all other elements being zero.

By (4.5.23), (4.5.24), and (4.5.29), we conclude that, asymptotically,

$$\sqrt{T}(\tilde{\delta} - \delta) \sim N\left[0, \operatorname*{plim}_{T \to \infty} \left(\frac{Q'Q}{T}\right)^{-1} \frac{Q'}{\sqrt{T}} (\Sigma \otimes I_G) \frac{Q}{\sqrt{T}} \left(\frac{Q'Q}{T}\right)^{-1}\right] \qquad (4.5.31)$$

where I_G is the identity matrix of order G.

As an exercise the reader may verify, by extracting the 1st diagonal block of the covariance matrix in (4.5.31), that this is exactly the covariance matrix of the asymptotic distribution of $\sqrt{T}(\tilde{\delta}_{.1} - \delta_{.1})$ as given in (4.5.6).

As before, the argument may be simplified somewhat if the error terms of the system are assumed to be jointly normal, that is, if we assume

$$u'_{s.} \sim N(0, \Sigma) \qquad \text{all } s. \qquad (4.5.32)$$

The discussion following (4.5.6) is fully applicable, *mutatis mutandis*, in the present case as well and for that reason it need not be repeated. The same applies to our earlier remarks regarding the presence of *lagged endogenous* among the *predetermined* variables of the system.

To complete the solution of the inference problem for the 2SLS estimator, we ought to produce a consistent estimator of the covariance matrix of its asymptotic distribution. But this is rather simple.

From (4.5.6) it is apparent that a consistent estimator for the covariance matrix may be obtained by

$$\hat{\sigma}_{11} \left(\frac{Q_1 Q_1}{T}\right)^{-1}$$

where

$$\hat{\sigma}_{11} = \frac{\tilde{u}'_{.1} \tilde{u}_{.1}}{T} = \frac{(y_{.1} - Z_1 \tilde{\delta}_{.1})'(y_{.1} - Z_1 \tilde{\delta}_{.1})}{T} \qquad (4.5.33)$$

The consistency of $\hat{\sigma}_{11}$ is established as follows. By the definition of $y_{.1}$ in (4.4.1), we can write

$$\tilde{u}_{.1} = y_{.1} - Z_1 \tilde{\delta}_{.1} = u_{.1} - Z_1(\tilde{\delta}_{.1} - \delta_{.1}) \qquad (4.5.34)$$

Thus

$$\hat{\sigma}_{11} = \frac{u'_{.1} u_{.1}}{T} - \frac{u'_{.1} Z_1}{T}(\tilde{\delta}_{.1} - \delta_{.1}) - (\tilde{\delta}_{.1} - \delta_{.1})' \frac{Z_1' u_{.1}}{T}$$

$$+ (\tilde{\delta}_{.1} - \delta_{.1})' \frac{Z_1' Z_1}{T}(\tilde{\delta}_{.1} - \delta_{.1}) \qquad (4.5.35)$$

Since $\tilde{\delta}_{.1}$ is a consistent estimator of $\delta_{.1}$, we find

$$\operatorname*{plim}_{T \to \infty} \hat{\sigma}_{11} = \operatorname*{plim}_{T \to \infty} \frac{u'_{.1} u_{.1}}{T} = \sigma_{11} \qquad (4.5.36)$$

This is so since

$$\text{plim}_{T \to \infty} \frac{u'_{\cdot 1} Z_1}{T}$$

is a finite nonstochastic quantity; indeed, an expression for it was established in equations (4.3.35) through (4.3.42) of Section 4.3. Similarly for

$$\text{plim}_{T \to \infty} \frac{Z'_1 Z_1}{T}$$

The reader who desires greater detail may actually express $\hat{\sigma}_{11}$ in terms of the moment matrices of the variables of the system and verify its consistency directly.

Similarly the covariance matrix in (4.5.31) may be consistently estimated by

$$\left(\frac{Q'Q}{T}\right)^{-1} \frac{Q'}{\sqrt{T}} (\hat{\Sigma} \otimes I_G) \frac{Q}{\sqrt{T}} \left(\frac{Q'Q}{T}\right)^{-1}$$

where

$$\hat{\Sigma} = (\hat{\sigma}_{ij}) \quad \hat{\sigma}_{ij} = \frac{\tilde{u}'_{\cdot i} \tilde{u}_{\cdot j}}{T} \qquad i, j = 1, 2, \ldots, m \tag{4.5.37}$$

and

$$\tilde{u}_{\cdot i} = y_{\cdot i} - Z_i \hat{\delta}_{\cdot i} \tag{4.5.38}$$

Tests of significance based on the asymptotic distribution of the estimators may be conducted in terms of the quantities

$$\frac{\sqrt{T}(\hat{\delta}_{ki} - \delta_{ki})}{\sqrt{q^i_{kk}}}$$

where δ_{ki} is the kth element of $\delta_{\cdot i}$ and q^i_{kk} is the kth diagonal element of

$$\hat{\sigma}_{ii} \left(\frac{Q'_i Q_i}{T}\right)^{-1}$$

It is easily verified that, asymptotically,

$$\frac{\sqrt{T}(\hat{\delta}_{ki} - \delta_{ki})}{\sqrt{q^i_{kk}}} \sim N(0, 1) \tag{4.5.39}$$

An interesting result, although of minor importance, may be established for the residuals of a just identified equation.

Proposition 1: The 2SLS residuals of a just identified equation are orthogonal to the predetermined variables of the system.

PROOF: Consider the first equation and let it be just identified. The 2SLS residuals are given by

$$\tilde{u}._1 = y._1 - Z_1\tilde{\delta}._1 \tag{4.5.40}$$

Thus

$$X'\tilde{u}._1 = X'y._1 - X'Z\tilde{\delta}._1 \tag{4.5.41}$$

But from (4.4.9) and (4.4.19) we find

$$X'Z_1\tilde{\delta}._1 = X'Z_1(Q_1'Q_1)^{-1}Q_1'w._1 = X'Z_1Q_1^{-1}w._1 = X'Z_1(X'Z_1)^{-1}X'y._1$$
$$= X'y._1 \tag{4.5.42}$$

As a result of (4.5.41), we conclude

$$X'\tilde{u}._1 = 0 \qquad\qquad\qquad\qquad\qquad\qquad \text{Q.E.D.} \tag{4.5.43}$$

Remark 14: In (4.5.31) we have obtained the (joint) asymptotic distribution of the 2SLS estimator of *all* the parameters of the system. The covariance matrix of that distribution is *not block diagonal unless* $\sigma_{ij} = 0$ *for* $i \neq j$.[14] It is clear, then, that when we derive the asymptotic distribution of the parameter estimators, one equation at a time, as we did in Section 4.3, we obtain, in fact, the *marginal distribution* of the estimator of the parameters contained in that equation. However, it is intuitively clear that other equations convey information regarding the parameters of the equation under consideration. Thus we conjuecture that the "single equation at a time" procedure may not make as effective a use of the information conveyed by the sample as might be possible. It is exactly this deficiency of 2SLS that one attempts to correct by the technique of *three-stage least squares*; we shall study the latter procedure at some length.

To conclude this section, we summarise the main conclusions of the present discussion in

Theorem 11: Consider the structural system of (identifiable) equations

$$y._i = Z_i\delta._i + u._i \qquad i = 1, 2, \ldots, m \tag{4.5.44}$$

and suppose the system contains no lagged endogenous variables. Suppose, also, that the error terms of the model $u_s. = (u_{s1}, u_{s2}, \ldots, u_{sm})$ are mutually independent for all s and such that

$$E(u_s'.) = 0 \quad \text{Cov}(u'._s) = \Sigma \quad E(X'u._i) = 0 \qquad \text{all } s, i \tag{4.5.45}$$

where

$$u._i = (u_{1i}, \ldots, u_{Ti})' \tag{4.5.46}$$

---

[14] As an exercise, the reader should verify the truth of this assertion.

is the vector of the errors appearing in the ith equation over the entire sample period. Let Y, X be, respectively, the matrices of observations on the current endogenous and predetermined variables of the system and suppose

$$\operatorname*{plim}_{T \to \infty} \frac{1}{T} \begin{bmatrix} Y'Y & Y'X \\ X'Y & X'X \end{bmatrix} = M \tag{4.5.47}$$

exists as a nonsingular matrix with nonstochastic elements. Then
  i. The asymptotic distribution of the 2SLS estimator of all parameters of the system is given by

$$\sqrt{T}(\tilde{\delta} - \delta) \sim N\left[0, \operatorname*{plim}_{T \to \infty} \left(\frac{Q'Q}{T}\right)^{-1} \frac{Q'}{\sqrt{T}} (\Sigma \otimes I_G) \frac{Q}{\sqrt{T}} \left(\frac{Q'Q}{T}\right)^{-1}\right] \tag{4.5.48}$$

provided the vectors u_s. in (4.5.46) obey, for every $\varepsilon > 0$,

$$\lim_{T \to \infty} \frac{1}{T} \sum_{s=1}^{T} \int_{|\phi| \geq \varepsilon\sqrt{T}} |\phi|^2 \, dF_s(\phi) = 0 \tag{4.5.49}$$

$F_s(\cdot)$ being the joint distribution of the elements of u_s..
 ii. If, in lieu of (4.5.45), we assert that

$$u'_s. \sim N(0, \Sigma) \qquad \text{all } s \tag{4.5.50}$$

then the conclusion in (4.5.48) is valid without the additional assumption in (4.5.49).
iii. If $\tilde{\delta}._1$ is the 2SLS estimator of the parameters of the first structural equation, then asymptotically

$$\sqrt{T}(\tilde{\delta}._1 - \delta._1) \sim N\left[0, \sigma_{11} \operatorname*{plim}_{T \to \infty} \left(\frac{Q_1'Q_1}{T}\right)^{-1}\right] \tag{4.5.51}$$

provided either (4.5.49) or (4.5.50) is valid.
 iv. Consistent estimators for the parameters of the asymptotic distribution in (4.5.48) and (4.5.51), respectively, may be obtained by

$$\left(\frac{Q'Q}{T}\right)^{-1} \frac{Q'}{\sqrt{T}} (\hat{\Sigma} \otimes I_G) \frac{Q}{\sqrt{T}} \left(\frac{Q'Q}{T}\right)^{-1}$$

and

$$\hat{\sigma}_{11} \left(\frac{Q_1'Q_1}{T}\right)^{-1}$$

where

$$\hat{\Sigma} = (\hat{\sigma}_{ij}) \quad \hat{\sigma}_{ij} = \frac{1}{T} \tilde{u}'._i \tilde{u}'._j \quad \tilde{u}._i = y._i - Z_i \tilde{\delta}._i \qquad i = 1, 2, \ldots, m \tag{4.5.52}$$

v. Tests of significance on individual 2SLS estimated parameters may be based (asymptotically) on the $N(0, 1)$ distribution.

vi. If an equation, say the ith, is just identified, then the 2SLS residuals, as given in (4.5.52), are orthogonal to the matrix of observations on the predetermined variables of the system, in the sense that $X'\tilde{u}._i = 0$.

4.6 THE GENERAL k-CLASS ESTIMATOR

The original motivation for the general k-class estimator is best understood by referring to the expression for the 2SLS estimator given in (4.3.89). Thus

$$\tilde{\delta}._1 = \begin{bmatrix} Y_1'Y_1 - \tilde{V}_1'\tilde{V}_1 & Y_1'X_1 \\ X_1'Y_1 & X_1'X_1 \end{bmatrix}^{-1} \begin{bmatrix} Y_1' - \tilde{V}_1' \\ X_1' \end{bmatrix} y._1 \tag{4.6.1}$$

The expression in (4.6.1) indicates that the 2SLS estimator is obtained by "purging" the explanatory current endogenous variables of their (estimated) components which are correlated with the error term in the relevant equation. Well, what if we remove not $\tilde{V}_1$ but something proportional to it? This is certain to give some flexibility. In this heuristic fashion, the *general k-class estimator of $\delta._1$ is defined by*

$$\tilde{\delta}._1(k) = \begin{bmatrix} Y_1'Y_1 - k\tilde{V}_1'\tilde{V}_1 & Y_1'X_1 \\ X_1'Y_1 & X_1'X_1 \end{bmatrix}^{-1} \begin{bmatrix} Y_1' - k\tilde{V}_1' \\ X_1' \end{bmatrix} y._1 \tag{4.6.2}$$

In (4.6.2) notice that whether we write $(Y_1 - k\tilde{V}_1)'X_1$ or simply $Y_1'X_1$ for the off-diagonal blocks is irrelevant, for the matrices $\tilde{V}_1$ and X are orthogonal and thus

$$\tilde{V}_1'X = 0. \tag{4.6.3}$$

This is certainly an interesting device in that it serves to unify the expressions for certain classes of estimators. Thus, the OLS estimator corresponds to $k = 0$, while 2SLS corresponds to $k = 1$. The limited-information, maximum likelihood estimator, which shall be developed later, is a k-class estimator as well. But beyond these interesting and rather minor properties it does not appear that this estimator is of particular usefulness except possibly in connection with the small sample properties of such estimators, were they to be satisfactorily established. Unfortunately, this is not yet the case, as we shall show at a later stage.

The reason the k-class estimator is of limited usefulness is that one can show easily in view of the discussion in Sections 4.3 and 4.4 that

$$\operatorname*{plim}_{T \to \infty} \tilde{\delta}._1(k) = \delta._1 + \begin{bmatrix} \Pi_1'M\Pi_1 + \operatorname*{plim}_{T \to \infty}(1 - k)D_1'\Sigma D_1\Pi_1'\begin{pmatrix} M_{11} \\ M_{21} \end{pmatrix} & \\ (M_{11}, M_{12})\Pi_1 & M_{11} \end{bmatrix}^{-1}$$

$$\times \begin{bmatrix} \operatorname*{plim}_{T \to \infty}(1 - k)D_1'\sigma._1 \\ 0 \end{bmatrix} \tag{4.6.4}$$

where Σ is the covariance matrix of the error terms in the entire structural system, $\sigma._1$ its first column, and D_1 is as defined in (4.3.36).

Hence we see that if k is stochastic, the k-class estimator will be consistent if and only if

$$\operatorname*{plim}_{T \to \infty} k = 1 \qquad\qquad (4.6.5)$$

so that the estimator asymptotically coincides with the 2SLS one. If k is non-stochastic, but nonetheless depends on the sample size, to emphasize this write $k(T)$, then $\tilde{\delta}._1(k)$ will be consistent if and only if

$$\lim_{T \to \infty} k(T) = 1 \qquad\qquad (4.6.6)$$

This is again a case of asymptotic coincidence with the 2SLS estimator. Finally, if k is a fixed constant, then $\tilde{\delta}._1(k)$ will be consistent if and only if

$$k = 1 \qquad\qquad (4.6.7)$$

But then we are reduced once more to the 2SLS estimator.

Some possible uses to which such estimators may be put will be considered at the end of the next section after we examine h- and double k-class estimators.

h- AND DOUBLE k-CLASS ESTIMATORS

If certain modifications are made to the k-class estimator, we obtain the h- and double k-class estimators. The modifications are as follows.

Consider the first structural equation again; thus

$$y._1 = Y_1\beta._1 + X_1\gamma._1 + u._1 \qquad\qquad (4.6.8)$$

In obtaining the k-class estimator, we employed an ad hoc procedure by operating on the expression for the 2SLS estimator. Suppose that we follow up, systematically, the line of reasoning implicit in that procedure and argue, instead, as follows. In (4.6.8) let us purge Y_1, not of the estimated residuals of its reduced form but rather of something proportional to them.

Thus in obtaining—hopefully consistent—estimators for the parameters in (4.6.8), we shall substitute for Y_1, $Y_1 - h\tilde{V}_1$, where as before $\tilde{V}_1$ is the matrix of reduced form residuals corresponding to Y_1.

Consequently, rewrite (4.6.8) as

$$y._1 = (Y_1 - h\tilde{V}_1)\beta._1 + X_1\gamma._1 + u._1 + h\tilde{V}_1\beta._1 \qquad\qquad (4.6.9)$$

and obtain the h-class estimator of

$$\delta._1 = \begin{pmatrix} \beta._1 \\ \gamma._1 \end{pmatrix}$$

as the OLS estimator of the parameters in (4.6.9). Thus we obtain[15]

$$\tilde{\delta}_{\cdot 1}(h) = \begin{bmatrix} Y_1'Y_1 - h(2-h)\tilde{V}_1'\tilde{V}_1 & Y_1'X_1 \\ X_1'Y_1 & X_1'X_1 \end{bmatrix}^{-1} \begin{bmatrix} Y_1' - h\tilde{V}_1' \\ X_1' \end{bmatrix} y_{\cdot 1} \qquad (4.6.10)$$

As in the case of the k-class estimators, we note that $\tilde{\delta}_{\cdot 1}(0)$ is the OLS estimator of the parameters in (4.6.8) and $\tilde{\delta}_{\cdot 1}(1)$ is the 2SLS estimator.

The double k-class is a modification of the h-class as follows. In (4.6.10) we note that there is a functional relation between the parameters ($2h - h^2$ and h, respectively) by which we operate on the matrix of reduced form residuals. It would certainly give us more flexibility if we could vary these parameters arbitrarily. Thus one may define the double k-class as

$$\tilde{\delta}_{\cdot 1}(k_1, k_2) = \begin{bmatrix} Y_1'Y_1 - k_1\tilde{V}_1'\tilde{V}_1 & Y_1'X_1 \\ X_1'Y_1 & X_1'X_1 \end{bmatrix}^{-1} \begin{bmatrix} Y_1' - k_2\tilde{V}_1' \\ X_1' \end{bmatrix} y_{\cdot 1} \qquad (4.6.11)$$

In view of the preceding discussion, one might ask: What is the motivation for considering such estimators? It is true that the k-class has considerable appeal as a summary statement of several commonly occurring estimators, but unless k converges to unity such estimators are inconsistent. On the other hand, if small sample properties of such estimators could be derived, the flexibility afforded us by the parameters of the k- or double k-class would be considerable.

It is developments along such lines that motivated the introduction of these estimators. Unfortunately, however, the results obtained are rather meager and thus the usefulness of such estimators is severely restricted. The small sample properties referred to above are largely due to Nagar [36]. We shall give a brief account of them and indicate their (considerable) limitations.

For simplicity and brevity, let us confine our discussion to the k-class. The arguments are essentially similar in the case of the h- or double k-class.

From the reduced form, we have

$$Y_1 = X\Pi_1 + V_1 \qquad (4.6.12)$$

For economy of notation, let

$$\bar{Y}_1 = X\Pi_1 \qquad (4.6.13)$$

Notice, also, that we can always write V_1 as a sum of two components such that one is a set of linear combinations of the elements of $u_{\cdot 1}$ and the other is uncorrelated with (in the case of normality independent of) $u_{\cdot 1}$. For example, write

$$V_1 = u_{\cdot 1}\xi' + W_1 \qquad (4.6.14)$$

where ξ is a column vector, the elements of which are to be determined.

---

[15] Notice that if we put $h = 1 - h^*$, then the h-class estimator can be also written in the form

$$\tilde{\delta}_{\cdot 1}(h^*) = \begin{bmatrix} Y_1'Y_1 - (1-h^{*2})\tilde{V}_1'\tilde{V}_1 & Y_1'X_1 \\ X_1'Y_1 & X_1'X_1 \end{bmatrix}^{-1} \begin{bmatrix} Y_1' - (1-h^*)\tilde{V}_1' \\ X_1' \end{bmatrix} y_{\cdot 1}$$

We see, therefore, that generally we would want $h^* \in (0, 1)$.

Since $V_1 = UD_1$, consider the expectation of $V_1'u._1$. It is

$$E(V_1'u._1) = D_1'E(U'u._1) = TD_1'\sigma._1 \tag{4.6.15}$$

Let

$$\xi = \frac{D_1'\sigma._1}{\sigma_{11}} \tag{4.6.16}$$

and thus observe

$$E(V_1'u._1) = \xi E(u'._1u._1) + E(W_1'u._1) = T\xi\sigma_{11} + E(W_1'u._1) \tag{4.6.17}$$

By (4.6.15) and (4.6.16), we conclude

$$E(W_1'u._1) = 0 \tag{4.6.18}$$

Next notice that the k-class estimator of the parameters of the first structural equation can be written as

$$\tilde{\delta}._1(k) = \delta._1 + \begin{bmatrix} Y_1'Y_1 - k\tilde{V}_1'\tilde{V}_1 & Y_1'X_1 \\ X_1'Y_1 & X_1'X_1 \end{bmatrix}^{-1} \begin{bmatrix} Y_1' - k\tilde{V}_1' \\ X_1' \end{bmatrix} u._1 \tag{4.6.19}$$

If we define

$$\bar{Z}_1 = (\bar{Y}_1, X_1) \quad V_1^* = (V_1, 0) \quad N^* = X(X'X)^{-1}X \tag{4.6.20}$$

then the matrix to be inverted in (4.6.19) is simply

$$\begin{bmatrix} Y_1'Y_1 - k\tilde{V}_1'\tilde{V}_1 & Y_1'X_1 \\ X_1'Y_1 & X_1'X_1 \end{bmatrix} = \bar{Z}_1'\bar{Z}_1 + V_1^{*'}\bar{Z}_1 + \bar{Z}_1'V_1^* + (1-k)V_1^{*'}V_1^*$$

$$+ kV_1^{*'}N^*V_1^* \tag{4.6.21}$$

where, we should observe, the zero matrix involved in the definition of V_1^* is of the same dimension as X_1. Note that

$$\tilde{V}_1 = NV_1 = V_1 - N^*V_1 \quad \dot{N} = I - N^* \tag{4.6.22}$$

Hence

$$\begin{bmatrix} Y_1' - k\tilde{V}_1' \\ X_1' \end{bmatrix} u._1 = \bar{Z}_1'u._1 + (1-k)V_1^{*'}u._1 + kV_1^{*'}N^*u._1 \tag{4.6.23}$$

Putting

$$\bar{Z}_1'\bar{Z}_1 = \bar{Q}_1^{-1} \tag{4.6.24}$$

we can then write the k-class estimator as

$$\tilde{\delta}._1(k) = \delta._1 + (I + Q_1F)^{-1}\bar{Q}_1[\bar{Z}_1' + (1-k)V_1^{*'} + kV_1^{*'}N^*]u._1 \tag{4.6.25}$$

where

$$F = V_1^{*'}\bar{Z}_1 + \bar{Z}_1'V_1^* + (1-k)V_1^{*'}V_1^* + kV_1^{*'}N^*V_1^* \tag{4.6.26}$$

One then proceeds to expand $(I + \bar{Q}_1 F)^{-1}$ by power series to obtain, formally,

$$(I + \bar{Q}_1 F)^{-1} = \sum_{s=0}^{\infty} (-1)^s (\bar{Q}_1 F)^s \tag{4.6.27}$$

One retains, at most, the two initial terms and argues that, approximately,

$$
\begin{aligned}
e_{.1}(k) = \tilde{\delta}_{.1}(k) - \delta_{.1} &= Q_1 [\bar{Z}_1' + (1-k)V_1^{*'} + kV_1^{*'}N^*]u_{.1} \\
&- \bar{Q}_1 F \bar{Q}_1 [\bar{Z}_1' + (1-k)V_1^{*'} + kV_1^{*'}N^*]u_{.1}{}^{16}
\end{aligned} \tag{4.6.28}
$$

Then by obtaining the expectation of $e_{.1}(k)$ and $e_{.1}(k)e_{.1}'(k)$, one argues that one has obtained the approximate small sample bias and covariance matrix characteristics of the k-class estimator. It is then further argued that one can choose k (or h or k_1 and k_2) so as to minimize the "small sample bias," or "small sample generalized variance," or some other appropriate objective function.

Even though this line of argument is intuitively very appealing, its usefulness in econometric research is extremely limited. It suffers from three major defects.

First, as we have shown in earlier discussion, the 2SLS estimator need not possess finite small sample moments.[17] If this is so, then it is certainly absurd to consider the expectation of the truncated sampling error $(\tilde{\delta}_{.1}(k) - \delta_{.1})$ in (4.6.28). Second, even if the small sample first- and second-order moments of the 2SLS estimator exist, the expansion in (4.6.27) may not be valid.

Finally, even if the expansion is valid, its expectation term by term may not be a valid procedure for obtaining the expectation of the sampling error.

Thus for k-class estimators to possess a rigorous basis and to be useful in empirical applications, the following conditions must hold.

i. The existence of finite moments up to at least second order must be established for the k-class estimator.
ii. The expansion in (4.6.27) must be valid, at least in probability.
iii. The term by term expectation of the series must be justified and its convergence to the expectation of the sampling error demonstrated.

If i does not hold, then we are trying to approximate an infinite quantity by a finite one and this is patently absurd. If i holds but ii does not, then considering the first two (or any finite number of) terms of that expansion has no meaning in terms of the quantity $e_{.1}(k)$, for the expansion in no way represents $e_{.1}(k)$.

---

[16] Incidentally, it is because of this development that the decomposition of V_1 in (4.6.14) is useful.

[17] It has been conjectured (but *not* proven) by Basmann [6] that the 2SLS estimator of the parameters of the ith structural equation has finite small sample moments up to order $G - G_i - m_i$, where $G_i + m_i$ is the number of parameters to be estimated in the ith structural equation and G is the number of predetermined variables in the entire system. Thus $G - G_i - m_i$ is the extent to which the ith equation is overidentified, and we see that for a just identified equation no finite small sample moments exist.

Finally, if i and ii hold but iii does not, then the expectation of the first few terms of the expansion has no meaning in terms of the *moments of e.₁(k) because the term-by-term expectation of the series does not converge to the expectation of the appropriate function of e.₁(k).*

The preceding points are best clarified through examples.

Example 3: Let $\{x_T : T = 1, 2, \ldots,\}$ be a family of random variables with the distribution

$$\Pr \{x_T = a\} = 1 - \frac{1}{T}$$

$$\Pr \{x_T = T^v\} = \frac{1}{T} \tag{4.6.29}$$

where v is some constant to be specified later, and consider

$$y_T = \frac{1}{1 + x_T} \tag{4.6.30}$$

Clearly,

$$E(y_T) = \frac{1}{1 + a} \left(1 - \frac{1}{T}\right) + \frac{1}{1 + T^v} \frac{1}{T} \tag{4.6.31}$$

which is finite for all T provided $a \neq -1$.

Now if we assume that $|a| < 1$, then, for given $v > 0$, there certainly exists a T^* such that for $T > T^*$

$$\Pr \{|x_T - a| > \delta\} < \varepsilon \tag{4.6.32}$$

for any preassigned (and small) $\delta, \varepsilon > 0$. Hence the expansion

$$y_T = \sum_{\tau=0}^{\infty} (-1)^{\tau} x_T^{\tau} \tag{4.6.33}$$

is valid (for $T > T^*$) with probability greater then $1 - \varepsilon$, where ε is arbitrarily small. On the other hand,

$$E(x_T^{\tau}) = a^{\tau} \left(1 - \frac{1}{T}\right) + T^{v\tau - 1} \tag{4.6.34}$$

and from (4.6.33) we shall then find, expecting term by term,

$$E(y_T) = \sum_{\tau=0}^{\infty} (-1)^{\tau} \left[a^{\tau} \left(1 - \frac{1}{T}\right) + T^{v\tau - 1}\right] \tag{4.6.35}$$

If $v > 0$, however, the right-hand side of (4.6.35) *does not* converge, which clearly illustrates the importance of condition iii above. The point to realize in connection with this example is that a power series expansion brings into consideration moments *of all orders of the basic random variable*. As we see from (4.6.31), the fact that certain higher moments of x_T may not exist as $T \to \infty$ does not prevent $E(y_T)$ from being finite. However, by the expansion in (4.6.33), we seek to represent $E(y_T)$ as a function of the τth moment of x_T for $\tau = 0, 1, 2, \dots$. Depending on the value of v, such moments diverge as $\tau \to \infty$. The fact that (4.6.35) is not valid in *no way implies the nonexistence of $E(y_T)$; it merely means that we cannot obtain it by means of the power series expansion*. To use a more familiar example, for a real number α, $1/(1 - \alpha)$ is a perfectly well-defined number even for $|\alpha| > 1$; if so, however, $1/(1 - \alpha)$ does *not* have a valid expression as the geometric series $\sum_{i=0}^{\infty} \alpha^i$!

Lest it appear that such cases can be concocted only with pathological distributions, consider another example.

Example 4: Consider again Example 1 of Section 4.3. There, we had established that the 2SLS estimator, $\hat{\beta}$, of the marginal propensity to consume in the simple Keynesian model is given by

$$\frac{\hat{\beta} - \beta}{1 - \beta} = \frac{r}{1 + r} \tag{4.6.36}$$

where

$$r \sim N(0, \phi) \qquad \phi = \frac{\sigma^2}{a'a} \tag{4.6.37}$$

and

$$\lim_{T \to \infty} a'a = \infty \tag{4.6.38}$$

In view of (4.6.38), we can choose T large enough so that

$$\Pr\{|r| \geq 1\} < \varepsilon \tag{4.6.39}$$

for preassigned $\varepsilon > 0$, arbitrarily small. Thus the expansion

$$\frac{r}{1 + r} = \sum_{\tau=0}^{\infty} (-1)^{\tau} r^{\tau+1} \tag{4.6.40}$$

is valid with probability arbitrarily close to unity. On the other hand,

$$E\left[\sum_{\tau=0}^{\infty} (-1)^{\tau} r^{\tau+1}\right] = \sum_{\tau=0}^{\infty} (-1)^{\tau} \frac{(2\tau + 2)!}{2^{\tau+1}(\tau + 1)!} \phi^{\tau+1} \tag{4.6.41}$$

which does not converge however small ϕ may be. But, of course, as we pointed out earlier, the expectation of $r/(1 + r)$ does not exist for any finite T even though the fraction converges in probability to zero.

Thus, minimally, one ought to verify that the expectation in (4.6.25) exists before the expansion in (4.6.27) is undertaken, and arguments are based on the

4.7 THREE-STAGE LEAST SQUARES (3SLS)

MOTIVATION

Earlier we saw that the problem of estimating the parameters of a structural system of equations by 2SLS can be reduced to the problem of estimating by ordinary least squares, the parameters of a "single equation" in the notation of (4.4.23).

However, it was also shown in Section 4.1 that in this context whether such a procedure is efficient or not depends on the covariance structure of the error terms in the various equations of the system. In particular, it was shown that if the error terms between any two equations were correlated, then a gain in efficiency would result by applying Aitken's procedure provided that not all equations contain the same variables. There is an exact parallel in the present case, which would thus lead us to conjecture that, at least in some asymptotic sense, a procedure that would take into account this postulated covariance structure will be efficient relative to the 2SLS procedure, which does not. Of course, it is apparent on intuitive grounds that 2SLS estimation does not use the sample on the entire system efficiently. This is so since, in general, different equations will contain different explanatory variables. If their respective error terms are correlated, then by focusing our attention on one equation at a time we are neglecting the information conveyed by the rest of the system. If we could use such information, then clearly we would improve on 2SLS.

THE THREE-STAGE LEAST SQUARES ESTIMATOR

Consider again the system

$$y_{.i} = Y_i\beta_{.i} + X_i\gamma_{.i} + u_{.i} \qquad i = 1, 2, \ldots, m \tag{4.7.1}$$

and its associated transform

$$R^{-1}X'y_{.i} = R^{-1}X'Y_i\beta_{.i} + R^{-1}X'X_i\gamma_{.i} + R^{-1}X'u_{.i} \qquad i = 1, 2, \ldots, m \tag{4.7.2}$$

where R is a *nonsingular matrix* such that

$$RR' = X'X \tag{4.7.3}$$

One of the assumptions underlying this entire estimation scheme is that[18]

$$\operatorname*{plim}_{T \to \infty} \frac{X'X}{T} = M_{xx} \tag{4.7.4}$$

exists as a nonsingular matrix.

---

[18] Evidently if all predetermined variables are assumed to be nonstochastic, then $\operatorname{plim}_{T\to\infty}$ should be replaced by $\lim_{T\to\infty}$ in (4.7.4) as well as (4.7.6).

Since

$$\left(\frac{X'X}{T}\right)^{-1} = TR'^{-1}R^{-1} \tag{4.7.5}$$

we conclude that

$$\operatorname*{plim}_{T \to \infty} \sqrt{T}R^{-1} = \bar{R} \tag{4.7.6}$$

exists as a matrix with finite elements. If we define w, Q, δ, and r as in (4.4.21) and (4.4.22), we have

$$w = Q\delta + r \tag{4.7.7}$$

Now, by definition,

$$r = Fu \quad F = I_m \otimes R^{-1}X' \quad u = \begin{pmatrix} u_{.1} \\ u_{.2} \\ \vdots \\ u_{.m} \end{pmatrix} \tag{4.7.8}$$

and we see that if the system does not contain any lagged endogenous variables, we can argue as follows: We know that

$$E(u) = 0 \quad \operatorname{Cov}(u) = \Sigma \otimes I_T \tag{4.7.9}$$

and thus, conditionally on X, we find

$$E(r) = 0 \quad \operatorname{Cov}(r) = F(\Sigma \otimes I_T)F' = \Sigma \otimes R^{-1}X'XR'^{-1} = \Sigma \otimes I_G \tag{4.7.10}$$

But (4.7.10) implies that *even unconditionally* on F the mean vector and covariance matrix of r do not depend on X. Now, if 2SLS estimation of δ is OLS estimation in the context of (4.7.7) and if the covariance matrix of r is not scalar, then we are encouraged to think that Aitken methods applied to the problem will yield relatively efficient estimators. Notice, also, that in this formulation the dimensions of the covariance matrix of the system have been reduced from mT to mG.

Now, in the context of (4.7.7), the Aitken estimator of δ is given by

$$\bar{\delta} = (Q'\Phi^{-1}Q)^{-1}Q'\Phi^{-1}w \tag{4.7.11}$$

where

$$\Phi = \Sigma \otimes I_G = \operatorname{Cov}(r) \tag{4.7.12}$$

Clearly, since Σ will typically be unknown, the estimator in (4.7.11) is not feasible. If a consistent estimator of the $(m \times m)$ matrix Σ exists, say $\hat{\Sigma}$, then the feasible Aitken estimator is given by

$$\hat{\delta} = (Q'\hat{\Phi}^{-1}Q)^{-1}Q'\hat{\Phi}^{-1}w \quad \hat{\Phi} = \hat{\Sigma} \otimes I_G \tag{4.7.13}$$

A consistent estimator of Σ does indeed exist, and in fact it was given in (4.5.37). It is simply the "sample" covariance matrix of the 2SLS residuals of the system.

The estimator in (4.7.13) was termed by its discoverers, H. Theil and A. Zellner, the *three-stage least squares* (3SLS) estimator. Perhaps it would be more appropriate to call it the Aitken structural estimator, while the 2SLS should be termed the OLS structural estimator. The term 3SLS has the following intuitive interpretation: Proceeding from first principles, as in Section 4.3, in the "first" stage we purge from the explanatory current endogenous variables their stochastic components; in the "second" stage we obtain a consistent estimator for Σ; in the "third" stage we obtain the desired estimator of the structural parameters. Although a rather cumbersome view of the process, it is, for better or worse, the historically initial and established view.

Actually, and despite the terminology, the 3SLS estimator in (4.7.13) can be computed *in one operation*. The reason is that the typical element of the matrix $\hat{\Sigma}$ can be expressed solely in terms of the moment matrices of the data. For example,

$$\hat{\sigma}_{ij} = \frac{1}{T} y'_{\cdot i} A_{ij} y_{\cdot j} \qquad i, j = 1, 2, \ldots, m \tag{4.7.14}$$

where A_{ij} is the $T \times T$ matrix

$$A_{ij} = [I - Z_i(Q'_i Q_i)^{-1} Q'_i R^{-1} X'][I - Z_j(Q'_j Q_j)^{-1} Q'_j R^{-1} X'] \tag{4.7.15}$$

Having defined what we wish to mean by the 3SLS estimator, let us take a more detailed view of it.

Expanding (4.7.13), we see that

$$\hat{\delta} = \begin{bmatrix} \hat{\sigma}^{11} Q'_1 Q_1 & \hat{\sigma}^{12} Q'_1 Q_2 & \cdots & \hat{\sigma}^{1m} Q'_1 Q_m \\ \hat{\sigma}^{21} Q'_2 Q_1 & \hat{\sigma}^{22} Q'_2 Q_2 & \cdots & \hat{\sigma}^{2m} Q'_2 Q_m \\ \cdot & \cdot & \cdot & \cdot \\ \hat{\sigma}^{m1} Q'_m Q_1 & \hat{\sigma}^{m2} Q'_m Q_2 & \cdots & \hat{\sigma}^{mm} Q'_m Q_m \end{bmatrix}^{-1} \begin{bmatrix} \sum_{j=1}^{m} \hat{\sigma}^{1j} Z'_1 X(X'X)^{-1} X' y_{\cdot j} \\ \sum_{j=1}^{m} \hat{\sigma}^{2j} Z'_2 X(X'X)^{-1} X' y_{\cdot j} \\ \cdot \quad \cdot \quad \cdot \quad \cdot \quad \cdot \quad \cdot \\ \sum_{j=1}^{m} \hat{\sigma}^{mj} Z'_m X(X'X)^{-1} X' y_{\cdot j} \end{bmatrix} \tag{4.7.16}$$

where, we remind the reader,

$$Q_i = R^{-1} X' Z_i \quad \hat{\Sigma}^{-1} = (\hat{\sigma}^{ij}) \quad Z_i = (Y_i, X_i) \qquad i = 1, 2, \ldots, m \tag{4.7.17}$$

CONSISTENCY OF THE 3SLS ESTIMATOR

The approach in establishing the consistency of this estimator is exactly parallel to that employed in dealing with 2SLS. Substituting (4.7.7) into (4.7.13), we find

$$\hat{\delta} = \delta + (Q'\hat{\Phi}^{-1}Q)^{-1} Q'\hat{\Phi}^{-1} r \tag{4.7.18}$$

Now

$$(Q'\hat{\Phi}^{-1}Q)^{-1} Q'\hat{\Phi}^{-1} r = \left(\frac{Q'\hat{\Phi}^{-1}Q}{T} \right)^{-1} \frac{Q'}{\sqrt{T}} \hat{\Phi}^{-1} \frac{r}{\sqrt{T}} \tag{4.7.19}$$

Consider, first, the probability limit of the first matrix in the right-hand side of (4.7.19). In (4.7.16) we have given a fuller expression of it, and we see that the existence of that limit as a matrix with nonstochastic elements entails a nonstochastic probability limit for the quantities $\hat{\sigma}^{ij}(Q_i'Q_j/T)$. But

$$\hat{\sigma}^{ij}\frac{Q_i'Q_j}{T} = \hat{\sigma}^{ij}\frac{Z_i'X}{T}\left(\frac{X'X}{T}\right)^{-1}\frac{X'Z_j}{T} \tag{4.7.20}$$

and since $\hat{\sigma}_{ij}$ is a consistent estimator of σ^{ij}, we conclude in view of the assumption in (4.5.47) that the probability limit in question is a nonstochastic matrix with finite elements. By the same arguments we establish that the probability limit of $(Q'/\sqrt{T})\hat{\Phi}^{-1}$ is also a nonstochastic matrix with finite elements. Hence whether $\hat{\delta}$ is consistent or not hinges on the probability limit of $r/\sqrt{T}$. By definition, however, we have

$$\frac{r}{\sqrt{T}} = \frac{Fu}{\sqrt{T}} \tag{4.7.21}$$

where F is as defined in (4.7.8). The ith subvector of this is given by

$$\frac{R^{-1}X'u_{\cdot i}}{\sqrt{T}} = \sqrt{T}R^{-1}\frac{X'u_{\cdot i}}{T} \tag{4.7.22}$$

By (4.7.6) we see that the probability limit of the right-hand side of (4.7.22) is given by

$$\bar{R}\plim_{T\to\infty}\frac{X'u_{\cdot i}}{T}$$

Since $\bar{R}$ is a nonstochastic matrix with finite elements and

$$\plim_{T\to\infty}\frac{X'u_{\cdot i}}{T} = 0 \qquad i = 1, 2, \ldots, m \tag{4.7.23}$$

we conclude, from (4.7.18),

$$\plim_{T\to\infty}\hat{\delta} = \delta \tag{4.7.24}$$

which establishes the consistency of 3SLS.

ASYMPTOTIC DISTRIBUTION OF 3SLS

The perceptive reader will have noticed that the consistency property of 3SLS has been established in a rather straightforward fashion *without the necessity of assuming that the system contains no lagged endogenous variables.* Although the asymptotic distribution of 3SLS can be similarly established without this restrictive assumption, nonetheless, in this case the proof becomes rather involved. Consequently, in the following argument we shall assume that the system does not contain (amongst its predetermined variables) lagged endogenous variables.

We can rewrite (4.7.18) as

$$\sqrt{T}(\hat{\delta} - \delta) = \left(\frac{Q'\hat{\Phi}^{-1}Q}{T}\right)^{-1} \frac{Q'\hat{\Phi}^{-1}r}{\sqrt{T}} \qquad (4.7.25)$$

From (4.7.25) it is easily seen that the question of the asymptotic distribution of $\sqrt{T}(\hat{\delta} - \delta)$ resolves into the question of the asymptotic distribution of $Q'\hat{\Phi}^{-1}r/\sqrt{T}$. First, we note that the asymptotic distribution of the latter is exactly the asymptotic distribution of $Q'\Phi^{-1}r/\sqrt{T}$, where

$$\Phi = \Sigma \otimes I_G \qquad (4.7.26)$$

Now, by definition of the quantities involved,

$$Q'\Phi^{-1}r = Q'(\Sigma^{-1} \otimes I_G)(I_m \otimes R^{-1}X')u \qquad (4.7.27)$$

where u is as defined in (4.7.8). Moreover, if we define

$$Q_i^{*'} = Q_i' R^{-1}X' \qquad Q^{*'} = \text{diag}\,(Q_1^{*'}, Q_2^{*'}, \ldots, Q_m^{*'}) \qquad (4.7.28)$$

we easily verify that

$$Q'\Phi^{-1}r = Q^{*'}(\Sigma^{-1} \otimes I_T)u \qquad (4.7.29)$$

and we further observe

$$Q^{*'} = Q'(I_m \otimes R^{-1})(I_m \otimes X'). \qquad (4.7.30)$$

Let

$$B = \text{diag}\,(B_1, B_2, \ldots, B_m) \qquad B_i = Q_i' R^{-1} \qquad = 1, 2, \ldots, m \qquad (4.7.31)$$

and notice that the quantities

$$\underset{T \to \infty}{\text{plim}}\, B_i = \underset{T \to \infty}{\text{plim}}\, \frac{Q_i'}{\sqrt{T}} \sqrt{T}R^{-1} \qquad i = 1, 2, \ldots, m \qquad (4.7.32)$$

exist as nonstochastic matrices with finite elements. Also, let $\sigma^{i\cdot}$ be *the* ith row of Σ^{-1}, $u_{s\cdot}$ the row vector containing the error terms of the m equations of the system at "time" s and x_s'. the sth column of X'. One easily verifies that

$$\frac{Q'\Phi^{-1}r}{\sqrt{T}} = B \sum_{s=1}^{T} \frac{V_s u_{s\cdot}'}{\sqrt{T}} \qquad (4.7.33)$$

where

$$V_s = \begin{bmatrix} V_s^{(1)} \\ V_s^{(2)} \\ \vdots \\ V_s^{(m)} \end{bmatrix} \qquad V_s^{(i)} = x_s'. \,\sigma^{i\cdot} \qquad (4.7.34)$$

Since B has a well-defined nonstochastic probability limit, we conclude that the asymptotic distribution of $Q'\Phi^{-1}r/\sqrt{T}$ is determined essentially by the asymptotic distribution of

$$\frac{1}{\sqrt{T}} \sum_{s=1}^{T} V_s u_s'.$$

If, as we customarily assume, observations on the variables of the system constitute a random sample, then the $V_s u_s'.$, $s = 1, 2, \ldots,$ constitute a set of mutually independent random vectors.[19] Let $F_s(\cdot)$ be the joint distribution of the (mG) elements of $V_s u_s'.$ and suppose that for every $\varepsilon > 0$ the convergence condition

$$\lim_{T \to \infty} \frac{1}{T} \sum_{s=1}^{T} \int_{|\phi| > \varepsilon \sqrt{T}} |\phi|^2 dF_s(\phi) = 0 \tag{4.7.35}$$

is satisfied. Then by Theorem 6 of Chapter 3, we conclude that, asymptotically,

$$\frac{1}{\sqrt{T}} \sum_{s=1}^{T} V_s u_s'. \sim N\left(0, \lim_{T \to \infty} \frac{1}{T} \sum_{s=1}^{T} V_s \Sigma V_s'\right) \tag{4.7.36}$$

If the elements of X are stochastic, then the term $V_s \Sigma V_s'$ is to be replaced by $E(V_s \Sigma V_s')$, assuming that the elements of $x_s.$ have finite second moments. In that case, the covariance matrix in (4.7.36) may be replaced by

$$\underset{T \to \infty}{\text{plim}} \frac{1}{T} \sum_{s=1}^{T} V_s \Sigma V_s' \tag{4.7.37}$$

From (4.7.36) and Proposition 2 of Chapter 3, we conclude that the asymptotic distribution of the 3SLS estimator is given by

$$\sqrt{T}(\hat{\delta} - \delta) \sim N\left[0, \underset{T \to \infty}{\text{plim}} \left(\frac{Q'\Phi^{-1}Q}{T}\right)^{-1}\right] \tag{4.7.38}$$

To see how the covariance matrix of this distribution is obtained, we first consider the covariance matrix in (4.7.36). From the definition of V_s in (4.7.34), we see that the (i, j) block (matrix) element of $V_s \Sigma V_s'$ is given by $V_s^{(i)} \Sigma V_s^{(j)'}$. The (r, α) (scalar) element of the latter is given by

$$\sum_{v=1}^{m} \sum_{\tau=1}^{m} x_{sr} \sigma^{i\tau} \sigma_{\tau v} \sigma^{vj} x_{s\alpha} = \sum_{v=1}^{m} \delta_{iv} x_{sr} x_{s\alpha} \sigma^{vj} = x_{sr} x_{s\alpha} \sigma^{ij} \tag{4.7.39}$$

where δ_{iv} is the Kronecker delta. Thus, summing over s, we conclude

$$\sum_{s=1}^{T} V_s^{(i)} \Sigma V_s^{(j)'} = \sigma^{ij} X'X \tag{4.7.40}$$

---

[19] Notice that if the vector $x_s.$ contains lagged endogenous variables, it cannot be so easily established that the vectors $V_s u_s'.$ are mutually independent, even if we assume that the exogenous variables and error terms are *intertemporally mutually independent*.

Therefore

$$\sum_{s=1}^{T} V_s \Sigma V'_s = \Sigma^{-1} \otimes X'X \qquad (4.7.41)$$

It follows that the covariance matrix of the asymptotic distribution of $Q'\Phi^{-1}r/\sqrt{T}$ is given by

$$\operatorname*{plim}_{T \to \infty} \frac{1}{T} B(\Sigma^{-1} \otimes X'X)B' = \operatorname*{plim}_{T \to \infty} \frac{1}{T} Q'(\Sigma^{-1} \otimes I_G)Q$$

$$= \operatorname*{plim}_{T \to \infty} \frac{Q'\Phi^{-1}Q}{T} \qquad (4.7.42)$$

Since the asymptotic distribution of $\sqrt{T}(\hat{\delta} - \delta)$ is exactly that of

$$\left(\frac{Q'\Phi^{-1}Q}{T}\right)^{-1} \frac{Q'\Phi^{-1}r}{\sqrt{T}}$$

the conclusion in (4.7.38) follows immediately.

The discussion above may be summarized in

Theorem 12: Let

$$y_{\cdot i} = Y_i \beta_{\cdot i} + X_i \gamma_{\cdot i} + u_{\cdot i} \qquad i = 1, 2, \ldots, m \qquad (4.7.43)$$

be a system of structural equations (not containing identities), X be the matrix of observations on the predetermined variables of the system, and

$$u_{s\cdot} = (u_{s1}, u_{s2}, \ldots, u_{sm}) \qquad (4.7.44)$$

the vector of disturbances in the equations of the system at "time" s. Suppose, also, that

$$E(u'_{s\cdot}) = 0 \quad E(Xu'_{s\cdot}) = 0 \quad \operatorname{rank}(X) = G \quad \operatorname{Cov}(u'_{s'\cdot}, u'_{s\cdot}) = \delta_{ss'} \Sigma \qquad \text{all } s, s' \qquad (4.7.45)$$

$\delta_{ss'}$ being the Kronecker delta. Then the 3SLS estimator defined by

$$\hat{\delta} = (Q'\hat{\Phi}^{-1}Q)^{-1}Q'\hat{\Phi}^{-1}w \qquad (4.7.46)$$

where δ, Q, w are as defined in (4.4.22) and $\hat{\Phi}$ is as defined in (4.7.13), is a consistent estimator of δ provided

$$\operatorname*{plim}_{T \to \infty} \left(\frac{Q'\Phi^{-1}Q}{T}\right)^{-1}$$

exists as a nonstochastic matrix with finite elements. If, in addition, we assume that the vectors $u_{s\cdot}$ are mutually independent, that the system does not contain lagged endogenous amongst its predetermined variables, and that the vectors

$V_s u_s'$, as defined in (4.7.34), obey (4.7.35), then the asymptotic distribution of the 3SLS estimator is given by

$$\sqrt{T}(\hat{\delta} - \delta) \sim N\left[0, \operatorname*{plim}_{T\to\infty} \left(\frac{Q'\Phi^{-1}Q}{T}\right)^{-1}\right] \tag{4.7.47}$$

EFFICIENCY OF 3SLS RELATIVE TO 2SLS AND RELATED ASPECTS

From the preceding discussion it is apparent that the 3SLS estimator is far more complex and computationally burdensome than the 2SLS one. Thus we are entitled to ask: What do we gain by it and under what circumstances does the gain, if any, materialize?

In this section we shall establish that 3SLS is efficient relative to 2SLS in the sense that the difference of the covariance matrices of the asymptotic distribution of the two estimators forms a positive semidefinite matrix. We shall also determine the circumstances under which 3SLS is *strictly efficient relative to* 2SLS in a sense to be made clear below. It is interesting that in dealing with these questions exactly the same arguments may be employed as in Sections 4.1, 4.2 where we dealt with the question of the efficiency of Aitken relative to OLS estimators in the context of a system of regression equations. Thus define a matrix A by

$$(Q'Q)^{-1}Q' = (Q'\Phi^{-1}Q)^{-1}Q'\Phi^{-1} + A \tag{4.7.48}$$

and note that A has the property

$$AQ = 0 \tag{4.7.49}$$

Further, note that

$$\sqrt{T}A = \left(\frac{Q'Q}{T}\right)^{-1}\frac{Q'}{\sqrt{T}} - \left(\frac{Q'\Phi^{-1}Q}{T}\right)^{-1}\frac{Q'}{\sqrt{T}}\Phi^{-1} \tag{4.7.50}$$

Since the matrices in the right-hand member of (4.7.50) were earlier shown to have well-defined nonstochastic probability limits, we conclude that

$$\operatorname*{plim}_{T\to\infty} \sqrt{T}A = \bar{A} \tag{4.7.51}$$

exists as a nonstochastic matrix with finite elements. We remind the reader that A and hence $\bar{A}$ are both of finite dimensions; in particular, they have $\sum_{i=1}^{m}(m_i + G_i)$ rows and mG columns.

Notice that

$$[\sqrt{T}(Q'Q)^{-1}Q']\Phi[\sqrt{T}Q(Q'Q)^{-1}] = \left(\frac{Q'Q}{T}\right)^{-1}\frac{Q'\Phi Q}{T}\left(\frac{Q'Q}{T}\right)^{-1} \tag{4.7.52}$$

In view of (4.7.48) the matrix in (4.7.52) can be written as

$$\left(\frac{Q'Q}{T}\right)^{-1}\frac{Q'\Phi Q}{T}\left(\frac{Q'Q}{T}\right)^{-1} = \left[\left(\frac{Q'\Phi^{-1}Q}{T}\right)^{-1}\frac{Q'}{\sqrt{T}}\Phi^{-1} + \sqrt{T}A\right]\Phi$$

$$\times\left[\Phi^{-1}\frac{Q}{\sqrt{T}}\left(\frac{Q'\Phi^{-1}Q}{T}\right)^{-1} + \sqrt{T}A'\right]$$

$$= \left(\frac{Q'\Phi^{-1}Q}{T}\right)^{-1} + (\sqrt{T}A)\Phi(\sqrt{T}A)' \qquad (4.7.53)$$

The last equality of (4.7.53) holds by (4.7.49). Taking probability limits, we conclude

$$\operatorname*{plim}_{T\to\infty}\left[\left(\frac{Q'Q}{T}\right)^{-1}\frac{Q'\Phi Q}{T}\left(\frac{Q'Q}{T}\right)^{-1}\right] = \operatorname*{plim}_{T\to\infty}\left(\frac{Q'\Phi^{-1}Q}{T}\right)^{-1} + \bar{A}\Phi\bar{A}' \qquad (4.7.54)$$

But the left-hand side of (4.7.54) is the covariance matrix of the asymptotic distribution of the 2SLS estimator of the parameters of the entire system, say C_2; the first term in the right-hand side is similarly the covariance matrix of the asymptotic distribution of the 3SLS estimator, say C_3. Thus (4.7.54) states

$$C_2 - C_3 = \bar{A}\Phi\bar{A}' \qquad (4.7.55)$$

Since Φ is a positive definite matrix, clearly $\bar{A}\Phi\bar{A}'$ is *at least positive semidefinite*.

We therefore conclude from Corollary 5 of the Mathematical Appendix that unless

$$\operatorname{rank} \bar{A} = 0 \qquad (4.7.56)$$

we should have

$$|C_2| > |C_3| \qquad (4.7.57)$$

In any event, *it is generally true that*

$$|C_2| \geq |C_3| \qquad (4.7.58)$$

Similarly, if c_{ii}^2, c_{ii}^3 are, respectively, the ith diagonal (scalar) element of C_2 and C_3, then

$$c_{ii}^2 \geq c_{ii}^3 \qquad i = 1, 2, \ldots, \sum_{j=1}^{m}(m_j + G_j) \qquad (4.7.59)$$

and unless (4.7.56) *holds, the strict inequality obtains for at least one index i.*

Remark 15: Although the preceding discussion establishes the precise conditions under which one might expect to gain in efficiency by using the 3SLS estimator, it should be noted that the condition (4.7.56) cannot, in general, be verified empirically. As a rough rule (which, however, cannot be supported rigorously), one might conjecture that (4.7.56) would not generally hold unless $\bar{A}$ is the zero matrix and that the latter is unlikely to hold unless A is the *zero matrix*. Hence one would expect a gain in efficiency unless the 3SLS and 2SLS estimators coincide.

The remark above, would naturally motivate the question: When is there no gain in efficiency by the use of the 3SLS estimator? Clearly, if it is known that the error terms in distinct equations are uncorrelated, that is, if it is known that

$$\sigma_{ij} = 0 \qquad i \neq j \tag{4.7.60}$$

then

$$(Q'\Phi^{-1}Q)^{-1}Q'\Phi^{-1} = \operatorname{diag}\left[\sigma_{11}(Q_1'Q_1)^{-1}, \ldots, \sigma_{mm}(Q_m'Q_m)^{-1}\right]$$

$$\times \operatorname{diag}\left[\frac{Q_1'}{\sigma_{11}}, \ldots, \frac{Q_m'}{\sigma_{mm}}\right] = (Q'Q)^{-1}Q' \tag{4.7.61}$$

Hence in this case

$$A = 0 \tag{4.7.62}$$

and

$$C_2 = C_3 \tag{4.7.63}$$

so that no gain results.

Indeed, one can show directly from (4.7.61), replacing σ_{ii} by $\hat{\sigma}_{ii}$, that 2SLS and 3SLS are *exactly identical*.

When we dealt with the case of systems of regression equations in Section 4.1, there was another circumstance under which OLS and Aitken estimators coincided. That was when all regressions contained the *same* explanatory variables. What corresponds to this case here? Well, it is interesting that this is the case where each equation of the system is *just identified*. Notice that when this is so, the matrices Q_i are square matrices of order $m_i + G_i = G$ and thus, we would expect, nonsingular. So,

$$(Q'\Phi^{-1}Q)^{-1}Q'\Phi^{-1} = Q^{-1}\Phi Q'^{-1}Q'\Phi^{-1} = Q^{-1} \tag{4.7.64}$$

On the other hand,

$$(Q'Q)^{-1}Q' = Q^{-1}Q'^{-1}Q' = Q^{-1} \tag{4.7.65}$$

which again shows that (4.7.62) holds. Of course, (4.7.64) would still be valid if Φ^{-1} is replaced by $\hat{\Phi}^{-1}$ so that 2SLS and 3SLS are exactly identical. Incidentally, notice that in this case computations are considerably simplified, for

$$\tilde{\delta} = \hat{\delta} = Q^{-1}w \tag{4.7.66}$$

It has also been shown by Zellner and Theil [58] that if m^* of the equations of the system are *overidentified*, while the remaining $m - m^*$ are *just identified*, then the 3SLS estimator of the parameters of the former set would be the same whether they are derived solely on the basis of the first subsystem or on the basis of the entire system.

Of course, it should be obvious that if the entire system can be decomposed into distinct subsystems so that the error terms in one subsystem are *uncorrelated with those of another*, then there is no gain in efficiency by considering the system as a whole. Rather, we should estimate by 3SLS the parameters within each subsystem separately.

The major conclusions of this section may be summarized in

Theorem 13: Consider the model and the assumptions set forth in the statement of Theorem 12 and let C_2, C_3 be, respectively, the covariance matrices of the asymptotic distribution of the 2SLS and 3SLS estimators. Then

$$C = C_2 - C_3 \tag{4.7.67}$$

is a positive semidefinite matrix. In special cases where

$$\sigma_{ij} = 0 \qquad i \neq j \tag{4.7.68}$$

or every equation in the system is just identified, then

$$C = 0 \tag{4.7.69}$$

and the 2SLS and 3SLS estimators exactly coincide.

REFERENCES

1. Aitken, A. C., "On Least Squares and Linear Combinations of Observations," *Proceedings of the Royal Society*, Edinburgh, vol. 55, 1935, pp. 42–48.
2. Basmann, R. L., "A Generalized Classical Method of Linear Estimation of Coefficients in a Structural Equation," *Econometrica*, vol. 25, 1957, pp. 77–83.
3. Basmann, R. L., "The Computation of Coefficients in a Structural Equation," *Econometrica*, vol. 27, 1959, pp. 72–81.
4. Basmann, R. L., "On Finite Sample Distributions of Generalized Classical Linear Identifiability Test Statistics," *Journal of the American Statistical Association*, vol. 55, 1960, pp. 650–659.
5. Basmann, R. L., "On the Assymptotic Distribution of Generalized Linear Estimators," *Econometrica*, vol. 28, 1960, pp. 97–107.
6. Basmann, R. L., "A Note on the Exact Finite Sample Frequency Functions of Generalized Classical Linear Estimators in Two Leading Overidentified Cases," *Journal of the American Statistical Association*, vol. 56, 1961, pp. 619–636.
7. Bronfenbrenner, J., "Sources and Size of Least Squares Bias in a Two-Equation Model," Chapter 9 in *Studies in Econometric Methods*, W. C. Hood and T. C. Koopmans (Eds.), Cowles Foundation for Research in Economics, Monograph No. 14, New York, Wiley, 1953.
8. Chow, G. C., "Tests of Equality Between Sets of Coefficients in Two Linear Regressions," *Econometrica*, vol. 28, 1960, pp. 591–605.
9. Chow, G. C., "A Comparison of Alternative Estimators for Simultaneous Equations," *Econometrica*, vol. 32, 1964, pp. 532–553.

10. Chow, Gregory C., and D. K. Ray-Chandhuri, "An Alternative Proof of Hannan's Theorem on Canonical Correlation and Multiple Equation Systems, *Econometrica*, vol. 35, 1967, pp. 139–142.
11. Christ, C. F., "Aggregate Econometric Models" in the American Economic Association *Readings in Business Cycles*, R. A. Gordon and L. R. Klein (Eds.), pp. 307–333, Homewood, Illinois, Richard D. Irwin, May, 1965.
12. Christ, C. F., *Econometric Models and Methods*, New York, Wiley, 1966. Part 3 deals with the theoretical issues regarding inference in econometric models.
13. Christ, C. F., C. Hildreth, T. Liu, and L. R. Klein, "A Symposium on Simultaneous Equation Estimation," *Econometrica*, vol. 28, 1960, pp. 835–871.
14. Durbin, J., "Maximum Likelihood Estimation of the Parameters of a System of Simultaneous Regression Equations." Paper presented at the Economectric Society meetings, Copenhagen, 1963.
15. Fisher, F. M., "Generalization of the Rank and Order Conditions for Identifiability," *Econometrica*, vol. 27, 1959, pp. 431–447.
16. Fisk, P. R., *Stochastically Dependent Equations: An Introductory Text for Econometricians*, New York, Hafner Publishing Co., 1967.
17. Fox, Karl, "Econometric Models of the United States," *Journal of Political Economy*, vol. 64, 1956, pp. 128–142.
18. Goldberger, A. S., A. L. Nagar, and H. S. Odeh, "The Covariance Matrices of Reduced-Form Coefficients and of Forecasts for a Structural Econometric Model," *Econometrica*, vol. 29, 1961, pp. 556–573.
19. Goldberger, A. S., *Econometric Theory*, New York, Wiley, 1964.
20. Haavelmo, T., "The Statistical Implications of a System of Simultaneous Equations," *Econometrica*, vol. 11, 1943, pp. 1–12.
21. Haavelmo, T., "Methods of Measuring the Marginal Propensity to Consume," Chapter 4 in *Studies in Econometric Methods*, W. C. Hood and T. C. Koopmans (Eds.), Cowles Foundation for Research in Economics, Monograph No. 14, New York, Wiley, 1953.
22. Hannan, E. J., "Canonical Correlation and Multiple Equation Systems in Economics," *Econometrica*, vol. 35, 1967, pp. 123–138.
23. Hooper, J. W., "Simultaneous Equations and Canonical Correlation Theory," *Econometrica*, vol. 27, 1959, pp. 245–256.
24. Hooper, J. W., and A. Zellner, "The Error of Forecast for Multivariate Regression Models," *Econometrica*, vol. 29, 1961, pp. 544–555.
25. Johnston, J., *Econometric Methods*, New York, McGraw-Hill, 1963.
26. Kabe, D. G., "On the Exact Distributions of the GCL Estimators in a Leading Three Equation Case," *Journal of the American Statistical Association*, vol. 59, 1964, pp. 881–894.
27. Klein, L. R., *An Introduction to Econometrics*, Englewood Cliffs, N.J., Prentice-Hall, 1962.
28. Kloek, T., and L. B. M. Mennes, "Simultaneous Equations Estimation Based on Principal Components of Predetermined Variables," *Econometrica*, vol. 28, 1960, pp. 45–61.
29. Koopmans, T. C., "Identification Problems in Economic Model Construction," Chapter 2 in *Studies in Econometric Methods*, W. C. Hood and T. C. Koopmans (Eds.), Cowles Foundation for Research in Economics, Monograph No. 14, New York, Wiley, 1953.
30. Koopmans, T. C., and W. C. Hood, "The Estimation of Simultaneous Linear Economic Relationships," Chapter 6 in *Studies in Econometric Method*, W. C. Hood and T. C. Koopmans (Eds.) Cowles Foundation for Research in Economics, Monograph No. 14, New York, Wiley, 1953.
31. Leser, C. E. V., "The Role of Macroeconomic Models in Short-Term Forecasting," *Econometrica*, vol. 34, 1966, pp. 862–872.
32. Madansky, A., "On the Efficiency of Three-Stage Least Squares Estimation," *Econometrica*, vol. 32, 1964, pp. 51–56.
33. Malinvaud, E., *Statistical Methods of Econometrics*, Chicago, Rand McNally, 1966.
34. Markov, A. A., *Wahrscheinlichkeitsrechnung*, Leipzig, Teubner, 1900.
35. Nagar, A. L., *Statistical Estimation of Simultaneous Economic Relationships*, Ph.D. dissertation, Netherlands School of Economics, Rotterdam, 1959.
36. Nagar, A. L., "The Bias and Moment Matrix of the General k-Class Estimators of the Parameters in Simultaneous Equations," *Econometrica*, vol. 27, 1959, pp. 575–595.

37. Nagar, A. L., "A Note on the Residual Variance Estimation in Simultaneous Equations," *Econometrica*, vol. 29, 1961, pp. 238–243.
38. Nagar, A. L., " Double *k*-Class Estimators of Parameters in Simultaneous Equations and Their Small Sample Properties," *International Economic Review*, vol. 3 (1962), pp. 168–188.
39. Park, E., "Estimation with Heteroscedastic Error Terms," *Econometrica*, vol. 34, 1966, p. 888.
40. Quandt, R. E., " On Certain Small Sample Properties of *k*-Class Estimators," *International Economic Review*, vol. 6, 1965, pp. 92–104.
41. Rothenberg, T. J., and C. T. Leenders, " Efficient Estimation of Simultaneous Equation Systems," *Econometrica*, vol. 32, 1964, pp. 57–76.
42. Sargan, J. D., " The Estimation of Economic Relationships Using Instrumental Variables," *Econometrica*, vol. 26, 1958, pp. 393–415.
43. Sargan, J. D., "The Maximum Likelihood Estimation of Economic Relationships with Autoregressive Residuals," *Econometrica*, vol. 29, 1961, pp. 414–426.
44. Sargan, J. D., "Three-Stage Least Squares and Full Maximum Likelihood Estimates," *Econometrica*, vol. 32, 1964, pp. 77–81.
45. Scheffé, H., *The Analysis of Variance*, New York, Wiley, 1959.
46. Stuvel, G., "A Systematic Approach to Macroeconomic Policy Design," *Econometrica*, vol. 33, 1965, pp. 114–140
47. Suits, D. B., "Forecasting with an Econometric Model," in the American Economic Association *Readings in Business Cycles*, R. A. Gordon and L. R. Klein (Eds.), pp. 597–625, Homewood, Illinois, Richard D. Irwin, May 1965.
48. Theil, H., "Estimation and Simultaneous Correlation in Complete Equation Systems," The Hague: Central Plan Bureau, 1953.
49. Theil, H., *Economic Forecasts and Policy*, Chapter 6, Amsterdam, North Holland Publishing Co., 1958. *Note:* Second revised edition appeared in 1961.
50. Theil, H. and A. S. Goldberger, " On Pure and Mixed Statistical Estimation in Economics," *International Economic Review*, vol. 2, 1961, pp. 65–78.
51. Tintner, G., " The Definition of Econometrics," *Econometrica*, vol. 21, 1953, pp. 31–40.
52. Waugh, Frederick V., " The Place of Least Squares in Econometrics," *Econometrica*, vol. 29, 1961, pp. 386–396.
53. Working, E. J., "What do Statistical Demand Curves Show?" *Quarterly Journal of Economics*, vol. 41, 1927, pp. 212–235.
54. Zellner, A., " Econometric Estimation with Temporally Dependent Disturbance Terms," *International Economic Review*, vol. 2, 1961, pp. 164–178.
55. Zellner, A., " Linear Regression with Inequality Constraints on the Coefficients: An Application of Quadratic Programming and Linear Decision Rules," International Centre for Management Science, Report 6109 (MS No. 9).
56. Zellner, A., "An Efficient Method of Estimating Seemingly Unrelated Regressions and Tests for Aggregation Bias," *Journal of the American Statistical Association*, vol. 57, 1962, pp. 348–368.
57. Zellner, A., and D. S. Huang, "Further Properties of Efficient Estimators for Seemingly Unrelated Regression Equations," *International Economic Review*, vol. 3, 1962, pp. 300–313.
58. Zellner, A., and H. Theil, "Three-Stage Least Squares: Simultaneous Estimation of Simultaneous Equations," *Econometrica*, vol. 30, 1962, pp. 54–78.

APPLICATIONS OF
CLASSICAL AND SIMULTANEOUS
EQUATIONS TECHNIQUES
AND RELATED PROBLEMS

5

In this chapter we shall examine some applications of the techniques developed earlier and discuss some of the problems arising in such applications. We shall be led to consider *inter alia* certain elementary aspects of specification error theory, the relevance of canonical correlations in appraising the "goodness of fit" of simultaneous equations systems, and the application of principal component theory in the estimation of economy-wide (large) econometric models.

5.1 ESTIMATION OF PRODUCTION AND COST FUNCTIONS AND SPECIFICATION ERROR ANALYSIS

Recall from economic theory that a production function

$$Q = F(x) \tag{5.1.1}$$

where Q is (the homogeneous) output and x is the n-dimensional vector of (homogeneous) inputs, is a technically prescribed relationship such that if Q and all inputs but one, say x_n, are specified, then the function in (5.1.1) yields the *minimum* quantity of x_n necessary in order to produce the output Q. Conversely, if all inputs were specified, then (5.1.1) yields the maximum output obtained from such inputs. In econometric work, one customarily assumes that the production function is known only up to a stochastic term. It is often convenient to assume that the stochastic term enters multiplicatively, although this assumption has mainly convenience to recommend it. Thus, as an example, consider the well-known Cobb-Douglas function, perhaps more appropriately called the Wicksell function,[1]

$$Q = AK^{\alpha}L^{\beta} \tag{5.1.2}$$

Observe that the function is nonlinear in the parameters α and β and thus cannot be directly estimated by OLS techniques, even if the latter were appropriate. Notice, further, that in (5.1.2) A is a parameter that crucially depends on the units of measurement. Thus suppose we redefine variables

$$Q^* = k_0 Q \quad K^* = k_1 K \quad L^* = k_2 L \tag{5.1.3}$$

where the k_i, $i = 0, 1, 2$, represent the new scale of measurement. Expressing (5.1.2) in terms of the new variables, we see that

$$Q^* = k_0 k_1^{-\alpha} k_2^{-\beta} A K^{*\alpha} L^{*\beta} = A^* K^{*\alpha} L^{*\beta} \tag{5.1.4}$$

Hence the new parameter, $A^* = Ak_0 k^{-\alpha} k_2^{-\beta}$, reflects the scale of measurement of output, capital, and labor. On the other hand, note that the parameters α and β are invariant to scale of measurement changes. Thus in empirical results the magnitude of the estimate of A will not, per se, be of any significance. The parameters α and β, however, have fundamental economic significance as indicated below. We have

$$\frac{\partial Q}{\partial K}\frac{K}{Q} = \alpha \qquad \frac{\partial Q}{\partial L}\frac{L}{Q} = \beta \tag{5.1.5}$$

and we see that they represent, respectively, the (partial) elasticity of output with respect to capital and labor. It is an implication of the Cobb-Douglas function that these elasticities are constant. If the firm or industry whose production process is assumed to be given by (5.1.2) is perfectly competitive, then standard economic theory indicates that, under profit maximization, the following relations will hold

$$p\frac{\partial Q}{\partial K} = r \qquad p\frac{\partial Q}{\partial L} = w \tag{5.1.6}$$

where p, r, w are, respectively, the price of output, rental, and wage rate.

Carrying out the operations indicated in (5.1.6), we find

$$\alpha = \frac{rK}{pQ} \qquad \beta = \frac{wL}{pQ} \tag{5.1.7}$$

But the right-hand sides of the equations in (5.1.7) represent, respectively, the share of capital and labor. Since the returns to capital and labor are, respectively,

---

[1] In *Lectures on Political Economy* [33, p. 285], Wicksell derives this function from elementary economic considerations and assumptions. It is known, however, as the "Cobb-Douglas" function due to its extensive application in early econometric work by Cobb and Douglas.

rK and wL and since all output accrues to someone as income while the model specifies capital and labor as the only factors of production, it follows that if we wish to structure the model according to standard competitive theory, then we need to assume additionally that

$$\alpha + \beta = 1 \tag{5.1.8}$$

If (5.1.8) does not hold, then product will be either overexhausted ($\alpha + \beta > 1$) or underexhausted ($\alpha + \beta < 1$). If we do make the assumption in (5.1.8), then α (or β) may be interpreted as a distributive parameter, indicating the share of capital (or labor) in the output of the unit in question. Now, as a matter of fact, it is difficult to find a sector of the U.S. economy at least, for which the share of capital (or labor) is strictly constant. Hence if we wish to apply this production model to some specified real world situation and if we wish to retain the perfect competition assumption with respect to this sector, then we can no longer rule out randomness in (5.1.2). This is at least a partial motivation for introducing the stochastic production function

$$Q = AK^\alpha L^\beta \exp u \tag{5.1.9}$$

where u is a random variable. We have entered the latter in exponential form only because it is convenient to do so; this in itself does not involve any restrictive assumption. The restrictive assumption is that the error term enters multiplicatively and that it has range $(0, \infty)$. If U is such a variable and the production function in fact is

$$Q = AK^\alpha L^\beta U \tag{5.1.10}$$

then define

$$u = \ln U \tag{5.1.11}$$

to obtain the expression in (5.1.9). It is convenient and involves no loss in generality to assume

$$E(u) = 0 \tag{5.1.12}$$

Notice that this *does not* imply

$$E(U) = 1 \tag{5.1.13}$$

Making use of (5.1.11), we notice that

$$E(U) = E(\exp u) = \phi(1) \tag{5.1.14}$$

where $\phi(\cdot)$ is the *moment generating* function of u. If, for example, $u \sim N(0, \sigma^2)$, then

$$\phi(s) = \exp\left(\tfrac{1}{2}\sigma^2 s^2\right) \qquad \phi(1) = \exp\left(\tfrac{1}{2}\sigma^2\right) > 1 \tag{5.1.15}$$

As we remarked above, the assumption that the random term enters multiplicatively is a restrictive one; on the other hand, it would be patently inconvenient in (5.1.9) to enter the stochastic component linearly. The (multiplicative) assumption is made more palatable if we admit as correct the proposition that errors are proportional to the scale of operation. Now if (5.1.9) is the specified production function, then, taking the logarithm of both sides, we find

$$\ln Q = \ln A + \alpha \ln K + \beta \ln L + u \qquad (5.1.16)$$

and thus the function now exhibits *linearity in its parameters* except for A. But then if we have observations

$$\ln Q_t = \ln A + \alpha \ln K_t + \beta \ln L_t + u_t \qquad t = 1, 2, \ldots, T \qquad (5.1.17)$$

we might be tempted to estimate the parameters by ordinary least squares. Estimators for α and β are then obtained directly, while an estimator for A can be easily obtained from that of $\ln A$. In this scheme we might either incorporate the assumption (5.1.8) in (5.1.17) and estimate instead

$$\ln Q_t - \ln L_t = \ln A + \alpha(\ln K_t - \ln L_t) + u_t \qquad (5.1.18)$$

or we might estimate (5.1.17) and then *test* the validity of (5.1.8). Although this is a singularly simple scheme, let us inquire into the properties of the estimators so obtained.

First we note that the conditions of the Markov theorem—that is, the conditions under which OLS estimators of the parameters in (5.1.17) are BLUE— require that $\ln K_t$, $\ln L_t$ be either nonrandom or independent of the error terms u_t. If, for example, we had a sample obtained by varying independently (K, L) and then observing the resulting output, then the Markov theorem would be valid, provided that the quantities $Q_t / A K_t^\alpha L_t^\beta$ for any two time periods are uncorrelated. Unfortunately, such a circumstance holds very rarely, if ever. In general, how much of a given factor is employed, in a somewhat aggregative context, would depend on expected output and expected factor prices and all these are economic, not technical, considerations. One could easily imagine circumstances under which the explanatory variables (K, L) would be correlated with the error component of the production function. In particular, suppose that the extent of deviations of Q from $A K^\alpha L^\beta$ depends in part on the age composition of the otherwise homogeneous capital stock. Then clearly capital will be correlated with the stochastic component of the production function, whether we deal with a time series or cross section except under highly specific circumstances. In addition, it is an empirical fact that in many sectors of the U.S. economy at least $\ln L_t$ and $\ln K_t$ are highly collinear. Due to these and other considerations it is not indicated that ordinary least squares be employed in the context of (5.1.9) in estimating the parameters α, β and $\ln A$. This is not to say that such estimation has not been carried out in the literature. Indeed, the pioneering work of Cobb and Douglas [4] employs precisely this approach. Let us put aside our qualms about the propriety of OLS in the context of (5.1.9) for the moment and ask: If it were appropriate for us to estimate the parameters of (5.1.9) by OLS, what sort of data do we require? From the economic theoretical conception of the production function, we note that we require the inputs of *capital and labor services*. We also require a measure of final output. Unfortunately, none of these quantities is actually available in practice. At best we can obtain a series of manhours worked and a dollar measure of capital available to the given economic unit. As a measure of output, we can obtain a value added series. If the sample is a time series one, then such a measure must be a deflated one; otherwise movements in that series need not reflect changes in physical volume but rather simply movements in the relevant prices.

While we may take the measures of labor and output as tolerable in the context of this model, the measure of capital is patently inappropriate. What we have is not a measure of capital services even if it were a perfectly accurate measure of the physical stock of capital available to the unit. This is so since it *does not* take into account the extent to which the capital stock is utilized. If the latter were utilized at a constant rate, no difficulties will arise for capital services would be proportional to capital stock. Hence using capital stock in lieu of capital services would constitute a change in the units of measurement and thus would affect the scale constant A—as we remarked earlier. On the other hand, if the rate at which capital is utilized varies from observation to observation, this is a far more serious problem and raises the general question: In the context of the general linear model, suppose one (or more) variable is misspecified; what is the effect of this on the properties of the OLS estimator of the parameters?

Analysis of this type of problem is called *specification* or *specification error* analysis. The analytical apparatus employed is quite simple. We first indicate the nature of the incorrect specification as well as that of the correct one. We then subject the *incorrectly specified* model to the relevant estimation process and seek to establish the properties of the resulting estimators. If, in ascertaining the latter, we need to make use of the structure of the model, then of course we employ the correctly specified one. The general theory of specification analysis and the specific consequences of misspecifying capital will become clearer as we carry out the analysis. Thus suppose we are dealing with the model:

$$y - X\beta + u \tag{5.1.19}$$

where y, X are, respectively, the vector and matrix of observations on the dependent and explanatory variables, β is the vector of coefficients to be estimated, and u is the vector of disturbances having the properties

$$E(u) = 0 \qquad \text{Cov}(u) = \sigma^2 I \tag{5.1.20}$$

and is further independent of the columns of X.

We assert that (5.1.19) represents the "true" model. Now, suppose that through ignorance or lack of data we use, instead of X, another matrix X^*. In general, X^* will contain some columns in common with X although it will differ in at least one column (corresponding to the "misspecified" variable). If we regress the dependent variable on the variables contained in X^*, we obtain the "estimator" of β

$$\tilde{\beta}^* = (X^{*\prime}X^*)^{-1}X^{*\prime}y \tag{5.1.21}$$

What are the properties of $\tilde{\beta}^*$ as an estimator of β? Substituting from (5.1.19), we find

$$\tilde{\beta}^* = (X^{*\prime}X^*)^{-1}X^{*\prime}X\beta + (X^{*\prime}X^*)^{-1}X^{*\prime}u \tag{5.1.22}$$

If the misspecified variables are *independent* of the error term, then

$$E(\tilde{\beta}^*) = E[(X^{*\prime}X^*)^{-1}X^{*\prime}X]\beta = P\beta \tag{5.1.23}$$

But we recognize $(X^{*\prime}X^*)^{-1}X^{*\prime}X$ as the *matrix of regression coefficients of the explanatory variables in the true model on the explanatory variables in the misspecified model*. Thus we conclude that, in general, $\tilde{\beta}^*$ is a biased estimator of β and the specification bias of $\tilde{\beta}^*$ is given by

$$b(\tilde{\beta}^*) = (P - I)\beta \tag{5.1.24}$$

where I is a suitable identity matrix.

Although equation (5.1.24) is the result usually quoted in the literature, it should be pointed out that if the *misspecified variables are not independent of u*, then (5.1.23) does not hold except possibly asymptotically. Because even if $E[X^{*\prime}u] = 0$, it does not follow that for every sample size $E[(X^{*\prime}X^*)^{-1}X^{*\prime}u] = 0$. This will be so either if X^* is nonstochastic or if its columns are independent of u. However, if the second-order moment matrix of the misspecified variables exists, as well as the cross moment matrix between the misspecified and true variables, then we can write

$$\operatorname*{plim}_{T \to \infty} \tilde{\beta}^* = M_{**}^{-1}M_*\beta \tag{5.1.25}$$

where

$$M_{**} = \operatorname*{plim}_{T \to \infty} \frac{X^{*\prime}X^*}{T} \qquad M_* = \operatorname*{plim}_{T \to \infty} \frac{X^{*\prime}X}{T} \tag{5.1.26}$$

Thus the estimator $\tilde{\beta}^*$ is inconsistent and its inconsistency is given by

$$i(\tilde{\beta}^*) = (M_{**}^{-1}M_* - I)\beta \tag{5.1.27}$$

If the matrix

$$P = E[(X^{*\prime}X^*)^{-1}X^{*\prime}X] \tag{5.1.28}$$

exists and the elements of the matrix in square brackets obey at least the weak law of large numbers, then

$$M_{**}^{-1}M_* = P \tag{5.1.29}$$

and the *specification bias* of $\tilde{\beta}^*$ coincides with its *specification inconsistency*.

We have therefore proved

Theorem 1: Suppose that we have the standard general linear model

$$y = X\beta + u \tag{5.1.30}$$

and suppose that in estimating its parameters we use, instead of the variables appearing in X, an alternative set of variables, the observations on which are given in the matrix X^*. Let the estimator of β be

$$\tilde{\beta}^* = (X^{*\prime}X^*)^{-1}X^{*\prime}y \tag{5.1.31}$$

Suppose, also, that the misspecified and true variables have a well-defined (finite) second-moment matrix. Then

i. if the "misspecified" and "true" variables are nonstochastic,

$$E(\tilde{\beta}^*) = P\beta \qquad P = (X^{*\prime}X^*)^{-1}X^{*\prime}X \tag{5.1.32}$$

Thus the *specification bias* is given by

$$b(\tilde{\beta}^*) = (P - I)\beta \tag{5.1.33}$$

and the specification inconsistency by

$$i(\tilde{\beta}^*) = (M_{**}^{-1}M_* - I)\beta \tag{5.1.34}$$

where M_{**}, M_* are defined in (5.1.26), the operations there being taken as simple limits and *not* (obviously) as probability limits.

ii. if the misspecified variables are stochastic but independent of the vector u,

$$E(\tilde{\beta}^*) = P\beta \qquad P = E[(X^{*\prime}X^*)^{-1}X^{*\prime}X] \tag{5.1.35}$$

provided P is defined.

The *specification bias* of $\tilde{\beta}^*$ is given by

$$b(\tilde{\beta}^*) = (P - I)\beta \tag{5.1.36}$$

while its *specification inconsistency* is given by

$$i(\tilde{\beta}^*) = (M_{**}^{-1}M_* - I)\beta \tag{5.1.37}$$

where M_{**}, M_* are now as defined in (5.1.26).

iii. if the misspecified variables are stochastic but merely uncorrelated with the vector u, the result in (5.1.35) will not hold except possibly asymptotically; the result in (5.1.37) will continue to hold.

In order to determine the consequence of misspecifying capital in the production model discussed earlier, we need to specialize the results above to the case where only one input is misspecified, say the nth.

For simplicity, let us consider this in the context of i. Nothing of substance will be different if we choose to discuss it in the context of ii although the notation will be a bit more cumbersome. Let

$$X^* = (X_1, x_{\cdot n}^*) \qquad X = (X_1, x_{\cdot n}) \tag{5.1.38}$$

where $x^*_{.n}$ and $x_{.n}$ are, respectively, the vectors of observations on the misspecified and true variable and X_1 is the matrix of observations on the $(n-1)$ variables which are correctly specified. Notice that we can write

$$X = (X_1, x_{.n}) = X^* \begin{bmatrix} I_{n-1} & 0 \\ 0 & 0 \end{bmatrix} + (0, x_{.n}) \begin{bmatrix} 0 & 0 \\ 0 & 1 \end{bmatrix} \tag{5.1.39}$$

Hence we find

$$(X^{*\prime}X^*)^{-1}X^{*\prime}X = (X^{*\prime}X^*)^{-1}X^{*\prime}X^* \begin{bmatrix} I_{n-1} & 0 \\ 0 & 0 \end{bmatrix}$$

$$+ (X^{*\prime}X^*)^{-1}X^{*\prime}(0, x_{.n}) \begin{bmatrix} 0 & 0 \\ 0 & 1 \end{bmatrix}$$

$$= \begin{bmatrix} I_{n-1} & 0 \\ 0 & 0 \end{bmatrix} + [0, (X^{*\prime}X^*)^{-1}X^{*\prime}x_{.n}] \tag{5.1.40}$$

Thus if

$$\tilde{\beta}^* = (X^{*\prime}X^*)^{-1}X^{*\prime}y \tag{5.1.41}$$

then

$$b(\tilde{\beta}^*) = \left\{ (X^{*\prime}X^*)^{-1}X^{*\prime}x_{.n} + \begin{bmatrix} 0 \\ 0 \\ \vdots \\ -1 \end{bmatrix} \right\} \beta_n \tag{5.1.42}$$

We see, then, that even if a single variable is misspecified in a regression, the entire set of coefficient estimators is biased and not merely the coefficient corresponding to the misspecified variable. Furthermore, we recognize the first term in the right-hand side of (5.1.42) as the regression of the (true) omitted variable on the included—both true and misspecified—variables.

Specializing this result to the production model, let us consider the case in which output, Q, and labor, L, are correctly specified. We are only concerned about the misspecification of capital, resulting from the fact that we are using a measure of the capital stock rather than capital services when in fact the rate of utilization of the stock is not constant.[2] Let us denote capital services by K, and the capital stock by K^*.

If we put

$$\gamma = \begin{bmatrix} \ln A \\ \beta \\ \alpha \end{bmatrix} \tag{5.1.43}$$

---

[2] We should stress that these statements are made simply for illustration and that we do not mean that these output and labor measures are the absolutely correct ones.

then (5.1.40) implies

$$b(\tilde{\gamma}^*) = \begin{bmatrix} p_0\alpha \\ p_1\alpha \\ (p_2-1)\alpha \end{bmatrix} \tag{5.1.44}$$

where the p_i are the regression coefficients in

$$\ln K_t = p_0 + p_1 \ln L_t + p_2 \ln K_t^* + v_t \tag{5.1.45}$$

v_t being the residuals of the regression.

Now, typically, in time series we would expect capital services, K_t, to vary directly with labor services, L_t, and thus we could expect the coefficient p_1 to be positive, if such a regression could in fact be carried out.[3] On the other hand, since capital utilization would tend to fluctuate—perhaps considerably—due to cyclical factors, one would expect the coefficient of $\ln K_t^*$ to be certainly less than unity. From (5.1.44) we see then that the estimated exponent of labor is likely to be biased upward (positively), while the estimated coefficient of capital is likely to be biased downward (negatively). Of course, it should be pointed out that generally, OLS is not the appropriate technique in estimating the parameters of the production function in (5.1.9). Thus the preceding is best construed as an illustrative exercise and as a warning that if OLS, applied to (5.1.17), yields a negative coefficient for capital, then in the face of misspecification, this result need not mean that the Cobb-Douglas function is inapplicabe to the sector under consideration; it might only be the result of a serious specification error.[4]

Perhaps the main attraction of the estimation procedure outlined above is that it does not rely on the perfect competition assumption and thus does not require the constant returns to scale assumption in (5.1.8). Its disadvantages are that it probably leads to inconsistent estimators because the assumption that capital is independent of the error term is not likely to be a correct one. Finally, even if it were, we typically do not have observations on capital services. Using capital stock instead is likely to lead to specification bias and inconsistency due to nonconstant utilization of the capital stock.

Since many of the problems involved in the application of OLS to (5.1.17) deal with the capital input, it would seem desirable to provide an alternative estimation procedure that does not require information on capital. We shall outline such a procedure below. A price has to be paid for it, however, namely, we must now *assume* constant returns to scale ($\alpha + \beta = 1$).

Suppose we specify that we are concerned with an industry consisting of

---

[3] Obviously (5.1.45) is not an operational relation, for $\ln K_t$ cannot be observed. If it could, then the entire problem would have been obviated.

[4] It might also be due to a severe incidence of collinearity as between the capital and labor inputs.

identical firms, having the production function (5.1.9) and such that they determine their factor employment by

$$\frac{\partial Q^*}{\partial K} = r^* \qquad \frac{\partial Q^*}{\partial L} = w^* \qquad\qquad\qquad (5.1.46)$$

where

$$Q^* = Q \exp -u \qquad\qquad\qquad (5.1.47)$$

that is, it is the nonstochastic component of the production function. This can be interpreted as stating that firms know their production function only up to a stochastic component and act solely on the basis of this knowledge. The quantities r^*, w^* are (real) anticipated rentals and wages with the output of the industry used as the *numeraire*. If it is also the case that factor prices are correctly anticipated only up to a stochastic component, then we can write

$$r_t^* = r_t \exp [v_1(t)] \qquad w_t^* = w_t \exp [v_2(t)] \qquad\qquad (5.1.48)$$

where the $v_i(t)$ are suitable random variables, at time t, and r_t, w_t are, respectively, the observed (real) rentals and wages. Carrying out the operations indicated in (5.1.46), we obtain for each time t

$$\left(\frac{rK}{Q}\right)_t = \alpha \exp [-u(t) - v_1(t)] \qquad \left(\frac{wL}{Q}\right)_t = \beta \exp [-u(t) - v_2(t)] \qquad (5.1.49)$$

But the left-hand side of these equations is easily recognized as the observed share of *capital and labor respectively*. Denoting them by $\alpha(t)$, $\beta(t)$, respectively, and taking logarithms, we have

$$\ln \alpha(t) = \ln \alpha + [-u(t) - v_1(t)] \qquad \ln \beta(t) = \ln \beta + [-u(t) - v_2(t)] \qquad (5.1.50)$$

We should remark that in virtue of the constant returns to scale assumption only one of these two equations is independent. Thus we need estimate only α (or β), the other being derived residually as $1 - \hat{\alpha}$ (or $1 - \hat{\beta}$). If we eliminate the first equation, it seems that we can estimate β from share of labor data by OLS as follows:

$$\widetilde{\ln \beta} = \frac{1}{T} \sum_{t=1}^{T} \ln \beta(t) \qquad \hat{\beta} = \exp (\widetilde{\ln \beta}) \qquad\qquad (5.1.51)$$

We note that

$$\hat{\beta} = \left[\prod_{t=1}^{T} \beta(t)\right]^{1/T} \qquad\qquad (5.1.52)$$

that is, it is the geometric mean of observed labor shares. We further observe that if the error term

$$w(t) = -u(t) - v_2(t) \qquad\qquad (5.1.53)$$

has mean zero and is intertemporally nonautocorrelated, then the estimator $\widetilde{\ln \beta}$ is consistent and BLUE. However, this *is not so* for $\hat{\beta}$. In particular, if we also have

$$w_t \sim N(0, \sigma^2) \qquad t = 1, 2, \ldots \tag{5.1.54}$$

then

$$E(\hat{\beta}) = \beta \exp \frac{1}{2T} \sigma^2 \tag{5.1.55}$$

An unbiased consistent and efficient estimator nonetheless may be obtained, as was determined in Chapter 3.

It is interesting that this technique easily leads to estimation of technical progress parameters. Observe that in the derivation of $\hat{\beta}$ we have nowhere encountered the scale constant A. If, as a matter of fact, neutral technical change were present in the industry under consideration, it is conceivable that the industry production function could be written as

$$Q_t = A_0 \exp{(\lambda t)} K_t^\alpha L_t^\beta \exp{[u(t)]} \tag{5.1.56}$$

where A_0 is a fixed constant—depending on the units of measurement—and λ is the rate at which neutral technical change occurs. If α and β are estimated, for example, as above and if observations are available on output capital and labor, then we note that

$$Q_t K_t^{-\hat{\alpha}} L_t^{-\hat{\beta}} = A_0 \exp{(\lambda t)} K_t^{-(\hat{\alpha}-\alpha)} L_t^{-(\hat{\beta}-\beta)} \exp{[u(t)]} \tag{5.1.57}$$

Upon taking logarithms, we see

$$\ln Z(t) = \ln A_0 + \lambda t + \phi(t) \tag{5.1.58}$$

where

$$\phi(t) = -(\hat{\alpha} - \alpha) \ln K_t - (\hat{\beta} - \beta) \ln L_t + u(t) \tag{5.1.59}$$

If the sample is sufficiently large, then $\phi(t) \approx u(t)$, for $\hat{\alpha}$, $\hat{\beta}$ are, respectively, consistent estimators of α and β. Thus we may estimate λ and $\ln A_0$ by OLS, and the estimators will be unbiased and consistent.

In many instances, estimation of cost functions is equivalent to estimation of production functions. Indeed—see Sheppard [28]—under certain broad conditions there exists a one-to-one relation between cost and production functions. Let us see specifically what is the cost function implied by the Cobb-Douglas production function, under cost minimization. If a firm has the production function

$$Q = AK^\alpha L^\beta \tag{5.1.60}$$

and if it determines factor inputs by minimizing cost for given output and exogenously determined factor prices, then we obtain desired factor inputs by minimizing

$$\Lambda = rK + wL + \mu(Q - AK^\alpha L^\beta) \qquad (5.1.61)$$

First-order conditions are

$$\frac{\partial \Lambda}{\partial K} = r - \mu\alpha AK^{\alpha-1}L^\beta = 0$$

$$\frac{\partial \Lambda}{\partial L} = w - \mu\beta AK^\alpha L^{\beta-1} = 0$$

$$\frac{\partial \Lambda}{\partial \mu} = Q - AK^\alpha L^\beta = 0 \qquad (5.1.62)$$

Solving, we obtain the cost function

$$C = A^{-1/\alpha+\beta}\left[\left(\frac{\alpha}{\beta}\right)^{\beta/\alpha+\beta} + \left(\frac{\alpha}{\beta}\right)^{-\alpha/\alpha+\beta}\right] r^{\alpha/\alpha+\beta} w^{\beta/\alpha+\beta} Q^{1/\alpha+\beta} \qquad (5.1.63)$$

In a sense (5.1.63) is a reduced form for the set of structural equations in (5.1.62). However, as it stands, (5.1.63) is not an econometrically operational relation because it is not quite clear what is exogenous and what is endogenous or what is random and what is not. In the context of perfect certainty and perfect competition, r and w would be taken as given irrespectively of the firm's activity and thus exogenous in a statistical sense. If (5.1.60) in fact represents the production function, then there is no randomness in this simple context and we are reduced to curve fitting. However, if instead of (5.1.60) we have

$$Q = AK^\alpha L^\beta \exp u \qquad (5.1.64)$$

where u is a random variable with mean zero, then we can visualize the firm as determining optimal factor employment on the basis of an expected output constraint. Thus we now need to solve the problem of minimizing

$$\Lambda = rK + wL + \mu[Q^* - A^*K^\alpha L^\beta] \qquad (5.1.65)$$

where

$$Q^* = E(Q) \qquad A^* = AE[\exp u] \qquad (5.1.66)$$

Proceeding as before, we obtain

$$C = A^{*(-1/\alpha+\beta)}\left[\left(\frac{\alpha}{\beta}\right)^{\beta/\alpha+\beta} + \left(\frac{\alpha}{\beta}\right)^{-\alpha/\alpha+\beta}\right] r^{\alpha/\alpha+\beta} w^{\beta/\alpha+\beta} Q^{*(1/\alpha+\beta)} \qquad (5.1.67)$$

But Q^* is not observable; from (5.1.66) we note that

$$Q^* = \frac{A^*}{A} Q \exp(-u) \qquad (5.1.68)$$

Substituting (5.1.68) in (5.1.67), we have

$$\ln Q = c_0 + \alpha[\ln C - \ln r] + \beta[\ln C - \ln w] + u \qquad (5.1.69)$$

where c_0 is a complicated function of the parameters A^*, A, α, and β. At least under our assumptions $(\ln C - \ln r)$, $(\ln C - \ln w)$ are nonstochastic or, if stochastic, are independent of u and thus application of OLS to (5.1.69) will yield efficient estimators of α and β.

Notice that this approach does not explicitly require α and β to sum to unity although the second-order conditions for a minimum will either impose some conditions on the parameters α, β or on the permissible range of r and w.

However, the econometric model above is difficult to accept at face value in that we are regressing *physical* output on *monetary* costs of one variety or another and the underlying rationale may be less than perfectly convincing.

Nonetheless, in certain industries (e.g., the electric generating industry) it is possible to argue that output is completely determined by demand conditions which are taken to be exogenous to the firm(s). If the production decision is taken in accordance with a cost minimization scheme and if the production function is in fact (5.1.60), then we shall arrive at the cost function (5.1.63), with a random term, provided we argue that *cost minimization* is *imperfect* so that in each of the first two equations in (5.1.62) we add a random term. In this case, all explanatory variables (r, w, Q) are exogenous and thus estimation of the parameters of the Cobb-Douglas function can be carried out by OLS through a variant of (5.1.63). Nerlove [24], in his study of electricity supply, follows essentially this approach although he chooses to express the cost function solely in terms of factor prices. If one deals with a cross-sectional sample, this might not be particularly appropriate because even if the firms are geographically dispersed it is unlikely that factor prices will vary sufficiently over the sample to justify an acceptable degree of confidence in the estimators. We shall not pursue this matter here, for an exhaustive recent review of econometric techniques and findings with respect to production functions is available in Walters [32].

5.2 AN EXAMPLE OF EFFICIENT ESTIMATION OF A SET OF GENERAL LINEAR (REGRESSION) MODELS

In his paper Zellner [34] considers the following simple investment model:

$$I_t = \alpha_0 + \alpha_1 C_{t-1} + \alpha_2 F_{t-1} + u_t \qquad (5.2.1)$$

where I, C, F are, respectively, gross invetsment, capital stock, and market value of the firm's outstanding (common) stock. We are not concerned here with the propriety of (5.2.1) as a microinvestment function and thus we shall not comment on its form. Now, suppose that we consider (5.2.1) as an appropriate investment function for firms of a certain type and suppose that we have a time

TABLE 5.1.[a]   OLS parameter estimates of

$$I_t = \alpha_0 + \alpha_1 C_{t-1} + \alpha_2 F_{t-1} + u_t$$

	α_0	α_1	α_2
General Electric	-9.95	(.1517	(.0266
		(.00066)	(.00024)
Westinghouse	-0.5094	.0924	.0529
		(.00314)	(.00024)

[a] Numbers in parentheses are standard errors of the estimators.

series sample for two such firms. How do we best go about estimating the parameters of the model? First, we determine whether the two firms have identical investment functions. If they do, then we obviously pool the two samples. If they do not, then, of course, we ought to estimate two sets of parameters, one for each firm. The results are given in Table 5.1.

It is clear from the table that the two parameter sets are quite different and that pooling of the samples is not indicated. On the other hand, we saw in Chapter 4 that such estimators may not be efficient if the error terms of the two equations are correlated.[5] The correlation between the two error terms can be (consistently) estimated from the regression residuals. In fact, one obtains $r \approx .8$, which, by the conventional tests, is certainly highly significant.

Applying Aitken (efficient) estimation to the two equations, we obtain Table 5.2. Comparing the entries in the two tables, we see that there is an

TABLE 5.2.[a]   Aitken (efficient) estimates of the parameters
of $I_t = \alpha_0 + \alpha_1 C_{t-1} + \alpha_2 F_{t-1} + u_t$

	α_0	α_1	α_2
General Electric	-32.480	.1326	.0421
		(.00060)	(.00018)
Westinghouse	-2.011	.0459	.0611
		(.00269)	(.00019)

[a] Number in parentheses is standard error of the estimator.

[5] It must not be thought that the variables in the two equations are the same and thus that Aitken estimation is unnecessary. Clearly the observations on C_{t-1}, F_{t-1} for General Electric and Westinghouse will, in general, differ and thus the two data matrices will be far from identical.

appreciable change in the magnitude of the estimates as between the two procedures and also that although standard errors are quite small in both cases, they are appreciably smaller in the case of Aitken estimation as we would expect.

5.3 AN EXAMPLE OF 2SLS AND 3SLS ESTIMATION

The behavior of firms with respect to their dividend, investment, and external finance policies has been extensively studied in the econometric literature. Dhrymes and Kurz [6] consider these three policies as simultaneously determined and thus they argue that, econometrically, such relations ought to be considered as a simultaneous equations system and be estimated by simultaneous equations techniques. Their basic model is

$$\frac{D}{S} = \alpha_0 + \alpha_1 \frac{P}{K} + \alpha_2 \frac{N}{K} + \alpha_3 \frac{I}{K} + \alpha_4 \frac{F}{S} + u_1$$

$$\frac{I}{S} = \beta_0 + \beta_1 \left(\frac{P}{K}\right)_{-1} + \beta_2 \frac{N}{K} + \beta_3 S^*_{-2} + \beta_4 \frac{D}{S} + \beta_5 \frac{F}{S} + u_2$$

$$\frac{F}{S} = \gamma_0 + \gamma_1 \left[\frac{LTD}{K\text{-}LTD}\right] + \gamma_2 i + \gamma_3 \frac{Dep.}{K} + \gamma_4 \frac{P}{K} + \gamma_5 \frac{D}{S}$$

$$+ \gamma_6 \frac{I}{S} + u_3 \tag{5.3.1}$$

where D is (common stock) dividend disbursements, I is investment in plant and equipment, F is external (bond) finance, P is profits before taxes, S is sales, N is the net short-run position of the firm, LTD is long-term debt outstanding, i is an appropriate interest rate, Dep. is depreciation, K is gross (book) value of capital stock minus retirements, and S^*_{-2} is the relative rate of change of sales over a two-year period. The sample is a cross-sectional one covering 181 firms, chiefly in the manufacturing and retail sectors, although the primary activity of a few appears to be in mining. The assumption is that all firms in the sample have the same decision rule with respect to the three policies under consideration. Actually, Dhrymes and Kurz modify the model in (5.3.1) to allow for variation of the constant term according to the type of activity characteristic of the firm in the manner common to covariance analysis models. This modification is unimportant from the point of view of our interests here and thus we shall disregard it.

The parameters of the equations above were estimated by 2SLS; the results are given in Table 5.3.

TABLE 5.3.[a] **2SLS estimates of the system (1956)**

					Coefficients of						
	Const.	$\frac{P}{K}$	$\left(\frac{P}{K}\right)_{-1}$	$\left(\frac{N}{K}\right)$	$\frac{\text{LTD}}{K-\text{LTD}}$	S^*_{-2}	i	$\frac{\text{Dep.}}{K}$	$\frac{D}{S}$	$\frac{I}{S}$	$\frac{F}{S}$
Dividend equation	.0196 (1.8840)	.0666 (3.1867)		-0.0078 (-1.8377)						-0.3071 (-1.3858)	.3505 (.6248)
Investment equation	.0494 (2.1478)		.0498 (.7674)	-0.0141 (-2.0068)		.0409 (2.0248)			-0.8174 (-1.0164)		.2039 (.2319)
External finance equation	.0195 (1.2936)	-0.0096 (-0.4048)			.0091 (.6755)		-0.1871 (-1.3453)	.0029 (.0238)	-0.2618 (-0.7325)	.2593 (2.2752)	

[a] Number in parentheses is t ratio.

Accepting, for the purposes of this illustration, that the specification of the model is correct, we note from the table that the results do not support the hypothesis that investment is influenced by the rate of profit or that dividend policy is affected by investment and vice versa. Thus the t ratio for the coefficient of I/S in the dividend equation is -1.3858, while that for the coefficient of D/S in the investment equation is -1.0164. It would appear, then, that there is no strong evidence of interaction as between these two policies for the firm. We may, however, ask: Is 2SLS estimation efficient? To answer that question, we need to inquire as to the covariance structure of the error terms of the three equations; it is actually simpler to work with the correlation matrix. We may estimate the latter, consistently, from the 2SLS residuals of the three equations. The estimates are given in Table 5.4. It is apparent from the table that the correlation between the error terms in the dividend and the other two equations is nonzero. This is probably not so regarding the correlation between the error terms in the investment and external finance equations. Thus we conclude that the covariance matrix of the model's error terms is not diagonal and 3SLS is the efficient estimation procedure, for every equation of the system is overidentified, as was shown in Section 4.7 of the previous chapter. If we employ 3SLS, we obtain the results given in Table 5.5.

A comparison of Tables 5.3 and 5.5 indicates two major differences in the conclusions to be drawn from these two sets of empirical results. The simultaneous character of these three policies is more firmly established as evidenced by the "significance" of the jointly dependent variables entering as explanatory variables in the investment and external finance equation—and to a lesser degree in the dividend equation. Second, there is a change in the substantive content of the two sets of results. From the 2SLS results we would conclude that there is no empirical support for a "profits" or "rate of profit" theory of investment, for the coefficient of the rate of profit variable $(P/K)_{-1}$ is insignificant. There is support only for an "accelerator" theory, as evidenced by the significance of S^*_{-2}, which is reasonably close to the change in sales variable that is usually encountered in the accelerator formulation of investment theory. On the other hand, arguing on the basis of the 3SLS (efficient) results, we see that there is support for a theory of investment that includes both "profits" and "accelerator" elements.

In conclusion, it must be emphasized that very often the substantive economic conclusions obtained as a result of an empirical investigation would generally

TABLE 5.4. Correlation matrix of 2SLS residuals (1956)

Dividend equation	1.000	.7517	-0.2722
Investment equation		1.0000	-0.0492
External finance equation			1.0000

TABLE 5.5.[a] 3SLS estimates of the system (1956)

					Coefficients of						
	Const	$\dfrac{P}{K}$	$\left(\dfrac{P}{K}\right)_{-1}$	$\dfrac{N}{K}$	$\dfrac{\text{LTD}}{K-\text{LTD}}$	S^*_{-2}	i	$\dfrac{\text{Dep.}}{K}$	$\dfrac{D}{S}$	$\dfrac{I}{S}$	$\dfrac{F}{S}$
Dividend equation	.0186 (1.8806)	.0634 (3.4194)		-0.0065 (-1.8040)						-0.2727 (-1.5124)	.3289 (.6715)
Investment equation	.0727 (3.4825)		.1236 (2.4919)	-0.0193 (-3.0976)		.0447 (2.6648)			-2.3647 (-4.1750)		-0.8921 (-1.1444)
External finance equation	.0174 (1.2117)	-0.0093 (-0.3925)			.0032 (.2462)		-0.2066 (-1.5273)	-0.0514 (-0.4373)	-0.2575 (-0.7254)	.2596 (2.2882)	

[a] Number in parentheses is t ratio.

depend (often critically) on the choice of estimation procedure. Hence it is quite important for the investigator to be careful in specifying the model and in choosing an efficient estimation technique. Assuming the specification of the model to be correct, the results above illustrate the critical importance of the choice regarding the estimation procedure.

5.4 MEASURES OF GOODNESS OF FIT IN MULTIPLE EQUATIONS SYSTEMS: COEFFICIENTS OF (VECTOR) ALIENATION AND CORRELATION

We recall that when dealing with the general linear model[6]

$$y = X\beta + u \tag{5.4.1}$$

where the error term u has the properties

$$E(u) = 0 \qquad \text{Cov}(u) = \sigma^2 I \tag{5.4.2}$$

we measure the "goodness of fit" of the model by the coefficient of determination (of multiple regression). One definition of the latter (the so-called "unadjusted" coefficient) is

$$R^2 = 1 - \frac{\hat{u}'\hat{u}}{(y - e\bar{y})(y - e\bar{y})} \tag{5.4.3}$$

where

$$\hat{u} = y - X\hat{\beta} \quad e = (1, 1, 1, \ldots, 1)' \quad \bar{y} = \frac{1}{T}\sum_{t=1}^{T} y_t \tag{5.4.4}$$

and $\hat{\beta}$ is the OLS estimator of β given by

$$\hat{\beta} = (X'X)^{-1}X'y \tag{5.4.5}$$

The "adjusted" coefficient is given by

$$\bar{R}^2 = 1 - \frac{\hat{u}'\hat{u}/T - k}{(y - e\bar{y})'(y - e\bar{y})/T - 1} \tag{5.4.6}$$

It will be simpler to deal with the unadjusted coefficient.

By "goodness of fit" in this context, we simply mean the extent to which the variables $x_2, \ldots, x_k$ contribute to the "explanation" of the dependent variable

---

[6] As is customary, y (of dimension $T \times 1$) and X (of dimension $T \times k$) represent the observations on the dependent and (k) explanatory variables respectively; the first column of X consists solely of ones—the dummy variable corresponding to the constant term of the equation—and β is the vector of unknown coefficients to be estimated, its first element being the constant term referred to below.

y—recall that x_1 is the fictitious variable "1." In view of the fact that the denominator of R^2 in (5.4.3) is expressed in terms of deviations from the sample mean of y and the fact that we are only interested in the role of the x_i, $i = 2, \ldots,$ k, in explaining the dependent variable, it will be more convenient to operate entirely in terms of deviations from sample means, thus eliminating the constant term. Hence let

$$y^* = y - e\bar{y} \quad X^* = X_2 - \frac{ee'}{T} X_2 \quad X_2 = (x_{.2}, \ldots, x_{.k})$$

$$\beta^* = (\beta_2, \beta_3, \ldots, \beta_k)' \quad u^* = u - e\bar{u} \quad \bar{u} = \frac{1}{T} \sum_{t=1}^{T} u_t \tag{5.4.7}$$

where $x_{.i}$ is the $(T \times 1)$ vector of observations on the variable x_i. The model may now be written as

$$y^* = X^*\beta^* + u^* \tag{5.4.8}$$

and the OLS estimator of β^* is easily obtained as

$$\tilde{\beta}^* = (X^{*'}X^*)^{-1}X^{*'}y^* = \beta^* + (X^{*'}X^*)^{-1}X^{*'}u \tag{5.4.9}$$

Noting that $e'e = T$ and thus that $X^{*'}e = 0$ we see that the last equality of (5.4.9) holds in virtue of

$$X^{*'}u^* = X^{*'}(u - e\bar{u}) = X^{*'}u - \bar{u}X^{*'}e = X^{*'}u \tag{5.4.10}$$

Now, it is easily established that $\tilde{\beta}^*$ of (5.4.9) is identical with the corresponding subvector of $\hat{\beta}$ in (5.4.5). To see this, note that

$$X = (e, X_2) \tag{5.4.11}$$

and that the equations defining $\hat{\beta}$ can be written as

$$X'y = (X'X)\hat{\beta} \tag{5.4.12}$$

Using the notation $\hat{\beta} = (\hat{\beta}_1, \hat{\beta}^{*'})'$, we can express (5.4.12) as

$$e'y = e'e\hat{\beta}_1 + e'X_2 \hat{\beta}^*$$
$$X_2'y = X_2'e\hat{\beta}_1 + X_2'X_2 \hat{\beta}^* \tag{5.4.13}$$

Solving the first equation for $\hat{\beta}_1$, we find

$$\hat{\beta}_1 = \bar{y} - \frac{e'X_2}{T} \hat{\beta}^* \tag{5.4.14}$$

Substituting in the second set, we obtain

$$X_2'y = X_2'e\left(\bar{y} - \frac{e'X_2}{T} \hat{\beta}^*\right) + X_2'X_2 \hat{\beta}^* \tag{5.4.15}$$

Since

$$\left(\frac{ee'}{T}X_2\right)'(y - e\bar{y}) = X_2'\left(\frac{ee'}{T}y - e\frac{e'e}{T}\bar{y}\right) = X_2'(e\bar{y} - e\bar{y}) = 0 \tag{5.4.16}$$

we conclude that (5.4.15) can also be written as

$$\left(X_2 - \frac{ee'}{T}X_2\right)'(y - e\bar{y}) = X_2'\left(I - \frac{ee'}{T}\right)X_2\hat{\beta}* \tag{5.4.17}$$

From (5.4.7) and (5.4.9), we conclude that

$$\tilde{\beta}* = \hat{\beta}* \tag{5.4.18}$$

The coefficient of determination computed on the basis of (5.4.8) is given by

$$R^{*2} = 1 - \frac{\hat{u}*'\hat{u}*}{y*'y*} \tag{5.4.19}$$

where

$$\hat{u}* = y* - X*\hat{\beta}* \tag{5.4.20}$$

However, from (5.4.14) we have

$$\hat{u}* = y - e\bar{y} + \frac{ee'}{T}X_2\hat{\beta}* - X_2\hat{\beta}* = y - e\left(\bar{y} - \frac{e'X_2}{T}\hat{\beta}*\right) - X_2\hat{\beta}*$$

$$= y - e\hat{\beta}_1 - X_2\hat{\beta}* = y - (e, X_2)\hat{\beta} = \hat{u} \tag{5.4.21}$$

Consequently, we see immediately that $R^2 = R^{*2}$ and thus we may indeed conduct our discussion in terms of the more convenient notation of (5.4.7) without loss of relevance.

Now

$$1 - R^2 = \frac{\hat{u}*'\hat{u}*}{y*'y*} \tag{5.4.22}$$

and thus

$$\frac{R^2}{1 - R^2} = \frac{y*'y* - \hat{u}*'\hat{u}*}{\hat{u}*'\hat{u}*} = \frac{\hat{\beta}*'X*'X*\hat{\beta}*}{\hat{u}*'\hat{u}*} \tag{5.4.23}$$

The last equality holds, since we may write

$$y* = X*\hat{\beta}* + \hat{u}* \tag{5.4.24}$$

and since $\hat{u}*$ is orthogonal to $X*$.

We now wish to show that $\hat{\beta}*'X*'X*\hat{\beta}*$ is distributed independently of $\hat{u}*'\hat{u}*$. But notice

$$\hat{u}*'\hat{u}* = u*'(I - N*)u* \qquad N* = X*(X*'X*)^{-1}X*' \tag{5.4.25}$$

Furthermore,

$$u^{*'}(I - N^*)u^* = u'\left(I - \frac{ee'}{T}\right)(I - N^*)\left(I - \frac{ee'}{T}\right)u$$

$$= u'\left(I - N^* - \frac{ee'}{T}\right)u \qquad (5.4.26)$$

Thus

$$u'u = u'\left(I - N^* - \frac{ee'}{T}\right)u + u'\left(\frac{ee'}{T}\right)u + u'N^*u$$

$$= u'A_1 u + u'A_2 u + u'A_3 u \qquad (5.4.27)$$

Now, it is apparent that the A_i, $i = 1, 2, 3$, are symmetric, mutually orthogonal, idempotent matrices and thus

$$\text{rank } (A_1) = \text{tr } \left[I - N^* - \frac{ee'}{T}\right] = T - (k - 1) - 1$$

$$\text{rank } \left(\frac{ee'}{T}\right) = \text{tr } \left(\frac{ee'}{T}\right) = 1$$

$$\text{rank } (N^*) = \text{tr } N^* = k - 1 \qquad (5.4.28)$$

Since $u \sim N(0, \sigma^2 I)$ by hypothesis, we conclude, by Cochran's theorem, Scheffé [27, p. 420], that

$$\frac{u'A_i u}{\sigma^2} \sim \chi^2_{r_i} \qquad r_i = \text{rank } (A_i) \qquad i = 1, 2, 3 \qquad (5.4.29)$$

and, moreover, that they are mutually independent. On the other hand, it is immediately obvious that

$$u'A_1 u = u^{*'}(I - N^*)u^* = \hat{u}^{*'}\hat{u}^*$$
$$u'A_3 u = (\hat{\beta}^* - \beta^*)X^{*'}X^*(\hat{\beta}^* - \beta^*) \qquad (5.4.30)$$

If we wish to test the hypothesis that the dependent variable does not depend on $x_2, x_3, \ldots, x_k$ (or, alternatively, that the fit does not improve by introducing them as explanatory variables), this can be carried out as a test of the null hypothesis

$$H_0: \beta^* = 0 \qquad (5.4.31)$$

But under the null hypothesis,

$$u'A_3 u = \hat{\beta}^{*'} X^{*'} X^* \hat{\beta}^* \qquad (5.4.32)$$

and is thus a statistic; that is, it is a quantity that depends solely on the observations and not on any unknown parameters. Hence under the null hypothesis,

$$\frac{u'A_3 u}{u'A_1 u} \frac{T-k}{k-1} = \frac{\hat{\beta}^{*'}X^{*'}X^*\hat{\beta}^*}{\hat{u}^{*'}\hat{u}^*} \frac{T-k}{k-1}$$

$$= \frac{R^2}{1-R^2} \frac{T-k}{k-1} = F_{k-1, T-k} \qquad (5.4.33)$$

and a test of the hypothesis in (5.4.31)—or a test of significance on R^2—can be based on the central F distribution, which is well tabulated.

More precisely, we would reject the null hypothesis in (5.4.31) at the level of significance α if

$$\frac{R^2}{1-R^2} \frac{T-k}{k-1} \geq F_\alpha \qquad (5.4.34)$$

and F_α is a number such that

$$\Pr\{F \geq F_\alpha\} = \alpha \qquad (5.4.35)$$

F being a central F variable with degrees of freedom $(k-1, T-k)$.

Suppose now that we are dealing with a system of general linear models, say

$$y_{\cdot i} = X_i \beta_{\cdot i} + u_{\cdot i} \qquad i = 1, 2, \ldots, m \qquad (5.4.36)$$

In this context, what would (or should) we mean by the "goodness of fit" of the model?

First, it occurs to us that we might employ a simple extension of the goodness of fit criterion (R^2) for the single equation model. The intuitive attractiveness of this approach is enhanced by the fact that by a change in notation we can express the multiple equations model of (5.4.36) in the form of a single equation.

Again, express all variables as deviations from sample means and put

$$y^* = \begin{pmatrix} y^*_{\cdot 1} \\ y^*_{\cdot 2} \\ \vdots \\ y^*_{\cdot m} \end{pmatrix} \qquad X^* = \operatorname{diag}(X^*_1, X^*_2, \ldots, X^*_m)$$

$$\beta^* = \begin{pmatrix} \beta^*_{\cdot 1} \\ \beta^*_{\cdot 2} \\ \vdots \\ \beta^*_{\cdot m} \end{pmatrix} \qquad u^* = \begin{pmatrix} u^*_{\cdot 1} \\ u^*_{\cdot 2} \\ \vdots \\ u^*_{\cdot m} \end{pmatrix} \qquad (5.4.37)$$

The starred symbols above have the same interpretation as the notation given in (5.4.7).

Using (5.4.37), we can write the system of equations in (5.4.36) as

$$y^* = X^*\beta^* + u^* \qquad (5.4.38)$$

nd thus we could formally define the goodness of fit statistic by

$$R^2 = 1 - \frac{\hat{u}^{*\prime}\hat{u}^*}{y^{*\prime}y^*} = \frac{y^{*\prime}y^* - \hat{u}^{*\prime}\hat{u}^*}{y^{*\prime}y^*} \tag{5.4.39}$$

here $\hat{u}^*$ is simply the OLS residual vector.

It can be easily shown that R^2 in (5.4.39) is a weighted average of the coefficients f determination of the individual equations (R_i^2), the weights being the fraction f total variability in the dependent variables accounted by the ith dependent ariable.

Thus we have

$$R^2 = \sum_{i=1}^{n} R_i^2 \left(\frac{y_{\cdot i}^{*\prime} y_{\cdot i}^*}{y^{*\prime}y^*} \right) \tag{5.4.40}$$

Although this scheme is intuitively appealing and the statistic R^2 is easily calcu-ated, it has the significant disadvantage that its distribution cannot be deter-mined because it will generally involve the unknown covariance parameters of he joint distribution of the error terms of the system in (5.4.36). Let us illustrate he nature of the difficulty. Suppose we were willing to specify that

$$\text{Cov}(u_{\cdot i}, u_{\cdot j}) = 0 \qquad i \neq j$$
$$\text{Cov}(u_{\cdot i}) = \sigma_{ii} I \qquad i = 1, 2, \ldots, m \tag{5.4.41}$$

so that OLS estimation of the parameters of (5.4.36) is efficient. If we proceed as n the case of the single general linear model, then

$$\frac{R^2}{1 - R^2} = \frac{y^{*\prime}y^* - \hat{u}^{*\prime}\hat{u}^*}{\hat{u}^{*\prime}\hat{u}^*} \tag{5.4.42}$$

We further note that

$$y^{*\prime}y^* - \hat{u}^{*\prime}\hat{u}^* = \sum_{i=1}^{n} (y_{\cdot i}^{*\prime} y_{\cdot i}^* - \hat{u}_{\cdot i}^{*\prime} \hat{u}_{\cdot i}^*)$$

$$= \sum_{i=1}^{n} (\hat{\beta}_{\cdot i}^{*\prime} X_i^{*\prime} X_i^* \hat{\beta}_{\cdot i}^*) \tag{5.4.43}$$

$$\hat{u}^{*\prime}\hat{u}^* = \sum_{i=1}^{m} \hat{u}_{\cdot i}^{*\prime} \hat{u}_{\cdot i}^* \tag{5.4.44}$$

If we wish to test the null hypothesis

$$H_0 : \beta_{\cdot i}^* = 0 \qquad i = 1, 2, \ldots, m \tag{5.4.45}$$

then under H_0,

$$\frac{\hat{\beta}_{\cdot i}^{*\prime} X_i^{*\prime} X_i^* \hat{\beta}_{\cdot i}^*}{\sigma_{ii}}$$

is a chi-square variable distributed independently of $\hat{u}^{*\prime}_{\cdot i}\hat{u}^{*}_{\cdot i}/\sigma_{ii}$, which is also chi-square variable. Unfortunately, however, $R^2/1 - R^2$ cannot be expressed solely as a function of the observations unless it so happens that $\sigma_{ii} = \sigma_{jj}$, all and j. This is quite apparent from (5.4.42), (5.4.43), and (5.4.44).

Moreover, if $\sigma_{ij} \neq 0$, then the efficient estimator of $\beta_{\cdot i}$ will not admit a orthogonality relation between the residuals of that regression and the explana tory variables so that it will not be the case that

$$y^{*\prime}_{\cdot i}y^{*}_{\cdot i} - \tilde{u}^{*\prime}_{\cdot i}\tilde{u}^{*}_{\cdot i} = \tilde{\beta}^{*\prime}_{\cdot i}X^{*\prime}_i X^{*}_i \tilde{\beta}^{*}_{\cdot i} \tag{5.4.46}$$

where now $\tilde{\beta}_{\cdot i}$ indicates the efficient (Aitken) estimator and $\tilde{u}_{\cdot i} = y^{*}_{\cdot i} - X_i \tilde{\beta}^{*}_{\cdot i}$
Finally, even if

$$X_i = X \qquad i = 1, 2, \ldots, m \tag{5.4.47}$$

as we are bound to have in the unrestricted reduced form of a structural system the problem still remains. Though the orthogonality condition will hold—since the efficient (Aitken) estimator is just the OLS estimator of $\beta^{*}_{\cdot i}$ and thus the statistics in (5.4.40) and (5.4.43) make perfectly good sense—still these statistics are not very useful, for their distribution depends on the unknown parameters σ_{ij}. Thus, even though one might wish to compute a statistic like (5.4.40) for the intuitive appeal it may possess, nonetheless, in order to conduct a statistically rigorous test of the hypothesis in (5.4.45) one will need a somewhat different apparatus.

So let us consider in some detail the problem of appraising the "goodness of fit" in the context of a reduced form model. In studying this problem, certain new concepts will be needed, and to these we now turn.

In the case of the single general linear model, goodness of fit questions are equivalent to questions about the correlation between a scalar random variable and a vector random variable. Recall our discussion of the multiple correlation coefficient in Chapter 1 and note that for that purpose the usual notions regarding correlations between two *scalar* variables will suffice. In a reduced form, however, we are dealing, in some sense, with the *correlation between two sets of random variables*. Thus we would need a generalization of the basic notion of correlation coefficients as follows:

Definition 1: Let

$$z = \begin{pmatrix} y \\ x \end{pmatrix} \quad y = (y_1, y_2, \ldots, y_m)' \quad x = (x_1, x_2, \ldots, x_G) \quad m \leq G \tag{5.4.48}$$

be a random variable having the distribution

$$z \sim N(0, \Sigma) \tag{5.4.49}$$

Partition Σ conformally with z so that

$$\Sigma = \begin{bmatrix} \Sigma_{11} & \Sigma_{12} \\ \Sigma_{21} & \Sigma_{22} \end{bmatrix} \tag{5.4.50}$$

t is apparent from (5.4.50) that[7]

$$\Sigma_{11} = \text{Cov}(y) \quad \Sigma_{22} = \text{Cov}(x) \quad \Sigma_{12} = \text{Cov}(y, x) \tag{5.4.51}$$

The coefficient of alienation (ρ_A) between the vectors y and x is defined by

$$\rho_A = \frac{\begin{vmatrix} \Sigma_{11} & \Sigma_{12} \\ \Sigma_{21} & \Sigma_{22} \end{vmatrix}}{|\Sigma_{11}| |\Sigma_{22}|} \tag{5.4.52}$$

Remark 1: The definition may appear a bit odd at first, so let us try to elucidate it. On intuitive or mnemonic grounds, one might think of $|\Sigma|$ as a quantity analogous to the square of the "covariance between y and x" if the latter were scalar variables. This might be thought appropriate, for $|\Sigma|$ is a (nonnegative) positive quantity; $|\Sigma_{11}|$ and $|\Sigma_{22}|$ may then be thought of as the variances of y and x respectively. Thus one might surmise that ρ_A should be analogous to the (square of the) correlation coefficient between two scalar variables. A little reflection, however, will convince us that the opposite is true. First, as we (usually) define a correlation coefficient it assumes the value zero when the covariance between the two variables in question vanishes and it assumes the value unity when the two variables are connected by an exact linear relation. Now, if the covariance between these two vectors vanishes—and because of normality the two vectors are thus mutually independent—we have

$$|\Sigma| = \begin{vmatrix} \Sigma_{11} & \Sigma_{12} \\ \Sigma_{21} & \Sigma_{22} \end{vmatrix} = |\Sigma_{11}| |\Sigma_{22}| \tag{5.4.53}$$

since

$$\Sigma_{12} = 0 \quad \Sigma_{21} = 0. \tag{5.4.54}$$

Hence in this case,

$$\rho_A = 1 \tag{5.4.55}$$

On the other hand, suppose that the two vectors are connected by

$$y = Bx \tag{5.4.56}$$

B being a nonstochastic matrix of rank m. Then

$$\text{Cov}(y) = B\Sigma_{22}B' \quad \text{Cov}(y, x) = B\Sigma_{22} \quad \text{Cov}(x, y) = \Sigma_{22}B' \tag{5.4.57}$$

---

[7] To make the notation perfectly transparent, we should perhaps write $\text{Cov}(x, x)$ and $\text{Cov}(y, y)$ instead of $\text{Cov}(x)$ and $\text{Cov}(y)$, since

$$\text{Cov}(x, y) = E[(x - \mu)(y - \nu)'] \quad \mu = E(x) \quad \nu = E(y)$$

However, the meaning will usually be clear from the context.

and thus[8]

$$|\Sigma| = \begin{vmatrix} B\Sigma_{22}B' & B\Sigma_{22} \\ \Sigma_{22}B' & \Sigma_{22} \end{vmatrix} = \begin{vmatrix} 0 & 0 \\ \Sigma_{22}B' & \Sigma_{22} \end{vmatrix} = 0 \qquad (5.4.58)$$

Therefore

$$\rho_A = 0 \qquad (5.4.59)$$

Thus it is seen that the coefficient of alienation is exactly like $1 - \rho^2$, where ρ^2 is the square of the correlation coefficient between two scalars, for it assumes the value unity for mutually independent vectors and the value zero for linearly connected vectors.

Finally, it is easy to show that

$$\rho_A \in [0, 1] \qquad (5.4.60)$$

To this effect, consider the roots of

$$|\mu\Sigma_{11} - (\Sigma_{11} - \Sigma_{12}\Sigma_{22}^{-1}\Sigma_{21})| = 0 \qquad (5.4.61)$$

Now $\Sigma_{11} - \Sigma_{12}\Sigma_{22}^{-1}\Sigma_{21}$ is the conditional covariance matrix of y given x. If the joint distribution of y and x is nondegenerate—that is, if Σ is nonsingular—then it is trivial to show that $\Sigma_{11} - \Sigma_{12}\Sigma_{22}^{-1}\Sigma_{21}$ is positive definite. This is so because Σ is positive definite and thus so is

$$D\Sigma D' = \begin{bmatrix} \Sigma_{11} - \Sigma_{12}\Sigma_{22}^{-1}\Sigma_{21} & 0 \\ 0 & \Sigma_{22} \end{bmatrix} \qquad (5.4.62)$$

where

$$D = \begin{bmatrix} I & -\Sigma_{12}\Sigma_{22}^{-1} \\ D & I \end{bmatrix} \qquad (5.4.63)$$

and thus nonsingular. But if $D\Sigma D'$ is positive definite, then so must be $\Sigma_{11} - \Sigma_{12}\Sigma_{22}^{-1}\Sigma_{21}$.

Hence we conclude from (5.4.61) that if μ_i, $i = 1, 2, \ldots, m$, are the roots of that equation, then

$$\mu_i \geq 0 \qquad (5.4.64)$$

Indeed, the μ_i will be strictly positive if Σ is positive definite.

Now let

$$M = \text{diag}(\mu_1, \mu_2, \ldots, \mu_m) \qquad (5.4.65)$$

---

[8] This is obtained by multiplying the lower layer of the matrix on the left by B and subtracting from the upper layer. The operation does not alter the value of the determinant but gives the form following the next to the last equality sign.

and let W be the (orthogonal) matrix of characteristic vectors associated with these roots. Then we can write

$$\Sigma_{11} - \Sigma_{12}\Sigma_{22}^{-1}\Sigma_{21})W = \Sigma_{11}WM \tag{5.4.66}$$

Taking determinants of both sides, we conclude

$$\frac{|\Sigma_{11} - \Sigma_{12}\Sigma_{22}^{-1}\Sigma_{21}|}{|\Sigma_{11}|} = |M| \tag{5.4.67}$$

We shall complete the proof of (5.4.60) if we show that

$$|M| \leq 1 \tag{5.4.68}$$

since[9]

$$|\Sigma| = |\Sigma_{22}|\,|\Sigma_{11} - \Sigma_{12}\Sigma_{22}^{-1}\Sigma_{21}| \tag{5.4.69}$$

But we note that (5.4.61) can also be written as

$$|(1 - \mu)\Sigma_{11} - \Sigma_{12}\Sigma_{22}^{-1}\Sigma_{21}| = |\lambda\Sigma_{11} - \Sigma_{12}\Sigma_{22}^{-1}\Sigma_{21}| = 0 \tag{5.4.70}$$

where

$$\lambda = 1 - \mu \tag{5.4.71}$$

But the roots λ_i of $|\lambda\Sigma_{11} - \Sigma_{12}\Sigma_{22}^{-1}\Sigma_{21}| = 0$ must be nonnegative, for Σ_{11} and $\Sigma_{12}\Sigma_{22}^{-1}\Sigma_{21}$ are, respectively, positive definite and at least positive semidefinite. Since

$$\lambda_i = 1 - \mu_i \quad \mu_i \geq 0 \qquad i = 1, 2, \ldots, m \tag{5.4.72}$$

we conclude

$$\mu_i \in [0, 1] \tag{5.4.73}$$

In fact, the interval will be open in the left if Σ is nonsingular, that is, if the vectors y and x are not connected by an exact linear relation. Now (5.4.73) immediately implies

$$\lambda_i \in [0, 1] \tag{5.4.74}$$

and from (5.4.65), it follows that

$$|M| \leq 1 \tag{5.4.75}$$

From (5.4.67), (5.4.69), and (5.4.75), we have

$$\rho_A = \frac{|\Sigma|}{|\Sigma_{11}|\,|\Sigma_{22}|} = |M| \leq 1 \tag{5.4.76}$$

---

[9] This is the so-called formula of Schur. Recall the discussion in the Mathematical Appendix.

It is interesting that the above imply another inequality, which we shall presently find useful. For this reason it is expedient to derive it now.

We note that we can rewrite (5.4.66) as

$$\Sigma_{12}\Sigma_{22}^{-1}\Sigma_{21}W = \Sigma_{11}W(I - M) \tag{5.4.77}$$

But the nonzero elements of the diagonal matrix $I - M$ are the λ_i of (5.4.74). Thus let

$$I - M = \Lambda = \text{diag}(\lambda_1, \lambda_2, \ldots, \lambda_m) \tag{5.4.78}$$

Taking determinants of both sides of (5.4.77) and using (5.4.78), we conclude

$$\frac{|\Sigma_{12}\Sigma_{22}^{-1}\Sigma_{21}|}{|\Sigma_{11}|} = |\Lambda| \leq 1 \tag{5.4.79}$$

The coefficient of correlation between two vector random variables is given by

Definition 2: Let z be as in Definition 1; then the coefficient of (vector) correlation between y and x is defined by

$$\rho_c = (-1)^m \frac{\begin{vmatrix} 0 & \Sigma_{12} \\ \Sigma_{21} & \Sigma_{22} \end{vmatrix}}{|\Sigma_{11}||\Sigma_{22}|} \tag{5.4.80}$$

Remark 2: This definition is perhaps stranger in appearance than the previous one. Consequently, some additional explanation may be in order. First, notice that if the covariance between the two vectors vanishes, that is, $\Sigma_{12} = 0$ and $\Sigma_{21} = 0$, then

$$\rho_c = (-1)^m \frac{\begin{vmatrix} 0 & 0 \\ 0 & \Sigma_{22} \end{vmatrix}}{|\Sigma_{11}||\Sigma_{22}|} = 0 \tag{5.4.81}$$

On the other hand, by the formula of Schur

$$\begin{vmatrix} 0 & \Sigma_{12} \\ \Sigma_{21} & \Sigma_{22} \end{vmatrix} = \begin{vmatrix} -\Sigma_{12}\Sigma_{22}^{-1}\Sigma_{21} & 0 \\ \Sigma_{21} & \Sigma_{22} \end{vmatrix}$$

$$= |\Sigma_{22}||-\Sigma_{12}\Sigma_{22}^{-1}\Sigma_{21}| = (-1)^m |\Sigma_{22}||\Sigma_{12}\Sigma_{22}^{-1}\Sigma_{21}| \tag{5.4.82}$$

Hence

$$\rho_c = \frac{|\Sigma_{12}\Sigma_{22}^{-1}\Sigma_{21}||\Sigma_{22}|}{|\Sigma_{11}||\Sigma_{22}|} \tag{5.4.83}$$

But from (5.4.79), we immediately conclude

$$\rho_c \in [0, 1] \tag{5.4.84}$$

Now suppose that the two vectors are connected by an exact linear relation

$$y = Bx \tag{5.4.85}$$

where B is nonstochastic and of rank m. Then

$$\Sigma_{11} = \text{Cov}\,(y) = B\Sigma_{22}\,B'$$
$$\Sigma_{12} = \text{Cov}\,(y, x) = B\Sigma_{22}$$
$$\Sigma_{21} = \text{Cov}\,(x, y) = \Sigma_{22}\,B' \qquad (5.4.86)$$

In this case,

$$\rho_c = \frac{|\Sigma_{12}\,\Sigma_{22}^{-1}\,\Sigma_{21}|}{|\Sigma_{11}|} = \frac{|B\Sigma_{22}\,\Sigma_{22}^{-1}\,\Sigma_{22}\,B'|}{|B\Sigma_{22}\,B'|} = 1 \qquad (5.4.87)$$

Thus we see that ρ_c satisfies the usual properties associated with the correlation coefficient between two scalar random variables so that the definition given for ρ_c and its name are quite appropriate.

It should be pointed out that although in some sense ρ_c and ρ_A are analogous to ρ^2 and $1 - \rho^2$, respectively, nonetheless, they *do not* satisfy the condition

$$\rho_A + \rho_c = 1 \qquad (5.4.88)$$

except when one of the two quantities vanishes. As a matter of fact, from (5.4.76) and (5.4.79) we see that

$$\rho_A + \rho_c = \prod_{i=1}^{m}(1 - \lambda_i) + \prod_{i=1}^{m}\lambda_i < 1 \qquad (5.4.89)$$

unless all $\lambda_i = 0$ or $\lambda_i = 1$.

Remark 3: Corresponding to the parameters ρ_A and ρ_c, we can obtain their respective estimators from a sample of size T on the vector z by obtaining the maximum likelihood estimators of $\Sigma_{11}, \Sigma_{12}, \Sigma_{22}$.

Thus if

$$Z = (y._1, y._2, \ldots, y._m, x._1, x._2, \ldots, x._G) = (Y, X) \qquad (5.4.90)$$

$y._i$ and $x._j$ being, respectively, the $T \times 1$ vectors of observations on the variables y_i and x_j, then the maximum likelihood estimator of Σ is given by

$$\hat{\Sigma} = \frac{1}{T}\begin{bmatrix} Y'Y & Y'X \\ X'Y & X'X \end{bmatrix} = \frac{Z'Z}{T} \qquad (5.4.91)$$

Thus

$$\hat{\Sigma}_{11} = \frac{Y'Y}{T} \quad \hat{\Sigma}_{12} = \frac{Y'X}{T} \quad \hat{\Sigma}_{22} = \frac{X'X}{T}$$

$$Y = (y._1, y._2, \ldots, y._m) \qquad X = (x._1, x._2, \ldots, x._G) \qquad (5.4.92)$$

One further aspect regarding the quantities ρ_A and ρ_c should be noted. In general, the coefficient of alienation between y and x is the same as the coefficient of alienation between x and y. This is so because ρ_A is symmetric with respect to

Σ_{11} and Σ_{22}. The same is not true, however, for the coefficient of correlation. Thus

$$\rho_c(x, y) = \frac{|\Sigma_{21}\Sigma_{11}^{-1}\Sigma_{12}|}{|\Sigma_{22}|} \qquad (5.4.93)$$

while

$$\rho_c(y, x) = \frac{|\Sigma_{12}\Sigma_{22}^{-1}\Sigma_{21}|}{|\Sigma_{11}|} \qquad (5.4.94)$$

Now the rank of $\Sigma_{21}\Sigma_{11}^{-1}\Sigma_{21}$ cannot exceed that of Σ_{11}, which is m. But the dimension of $\Sigma_{21}\Sigma_{11}^{-1}\Sigma_{21}$ is $G \times G$. Thus since $G \geq m$, we conclude that unless $G = m$,

$$\rho_c(x, y) = 0 \qquad (5.4.95)$$

and, in general,

$$\rho_c(y, x) \neq \rho_c(x, y) \qquad (5.4.96)$$

Equality in (5.4.96) will hold when $m = G$. To see this, consider equations (5.4.93), (5.4.94) and observe that in the case under consideration Σ_{12} and (its transpose) Σ_{21} are square matrices. Since $|\Sigma_{12}| = |\Sigma_{21}|$, we see that

$$\rho_c(x, y) = \frac{|\Sigma_{21}||\Sigma_{12}|}{|\Sigma_{11}||\Sigma_{22}|} = \frac{|\Sigma_{12}|^2}{|\Sigma_{11}||\Sigma_{22}|} \qquad (5.4.97)$$

$$\rho_c(y, x) = \frac{|\Sigma_{12}||\Sigma_{21}|}{|\Sigma_{11}||\Sigma_{22}|} = \frac{|\Sigma_{12}|^2}{|\Sigma_{11}||\Sigma_{22}|} \qquad (5.4.98)$$

which proves our assertion.

It is interesting that the concepts developed above provide a solution to the problem of defining a goodness of fit measure for simultaneous equations models. To this effect, recall again the general model considered in Chapter 4. We have the set of observations

$$y_{ti}^* = \sum_{j=1}^{m} \beta_{ji}^* y_{tj}^* + \sum_{s=2}^{G} \gamma_{si}^* x_{ts}^* + u_{ti}^* \qquad \begin{aligned} i &= 1, 2, \ldots, m \\ t &= 1, 2, \ldots, T \end{aligned} \qquad (5.4.99)$$

where we now adopt the convention that all variables are measured as deviations from their respective means; thus $y_{ti}^* = y_{ti} - \bar{y}_i$, $x_{ts}^* = x_{ts} - \bar{x}_s$, $u_{ti}^* = u_{ti} - \bar{u}_i$, and so on. Notice also in (5.4.99) that the "first" predetermined variable x_{t1} has been eliminated. This is so because by convention it stands for the fictitious variable "1," which is the "variable" whose coefficient is the constant term of the equation in question. Obviously the equations in (5.4.99) do not contain a constant term. For identifiability, certain restrictions have to be imposed on the parameters β_{ji}^* and γ_{si}^*. In practice, however, such restrictions are ignored when estimating the reduced form, which in the present case is given by

$$Y^* = X^*\Pi^* + V^* \tag{5.4.100}$$

where

$$\Pi^* = C^{**}D \quad V^* = U^*D \quad D = (I - B^*)^{-1} \quad B^* = (\beta_{ji}^*) \quad i, j = 1, 2, \ldots, m$$
$$C^{**} = (\gamma_{si}^*) \quad s = 2, \ldots, G, \quad i = 1, 2, \ldots, m \tag{5.4.101}$$

Of course,

$$Y^* = (y_{\cdot 1}^*, y_{\cdot 2}^*, \ldots, y_{\cdot m}^*) \quad X^* = (x_{\cdot 2}^*, x_{\cdot 3}^*, \ldots, x_{\cdot G}^*)$$
$$U^* = (u_{\cdot 1}^*, u_{\cdot 2}^*, \ldots, u_{\cdot m}^*) \tag{5.4.102}$$

$y_{\cdot i}^*$, $x_{\cdot j}^*$ and $u_{\cdot k}^*$ being, respectively, the $T \times 1$ vectors of (centered) observations on the variables y_i, x_j and the error term of the kth equation. The connection between the notation of this model and that of the standard one as developed, say, in Section 4.3 of Chapter 4 is as follows:

$$Y^* = \left(I - \frac{ee'}{T}\right)Y \quad X^* = \left(I - \frac{ee'}{T}\right)X^0 \quad U^* = \left(I - \frac{ee'}{T}\right)U \tag{5.4.103}$$

where X^0 is the submatrix of X resulting when we delete the first column of the latter, and $e = (1, 1, 1, \ldots, 1)'$. Obviously C^{**} differs from C^* as defined in Section 4.3 of Chapter 4 only in that its first row is deleted. Finally, from (5.4.101) and (5.4.103) we see that

$$V^* = \left(I - \frac{ee'}{T}\right)UD \tag{5.4.104}$$

Now, it would be reasonable to expect that in the context of a set of regressions —as the reduced form is—the concepts of coefficient of (vector) alienation and correlation would have useful applications. We note that, in the case of a single general linear model, "goodness of fit" is measured by the multiple correlation coefficient, which—as developed in Section 1.4 of Chapter 1—is simply the correlation between a vector and a scalar. Here, in some sense, we are dealing with the correlation between two vector random variables, and as we saw earlier, ρ_A and ρ_c are well suited to measure the extent of correlation between them. Now, if we estimate Π^* by OLS, we obtain

$$P^* = (X^{*\prime}X^*)^{-1}X^{*\prime}Y^* \tag{5.4.105}$$

As we saw in Chapter 4, this is a best linear unbiased estimator of Π^*. We may also write

$$\tilde{V}^* = Y^* - X^*P^* \tag{5.4.106}$$

so that $\tilde{V}^*$ is the matrix of OLS residuals in the entire system and is orthogonal to the matrix of the explanatory variables. Thus we have

$$X^{*\prime}\tilde{V}^* = 0 \tag{5.4.107}$$

As observed in Remark 3 above, the coefficient of vector alienation may be estimated by

$$r_A = \frac{\begin{vmatrix} Y^{*\prime}Y^* & Y^{*\prime}X^* \\ X^{*\prime}Y^* & X^{*\prime}X^* \end{vmatrix}}{|Y^{*\prime}Y^*||X^{*\prime}X^*|} \tag{5.4.108}$$

From (5.4.107) we have

$$X^{*\prime}Y^* = X^{*\prime}X^*P^* \qquad Y^{*\prime}Y^* = P^{*\prime}X^{*\prime}X^*P^* + \tilde{V}^{*\prime}\tilde{V}^* \tag{5.4.109}$$

Using (5.4.109) and Schur's formula for the determinant of a partitioned matrix, we conclude

$$r_A = \frac{|\tilde{V}^{*\prime}\tilde{V}^*|}{|Y^{*\prime}Y^*|} \tag{5.4.110}$$

Thus we see that r_A is the analog of $1 - R^2$ in the single general linear model. In the latter context, $1 - R^2$ measures the residual variance as a fraction of the variance of the dependent variable. Similarly, r_A measures the residual variance as a fraction of the variance of the dependent variables; now, however, by variance we mean *generalized variance*. Thus r_A is simply the ratio of the *generalized variance* about the regression planes to the *generalized variance* of the jointly dependent variables (about their respective means) and thus measures the relative residual variability remaining after the influence of the explanatory (predetermined) variables on the jointly dependent variables has been removed.

Similarly, using the relations in (5.4.91), (5.4.92), (5.4.106), and (5.4.107), we can show that

$$r_c = \frac{|Y^{*\prime}X^*(X^{*\prime}X^*)^{-1}X^{*\prime}Y^*|}{|Y^{*\prime}Y^*|} = \frac{|P^{*\prime}X^{*\prime}X^*P^*|}{|Y^{*\prime}Y^*|} \tag{5.4.111}$$

We note that r_c indicates the fraction of the generalized variance of the jointly dependent variables "explained" by the reduced form. Thus it is completely analogous to R^2, the coefficient of determination of multiple regression.

Notice also that

$$\tilde{V}^* = Y^* - X^*(X^{*\prime}X^*)^{-1}X^{*\prime}Y^* = (I - N^*)V^* \qquad N^* = X^*(X^{*\prime}X^*)^{-1}X^{*\prime} \tag{5.4.112}$$

Thus, since both N^* and $I - N^*$ are idempotent, we conclude

$$\tilde{V}^{*\prime}\tilde{V}^* = V^{*\prime}(I - N^*)V^* \tag{5.4.113}$$

$$(P^* - \Pi^*)'X^{*\prime}X^*(P^* - \Pi^*) = V^{*\prime}N^*V^* \tag{5.4.114}$$

We have explored the coefficient of (vector) correlation (and alienation) alternative to the "goodness of fit" problem in the hope that it would yield more tractable statistics than the one obtained in (5.4.42). Let us see whether this expectation was justified.

Recall that in the notation of (5.4.99), (5.4.101), and (5.4.102),

$$V^* = U^*D \tag{5.4.115}$$

and thus the ith row of V^* is given by

$$v_{i\cdot}^* = u_{i\cdot}^* D \tag{5.4.116}$$

where $u_{i\cdot}^*$ is the ith row of U^*; that is, it is the (row) vector of observations at time i *on the error terms of all the equations in the system*, centered about its sample mean.

Although it might not have been explicitly stated before, we typically assume in such models that the *uncentered* vectors $u_{i\cdot}'$ are mutually independent, identically distributed, each with the distribution

$$u_{i\cdot}' \sim N(0, \Sigma) \qquad i = 1, 2, \dots, T. \tag{5.4.117}$$

Thus by Theorem 1 of Chapter 1,

$$v_{i\cdot}' \sim N(0, D'\Sigma D)^{10} \qquad i = 1, 2, \dots, T \tag{5.4.118}$$

where $v_{i\cdot}$ is the (corresponding) uncentered vector of reduced form errors at time i.

Thus V is a matrix whose rows are mutually independent, identically distributed variables with mean 0 and covariance matrix $D'\Sigma D$. Hence by Theorem 5 of Chapter 1, we conclude

$$V'V \sim W(D'\Sigma D, m, T) \tag{5.4.119}$$

that is, it has the *Wishart distribution* with parameters $D'\Sigma D$, m, and T.

Before we proceed, it will be useful to have the following generalization of Cochran's theorem, which we cite without proof.

Theorem 1: Let Z be a $T \times m$ matrix such that its ith row $z_{i\cdot}$ obeys

$$z_{i\cdot}' \sim N(0, \Phi) \tag{5.4.120}$$

Suppose that we can write

$$Z'Z = \sum_{i=1}^{p} Z'A^i Z \tag{5.4.121}$$

where the A^i are matrices with

$$\text{rank}\,(A^i) = r_i \tag{5.4.122}$$

---

[10] We use $v_{i\cdot}'$ because, by convention, we take all vectors unless otherwise indicated as being *column* vectors. Here by construction $v_{i\cdot}$ is a row vector; thus its transpose $v_{i\cdot}'$ is a column vector as desired.

Then a necessary and sufficient condition that

$$Z'A^iZ = \sum_{\alpha = r_1 + \cdots + r_{i-1} + 1}^{r_1 + r_2 + \cdots + r_i} q._\alpha q'._\alpha \qquad (5.4.123)$$

where the $q._\alpha$ are mutually independent, each with distribution

$$q._\alpha \sim N(0, \Phi) \qquad \alpha = 1, 2, \ldots, \sum_{i=1}^{p} r_i \qquad (5.4.124)$$

is that

$$\sum_{i=1}^{p} r_i = T \qquad (5.4.125)$$

Moreover, if $r_i \geq m$, then

$$Z'A^iZ \sim W(\Phi, m, r_i) \qquad i = 1, 2, \ldots, p \qquad (5.4.126)$$

PROOF: See Anderson [1, p. 165].
An additional useful result is

Theorem 2: Let

$$W \sim W(\Phi, m, n) \qquad n \geq m \qquad (5.4.127)$$

then

$$|W| = |\Phi| \prod_{i=0}^{m-1} \chi_{n-i}^2 \qquad (5.4.128)$$

where the χ_{n-i}^2 are mutually independent chi-square variables with $n - i$ degrees of freedom.

PROOF: See Anderson [1, p. 171].

Remark 4: Theorem 2 states that the *determinant* of a Wishart-distributed matrix is proportional to a quantity that is the product of mutually independent chi-square variables with *nonidentical distributions*. The distribution of the latter can easily be derived but it is a rather complicated one. Since the quantity has range $(0, \infty)$, it has been suggested that the mth root of it be approximated by a chi-square variable with appropriate degrees of freedom parameter. Thus the burden of the theorem is to suggest, first, that $|W|/|\Phi|$ has the distribution of a product of chi-square variables and, second, that the distribution of $\{|W|/|\Phi|\}^{1/m}$ can be approximated by a chi-square variable whose parameter would be chosen, for example, so as to coincide with the first moment of $\{|W|/|\Phi|\}^{1/m}$.

What is the relevance of these two theorems to our discussion? From equations (5.4.105), (5.4.106), (5.4.107), and the definition of V^*, we conclude that[11]

$$V^{*'}V^* = V'\left(I - \frac{ee'}{T}\right)V \tag{5.4.129}$$

Obviously

$$V^{*'}V^* = V^{*'}(I - N^*)V^* + V^{*'}N^*V^* \tag{5.4.130}$$

Substituting (5.4.129) in (5.4.130) and rearranging, we obtain

$$V'V = V'\left(I - N^* - \frac{ee'}{T}\right)V + V'N^*V + V'\left(\frac{ee'}{T}\right)V \tag{5.4.131}$$

This is so because

$$N^*\frac{ee'}{T} = 0 \tag{5.4.132}$$

It can easily be verified that $[I - N^* - (ee'/T)]$, N^*, and ee'/T are mutually orthogonal, idempotent symmetric matrices and thus

$$\text{rank}\left(\frac{ee'}{T}\right) = \text{tr}\left(\frac{ee'}{T}\right) = 1 \qquad \text{rank } N^* = \text{tr } N^* = G - 1$$

$$\text{rank}\left(I - N^* - \frac{ee'}{T}\right) = \text{tr}\left(I - N^* - \frac{ee'}{T}\right) = T - (G - 1) - 1 = T - G \tag{5.4.133}$$

But the (T) rows of V are mutually independent, identically distributed, each with the distribution given in (5.4.118). Thus, by Theorem 1, we conclude that $V'[I - N^* - (ee'/T)]V$, $V'N^*V$, and $V'(ee'/T)V$ are mutually independently distributed. Moreover, if

$$T - G \geq m \qquad G - 1 \geq m \tag{5.4.134}$$

then the first two matrices are Wishart distributed with parameters $(D'\Sigma D, m, T - G)$ and $(D'\Sigma D, m, G - 1)$ respectively.

Now suppose that we wish to test the null hypothesis

$$H_0: \Pi^* = 0 \tag{5.4.135}$$

---

[11] Since V^* is the centered matrix of "observations" on the reduced-form error terms, we have $V^* = V - e\bar{v}'$, where $e = (1, 1, 1, \ldots, 1)'$ and $\bar{v} = e'V/T$; that is, $\bar{v}$ is the vector of sample means for the error terms of the various reduced-form equations. Thus $V^* = [I - (ee'/T)]V$, and (5.4.129) follows immediately, if it is noted that $[I - (ee'/T)]$ is idempotent.

Strictly speaking, this is a hypothesis on the goodness of fit of the reduced form; recalling, however, that

$$\Pi^* = C^{**}(I - B^*)^{-1} \tag{5.4.136}$$

we notice that (5.4.135) holds if and only if

$$C^{**} = 0 \tag{5.4.137}$$

Thus the test implied by it can also be interpreted as testing the hypothesis that the simultaneous equations system in (5.4.99) *contains no predetermined variables*. From (5.4.114) we see that, under the null hypothesis,

$$P^{*\prime}X^{*\prime}X^*P^* = V^{*\prime}N^*V^* = V'N^*V \tag{5.4.138}$$

On the other hand, from (5.4.107) we have

$$\tilde{V}^{*\prime}\tilde{V}^* = V^{*\prime}(I - N^*)V^* = V'\left(I - N^* - \frac{ee'}{T}\right)V \tag{5.4.139}$$

Hence, under H_0, we have

$$\frac{r_c}{r_A} = \frac{|P^{*\prime}X^{*\prime}X^*P^*|}{|\tilde{V}^{*\prime}\tilde{V}^*|} = \frac{|V'N^*V|}{\left|V'\left(I - N^* - \dfrac{ee'}{T}\right)V\right|} \tag{5.4.140}$$

and thus by Theorems 1 and 2 we find

$$\frac{r_c}{r_A} = \frac{\prod_{i=0}^{m-1} \chi_{G-1-i}^2}{\prod_{i=0}^{m-1} \chi_{T-G-i}^2} \tag{5.4.141}$$

Although the exact distribution of r_c/r_A cannot be expressed in convenient closed form and tabulated, we may, as observed in Remark 4, approximate the mth root of the numerator and denominator by chi-square variables. In particular, we may take

$$\left(\prod_{i=0}^{m-1} \chi_{G-1-i}^2\right)^{1/m} \sim \chi_{C_1}^2 \tag{5.4.142}$$

where

$$C_1 = 2\,\frac{\prod\limits_{i=0}^{m-1} \Gamma\!\left(\dfrac{G-1-i}{2} + \dfrac{1}{m}\right)}{\prod\limits_{i=0}^{m-1} \Gamma\!\left(\dfrac{G-1-i}{2}\right)} \tag{5.4.143}$$

This constant is chosen so that

$$C_1 = E(\chi_{C_1}^2) = E\left(\prod_{i=0}^{m-1} \chi_{G-1-i}^2\right)^{1/m} = \prod_{i=0}^{m-1} E(\chi_{G-1-i}^2)^{1/m}$$

$$= \prod_{i=0}^{m-1} \int_0^\infty \frac{1}{2\Gamma\left(\dfrac{G-1-i}{2}\right)} 2^{1/m} \left(\frac{x}{2}\right)^{\frac{G-3-i}{2} + \frac{1}{m}} \exp\left(-\frac{1}{2}x\right) dx$$

$$= \prod_{i=0}^{m-1} \left[\frac{2^{1/m}\Gamma\left(\dfrac{G-1-i}{2} + \dfrac{1}{m}\right)}{\Gamma\left(\dfrac{G-1-i}{2}\right)}\right] \tag{5.4.144}$$

Other approximations are also reasonable. Thus Hoel [9] has suggested, in a different context, that we use the approximation

$$\left(\prod_{i=0}^{m-1} \chi_{G-1-i}^2\right)^{1/m} \sim \bar{C}_1 \chi_{C_1*}^2 \tag{5.4.145}$$

where

$$C_1^* = m(T-m) \qquad \bar{C}_1 = \left\{m\left[1 - \frac{(m-1)(m-2)}{2T}\right]\right\}^{-1} \tag{5.4.146}$$

Similarly, we may approximate the mth root of the denominator by

$$\left(\prod_{i=0}^{m-1} \chi_{T-G-i}^2\right)^{1/m} \sim \chi_{C_2}^2 \tag{5.4.147}$$

where

$$C_2 = \frac{2\prod_{i=0}^{m-1}\Gamma\left(\dfrac{T-G-i}{2} + \dfrac{1}{m}\right)}{\Gamma\left(\dfrac{T-G-i}{2}\right)} \tag{5.4.148}$$

But then it is apparent that the mth root of r_c/r_A may be approximated, under the null hypothesis, by a central F distribution with C_1 and C_2 degrees of freedom respectively, for the numerator and denominator of the fraction are mutually independent.

Thus we can write, approximately,

$$\left(\frac{r_c}{r_A}\right)^{1/m} \frac{C_2}{C_1} \sim F_{C_1, C_2} \tag{5.4.149}$$

and we may test H_0—or the goodness of fit of the reduced form model—by the following procedure. Select a level of significance α. Determine the critical value F_α^* by the condition

$$\Pr \{F_{C_1, C_2} \geq F_\alpha^*\} = \alpha \tag{5.4.150}$$

where F_{C_1, C_2} has the central F distribution with C_1 and C_2 degrees of freedom; if C_1 and C_2 are not integers, we may approximate them by the nearest integer. (This is necessary because tabulations of the F distribution exist only for integer values of the degrees of freedom parameters.) Compute

$$\left(\frac{r_c}{r_A}\right)^{1/m} \frac{C_2}{C_1}$$

and if the latter is less than or equal to F_α^*, *accept* H_0; otherwise reject it. In a sense, this is also a test of the "significance" of r_c, the fraction of the generalized variance of the endogenous variables "explained" by the reduced form.

The difficulty with this approach is that it requires the conditions (5.4.134). While the number of predetermined variables in an econometric model will typically exceed the number of jointly dependent variables, so that $G - 1 \geq m$ will be satisfied, very often in economy-wide models the number of *predetermined and jointly dependent* variables will be considerably larger than the number of observations at hand so that[12]

$$T - G - m < 0 \tag{5.4.151}$$

In such a case, the distribution of the ratio r_c/r_A is not well defined and indeed the ratio itself will not be well defined. This is so because the denominator of the fraction is given by the determinant of $V'[I - N^* - (ee'/T)]V$, which is an $m \times m$ matrix. But its rank cannot exceed $T - G$, for by (5.4.132) this is the rank of the matrix in parentheses. Since $T - G < m$ by (5.4.151), it follows that $V'[I - N^* - (ee'/T)]V$ is singular so that its determinant is zero. Of course, we should also note that if, in fact, we have

$$T - G < 0 \tag{5.4.152}$$

as is the case in certain economy-wide models, then we cannot even estimate the reduced form by OLS, let alone define unambiguously a "goodness of fit" measure. Finally, we note that if (5.4.151) does not hold but instead

$$G - 1 < m \tag{5.4.153}$$

---

[12] For instance the Brookings (quarterly) econometric model has the characteristics $T = 72$, $G = 240$, $m = 204$. This count is based on one of its more or less final versions currently researched at the University of Pennsylvania. This version contains *91 current and lagged exogenous variables, 149 lagged endogenous variables, and 204 current endogenous variables or equations.* Of these equations, 83 are identities and 121 are behavorial equations. The system contains two recursive blocks of 22 and 29 equations, respectively, and a simultaneous block of 153 equations. Also, in the Wharton (quarterly) model one has $T = 70$, $G = 95$, $m = 78$. Thus in both models the necessary conditions are violated and indeed we have $T - G < 0$ as well.

then, of course, $V'N*V$ is a singular matrix, for it is $m \times m$ and its rank cannot exceed $G - 1$ (which is the rank of $N*$). Thus r_c is zero no matter how well $X*P*$ "explains" $Y*$ within the sample.

Since situations where the conditions (5.4.134) do not hold arise quite commonly, it is necessary and useful for us to develop ways of coping with them.

5.5 CANONICAL CORRELATIONS AND GOODNESS OF FIT IN ECONOMETRIC SYSTEMS

Consider again the coefficient of (vector) correlation

$$\rho_c = \frac{|\Sigma_{12}\Sigma_{22}^{-1}\Sigma_{21}|}{|\Sigma_{11}|} = |C| \tag{5.5.1}$$

where

$$C = \Sigma_{11}^{-1}(\Sigma_{12}\Sigma_{22}^{-1}\Sigma_{21}) \tag{5.5.2}$$

Recall that, as we saw in Section 2.1 of Chapter 2, the set of canonical correlations between the y's and the x's is obtained as the solution of

$$\begin{vmatrix} -v\Sigma_{11} & \Sigma_{12} \\ \Sigma_{21} & -v\Sigma_{22} \end{vmatrix} = 0 \tag{5.5.3}$$

where the Σ_{ij}, $i, j = 1, 2$, have the meaning given them in the preceding section. By the formula of Schur, the determinantal equation in (5.5.3) is equivalent to

$$|-v\Sigma_{22}| \left| -v\Sigma_{11} + \frac{1}{v}\Sigma_{12}\Sigma_{22}^{-1}\Sigma_{21} \right|$$
$$= (-1)^{G+m}v^{G-m}|\Sigma_{22}| |v^2\Sigma_{11} - \Sigma_{12}\Sigma_{22}^{-1}\Sigma_{21}| = 0 \quad (5.5.4)$$

Thus if $G \geq m$—that is, the number of predetermined variables is not less than the number of current endogenous variables—then the squares of the canonical correlations are simply the solutions of

$$|v^2\Sigma_{11} - \Sigma_{12}\Sigma_{22}^{-1}\Sigma_{21}| = 0 \tag{5.5.5}$$

But from (5.4.79) and (5.4.83) we conclude that the coefficient of (vector) correlation ρ_c is simply the *product of the squares of all the canonical correlations* between the y's and x's. From (5.4.76), (5.4.78), (5.4.79), and the preceding discussion it is easily seen that if v_i is the ith canonical correlation, then the coefficient of (vector) alienation is given by

$$\rho_A = \prod_{i=1}^{m} (1 - v_i^2) \tag{5.5.6}$$

Obviously we can obtain maximum likelihood estimators for the canonical correlations v_i, $i = 1, 2, \ldots, m$, by solving

$$
\begin{vmatrix} -r\dfrac{Y'Y}{T} & \dfrac{Y'X}{T} \\[2ex] \dfrac{X'Y}{T} & -r\dfrac{X'X}{T} \end{vmatrix} = 0
\tag{5.5.7}
$$

where the matrices Y and X have the meaning given them in (5.4.92) or in (5.4.102); that is, they are matrices of (T) observations on $(m \times 1)$ and $(G \times 1)$ or $(G - 1 \times 1)$ multivariate normal vectors, respectively, with mean zero covariance matrices Σ_{11} and Σ_{22} and "cross covariance" Σ_{12}.

Thus the estimators for the v_i^2 are given by the solutions to (5.5.7), which are equivalent to the solutions of

$$
|r^2 \hat{\Sigma}_{11} - \hat{\Sigma}_{12} \hat{\Sigma}_{22}^{-1} \hat{\Sigma}_{21}| = 0
\tag{5.5.8}
$$

where

$$
\hat{\Sigma}_{11} = \frac{Y'Y}{T} \quad \hat{\Sigma}_{12} = \frac{Y'X}{T} \quad \hat{\Sigma}_{21} = \frac{X'Y}{T} \quad \hat{\Sigma}_{22} = \frac{X'X}{T}
\tag{5.5.9}
$$

If the solutions to (5.5.8) are denoted by r_i^2, then obviously

$$
r_c = \prod_{i=1}^{m} r_i^2 \qquad r_A = \prod_{i=1}^{m} (1 - r_i^2)
\tag{5.5.10}
$$

Thus the sample coefficients of (vector) correlation and alienation—the statistics in terms of which we proposed to judge the goodness of fit of the reduced form model in the discussion of the previous sections—turn out to be nothing more than the product, respectively, of the sample canonical correlations squared and one minus the square of the sample canonical correlations.

In particular, we see that

$$
r_c = \prod_{i=1}^{m} r_i^2 = |\hat{\Sigma}_{11}^{-1} (\hat{\Sigma}_{12} \hat{\Sigma}_{22}^{-1} \hat{\Sigma}_{21})|
\tag{5.5.11}
$$

As we saw earlier, the matrix $\hat{\Sigma}_{12} \hat{\Sigma}_{22}^{-1} \hat{\Sigma}_{21}$ will be singular if $G < m$, that is, if the number of predetermined variables is less than the number of current endogenous variables contained in the model. In this case, $r_c = 0$ no matter how closely in some other sense the predetermined variables "explain" the behavior of the current endogenous variables. This is a consequence of the fact that here some of the r_i must be zero. In order to obviate this difficulty and still keep within the current framework, Hooper [11] suggested that we take as a measure of goodness of fit not r_c, which is the product of the r_i^2, but rather the sum, or an average, of the latter. Thus he proposed

$$
\bar{r}_c = \frac{1}{m} \sum_{i=1}^{m} r_i^2
\tag{5.5.12}
$$

as a measure of the goodness of fit of the reduced form model. Notice that this is simply

$$\bar{r}_c = \frac{1}{m} \text{tr} \left[\hat{\Sigma}_{11}^{-1}(\hat{\Sigma}_{12}\hat{\Sigma}_{22}^{-1}\hat{\Sigma}_{21}) \right] \tag{5.5.13}$$

and thus it is also referred to as the *trace correlation*.

An interesting consequence of this approach is that $\bar{r}_c$ is not zero unless *all* the canonical correlations are zero; the latter will be so only if $\Sigma_{12} = 0$, that is, if the y's and the x's are mutually independent. This, of course, is exactly the property we would want for a goodness of fit measure. Thus we are able to define a sensible statistic even when $G < m$, in which case $r_c = 0$.

Of course, if we deal with $r_{c(x, y)}$ instead of $r_{c(y, x)}$, the former will not vanish. The only problem with the trace correlation is that its distribution is far less tractable than the distribution of r_c/r_A. Naturally we can also define the "trace" analog of the (sample) coefficient of (vector) alienation as

$$\bar{r}_A = \frac{1}{m} \text{tr} \left[\hat{\Sigma}_{11}^{-1}(\hat{\Sigma}_{11} - \hat{\Sigma}_{12}\hat{\Sigma}_{22}^{-1}\hat{\Sigma}_{21}) \right] = \frac{1}{m} \sum_{i=1}^{m} (1 - r_i^2) \tag{5.5.14}$$

and the population analogs of these quantities as

$$\bar{\rho}_c = \frac{1}{m} \text{tr} \left[\Sigma_{11}^{-1}(\Sigma_{12}\Sigma_{22}^{-1}\Sigma_{21}) \right]$$

$$\bar{\rho}_A = \frac{1}{m} \text{tr} \left[\Sigma_{11}^{-1}(\Sigma_{11} - \Sigma_{12}\Sigma_{22}^{-1}\Sigma_{21}) \right] \tag{5.5.15}$$

Another interesting property of the trace correlations is that

$$\bar{\rho}_c + \bar{\rho}_A = 1 \tag{5.5.16}$$

and that they are symmetrical in the following sense.

$$m\bar{\rho}_{c(y, x)} = \text{tr} \left[\Sigma_{11}^{-1}(\Sigma_{12}\Sigma_{22}^{-1}\Sigma_{21}) \right] = \text{tr} \left[\Sigma_{22}^{-1}(\Sigma_{21}\Sigma_{11}^{-1}\Sigma_{12}) \right]$$
$$= G\bar{\rho}_{c(x, y)} \tag{5.5.17}$$

Recall that it is not generally true that

$$\rho_{c(x, y)} = \rho_{c(y, x)} \tag{5.5.18}$$

unless $m = G$. From (5.5.17) we see that a certain multiple of the trace correlation between x and y is equal to the trace correlation between y and x.

However, unless $G < m$ there is not much point in using $\bar{r}_c$ as a measure of goodness of fit. It has no particular advantages, and we still have the complexity of its distribution to content with, although Hooper [11] has given an approximate expression for the asymptotic variance of $\bar{r}_c$.

5.6 APPLICATIONS OF PRINCIPAL COMPONENT THEORY IN ECONOMETRIC SYSTEMS

In the previous section we have attempted to give a measure of the goodness of fit of the reduced form of a model in terms of the coefficients of (vector) correlation and alienation. It was determined that in order for r_c/r_A to be a meaningful statistic and for its distribution to be determined, it was necessary that the conditions

$$G > m \qquad T - G - m \geq 0 \tag{5.6.1}$$

hold. It is easy to see that if the first condition fails, then $r_c = 0$. This is so since r_c is simply the determinant of the matrix

$$(Y^{*\prime}Y^*)^{-1}Y^{*\prime}X^*(X^{*\prime}X^*)^{-1}X^{*\prime}Y^* = \hat{C} \tag{5.6.2}$$

where the symbols Y^*, X^* were defined in (5.4.102) and (5.4.103). It is clear that if the dummy variable unity—corresponding to the constant terms of the various equations—is one of the predetermined variables, then $X^{*\prime}X^*$ is $(G-1) \times (G-1)$ and thus the matrix $\hat{C}$, which is $m \times m$, must be singular unless the first condition in (5.6.1) holds. On the other hand, if no equation contains a constant term, then the number of predetermined variables will be G and $X^{*\prime}X^*$ will be $G \times G$. In this case, the condition is to be replaced by

$$G \geq m \tag{5.6.3}$$

Since r_c is the product of the canonical correlations between the y's and x's and since at least one of these correlations is zero when the condition $G > m$ fails to hold, it was proposed that we use the sum of the canonical correlations as a measure of goodness of fit.

However, a more frequent difficulty with simultaneous equations systems by far is failure of the second condition in (5.6.1) to hold. The failure often occurs in the particularly severe form

$$T - G < 0 \tag{5.6.4}$$

that is, there are more predetermined variables in the model than there are observations. This is the case, for example, with the forecasting model of the Wharton School and the Brookings model.

The consequence of (5.6.4) is that neither r_c nor r_A is defined, for the matrix $X'X$—and hence $X^{*\prime}X^*$—is singular. But beyond that, the 2SLS and 3SLS estimators cannot be defined because of this singularity. Thus recall that the 2SLS estimator of the structural parameters appearing in the ith equation is given (Chapter 4) by

$$\tilde{\delta}_{\cdot i} = \left[\binom{Y_i'}{X_i'} X(X'X)^{-1}X'(Y_i, X_i) \right]^{-1} \binom{Y_i'}{X_i'} X(X'X)^{-1}X'y_{\cdot i} \tag{5.6.5}$$

Since (5.6.4) holds, X is, at most, of rank T, and thus the $G \times G$ matrix $X'X$ must be singular; hence $\tilde{\delta}_{.i}$ is not well defined.

How can this problem be handled? In this context it is preferable to think of the 2SLS estimator in the manner described in Section 4.3 of Chapter 4. Thus the problem arises "because" the "first stage" of 2SLS cannot be carried out, for unique estimators of the reduced form cannot be obtained.

On the other hand, arguing from first principles, we observe that what we seek to do in the "first stage" is not necessarily to estimate uniquely the matrix of parameters of the reduced form—Π. Rather, we seek a consistent estimator of the nonstochastic part of the jointly dependent variables, whenever they appear as explanatory variables.

The problem becomes more tractable when regarded in this fashion. Recall from Section 2.2 of Chapter 2 that if x is a $G \times 1$ random variable such that

$$E(x) = 0 \qquad \text{Cov}(x) = \Sigma \tag{5.6.6}$$

then the principal components of x are defined by

$$\zeta_i = a^{*\prime}_{.i} x \qquad i = 1, 2, \ldots, G \tag{5.6.7}$$

where $a^{*}_{.i}$ is the characteristic vector of Σ corresponding to its ith characteristic root. Of course, the $a^{*}_{.i}$ are normalized so that

$$a^{*\prime}_{.i} a^{*}_{.j} = \delta_{ij} \tag{5.6.8}$$

δ_{ij} being the Kronecker delta.

We further recall that if $\zeta = (\zeta_1, \zeta_2, \ldots, \zeta_G)'$, then

$$E(\zeta) = 0 \qquad \text{Cov}(\zeta) = A^{*\prime} E(xx') A^{*} = A^{*\prime} \Sigma A^{*} = \Lambda^{*} \tag{5.6.9}$$

where

$$A^{*} = (a^{*}_{.1}, a^{*}_{.2}, \ldots, a^{*}_{.G}) \qquad \Lambda^{*} = \text{diag}(\lambda^{*}_1, \lambda^{*}_2, \ldots, \lambda^{*}_G) \tag{5.6.10}$$

the λ^{*}_i obey $\lambda^{*}_1 \geqslant \lambda^{*}_2 \geqslant \cdots \geqslant \lambda^{*}_G$ and are the characteristic roots of Σ.

We also recall that the sum of the variances of the principal components equals the sum of the variances of the elements of x and, moreover, the generalized variance of ζ is equal to the generalized variance of x. Hence the principal components preserve the "variability" of the original set of random variables.

If, in addition to (5.6.6), we also assume

$$x \sim N(0, \Sigma) \tag{5.6.11}$$

then

$$\zeta \sim N(0, \Lambda^{*}) \tag{5.6.12}$$

so that the principal components are mutually independent.

Suppose that we select the set of the first k principal components. Since this is a set of k linear combinations of the elements of x, the characteristics of this set will in some measure reflect the characteristics of x. Neglecting the problem of units, it is apparent that the "fraction" of the generalized variance of x captured by the first k principal components is given by

$$\frac{|\Lambda_k^*|}{|\Lambda^*|} = \left(\prod_{i=k+1}^{G} \lambda_i^*\right)^{-1} \tag{5.6.13}$$

where

$$\Lambda_k^* = \text{diag}\,(\lambda_1^*, \lambda_2^*, \ldots, \lambda_k^*) \tag{5.6.14}$$

It should be noted that the word "fraction" is in quotes, for it is conceivable that $|\Lambda_k^*| > |\Lambda^*|$. This will be so, for example, if all the roots λ_i^*, $i = k+1, \ldots, G$, are less than unity. Another measure of the variability of the elements of x is the sum of their variances, which is simply

$$\text{tr}\,\Lambda^* = \sum_{i=1}^{G} \lambda_i^* \tag{5.6.15}$$

With this criterion, the fraction of the variability of x accounted by the first k principal components is

$$\phi(k) = \frac{\sum_{i=1}^{k} \lambda_i^*}{\sum_{i=1}^{G} \lambda_i^*} = \frac{\text{tr}\,\Lambda_k^*}{\text{tr}\,\Lambda^*} \tag{5.6.16}$$

By now it should be clear what it is that one might expect of principal component theory in this context. We have seen that when the number of predetermined variables exceeds the number of observations in an econometric model, then 2SLS estimators cannot be uniquely defined. On the other hand, it was noted that what fails is our ability to estimate uniquely the matrix of reduced form coefficients or an appropriate submatrix thereof. However, we are not interested in this matrix per se. We are only interested, in the logical framework of 2SLS, in obtaining a consistent estimator of the nonstochastic component of the current endogenous variables that serve as explanatory variables. Estimating, by OLS, the appropriate submatrix of reduced form coefficients is only one way of obtaining this end. We should be just as content if we could account for as much of the observed variation in the relevant current endogenous variables in terms of some other convenient function of the explanatory variables. In reduced form estimation, we try to account for the variation in any given endogenous variable through the *variations in all the predetermined variables of the system*. This is not possible in this case, for we cannot use all of the predetermined variables. On the other hand, if, through a relatively small number of linear combinations of the predetermined variables, we can account for "most" of the latter's variation, then clearly little will be lost in using this set of linear combinations to formulate our estimate of the nonstochastic component of the relevant endogenous variable. Thus little will be lost if, instead of regressing the latter on all the predetermined variables, we regressed it on a relatively small set of linear combinations of such variables. Hence the procedure to be outlined more fully below consists of estimating a set of k ($< T$) principal components of all the predetermined variables and then regressing the explanatory current endogenous variables on that set in order to obtain the consistent estimator of the latter's nonstochastic part.

Consequently, let us now give a formal account of this procedure. Consider the model in (5.4.100), where again all variables are measured as deviations from their respective sample means. For simplicity and ease of application, let us agree to deal with the problem of estimating consistently the nonstochastic component of all the current endogenous variables. Thus in estimating the parameters of any particular (structural) equation, all we need to do is to choose from the above the appropriate subset, that is, the one that enters the given equation in the form of explanatory variables.

Now we have to estimate the principal components of the $G - 1$ predetermined variables of the system. First, we obtain the characteristic roots and vectors of the "sample covariance matrix" $X^{*\prime}X^*/T$. Let the roots be denoted (in decreasing order of magnitude) by $\lambda_i: i = 1, 2, \ldots, G - 1$, and their (normalized) associated characteristic vectors by $a_{\cdot i}: i = 1, 2, \ldots, G - 1$, and suppose that we are interested in the first k principal components. Let

$$A_k = (a_{\cdot 1}, a_{\cdot 2}, \ldots, a_{\cdot k}) \tag{5.6.17}$$

and note that the matrix of observations on the (estimated) first k principal components is given by[13]

$$Z_k = X^* A_k \tag{5.6.18}$$

Having obtained the estimated principal components as above, we now estimate the nonstochastic part of the jointly dependent variables of the model by

$$\tilde{Y} = Z_k (Z_k' Z_k)^{-1} Z_k' Y^* \tag{5.6.19}$$

Formally, we may put

$$Y^* = Z_k \tilde{\Pi}_k + \tilde{V}_k \quad \tilde{\Pi}_k = (Z_k' Z_k)^{-1} Z_k' Y^* \quad \tilde{V}_k \equiv Y^* - \tilde{Y} \tag{5.6.20}$$

where $\tilde{\Pi}_k$ is merely a convenient notation and need not bear any explicit and unique relation to the matrix Π^* of reduced form coefficients in (5.4.100). The

---

[13] In many computer programs it is found computationally efficient to obtain the characteristic vectors defining principal components from the (sample) correlation rather than the covariance matrix; this would mean that in (5.6.18) we should define Z_k by $Z_k = X^* D^{-1} A_k$, where $D = (s_{22}^{1/2}, \ldots, s_{GG}^{1/2})$, the s_{ii} being the sample variances of the predetermined variables. Unfortunately, principal components are not invariant to the choice of units, and failure to scale the variables properly will result in loss of orthogonality as between (estimated) distinct principal components.

scheme above simply consists of regressing the current endogenous variables on the (estimated) first k principal components of the predetermined variables. But then it is clear how to proceed with a modified version of 2SLS estimation. If the ith equation of the system is written as

$$y^*_{\cdot i} = Y^*_i \beta_{\cdot i} + X^*_i \gamma_{\cdot i} + u^*_{\cdot i} \tag{5.6.21}$$

then the modified 2SLS estimator suggested here is obtained by applying OLS to

$$
\begin{aligned}
y^*_{\cdot i} &= \tilde{Y}_i \beta_{\cdot i} + X^*_i \gamma_{\cdot i} + \tilde{V}_{ki} \beta_{\cdot i} + u^*_{\cdot i} \\
&= (\tilde{Y}_i, X^*_i)\delta_{\cdot i} + \tilde{V}_{ki} \beta_{\cdot i} + u^*_{\cdot i}
\end{aligned} \tag{5.6.22}
$$

where

$$\delta_{\cdot i} = \begin{pmatrix} \beta_{\cdot i} \\ \gamma_{\cdot i} \end{pmatrix}$$

and $\tilde{Y}_i$, $\tilde{V}_{ki}$ are the appropriate submatrices of $\tilde{Y}$ and $\tilde{V}_k$ as defined in (5.6.19) and (5.6.20) respectively. Thus the modified 2SLS estimator of $\delta_{\cdot i}$, $\bar{\delta}_{\cdot i}$ is given by

$$\bar{\delta}_{\cdot i}(k) = \begin{bmatrix} \tilde{Y}'_i \tilde{Y}_i & \tilde{Y}'_i X^*_i \\ X^{*\prime}_i \tilde{Y}_i & X^{*\prime}_i X^*_i \end{bmatrix}^{-1} \begin{bmatrix} \tilde{Y}'_i y^*_{\cdot i} \\ X^{*\prime}_i y^*_{\cdot i} \end{bmatrix} \tag{5.6.23}$$

where the notation $\bar{\delta}_{\cdot i}(k)$ is used to make clear that k principal components are used.

Perhaps a computationally more convenient expression for the modified 2SLS estimator is the following:

$$\bar{\delta}_{\cdot i}(k) = \begin{bmatrix} Y^{*\prime}_i X^* M_k X^{*\prime} Y^*_i & Y^{*\prime}_i X^* M'_k X^*_i \\ X^{*\prime}_i X^* M_k X^{*\prime} Y^*_i & X^{*\prime}_i X^*_i \end{bmatrix}^{-1} \begin{bmatrix} Y^{*\prime}_i X^* M_k X^{*\prime} y^*_{\cdot i} \\ X^{*\prime}_i y^*_{\cdot i} \end{bmatrix} \tag{5.6.24}$$

where

$$M_k = A_k \Lambda_k^{-1} A'_k \tag{5.6.25}$$

Two questions arise in connection with this modified 2SLS estimator: Is it consistent? How should the number of principal components (k) be chosen?

The two questions are actually not distinct and thus we shall discuss them simultaneously. First, it should be noted that, on intuitive grounds, we cannot expect the estimator to be as efficient as 2SLS unless as $T \to \infty$ we use increasingly more, and ultimately all, of the principal components of the predetermined variables. Second, note that the greater the number of principal components employed, the greater the "explanation" attained for Y^* through $\tilde{Y}$ of (5.6.19); this seems to argue for as large a number of principal components as possible. On the other hand, if the number of principal components chosen is exactly T, then

$$Z_T = X^* A_T \tag{5.6.26}$$

which is a $T \times T$ matrix and thus ordinarily nonsingular. It follows then immediately from (5.6.19) that

$$\tilde{Y} = Y^* \qquad (5.6.27)$$

and thus our claim that $\tilde{Y}$ estimates the nonstochastic part of Y^* rests on zero degrees of freedom. Indeed, we are then reduced to OLS estimation, as (5.6.27) makes abundantly clear. The fact that we cannot use as many principal components as we can extract is perhaps sufficiently well established by the comment above so as not to require further elaboration. Let us state precisely the sense in which using more principal components results in a better "explanation" of Y^* by $\tilde{Y}$. The (sample) coefficient of (vector) correlation between the variables in Y^* and those in Z_k is by definition

$$r_c^{(1)} = \frac{|\tilde{\Pi}_k' Z_k' Z_k \tilde{\Pi}_k|}{|Y^{*\prime} Y^*|} \qquad (5.6.28)$$

Suppose now that we extract not k but n principal components (such that $k < n < T$) and regress the variables in Y^* on these n components. We obtain

$$\tilde{Y} = Z_n (Z_n' Z_n)^{-1} Z_n' Y^* = Z_n \tilde{\Pi}_n \qquad (5.6.29)$$

The statistic corresponding to $r_c^{(1)}$ of (5.6.28) is

$$r_c^{(2)} = \frac{|\tilde{\Pi}_n' Z_n' Z_n \tilde{\Pi}_n|}{|Y^{*\prime} Y^*|} \qquad (5.6.30)$$

We shall now show that

$$r_c^{(1)} \le r_c^{(2)} \qquad (5.6.31)$$

Employing the notation of (5.6.25), we have

$$\frac{r_c^{(1)}}{r_c^{(2)}} = \frac{|Y^{*\prime} X^* M_k X^{*\prime} Y|}{|Y^{*\prime} X^* M_n X^{*\prime} Y|} \qquad (5.6.32)$$

Write

$$A_n = (A_k, A^*) \qquad \Lambda_n = \begin{pmatrix} \Lambda_k & 0 \\ 0 & \Lambda^* \end{pmatrix} \qquad (5.6.33)$$

where $\Lambda^* = \operatorname{diag}(\lambda_{k+1}, \lambda_{k+2}, \ldots, \lambda_n)$, $A^* = (a_{\cdot k+1}, a_{\cdot k+2}, \ldots, a_{\cdot n})$, and observe that

$$M_n = (A_k, A^*) \begin{pmatrix} \Lambda_k^{-1} & 0 \\ 0 & \Lambda^{*-1} \end{pmatrix} \begin{pmatrix} A_k' \\ A^{*\prime} \end{pmatrix}$$

$$= A_k \Lambda_k^{-1} A_k' + A^* \Lambda^{*-1} A^{*\prime}$$

$$= M_k + A^* \Lambda^{*-1} A^{*\prime} \qquad (5.6.34)$$

Hence

$$Y^{*'}X^*M_n X^{*'}Y^* = Y^{*'}X^*M_k X^{*'}Y^* + Y^{*'}X^*(A^*\Lambda^{*-1}A^{*'})X^{*'}Y^* \qquad (5.6.35)$$

Thus the denominator in (5.6.32) can be expressed as the determinant of the sum of two matrices, the first of which is positive definite and the second is at least positive semidefinite. By the triangle inequality, we have

$$|Y^{*'}X^*M_n X^{*'}Y^*| \geq |Y^{*'}X^*M_k X^{*'}Y^*| + |Y^{*'}X^*(A^*\Lambda^{*-1}A^{*'})X^{*'}Y^*|$$
$$\geq |Y^{*'}X^*M_k X^{*'}Y^*| \qquad (5.6.36)$$

Therefore we conclude

$$r_c^{(2)} \geq r_c^{(1)} \qquad (5.6.37)$$

provided, of course, that $m < T$. If that does not hold, then $Y^{*'}Y^*$ is singular and neither $r_c^{(1)}$ nor $r_c^{(2)}$ is defined. But even if $m \geq T$, there is still a sense in which the more principal components we use, the more perfectly we "explain" Y^* by $\tilde{Y}$. Consider any column of $\tilde{Y}$, say $\tilde{y}_{\cdot i}$. It has the representation

$$\tilde{y}_{\cdot i} = Z_k(Z_k' Z_k)^{-1}Z_k' y_{\cdot i}^* \qquad (5.6.38)$$

The "regression sum of squares" is given by

$$y_{\cdot i}^{*'} Z_k(Z_k' Z_k)^{-1}Z_k' y_{\cdot i}^*$$

If n components are used, then by (5.6.34) we have

$$y_{\cdot i}^{*'} Z_n(Z_n' Z_n)^{-1}Z_n' y_{\cdot i}^* = y_{\cdot i}^{*'} X^*M_k X^{*'}y_{\cdot i}^* + y_{\cdot i}^{*'} X^*A^*\Lambda^{*-1}A^{*'}X^{*'}y_{\cdot i}^* \qquad (5.6.39)$$

Thus if our measure of goodness of fit consists of comparison of the regression sum of squares in all equations to the sum of the sample variances of all the endogenous variables, we have for the goodness of fit statistic

$$r_k^* = \frac{\text{tr } Y^{*'}X^*M_k X^{*'}Y^*}{\text{tr } Y^{*'}Y^*} \qquad (5.6.40)$$

where the subscript k is entered to indicate that k principal components are used. It is clear that if $n > k$, then

$$r_n^* \geq r_k^* \qquad (5.6.41)$$

so that if more principal components are used we cannot decrease the "regression sum of squares" corresponding to all the *endogenous variables of the system or, indeed, that corresponding to any particular endogenous variable.*

Recapitulating, the modified 2SLS estimator is obtained as follows:

i. Choose the desired "degrees of freedom" parameter, say q.
ii. From the centered moment matrix $X^{*'}X^*/T$, extract the largest[14] $k \leq T - q$

---

[14] Although little experience has been obtained with this procedure, perhaps a rule of the form $k \approx \sqrt{T}$ might prove reasonable, for samples of moderate size.

characteristic roots and obtain the matrix of principal components estimates, Z_k, as defined in (5.6.18).

iii. Regress the current endogenous variables on the k principal components above to obtain $\tilde{Y}$ of (5.6.19).

iv. To estimate the parameters of any structural equation, replace the current endogenous variables appearing as explanatory variables in that equation by the appropriate submatrix of $\tilde{Y}$ and apply OLS estimators to the resulting equation.

In ii it should be noted that as T becomes large, k will also increase. In particular, if $T \geq G + q$, then one can choose $k = G$ (or $G - 1$ as the case may be) so that as more observations become available we revert to the standard 2SLS procedure.

Turning now to the question of whether the modified 2SLS estimator above is consistent or not, it should be apparent from the preceding that indeed this is so since for large T it coincides with the 2SLS estimator. Clearly, the asymptotic distribution of the two estimators is identical. Thus in view of the preceding development and the discussion in Section 4.5, Chapter 4, a consistent estimator of the asymptotic covariance matrix of $\bar{\delta}._1(k)$, e.g., is given by

$$\mathrm{Cov} \, [\widetilde{\bar{\delta}}._1(k)] = T\bar{\sigma}_{11}(k) \begin{bmatrix} (Y_1^* - \tilde{V}_{k1})'(Y_1^* - \tilde{V}_{k1}) & (Y_1^* - \tilde{V}_{k1})'X_1^* \\ X_1^{*'}(Y_1^* - \tilde{V}_{k1}) & X_1^{*'}X_1^* \end{bmatrix}^{-1} \tag{5.6.42}$$

where

$$\bar{\sigma}_{11}(k) = \frac{1}{T}[y_{\cdot 1}^* - (\tilde{Y}_1, X_1^*)\bar{\delta}._1(k)]'[y_{\cdot 1}^* - (\tilde{Y}_1, X_1^*)\bar{\delta}._1(k)] \tag{5.6.43}$$

Before leaving this topic, two comments should be made. First, the choice of the parameter q—that is, the quantity by which T should minimally exceed the number of principal components (k) actually employed—is not something that is unambiguously determined by the procedure outlined above. Rather, this is left to the judgment of the individual investigator. Thus, to some extent, the choice is arbitrary. On the other hand, this is not such a crucial problem from the point of view of the properties implied for the resulting estimators, for the latter are large sample properties and in a large sample context the problem will not exist.

Second, it is important to stress that, in the preceding discussion, we had not employed principal components *because the predetermined variables were collinear (or nearly so)*. In such case, the matrix $X'X$ (or $X^{*'}X^*$) is singular (or nearly so) no matter how large T may be; hence, we are called upon to make a *permanent choice* regarding the number of principal components to be used. This is necessary since, no matter how large T is, the estimator of reduced form parameters is not defined; thus, the object of the device, in this scheme, is to transform the predetermined variables of the system into a smaller set such that the transformed variables do not exhibit linear dependence.

The reader should notice that the problem dealt with by this approach is not statistical, but one whose origin lies in the nature of the model and whose consequence is that, in the context of the reduced form, the influence of each predetermined variable on the current endogenous variables cannot be individually determined.

By contrast, the use of principal components outlined in the discussion of this section is designed to cope with the *"temporary" problem entailed by the fact that the number of predetermined variables exceeds the number of observations.* Clearly, the problem is obviated as $T \to \infty$.

5.7 ALTERNATIVE ASYMPTOTIC TESTS OF SIGNIFICANCE FOR 2SLS ESTIMATED PARAMETERS

In Chapter 4 (Section 4.5) we derived, under certain restrictions, the asymptotic distribution of the 2SLS estimator and formulated approximate tests of significance based on the normal distribution.

It is interesting, on the other hand, that if we exploit the formulation of the 2SLS estimator as given there, we can develop an almost exact parallel with the inference problem in the context of the general linear model and thus devise alternative tests of significance for 2SLS estimated parameters based, asymptotically, on the t distribution. In fact, such tests bear a striking similarity to the tests of identifiability we shall develop at a later stage.

In Chapter 4 (Section 4.5), we examined the structural system

$$y_{.i} = Y_i \beta_{.i} + X_i \gamma_{.i} + u_{.i} \qquad i = 1, 2, \ldots, m \tag{5.7.1}$$

and its associated transform

$$w_{.i} = Q_i \delta_{.i} + r_{.i} \qquad i = 1, 2, \ldots, m \tag{5.7.2}$$

where

$$w_{.i} = R^{-1} X' y_{.i} \quad Q_i = R^{-1} X'(Y_i, X_i) \quad \delta_{.i} = \begin{pmatrix} \beta_{.i} \\ \gamma_{.i} \end{pmatrix}$$
$$r_{.i} = R^{-1} X' u_{.i} \qquad RR' = X'X \tag{5.7.3}$$

and gave the meaning of the symbols, $y_{.i}$, Y_i, X_i, $\beta_{.i}$, $\gamma_{.i}$, $u_{.i}$.

It was further assumed that the system contained no lagged endogenous variables among its predetermined variables and that

$$u_{.i} \sim N(0, \sigma_{ii} I_T) \qquad \text{Cov}(u_{.i}, u_{.j}) = \sigma_{ij} I_T \tag{5.7.4}$$

Moreover, it was established that

$$\plim_{T \to \infty} \sqrt{T} R^{-1} = \bar{R}^{-1} \tag{5.7.5}$$

exists as a nonstochastic matrix with finite elements. Now, what is the distribution of $r_{\cdot i}$?

By definition, we have

$$r_{\cdot i} = \sqrt{T}\, R^{-1} \frac{X' u_{\cdot i}}{\sqrt{T}} \tag{5.7.6}$$

Thus the asymptotic distribution of $r_{\cdot i}$ *conditionally on X* is, from Proposition 2 of Chapter 3,

$$r_{\cdot i} \sim N(0, \sigma_{ii} I_G) \tag{5.7.7}$$

This is so since conditionally on X

$$\frac{X' u_{\cdot i}}{\sqrt{T}} \sim N\!\left(0, \sigma_{ii}\, \frac{X'X}{T}\right) \tag{5.7.8}$$

The conclusion in (5.7.7) follows immediately from (5.7.6). Further, since the conditional distribution of $r_{\cdot i}$ as exhibited in (5.7.6) does not depend on X, it follows *that* (5.7.7) *gives the unconditional one as well.* We next observe that $Q_i'/\sqrt{T}$ and $r_{\cdot i}$ are asymptotically uncorrelated because of the former's convergence to a nonstochastic probability limit. Thus we see that, for large T, the system in (5.7.2) bears a striking resemblance to a system of general linear models.

In what follows, we shall develop an inference theory exactly parallel to that obtaining in the context of ordinary regression analysis.

As shown in Chapter 4, the 2SLS estimator of $\delta_{\cdot i}$ is given by

$$\tilde{\delta}_{\cdot i} = (Q_i' Q_i)^{-1} Q_i' w_{\cdot i} = \delta_{\cdot i} + (Q_i' Q_i)^{-1} Q_i' r_{\cdot i} \tag{5.7.9}$$

We observe that

$$(\tilde{\delta}_{\cdot i} - \delta_{\cdot i})' Q_i' Q_i (\tilde{\delta}_{\cdot i} - \delta_{\cdot i}) = r_{\cdot i}' \frac{Q_i'}{\sqrt{T}} \left(\frac{Q_i' Q_i}{T}\right)^{-1} \frac{Q_i'}{\sqrt{T}}\, r_{\cdot i} \tag{5.7.10}$$

Consider now the residuals of (5.7.2)

$$\tilde{r}_{\cdot i} = w_{\cdot i} - Q_i \tilde{\delta}_{\cdot i} = [I - Q_i (Q_i' Q_i)^{-1} Q_i'] r_{\cdot i} \tag{5.7.11}$$

We therefore conclude that

$$\tilde{r}_{\cdot i}' \tilde{r}_{\cdot i} = r_{\cdot i}' \left[I - \frac{Q_i'}{\sqrt{T}} \left(\frac{Q_i' Q_i}{T}\right)^{-1} \frac{Q_i'}{\sqrt{T}}\right] r_{\cdot i} \tag{5.7.12}$$

Let

$$N_i = \frac{Q_i}{\sqrt{T}} \left(\frac{Q_i' Q_i}{T}\right)^{-1} \frac{Q_i'}{\sqrt{T}} \tag{5.7.13}$$

and notice that both N_i and $I - N_i$ are symmetric idempotent matrices that possess well-defined nonstochastic probability limits. Both $I - N_i$ and N_i are $G \times G$ matrices. Now it is obvious that

$$\frac{r'_{\cdot i} r_{\cdot i}}{\sigma_{ii}} = \frac{r'_{\cdot i} N_i r_{\cdot i}}{\sigma_{ii}} + \frac{r'_{\cdot i} (I - N_i) r_{\cdot i}}{\sigma_{ii}} \tag{5.7.14}$$

From (5.7.7) and the fact that

$$\text{rank } (N_i) = \text{tr } [Q_i (Q'_i Q_i)^{-1} Q'_i] = G_i + m_i$$
$$\text{rank } (I - N_i) = \text{tr } [I - Q_i (Q'_i Q_i)^{-1} Q'_i] = G - G_i - m_i \tag{5.7.15}$$

we conclude that, asymptotically,

$$\frac{r'_{\cdot i} N_i r_{\cdot i}}{\sigma_{ii}} \sim \chi^2_{G_i + m_i} \qquad \frac{r'_{\cdot i} (I - N_i) r_{\cdot i}}{\sigma_{ii}} \sim \chi^2_{G - G_i - m_i} \tag{5.7.16}$$

and, moreover, that the two quantities are mutually independent. Of course, for the result in (5.7.16) to be admissible we should have

$$G - G_i - m_i > 0 \tag{5.7.17}$$

so that we must be dealing with *an overidentified equation*. Thus if we estimate the parameter σ_{ii} by

$$\bar{\sigma}_{ii} = \frac{1}{G - G_i - m_i} \tilde{r}'_{\cdot i} \tilde{r}_{\cdot i} \tag{5.7.18}$$

we see that, asymptotically, $\bar{\sigma}_{ii}$ is proportional to a chi-square variable with $G - G_i - m_i$ degrees of freedom and is also an unbiased estimator of σ_{ii}.

Let δ_{ki} be the kth element of $\delta_{\cdot i}$, and $\bar{q}^i_{kk}$ be the kth diagonal element of $(Q'_i Q_i)^{-1}$. The development above implies that, asymptotically,

$$\frac{(\tilde{\delta}_{ki} - \delta_{ki})}{\sqrt{\bar{\sigma}_{ii} \bar{q}^i_{kk}}} \sim t_{G - G_i - m_i} \tag{5.7.19}$$

Hence we have produced an asymptotically exact test of significance that can be based on the t distribution. Notice that the degrees of freedom parameter involved is *the extent to which the equation* under discussion is overidentified. Thus *we have no test when the equation under consideration is just identified*. This is a consequence of the fact that, as pointed out in Chapter 4, for a just identified equation the 2SLS residuals

$$\tilde{u}_{\cdot i} = y_{\cdot i} - Z_i \tilde{\delta}_{\cdot i} \tag{5.7.20}$$

are orthogonal to the predetermined variables of the system in the sense that

$$X' \tilde{u}_{\cdot i} = 0 \tag{5.7.21}$$

Since $\bar{\sigma}_{ii}$ is simply a quadratic form in such residuals, namely,

$$\bar{\sigma}_{ii} = \frac{1}{G - G_i - m_i} [\tilde{u}'_{.i} X (X'X)^{-1} X' \tilde{u}_{.i}] \tag{5.7.22}$$

In the case of a just identified equation, $\bar{\sigma}_{ii}$ assumes the indeterminate form $0/0!$

To test, simultaneously, a hypothesis on a number of structural parameters, we may proceed as follows: Let it be desired to test a hypothesis on s (≥ 1) elements of $\delta_{.i}$. Let $\delta^{(s)}_{.i}$ be the subvector of $\delta_{.i}$ corresponding to these parameters. It should be clear from the preceding that if B_s is the submatrix of $(Q'_i Q_i)^{-1}$ consisting of the latter's rows and columns corresponding to the parameters in $\delta^{(s)}_{.i}$, then, asymptotically,

$$\frac{1}{\sigma_{ii}} (\tilde{\delta}^{(s)}_{.i} - \delta^{(s)}_{.i})' B_s^{-1} (\tilde{\delta}^{(s)}_{.i} - \delta_{.i}) \sim \chi^2_s \tag{5.7.23}$$

and, moreover, that the quantity in (5.7.23) is independent of $\bar{\sigma}_{ii}$. Thus we conclude

$$\frac{(\tilde{\delta}^{(s)}_{.i} - \delta^{(s)}_{.i})' B_s^{-1} (\tilde{\delta}^{(s)}_{.i} - \delta^{(s)}_{.i})}{\tilde{r}'_{.i} \tilde{r}_{.i}} \frac{G - G_i - m_i}{s} \sim F_{s, G - G_i - m_i} \tag{5.7.24}$$

so that a simultaneous test on all the parameters in $\delta^{(s)}_{.i}$ may be based on the central F distribution. In fact, the reader may easily verify that the quantity in (5.7.19) is a special case of that in (5.7.24) when in the latter we take

$$s = 1 \qquad B_s = \bar{q}^i_{kk} \tag{5.7.25}$$

The resulting quantity is then simply the square of the quantity in (5.7.19) and is thus distributed as central $F_{1, G - G_i - m_i}$.

Next we may ask: What is the difference in the test statistics entailed by the test of significance developed here and those obtained in Chapter 4?

The latter, based solely on the asymptotic distribution of $\sqrt{T}(\tilde{\delta}_{.i} - \delta_{.i})$, were formulated as follows.

Since, asymptotically,

$$\sqrt{T}(\tilde{\delta}_{.i} - \delta_{.i}) \sim N\left[0, \sigma_{ii} \plim_{T \to \infty} \left(\frac{Q'_i Q_i}{T}\right)^{-1}\right] \tag{5.7.26}$$

let

$$\tilde{\sigma}_{ii} = \frac{1}{T} \tilde{u}'_{.i} \tilde{u}_{.i} \qquad \tilde{u}_{.i} = y_{.i} - Z_i \tilde{\delta}_{.i}$$

In view of the consistency of $\tilde{\sigma}_{ii}$ as an estimator of σ_{ii}, we have, asymptotically,

$$\frac{\sqrt{T}(\tilde{\delta}_{ki} - \delta_{ki})}{\sqrt{\tilde{\sigma}_{ii} \bar{q}^{*i}_{kk}}} \sim N(0, 1) \tag{5.7.27}$$

where $\bar{q}_{kk}^{*i}$ is the kth diagonal element of $(Q_i'Q_i/T)^{-1}$. We note, however, that

$$\bar{q}_{kk}^{*i} = T\,\bar{q}_{kk}^{i} \qquad (5.7.28)$$

Thus (5.7.27) can be rewritten as

$$\frac{(\tilde{\delta}_{ki} - \delta_{ki})}{\sqrt{\tilde{\sigma}_{ii}\,\bar{q}_{kk}^{i}}} \sim N(0, 1) \qquad (5.7.29)$$

A comparison with (5.7.19) shows the two quantities to be identical except for the way in which the estimator for σ_{ii} is obtained. The choice in (5.7.18) results in a t distribution with $G - G_i - m_i$ degrees of freedom, while the customary choice, $\tilde{\sigma}_{ii}$, results in the standard normal distribution. In both cases we rely on asymptotic theory.

Since we seldom deal with samples large enough so that asymptotic distributions are, in fact, close approximations, it would be an interesting Monte Carlo experiment to investigate the relative performance of these two tests for samples of moderate size.

Finally, it might appear that the development above offers us the means of defining a goodness of fit criterion for structural equations. Thus, it might be argued, if by $\delta_{\cdot i}^{(s)}$ we denote the subvector of $\delta_{\cdot i}$ resulting when we eliminate from the latter the element corresponding to the constant term of the equation, then *mutatis mutandis* the quantity in (5.7.24) is similar to the quantity $R^2/(1 - R^2)$ we encounter in discussions of the general linear model, R^2 being the (unadjusted) coefficient of determination of multiple regression.

In order to make this line of argument perfectly clear, let us define starred variables as deviations from their respective sample means and $\delta_{\cdot i}^*$ as the subvector of $\delta_{\cdot i}$ resulting when we eliminate from the latter the element corresponding to the constant term. We see that if we define

$$R^{*2} = 1 - \frac{\tilde{r}_{\cdot i}'\tilde{r}_{\cdot i}}{w_{\cdot i}^{*\prime}w_{\cdot i}^{*}} = \frac{(\tilde{\delta}_{\cdot i}^* - \delta_{\cdot i}^*)'(Q_i^{*\prime}Q_i^*)(\tilde{\delta}_{\cdot i}^* - \delta_{\cdot i}^*)}{w_{\cdot i}^{*\prime}w_{\cdot i}^{*}} \qquad (5.7.30)$$

then

$$\frac{R^{*2}}{1 - R^{*2}} \frac{G - G_i - m_i}{G_i + m_i - 1} \sim F_{G_i + m_i - 1,\, G - G_i - m_i} \qquad (5.7.31)$$

The only difficulty with this is that while R^{*2} may serve as a plausible goodness of fit statistic, *it refers to the fit of the data to the model*

$$w_{\cdot i} = Q_i \delta_{\cdot i} + r_{\cdot i} \qquad (5.7.32)$$

and not to the model of interest, namely,

$$y_{\cdot i} = Z_i \delta_{\cdot i} + u_{\cdot i} \qquad (5.7.33)$$

Hence the procedure developed in this section is best viewed solely as providing an alternative set of asymptotic tests of significance for 2SLS estimated parameters and the statistic in (5.7.31) as being the appropriate one for testing the null hypothesis

$$H_0 : \delta^*_{\cdot i} = 0 \qquad\qquad (5.7.34)$$

as against the alternative

$$H_1 : \delta^*_{\cdot i} \neq 0 \qquad\qquad (5.7.35)$$

REFERENCES

1. Anderson, T. W., *An Introduction to Multivariate Statistical Analysis*, New York, Wiley, 1958.
2. Ando, A., and F. Modigliani, "The Relative Stability of Monetary Velocity and the Investment Multiplier," *The American Economic Review*, vol. 55, 1965, pp. 693–728.
3. Brown, T. M., "A Forecast Determination of National Product, Employment, and Price Level in Canada from an Econometric Model," in Conference on Research in Income and Wealth, *Models of Income Determination, Studies in Income and Wealth*, vol. 28, Princeton, Princeton University Press, 1964, pp. 11–96.
4. Cobb, C. W., and P. H. Douglas, "A Theory of Production," *American Economic Review*, vol. 18 (supplement), 1928, pp. 139–165.
5. Crouch, R. L., "A Model of the United Kingdom's Monetary Sector," *Econometrica*, vol. 35, 1967, pp. 398–418.
6. Dhrymes, P. J., and M. Kurz, "Investment, Dividend, and External Finance Behavior of Firms," in *Determinants of Investment Behavior*, R. Ferber and I. Friend (Eds.), New York, Columbia University Press, 1967, pp. 427–467.
7. Hoch, Irving, "Simultaneous Equation Bias in the Context of the Cobb-Douglas Production Function," *Econometrica*, vol. 26, 1958, pp. 566–578.
8. Hoch, Irving, "Estimation of Production Function Parameters Combining Time-series and Cross-section Data," *Econometrica*, vol. 30, 1962, pp. 34–53.
9. Hoel, P. G., "A Significance Test for Component Analysis," *Annals of Mathematical Statistics*, vol. 8, 1937, pp. 149–158.
10. Hooper, J. W., "Simultaneous Equations and Canonical Correlation Theory," *Econometrica*, vol. 27, 1959, pp. 245–256.
11. Hooper, J. W., "Partial Trace Correlations," *Econometrica*, vol. 30, 1962, pp. 324–331.
12. Hotelling, H., "Relations Between Two Sets of Variates," *Biometrika*, vol. 28, 1936, pp. 321–377.
13. Klein, L. R., "A Postwar Quarterly Model: Description and Applications," in Conference on Research in Income and Wealth, *Models of Income Determination, Studies in Income and Wealth*, vol. 28 Princeton, Princeton University Press, 1964, pp. 11–96.
14. Klein, L. R., R. J. Ball, A. Hazlewood, and P. Vandome, *An Econometric Model of the United Kingdom*, Oxford, Basil Blackwell, 1961.
15. Klein, L. R., R. J. Ball, A. Hazlewood, and P. Vandome, "Re-estimation of the Econometric Model of the United Kingdom and Forecasts for 1961," *Oxford Institute of Statistics Bulletin*, vol. 23, 1961, pp. 49–66.
16. Klein, L. R., and H. Barger, "A Quarterly Model of the U.S. Economy," *Journal of American Statistical Association*, vol. 49, 1954, pp. 413–437.
17. Klein, L. R., and A. S. Goldberger, *An Econometric Model of the United States, 1929–1952*, Amsterdam, North Holland Publishing Co., 1955.
18. Klein, L. R., and Y. Shinkai, "An Econometric Model of Japan, 1930–59," *International Economic Review*, vol. 4, 1962, pp. 1–28.

19. Kloek, T., and L. B. M. Mennes, "Simultaneous Equation Estimation Based on Principal Components of Predetermined Variables," *Econometrica*, vol. 28, 1960, pp. 45–61.
20. Kmenta, J., "Some Properties of Alternative Estimates of the Cobb-Douglas Production Function," *Econometrica*, vol. 32, 1964, pp. 183–188.
21. Maddala, G. S., and J. B. Kadane, "Estimation of Returns to Scale and the Elasticity of Substitution," *Econometrica*, vol. 35, 1967, pp. 419–423.
22. Mundlak, Yair, and Irving Hoch, "Consequences of Alternative Specifications in Estimation of Cobb-Douglas Production Functions," *Econometrica*, vol. 33, 1965, pp. 814–828.
23. Nerlove, M. "A Quarterly Econometric Model for the United Kingdom: A Review Article," *American Economic Review*, vol. 52, 1962, pp. 154–176.
24. Nerlove, M., "Returns to Scale in Electricity Supply," Chapter 7 in *Measurement in Economics: Studies in Mathematical Economics and Econometrics in Memory of Yehuda Gruenfeld*, C. Christ et al. (Eds.), Stanford, Stanford University Press, 1963.
25. Nerlove, M. "Two Models of the British Economy: A Fragment of a Critical Survey," *International Economic Review*, vol. 6, 1965, pp. 127–181.
26. Nerlove, M., *Estimation and Identification of Cobb-Douglas Production Functions*, Chicago, Rand McNally, 1965.
27. Scheffé, H., *The Analysis of Variance*, New York, Wiley, 1959.
28. Shephard, R., *Cost and Production Functions*, Princeton, N.J., Princeton University Press, 1953.
29. Teigen, R. L., "Demand and Supply Functions for Money in the United States: Some Structural Estimates," *Econometrica*, vol. 32, 1964, pp. 476–509.
30. Theil, H., "The Aggregation Implications of Identifiable Structural Macro-relations," *Econometrica*, vol. 27, 1959, pp. 14–29.
31. Ueno, Hiroya, "A Long-Term Model of the Japanese Economy, 1920–1958," *International Economic Review*, vol. 4, 1963, pp. 171–193.
32. Walters, A. A., "Production and Cost Functions: An Econometric Survey," *Econometrica*, vol. 31, 1963, pp. 1–66.
33. Wicksell, K., *Lectures on Political Economy*, vol. 2. New York, Macmillan, 1934.
34. Zellner, A., "An Efficient Method of Estimating Seemingly Unrelated Regressions and Tests for Aggregation Bias," *Journal of the American Statistical Association*, vol. 57, 1962, pp. 348–368.
35. Zellner, A., J. Kmenta, and J. Dreze, "Specification and Estimation of Cobb-Douglas Production Function Models," *Econometrica*, vol. 34, 1966, pp. 784–795.

ALTERNATIVE
ESTIMATION METHODS;
RECURSIVE SYSTEMS

6

6.1 INTRODUCTION

In this chapter we shall consider alternative distribution-free estimators, that is, estimators whose derivation does not depend on explicit specification of the form of the distribution of the error terms of the system. In particular, we shall consider indirect least squares and instrumental variables estimators, and in the context of the former we shall discuss, in somewhat greater detail than previously, the identification problem. Finally, we shall examine the simplifications that accrue to the estimation problem when the econometric model under consideration is recursive.

6.2 INDIRECT LEAST SQUARES (ILS)

FORMULATION OF THE PROBLEM

In previous chapters we considered in detail the problem of estimating the parameters of the structural system

$$y_{\cdot i} = Y_i \beta_{\cdot i} + X_i \gamma_{\cdot i} + u_{\cdot i} \qquad i = 1, 2, \ldots, m \qquad (6.2.1)$$

under certain assumptions on the predetermined variables and error terms of the model.

In dealing with the estimation problem, *we had always attempted to estimate the structural parameters directly*. Whenever transformations were employed, it was *always transformations of the data, not of the parameters,* to which we resorted.

In indirect least squares (ILS) estimation we do exactly the opposite; we resort to a transformation that *leaves the data intact but reparameterizes the problem.* By this transformation we simplify the estimation problem, generally at the cost of proliferating the number of parameters to be estimated. Having obtained estimators of the parameters in the context of the transformed (reparameterized) problem, we then employ the *inverse transformation* on the resulting estimators in order *to recover information on the structural parameters that are, presumably, of primary interest to us.* Here we shall study precisely the conditions under which this *last step yields (unique) estimators for the structural coefficients of the model.*

ILS AND IDENTIFIABILITY OF STRUCTURE

As indicated above, the ILS technique consists in estimating the structural para-meters *indirectly* through the estimation of a set of *transformed parameters.* Specifically, consider the *reduced form* of the system in (6.2.1). According to the notation of Chapter 4, it is given by

$$Y = X\Pi + V \tag{6.2.2}$$

where

$$\Pi = CD \quad V = UD \quad D = (I - B)^{-1} \tag{6.2.3}$$

and B, C are the matrices whose columns contain, respectively, the parameter vectors $\beta_{.i}$, $\gamma_{.i}$ of (6.2.1). Notice that B and C already incorporate all a priori information concerning inclusion and exclusion of variables from the structural equations of the model so that it will be known, for example, that certain ele-ments of the columns of B and C are zero. Notice, also, that we have imposed a normalization rule so that $\beta_{ii} = 0$, $i = 1, 2, \ldots, m$.[1] Now, it is possible that the a priori restrictions on the elements of B and C are such as to imply that certain elements of Π are zero or that they exhibit certain functional relations. Ordinarily we do not employ such (implied) restrictions on Π; rather, we treat all its elements as free parameters.

As pointed out in Chapter 4, the parameters of the (unrestricted) reduced form are efficiently estimated, under the standard assumptions, by the OLS estimator

$$\hat{\Pi} = (X'X)^{-1}X'Y \tag{6.2.4}$$

We remind the reader that

$$Y = (y_{.1}, y_{.2}, \ldots, y_{.m}) \qquad X = (x_{.1}, x_{.2}, \ldots, x_{.G}) \tag{6.2.5}$$

---

[1] This aspect of the problem will become clearer when we study maximum likelihood methods at a later stage.

$y_{\cdot i}$ and $x_{\cdot j}$ being, respectively, the $(T \times 1)$ vectors of observation on the ith jointly dependent variable (y_i) and the jth predetermined variable (x_j). The standard assumptions on the error terms are

$$E(u'_s.) = 0 \quad \text{Cov}(u'_s., u'_t.) = \delta_{st} \Sigma \quad u_s. = (u_{s1}, u_{s2}, \ldots, u_{sm}) \tag{6.2.6}$$

where $u_s.$ is the (row) vector of all the error terms of the system at "time" s and δ_{st} is the Kronecker delta.

Having obtained the estimator in (6.2.4), we now have the question: Under what circumstances, if any, can we derive estimators for the *structural parameters* possessing desirable properties? If such estimators can actually be obtained, the problem is solved; moreover, the term *indirect least squares* becomes quite intelligible.

To answer this question, let us concentrate on a specific structural equation, say the first. The reader may verify quite easily that the results we shall obtain are fully applicable to any structural equation.

We observe from (6.2.3) that we have the following relation between $\hat{\Pi}$ and the estimators we are seeking for B and C, namely, $\hat{B}$, $\hat{C}$.

$$\hat{\Pi} = (I - \hat{B})^{-1}\hat{C} \tag{6.2.7}$$

From the relation in (6.2.7), let us extract the equations containing the parameters appearing in the first structural equation. Recalling that, by our numbering convention, the first structural equation contains the variables $y_1, y_2, \ldots, y_{m_1+1}$ and $x_1, x_2, \ldots, x_{G_1}$, we conclude that the subset of the relations in (6.2.7) that is relevant to our discussion is

$$\hat{\Pi} \begin{pmatrix} -\overset{1}{\hat{\beta}}_{\cdot 1} \\ 0 \end{pmatrix} = \begin{pmatrix} \hat{\gamma}_{\cdot 1} \\ 0 \end{pmatrix} \tag{6.2.8}$$

We recall that $\beta_{\cdot 1}$ is $(m_1 \times 1)$, $\gamma_{\cdot 1}$ is $(G_1 \times 1)$, the zero subvector in the left member of (6.2.8) is $(m - m_1 - 1) \times 1$ and that in the right member is $(G - G_1) \times 1$. Now partition Π by

$$\hat{\Pi} = (\hat{\pi}_{\cdot 1}, \hat{\Pi}_{m_1}, \hat{\Pi}_{m*}) \tag{6.2.9}$$

so that $\hat{\pi}_1$ consists of the first column of $\hat{\Pi}$, $\hat{\Pi}_{m_1}$ consists of the following m_1 columns, and Π_{m*} consists of the last $(m - m_1 - 1)$ columns of Π.

Partition further

$$\hat{\pi}_{\cdot 1} = \begin{bmatrix} \hat{\pi}_{G_1 1} \\ \hat{\pi}_{G*1} \end{bmatrix} \quad \hat{\Pi}_{m_1} = \begin{bmatrix} \hat{\Pi}_{G_1 m_1} \\ \hat{\Pi}_{G*m_1} \end{bmatrix} \quad G^* = G - G_1, m^* = m - m_1 - 1 \tag{6.2.10}$$

and observe that (6.2.8) may be rewritten as

$$\hat{\Pi}_{G_1 m_1}\hat{\beta}_{\cdot 1} + \hat{\gamma}_{\cdot 1} = \hat{\pi}_{G_1 1}$$
$$\hat{\Pi}_{G*m_1}\hat{\beta}_{\cdot 1} = \hat{\pi}_{G*1} \tag{6.2.11}$$

We see, therefore, that we are dealing with a recursive system of equations and, moreover, that unique estimators for $\beta_{.1}$ and $\gamma_{.1}$ exist if and only if the second set of equations in (6.2.11) can be solved uniquely for $\hat{\beta}_{.1}$. Of course, if we do not insist on uniqueness, estimators for $\beta_{.1}$ and $\gamma_{.1}$ may be obtained if, from the second set of equations in (6.2.11), we can obtain *an* estimator for $\beta_{.1}$. Before examining both these alternatives, let us point out that there exists a subtle but important distinction between the solution to the mathematical problem of the existence of *a* solution to the equations in (6.2.11)—where $\hat{\beta}_{.1}$, $\hat{\gamma}_{.1}$ are treated as the unknowns—and the *statistical problem* of the existence of estimators, for the structural parameters $\beta_{.1}$, $\gamma_{.1}$, possessing some desirable statistical properties. Clearly, if

$$G^* < m_1 \tag{6.2.12}$$

then by considering a number, $m_1 - G^*$, of the elements of $\hat{\beta}_{.1}$ as arbitrary parameters and transposing them to the right members of the second set of equations in (6.2.11), it may be possible to solve uniquely for the remaining G^* elements of $\hat{\beta}_{.1}$. Thus we can generate not only *one but infinitely many solutions to the mathematical problem* of finding a solution to the system in (6.2.11).

However, *the statistical problem is not solved.* What we obtain is an expression for G^* ($< m_1$) "estimators" for G^* of the elements of $\beta_{.1}$ in terms of the elements of $\hat{\Pi}_{G^*m_1}$, $\hat{\Pi}_{G^*1}$ *and* the undetermined excess parameters ($m_1 - G^*$ in number) of $\beta_{.1}$. Thus we do not have a set of statistics for *any of the elements of $\beta_{.1}$, and hence of $\gamma_{.1}$, because a statistic (estimator) cannot depend on any unknown parameter of the problem.* Hence if (6.2.12) holds, the statistical problem is not soluble and the structural parameters cannot be identified, *for no estimator exists for $\beta_{.1}$ or $\gamma_{.1}$.*

Notice that, written out more fully, (6.2.12) becomes

$$G < G_1 + m_1 \tag{6.2.13}$$

and recall that in discussing the 2SLS estimator in Chapter 4 we observed that when a condition like (6.2.13) holds, the 2SLS estimator is not defined. Moreover, an equation characterized by (6.2.13) was termed *underidentified* or *nonidentified.*

Consequently, for ILS estimators to exist we must have, minimally,

$$G^* \geq m_1 \tag{6.2.14}$$

Consider, next, the case where strict equality holds in (6.2.14). Thus

$$G^* = m_1 \tag{6.2.15}$$

and we see from (6.2.11) that a necessary and sufficient condition for unique solutions for $\hat{\beta}_{.1}$ and $\hat{\gamma}_{.1}$ to exist is that

$$\text{rank} \, (\hat{\Pi}_{G^*m_1}) = m_1 \tag{6.2.16}$$

Here the meaning of the term solution coincides in both the mathematical and statistical sense. If (6.2.15) and (6.2.16) hold, then the system in (6.2.11) has a unique mathematical solution in terms of $\hat{\beta}_{.1}$ and $\hat{\gamma}_{.1}$. This solution is also the appropriate ILS estimator of $\beta_{.1}$ and $\gamma_{.1}$, which will later be shown to be consistent.

Suppose that (6.2.14) holds with strict inequality so that we have

$$G^* > m_1 \tag{6.2.17}$$

It is clear that if we wish to obtain a statistical solution, the condition in (6.2.16) must still hold! Why? Suppose that the rank is $m_1 - 1$. Then we may determine an $(m_1 - 1) \times (m_1 - 1)$ nonsingular submatrix of $\hat{\Pi}_{G*m_1}$, transpose one of the elements of $\hat{\beta}_{.1}$ to the right-hand side, and obtain a set of equations equivalent to the second set in (6.2.11) but whose matrix of coefficients is now nonsingular. Thus we may "solve" to obtain "estimators" for some of the elements of $\beta_{.1}$ in terms of the excess parameter. From the preceding discussion, however, obviously *this is no solution to the statistical problem at all.* Now, if (6.2.17) and (6.2.16) both hold, how do we obtain a solution to our statistical problem? This is rather simple. In general, we shall be able to determine an $m_1 \times m_1$ nonsingular submatrix of $\hat{\Pi}_{G*m_1}$. Thus, neglecting now the *excess* $(G^* - m_1)$ *equations*, we shall be able to solve for $\hat{\beta}_{.1}$ and hence for $\hat{\gamma}_{.1}$. An element of arbitrariness still exists, of course, because which of the G^* equations we are to ignore may be entirely arbitrary. Contrary to the previous case, however, now we have $\binom{G^*}{m_1}$ distinct estimators at most. Hence the statistical problem has a solution *although not a unique one.*

On the other hand, note that *if* (6.2.17) *and* (6.2.16) *hold, then the system of equations in* (6.2.11) *generally has no mathematical solution. Thus we cannot, as a rule, find a vector* $\hat{\beta}_{.1}$ *that satisfies all the equations of the second set in* (6.2.11).

The meaning of this informal discussion is as follows: When a unique solution to the second subset of equations in (6.2.11) exists, then we also have unique ILS estimators for the structural parameters $\beta_{.1}, \gamma_{.1}$. When that subsystem admits of more than one mathematical solution (indeed an infinitude of such solutions), then *no ILS estimators for* $\beta_{.1}$ *and* $\gamma_{.1}$ *exist.* Finally, when the subsystem admits of *no mathematical solution, then we have multiple ILS estimators* for $\beta_{.1}$ and $\gamma_{.1}$.

Having explained the difference between a solution to the estimation problem and a solution to the problem of finding vectors $\hat{\beta}_{.1}, \hat{\gamma}_{.1}$ satisfying the equations in (6.2.11), let us now deal with the estimation problem more systematically.

Obviously, a necessary and sufficient condition for the ILS estimators $\hat{\beta}_{.1}$ and $\hat{\gamma}_{.1}$ to be defined is that

$$\text{rank } (\hat{\Pi}_{G*m_1}) = m_1 \tag{6.2.18}$$

The proof is implicit in our previous discussion but is repeated here only for clarity.

Necessity: Suppose that (6.2.18) does not hold; since the matrix is $G^* \times m_1$, then

$$\text{rank}\,(\hat{\Pi}_{G*m_1}) < m_1 \tag{6.2.19}$$

Let

$$r = m_1 - \text{rank}\,(\hat{\Pi}_{G*m_1}) \tag{6.2.20}$$

and notice that by appropriate row and column operations we can reduce the second subset of equations in (6.2.11) into an equivalent (nonsingular) system of $m_1 - r$ equations in $m_1 - r$ unknowns, the excess r elements of $\hat{\beta}_{.1}$ being transposed to the right member of the equations and treated as parameters. Thus it is impossible to solve for the elements of $\hat{\beta}_{.1}$ solely in terms of the data of the problem. Hence no estimators exist for $\beta_{.1}$ or for $\gamma_{.1}$. Consequently, (6.2.19) cannot hold.

Sufficiency: We consider two cases. First, suppose that

$$G^* = m_1 \tag{6.2.21}$$

Thus obtain explicitly from (6.2.11)

$$\hat{\beta}_{.1} = \hat{\Pi}_{G*m_1}^{-1}\hat{\pi}_{G*1} \qquad \hat{\gamma}_{.1} = \hat{\pi}_{G_1 1} - \hat{\Pi}_{G_1 m_1}\hat{\Pi}_{G*m_1}^{-1}\hat{\pi}_{G*1} \tag{6.2.22}$$

Secondly, suppose that

$$G^* > m_1 \tag{6.2.23}$$

Then there exists at least one $m_1 \times m_1$ submatrix of $\hat{\Pi}_{G*m_1}$ that is nonsingular. Suppressing all equations *not corresponding to this submatrix*, we obtain an explicit solution for $\hat{\beta}_{.1}$ as follows

$$\hat{\beta}_{.1} = \hat{\Pi}_{m_1 m_1}^{-1}\hat{\pi}_{m_1 1} \tag{6.2.24}$$

where, for simplicity, we have taken this nonsingular matrix to be the one corresponding to be first m_1 *rows* of $\hat{\Pi}_{G*m_1}$.

The situation corresponding to (6.2.19) is the *nonidentified* or *underidentified* case. Notice that if

$$G^* < m_1 \tag{6.2.25}$$

then the condition in (6.2.19) must also hold; on the other hand, we may have

$$G^* \geq m_1 \tag{6.2.26}$$

which does not necessarily imply anything specific about the rank of $\hat{\Pi}_{G*m_1}$. This should make it clear that the *governing condition is that referring to the rank and not to the order (dimension) of the relevant matrix*.

The case corresponding to (6.2.18) and (6.2.21) is the *just identified* case, whereas that corresponding to (6.2.18) and (6.2.23) is the *overidentified case.*

Before formalizing this discussion perhaps a few words are needed to justify the terminology employed in discussing the identification problem in the present context.

If we imagine the problem as beginning with the general model

$$y_{ti} = \sum_{j=1}^{m} \beta_{ji}^{*} y_{tj} + \sum_{s=1}^{G} \gamma_{si}^{*} x_{ts} + u_{ti} \qquad \begin{array}{l} i = 1, 2, \ldots, m \\ t = 1, 2, \ldots, T \end{array} \qquad (6.2.27)$$

in which everything depends on everything else, and then placing restrictions on what variables appear in the various equations (as explanatory variables), we see that *underidentification* (of a given equation) results "because" *we did not place enough restrictions* (on the relevant equation). Stated another way, we did not exclude enough variables from it and thus it is not "sufficiently different" from other equations. Notice that underidentification occurs if, for example, in the first equation

$$G < G_1 + m_1 \qquad (6.2.28)$$

so that the number of explanatory variables asserted to be present is too large relative to the total number of predetermined variables. We did not place enough restrictions; hence the term "underidentification," the implication being that if more restrictions were placed (more variables excluded), identifiability will result. Conversely, in the *overidentified* case,

$$G > G_1 + m_1 \qquad (6.2.29)$$

so that "too many" explanatory variables have been excluded from the structural equation. Finally, for the *just identified* case, we have excluded "just enough" explanatory variables, for we have

$$G = G_1 + m_1 \qquad (6.2.30)$$

Remark 1: The preceding discussion is highly informal and is meant only to motivate and elucidate the rigorous derivation of identifiability conditions in Theorem 1 below. The reader will appreciate its limitations if he asks himself: What meaning is to be attached to the condition in equation (6.2.16)? The matrix $\hat{\Pi}_{G*m_1}$ is *random*, since it is the OLS estimator of the *parameter matrix* Π_{G*m_1}. If the sample on which the estimator is based is sufficiently small, it is conceivable that equation (6.2.16) does not hold even though

$$\mathrm{rank}\,(\Pi_{G*m_1}) = m_1 \qquad (6.2.31)$$

and conversely.

On the other hand, and as we shall stress at a later point, identifiability is a *property of the model not of the estimated parameter matrix*.

Hence conditions for identifiability should refer to *the (true) parameters of the model not to their estimators*. When we examine more precisely conditions for identifiability, we shall be dealing with the matrix Π_{G*m_1}, and we shall derive conditions analogous to those in (6.2.14) and (6.2.16), pertaining to its order (dimension) and rank.

Although the rank condition is the fundamental criterion of identifiability, in practice we can check only the order condition prior to actual estimation. Thus, in examining the identifiability properties of a model (prior to estimation) we are reduced to certain counting rules. These involve making sure that *the number of parameters to be estimated in any given structural estimation does not exceed the number of predetermined variables appearing in the model*. It is therefore important that, having obtained reduced form estimators, we should check the statistical significance of the estimated parameters since the identification of a given equation may be illusory. While this statement may be obscure at this stage, it will be elucidated when we examine the identification problem from a logical point of view in the next section.

As the preceding informal discussion implies the problem of identification relates to the following question: Given knowledge of reduced form parameters can we deduce from it the structural parameters? If so, under what circumstances is the correspondence between reduced form and structural parameters unique?

To answer these questions we have

Theorem 1: Consider the model in (6.2.1) subject to the assumptions developed in the subsequent discussion. Suppose that the reduced form

$$Y = X\Pi + V \tag{6.2.32}$$

is well defined and the symbols in (6.2.32) have the meaning given them in (6.2.3.) Suppose, that by appropriate renumbering, if necessary, the "explanatory" variables in, say, the first equation are $y_2, y_3, \ldots, y_{m_1+1}, x_1, x_2, \ldots, x_{G_1}$. Thus the first structural equation is

$$y_{.1} = Y_1 \beta_{.1} + X_1 \gamma_{.1} + u_{.1} \tag{6.2.33}$$

where

$$Y_1 = (y_{.2}, y_{.3}, \ldots, y_{.m_1+1}) \qquad X_1 = (x_{.1}, x_{.2}, \ldots, x_{.G_1}) \tag{6.2.34}$$

and $\beta_{.1}, \gamma_{.1}$ are, respectively, the m_1 and G_1 element vectors of the structural parameters appearing in that equation.

Partition the matrix Π analogously with the partition of $\hat{\Pi}$ in (6.2.9) and (6.2.10).

A necessary and sufficient condition for the existence of ILS estimators of the (structural) parameters $\beta_{.1}, \gamma_{.1}$ is that

$$\text{rank}\,(\Pi_{G*m_1}) = m_1 \tag{6.2.35}$$

If, in addition

$$G^* = m_1 \qquad (G^* = G - G_1) \tag{6.2.36}$$

then the ILS estimator is unique.

If, instead of (6.2.36), we have—in conjunction with (6.2.35)—

$$G^* > m_1 \tag{6.2.37}$$

then there exist at most

$$\frac{G^*!}{m_1!(G^* - m_1)!}$$

distinct ILS estimators. If

$$\text{rank}\,(\Pi_{G^*m_1}) < m_1 \tag{6.2.38}$$

then ILS estimators for $\beta_{.1}$, $\gamma_{.1}$ do not exist.

PROOF: Partitioning Π analogously with the partition of $\hat{\Pi}$ in (6.2.9) and (6.2.10) we can write the parameter analog of (6.2.11) as

$$\Pi_{G_1 m_1}\beta_{.1} + \gamma_{.1} = \pi_{G_1 1}$$
$$\Pi_{G^*m_1}\beta_{.1} = \pi_{G^*1} \tag{6.2.39}$$

The theorem will be proved if we can show that conditions (6.2.35) and (6.2.36) or (6.2.37) permit us to express $\beta_{.1}$, $\gamma_{.1}$ *solely* as functions of the reduced form parameters, while condition (6.2.38) implies that this is not possible. But this is obvious by a slight modification of the discussion following equation (6.2.18), and the argument need not be repeated.

Since $\hat{\Pi}_{G_1 m_1}$, $\hat{\Pi}_{G^*m_1}$, $\hat{\pi}_{G_1 1}$, $\hat{\pi}_{G^*1}$ are *consistent estimators* of the corresponding parameters it follows that if the conditions of the theorem are satisfied with respect to the *parameters* $\Pi_{G_1 m_1}$, $\Pi_{G^*m_1}$, $\pi_{G_1 1}$, π_{G^*1} they will be satisfied—with probability one—relative to their OLS estimators, at least for large samples.

The conclusions of the theorem follow, then, by the informal discussion following equation (6.2.11).

Remark 2: If an equation is characterized by (6.2.38), then it is said to be *underidentified* or *nonidentified*. In particular notice that

$$G^* < m_1 \tag{6.2.40}$$

implies (6.2.38).

If an equation is characterized by the condition in (6.2.35), then it is said to be *identified*. Such an equation is said to be *just identified* if (6.2.35) *and* (6.2.36) both hold. It is said to be *overidentified* if (6.2.35) *and* (6.2.37) both hold and there are more than one (distinct) submatrices of $\Pi_{G^*m_1}$ (of order m_1) which are nonsingular. The condition

$$G^* \geq m_1 \tag{6.2.41}$$

is often termed the *order condition* for identifiability, while the condition in (6.2.35) is said to be the *rank condition*. The former is only a necessary condition while the latter is a necessary and sufficient condition for identifiability.

If ILS estimators are unique, their consistency easily follows from Proposition 1 of Chapter 3. In the case of overidentification, there exist multiple ILS estimators for the (structural) parameters of a given equation. The reader may then wonder whether all such estimators are consistent. The answer is yes, as shown in

Corollary 1: Consider the model of Theorem 1 and suppose that, say, the first equation is identified so that

$$\text{rank } (\Pi_{G*m_1}) = m_1 \qquad G^* \geq m_1 \tag{6.2.42}$$

Then, (all) the ILS estimators of the structural parameters of the first equation are consistent.

PROOF: Partition the matrix $\hat{\Pi}_{G*m_1}$ and the vector $\hat{\pi}_{G*_1}$ by

$$\hat{\Pi}_{G*m_1} = \begin{bmatrix} \hat{\Pi}_{m_1 m_1} \\ \hat{\Pi}_{G*-m_1, m_1} \end{bmatrix} \qquad \hat{\pi}_{G*1} = \begin{pmatrix} \hat{\pi}_{m_1 1} \\ \hat{\pi}_{G*-m_1, 1} \end{pmatrix} \tag{6.2.43}$$

where, for simplicity, we have taken the first m_1 rows of $\hat{\Pi}_{G*m_1}$ to constitute a nonsingular matrix. Such a nonsingular submatrix of $\hat{\Pi}_{G*m_1}$ must exist in virtue of (6.2.42).

Consider now the following abbreviated subsystem of (6.2.11):

$$\hat{\Pi}_{G_1 m_1} \tilde{\beta}_{\cdot 1} + \hat{\gamma}_{\cdot 1} = \hat{\pi}_{G_1 1}$$
$$\hat{\Pi}_{m_1 m_1} \tilde{\beta}_{\cdot 1} = \hat{\pi}_{m_1 1} \tag{6.2.44}$$

and notice that it defines unique ILS estimators for $\beta_{\cdot 1}$ and $\gamma_{\cdot 1}$. In particular we obtain

$$\tilde{\beta}_{\cdot 1} = \hat{\Pi}_{m_1 m_1}^{-1} \hat{\pi}_{m_1 1}, \, \hat{\gamma}_{\cdot 1} = \hat{\pi}_{G_1 1} - \hat{\Pi}_{G_1 m_1} \hat{\Pi}_{m_1 m_1}^{-1} \hat{\pi}_{m_1 1} \tag{6.2.45}$$

Taking probability limits in the second subsystem of (6.2.44) we have

$$\Pi_{m_1 m_1} \left(\plim_{T \to \infty} \tilde{\beta}_{\cdot 1} \right) = \pi_{m_1 1} \tag{6.2.46}$$

From the reduced form model in (6.2.32) and the definitions in (6.2.3) we obtain

$$\Pi_{G*m_1} \beta_{\cdot 1} = \pi_{G*1} \tag{6.2.47}$$

Considering only the first m_1 equations in (6.2.47) and subtracting them from (6.2.46), we establish

$$\Pi_{m_1 m_1} \left(\plim_{T \to \infty} \tilde{\beta}_{\cdot 1} - \beta_{\cdot 1} \right) = 0 \tag{6.2.48}$$

Since $\Pi_{m_1 m_1}$ is nonsingular, (6.2.48) implies

$$\plim_{T \to \infty} \tilde{\beta}_{\cdot 1} = \beta_{\cdot 1} \tag{6.2.49}$$

Now, if $G^* = m_1$, there exists a unique ILS estimator of $\beta_{\cdot 1}$ and hence of $\gamma_{\cdot 1}$; if $G^* > m_1$ the argument above establishes that if we choose a (any) non-singular submatrix of $\hat{\Pi}_{G*m_1}$ and obtain ILS estimators as in (6.2.45) then the resulting estimators of $\beta_{\cdot 1}$, and hence $\gamma_{\cdot 1}$, are consistent. There are at most $\binom{G^*}{m_1}$ nonsingular submatrices of $\hat{\Pi}_{G*m_1}$ and the estimators induced by *any* particular choice *are consistent*.

6.3 THE IDENTIFICATION PROBLEM

In the preceding section, as well as in previous chapters, problems relating to the identifiability of structural parameters in the context of an estimation problem were discussed. Thus when we studied 2SLS, we observed that unless

$$G \geq G_i + m_i \tag{6.3.1}$$

the 2SLS estimator of the parameters of the ith structural equation is not defined. This arose as a purely mathematical problem relating to the existence of the inverse of

$$Q_i' Q_i = \binom{\tilde{Y}_i'}{X_i'}(\tilde{Y}_i, X_i) \tag{6.3.2}$$

Again when dealing with ILS we observed that *unless certain rank and dimension (order) conditions* were satisfied with respect, for example, to the matrix Π_{G*m_1}, the ILS estimator of the parameters of the first structural equation could not be defined.

At this point a somewhat different view of the identification problem will be enlightening. The problem is essentially a logical one involving the construction and specification of the structural model and is best examined as such. Earlier we had merely noted the mathematical or statistical consequences of a certain logical deficiency in model construction.

Consider the classic supply and demand model in the context of a single competitive market. We have

$$
\begin{aligned}
q_t^S &= \alpha + \beta p_t + u_t \\
q_t^D &= a + b p_t + v_t \\
q_t^S &= q_t^D + w_t
\end{aligned}
\tag{6.3.3}
$$

The first two relations are, respectively, the supply and demand equations, while the third is a clearing-of-market condition. Together they serve to determine the quantity sold and its price so that observations on this model consist, say, of the set $\{(q_t, p_t): t = 1, 2, \ldots, T\}$.

In (6.3.3) we have, of course, a simultaneous equations model, and in our customary notation the following conditions hold:

$$G = 1 \qquad m = 2 \tag{6.3.4}$$

The only predetermined variable of the model is the fictitious variable unity whose "coefficients" are the constant terms of the equations. The jointly dependent variables are price (p_t) and quantity (q_t). We make the customary assumptions about the error terms of the model:

$$E(u_t) = E(v_t) = 0 \qquad \text{Cov}(u_t, u_{t'}) = \delta_{tt'}\sigma_{11}$$
$$\text{Cov}(v_t, v_{t'}) = \delta_{tt'}\sigma_{22} \qquad \text{Cov}(u_t, v_{t'}) = \delta_{tt'}\sigma_{12} \tag{6.3.5}$$

In terms of the formal criteria developed earlier, we see that neither the supply nor the demand equation is identified. The reason is that

$$m_i = 1 \quad G_i = 1 \qquad i = 1, 2 \tag{6.3.6}$$

From a more fundamental point of view, we see that the two structural equations in (6.3.3) are *not statistically distinguishable, for, in view of the last equation, they are simply linear combinations of the same variables.* Thus, for example, if we regress quantity on price—or price on quantity—it is not clear which, if any, of the two equations we should be estimating, even apart from the question of (statistical) inconsistency for the resulting estimators.

Later we shall clarify this fundamental deficiency of the model in analytical fashion, but first a graphical illustration will be useful. In Figure 6.1 the line labeled D indicates the demand function and that labeled S the supply function. Essentially these depict the situation that would prevail if

$$w_t = v_t = u_t = 0 \qquad \text{all } t \tag{6.3.7}$$

If all error terms are identically zero, as in (6.3.7), then all observations should be at the point of intersection of the supply and demand function, and from quantity and price data alone no estimation will be possible. Because of the stochastic

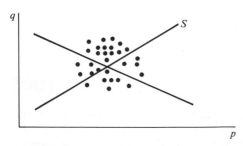

FIGURE 6.1 Lack of identification of supply and demand equations

nature of the equations in (6.3.3), observations will not necessarily lie at the intersection point but will be scattered randomly about it, as depicted in Figure 6.1.

Thus the observations on the model trace neither the supply nor the demand function but simply form a cluster about the intersection point. It should then be clear that such data cannot possibly discriminate between supply and demand, even though we are now able to fit a linear relationship to the data.

The problem arises because the specification of the model is not sufficiently tight to allow us statistical discrimination between the two functions. In view of the equilibrium condition, the observables of the model, quantity and price, are asserted to lie (approximately) on *both* the supply and the demand functions. Even if an acceptable estimation procedure were employed,[2], this fundamental interminacy in the interpretation of the estimated relation will still remain.

Let us consider the problem in a systematic way. The model as set forth in equations (6.3.3) and (6.3.5) states that quantity demanded (and supplied) depends linearly on price. The error terms of the system are characterized in (6.3.5) and the only constraints on the parameters there, are in effect,

$$\sigma_{ii} > 0 \quad \sigma_{12} \lessgtr 0 \quad i = 1, 2 \tag{6.3.8}$$

We shall now show that there exist other models which will generate similar relations between price and quantity and impose similar conditions on the error terms.

To this effect consider the convex combination

$$q_t^{*D} = \lambda q_t^D + (1 - \lambda)q_t^S \quad \lambda \in [0, 1] \tag{6.3.9}$$

Using the first two equations of (6.3.3), we find

$$q_t^{*D} = \lambda \alpha + \lambda \beta p_t + (1 - \lambda)a + (1 - \lambda)b p_t + \lambda u_t + (1 - \lambda)v_t \tag{6.3.10}$$

or

$$q_t^{*D} = \alpha^* + \beta^* p_t + u_t^* \tag{6.3.11}$$

where, obviously,

$$\alpha^* = \lambda \alpha + (1 - \lambda)a \quad \beta^* = \lambda \beta + (1 - \lambda)b \quad u_t^* = \lambda u_t + (1 - \lambda)v_t \tag{6.3.12}$$

If, in addition to (6.3.11), we consider the supply equation and equilibrium condition in (6.3.3), we have another model whose specification characteristics in no way differ from those of the model in (6.3.3) and (6.3.5). Clearly, in the new model the same conditions as in (6.3.5) will hold relative to means, variances, and covariances of the disturbances. Note, further, that since the observations

---

[2] If the equations in (6.3.3) were part of a larger model, we could, for example, use a 2SLS or instrumental variables estimation procedure that, apart from the nonidentification of the two equations, would yield consistent estimators.

(q_t, p_t) satisfy the equations of the original model, they will satisfy the equations of the new model as well. Thus if only the observation pairs (q_t, p_t) are available, we have no idea, when we process the sample to obtain estimators, which model's parameters we are estimating. The parameters of the demand function in the new model are radically different from those in the original model; as equation (6.3.12) makes abundantly clear, they are convex combinations of the *demand and supply* parameters in the original model.

Determining whether the equations of the system are sufficiently different so that they cannot be mistaken for linear combinations of several equations of the model is a relatively simple way of clarifying the difficulty presented by the identification problem. How can we cope with it? First, we note that the identification problem is not a sampling one; that is, it is not one that can be corrected by obtaining a larger or a different sample, as is typically the case with multicollinearity problems. The difficulty will persist no matter what the size of the sample. Second, since the problem results from the fact that the equations of the model, as originally specified, are not sufficiently different, it is clear that what is needed is a specification that makes them different so that, for example, we cannot mistake a linear combination of the two equations as one of the equations of the system.

Thus suppose we argue that the supply function depends not only on price but also on rainfall, r_t. This would be quite plausible if (6.3.3) refers to the market for an agricultural commodity. Clearly r_t is exogenous to this system. Hence the modified model is now

$$q_t^D = \alpha + \beta p_t + u_t$$
$$q_t^S = a + b p_t + c r_t + v_t$$
$$q_t^D = q_t^S + w_t \qquad (6.3.13)$$

Here it is clear that the two structural equations are different; on the other hand, the supply equation cannot be distinguished from a convex combination of the supply *and* demand equations. Thus it is *not identified*. The demand equation, however, cannot possibly be mistaken for such a linear combination, *for it does not contain the variable r_t and thus it is identified*.

Indeed, in terms of the formalism established in previous discussion, the model in (6.3.13) is characterized by

$$G = 2 \quad m = 2 \quad m_1 = 1 \quad G_1 = 1 \quad m_2 = 1 \quad G_2 = 2 \qquad (6.3.14)$$

Consequently, while we have

$$G = G_1 + m_1 \qquad (6.3.15)$$

for the first equation, for the second we obtain

$$G < G_2 + m_2 \qquad (6.3.16)$$

But (6.3.15) implies that the order condition for identifiability is satisfied with respect to the first equation, and (6.3.16) implies that the order criterion is *violated* with respect to the second equation.

A graphical illustration of the model in (6.3.13) may be useful. In Figure 6.2 we have plotted the supply and demand functions, *suppressing the error terms*. In plotting the supply function, we have given it a parametric representation in terms of the rainfall variable, r. Actually, we have assumed in this plotting that rainfall assumed only four values during the sample period, but this is only a simplification for pictorial exposition. The observation pairs (q_t, p_t) are now clustered about the intersection points of the (shifting) supply function with the demand function and are represented by the asterisks of Figure 6.2.

The supply function shifts in the (q, p) plane because the value assumed by the rainfall variable generally varies from observation to observation. It is pictorially clear *that the observations trace the demand but not the supply function.*

Using the same argument, we can establish the identifiability of the supply function if it can be validly made sufficiently different from a linear combination of the two structural equations of the system. But, in this context, this simply means that the demand equation must contain at least *one variable* not present in the supply equation. Thus suppose that we can argue quite plausibly that the demand for this commodity depends on the income, z_t, of the consumers of this commodity. The resulting system then becomes

$$q_t^D = \alpha + \beta p_t + \gamma z_t + u_t$$
$$q_t^S = a + b p_t + c r_t + v_t$$
$$q_t^D = q_t^S + w_t \qquad\qquad (6.3.17)$$

It may now be verified quite easily that the two structural equations of (6.3.17) are *just identified*.

In the preceding discussion we employed only exclusion restrictions in obtaining identifiability. The nature of such a procedure is to specify that certain variables are absent from certain equations. This, however, is not the only way

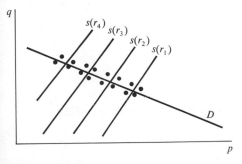

FIGURE 6.2 Identifiability of demand equation

in which identification may be obtained. In subsequent sections we shall show how restrictions on the probability structure of the error terms of the system will also produce identifiability.

Finally, to elucidate the nature of ILS estimation and the remark made at the end of the previous section relative to "illusory identifiability," and to disabuse the reader of the notion that identifiability is simply a condition the model builder imposes on the model, we consider the problem of estimating the parameters of (6.3.17) by ILS. Taking account of the equilibrium condition, we may rewrite (6.3.17) as

$$q_t = \alpha + \beta p_t + \gamma z_t + u_t - w_t$$
$$q_t = a + b p_t + c r_t + v_t \tag{6.3.18}$$

Normalizing the last equation above with respect to p_t, we have the standard form:

$$q_t - \beta p_t = \alpha + \gamma z_t + u_t - w_t$$

$$-\frac{1}{b} q_t + p_t = -\frac{a}{b} - \frac{c}{b} r_t - \frac{v_t}{b} \tag{6.3.19}$$

or, alternatively,

$$(q_t, p_t)\begin{bmatrix} 1 & -\dfrac{1}{b} \\ -\beta & 1 \end{bmatrix} = (1, z_t, r_t)\begin{bmatrix} \alpha & -\dfrac{a}{b} \\ \gamma & 0 \\ 0 & -\dfrac{c}{b} \end{bmatrix} + \left(u_t - w_t, \ -\dfrac{v_t}{b}\right) \tag{6.3.20}$$

The reduced form is obtained as

$$(q_t, p_t) = (1, z_t, r_t)\begin{bmatrix} \dfrac{\alpha b - a\beta}{b - \beta} & \dfrac{\alpha - a}{b - \beta} \\ \dfrac{\gamma b}{b - \beta} & \dfrac{\gamma}{b - \beta} \\ -\dfrac{c\beta}{b - \beta} & -\dfrac{c}{b - \beta} \end{bmatrix} + \text{error terms} \tag{6.3.21}$$

In the standard notation for reduced form systems, this may be written more conveniently as

$$q_t = \pi_{01} + \pi_{11} z_t + \pi_{21} r_t + \text{error}$$
$$p_t = \pi_{02} + \pi_{12} z_t + \pi_{22} r_t + \text{error} \tag{6.3.22}$$

The following relations exist between the reduced form and structural parameters of the first (demand) equation:

$$\begin{bmatrix} \pi_{01} & \pi_{02} \\ \pi_{11} & \pi_{12} \\ \pi_{21} & \pi_{22} \end{bmatrix} \begin{pmatrix} 1 \\ -\beta \end{pmatrix} = \begin{pmatrix} \alpha \\ \gamma \\ 0 \end{pmatrix} \tag{6.3.23}$$

or

$$\pi_{01} - \pi_{02}\,\beta = \alpha$$
$$\pi_{11} - \pi_{11}\,\beta = \gamma$$
$$\pi_{21} - \pi_{22}\,\beta = 0 \tag{6.3.24}$$

Obtaining the OLS estimators $\hat{\pi}_{ij}$, it is clear that from (6.3.24) we can derive the ILS estimators of α, β, γ.

Earlier we spoke of illusory identifiability. Indeed, the equations of the system in (6.3.17) satisfy the order condition for identifiability. However, the reader should not have the erroneous impression that simply writing down the system as in (6.3.17) gains us identifiability. In some fundamental sense, the variables we claim to be present in these equations must indeed belong there, that is, the specification must be correct. How can this be checked? Or, alternatively, how would we discover, after estimation, if we are really dealing with identifiable equations? Recall the sufficient condition for identifiability. In terms of the discussion in the previous section, it entails the condition

$$\operatorname{rank}\left(\Pi_{G*m_1}\right) = m_1 \tag{6.3.25}$$

In the present case,

$$\hat{\Pi}_{G*m_1} = \hat{\pi}_{22} \qquad m_1 = 1 \tag{6.3.26}$$

Together (6.3.25) and (6.3.26) imply that $\hat{\pi}_{22}$ must be significantly different from zero. If not, then, with probability equal to one minus the level of significance of the test, the condition (6.3.25) does not hold. Thus it would be rather pointless to solve the system in (6.3.23) to obtain "estimators" for α, β, and γ, for the identifiability of the demand equation is rather illusory.[3]

The discussion of identifiability problems may be extended to nonlinear systems and, indeed, in many other directions. We shall not do so here; the interested reader may consult the excellent monograph on the subject by Fisher [12].

---

[3] The reader should note that an estimated coefficient seldom turns out to be exactly zero. Thus "estimators" in (6.3.23) can always be defined by using $\hat{\pi}_{22}$ even though the latter's standard error might imply that the corresponding parameter, π_{22}, is zero with a high degree of confidence (probability).

6.4 INSTRUMENTAL VARIABLES ESTIMATION

Instrumental variables (I.V.) estimation is a technique with considerable intuitive appeal due to its simplicity; on the other hand, its importance in empirical applications is rather exaggerated.

Perhaps the simplest way of introducing the procedure is through an example involving the general linear model. Let

$$y = X\beta + u \tag{6.4.1}$$

where y, X are, respectively, the $(T \times 1)$ vector and $(T \times G)$ matrix of observations on the dependent and explanatory variables; β is the $(G \times 1)$ vector of parameters to be estimated and u is the $(T \times 1)$ vector of disturbances.

In addition, we have the usual conditions

$$\text{rank}\,(X) = G \quad E(u) = 0 \quad E(X'u) = 0 \quad \text{Cov}\,(u) = \sigma^2 I \tag{6.4.2}$$

Now, suppose we could find G variables, p_i, $i = 1, 2, \ldots, G$, which are independent of (minimally uncorrelated with) the error terms of the system. Let $p_{\cdot i}$ be the $(T \times 1)$ vector of observations on the ith variable and define the matrix

$$P = (p_{\cdot 1}, p_{\cdot 2}, \ldots, p_{\cdot G}) \tag{6.4.3}$$

Consider the transformed system

$$\frac{P'y}{T} = \frac{P'X}{T}\beta + \frac{P'u}{T} \tag{6.4.4}$$

and observe that by hypothesis

$$\plim_{T \to \infty} \frac{P'u}{T} = 0 \tag{6.4.5}$$

Since the last term in (6.4.4) vanishes in probability, it entails no loss to consider instead

$$\frac{P'y}{T} = \frac{P'X}{T}\beta \tag{6.4.6}$$

and derive the estimator

$$\tilde{\beta} = (P'X)^{-1}P'y \tag{6.4.7}$$

The variables p_i, $i = 1, 2, \ldots, G$, are termed the *instruments* or *instrumental variables* and $\tilde{\beta}$ of (6.4.7) is said to be the *instrumental variables (I.V.) estimator* of β. Thus an *instrument is a variable that is independent of (or minimally uncorrelated with) the disturbances of the equation and is correlated (presumably highly) with the explanatory variables appearing therein.* The latter is an important requirement. Suppose that the instruments are totally uncorrelated with the variables x_i, $i = 1, 2, \ldots, G$. For simplicity, suppose all variables are measured as deviations from their respective sample means. Thus in view of the uncorrelatedness of these two sets of variables,[4] we have

$$\plim_{T \to \infty} \frac{P'X}{T} = 0 \tag{6.4.8}$$

so that, at least asymptotically, the I.V. estimator will not be defined.

In the absence of the condition in (6.4.8) it is rather simple to show that I.V. estimators are consistent. Substituting from (6.4.1) in (6.4.7), we find

$$\tilde{\beta} = \beta + \left(\frac{P'X}{T}\right)^{-1} \frac{P'u}{T} \tag{6.4.9}$$

From (6.4.5) we conclude

$$\plim_{T \to \infty} \tilde{\beta} = \beta \tag{6.4.10}$$

If certain convergence criteria hold, we can easily establish (using the techniques of Chapter 3) that, asymptotically,

$$\sqrt{T}(\tilde{\beta} - \beta) \sim N\left[0, \sigma^2 \plim_{T \to \infty} \left(\frac{P'X}{T}\right)^{-1} \left(\frac{P'P}{T}\right)\left(\frac{X'P}{T}\right)^{-1}\right] \tag{6.4.11}$$

It is clear that conditionally on P and X, and for every sample size,

$$E(\tilde{\beta}) = \beta \qquad \text{Cov}(\tilde{\beta}) = \sigma^2 (P'X)^{-1}(P'P)(X'P)^{-1} \tag{6.4.12}$$

We noted earlier the need for the instruments to be correlated with the explanatory variables they replace. It is also apparent that there may exist many sets of instruments that one might consider using. Thus, we encounter the problem of making the appropriate choice of instruments. What criteria should we use? All I.V. estimators, no matter what the choice of instruments, are unbiased and consistent. If a choice is to be made, the criterion must be based on efficiency considerations. It is intuitively clear from the motivation we have given to I.V. estimators that instruments replace the explanatory variables of the model in forming the moment matrix to be inverted in the process of estimation. Hence it would be desirable to have instruments that are highly correlated with the variables they replace. Let us see whether we can relate these two considerations.

Notice that the *generalized variance* of the I.V. estimator in (6.4.7) is given by

$$\text{G.Var}(\tilde{\beta}) = |\text{Cov}(\tilde{\beta})| = \sigma^{2G} |(P'X)^{-1}(P'P)(X'P)^{-1}| \tag{6.4.13}$$

---

[4] It would be enlightening for the reader to ask himself why, in dealing with the general linear model, we were at pains to establish, by assumption or otherwise, that $\plim_{T \to \infty} X'X/T$ or $\lim_{T \to \infty} X'X/T$, depending on whether the elements of X were stochastic or not, was nonsingular. Also, why, in dealing with 2SLS estimation, we considered it necessary to demonstrate in the notation of Chapter 4 that $\plim_{T \to \infty}(Q_1'Q_1/T)$ was nonsingular.

The (sample) coefficient of vector correlation (see Chapter 5) between the instruments and the explanatory variables in (6.4.1) is given by

$$r_{c(x,\,p)} = (-1)^{G} \frac{\begin{vmatrix} 0 & X'P \\ P'X & P'P \end{vmatrix}}{|X'X|\,|P'P|} = \frac{|(X'P)(P'P)^{-1}(P'X)|}{|X'X|} \tag{6.4.14}$$

Thus we see that

$$G.\mathrm{Var}\,(\tilde{\beta}) = \frac{\sigma^{2G}}{|X'X|}\,\frac{1}{r_{c(x,\,p)}} \tag{6.4.15}$$

Since the first term in the right-hand side above does not depend on the choice of instruments, it is clear that the *generalized variance* of the I.V. estimator is *minimized* if the coefficient of vector correlation between the instruments and the explanatory variable they "replace" is *maximized*. We thus have, immediately, the desired connection between efficiency of I.V. estimators and a measure of correlation between instruments and "replaced" explanatory variables.

Of course, this is a rather trivial application, for it is apparent that the choice

$$P = X \tag{6.4.16}$$

yields the optimal I.V. estimator,[5] where optimality here means minimal generalized variance. This optimal I.V. estimator is, of course, the OLS one, as we already know from the Markov theorem of Chapter 4. The sole purpose of the discussion above was to introduce us to the nature of I.V. estimation and, in a simple context, make rigorous and clear the usual prescription that instruments be highly correlated with the explanatory variables they replace. Our discussion makes this aspect clear and, in addition, provides us with a well-formulated criterion for choice. As we shall see below, this is rather useful when we study I.V. estimation in the context of simultaneous equations systems.

To this effect, consider again the structural model of Section 6.1:

$$y_{\cdot i} = Z_i \delta_{\cdot i} + u_{\cdot i} \qquad i = 1, 2, \ldots, m \tag{6.4.17}$$

where

$$Z_i = (Y_i, X_i) \qquad \delta_{\cdot i} = \begin{pmatrix} \beta_{\cdot i} \\ \gamma_{\cdot i} \end{pmatrix} \tag{6.4.18}$$

Let

$$P = (p_{\cdot 1}, p_{\cdot 2}, \ldots, p_{\cdot n}) \tag{6.4.19}$$

---

[5] The reader may ask himself: What are the bounds of $r_{c(x,p)}$? What is $r_{c(x,p)}$ when the choice in (6.4.16) is made? Actually, the sample quantity $r_{c(x,p)}$ is not significant in itself. What we need is that the corresponding population parameter $\rho_{c(x,\,p)}$ be maximized. The latter, however, is consistently estimated by $r_{c(x,\,p)}$. Thus the considerations in the discussion above are equivalent, in probability, to considerations based on $\rho_{c(x,p)}$.

be a matrix of (T) observations on n potential instrumental variables of which, for the moment, we only require that they be independent of (or minimally uncorrelated with) the error terms of the system. Following the logic implicit in our earlier discussion, we must select a submatrix P_i containing $G_i + m_i$ instruments and solve the equation

$$P_i' y_{\cdot i} = P_i' Z_i \delta_{\cdot i} \tag{6.4.20}$$

in order to obtain the I.V. estimator

$$\tilde{\tilde{\delta}}_{\cdot i} = (P_i Z_i)^{-1} P_i' y_{\cdot i} = \delta_{\cdot i} + (P_i' Z_i)^{-1} P_i' u_{\cdot i} \tag{6.4.21}$$

We note that, because of the uncorrelatedness of instruments and error terms,

$$\underset{T \to \infty}{\text{plim}} \, (\tilde{\tilde{\delta}}_{\cdot i} - \delta_{\cdot i}) = \underset{T \to \infty}{\text{plim}} \left(\frac{P_i' Z_i}{T} \right)^{-1} \underset{T \to \infty}{\text{plim}} \left(\frac{P_i' u_{\cdot i}}{T} \right) = 0 \tag{6.4.22}$$

provided $\text{plim}_{T \to \infty} (P_i' Z_i / T)$ exists as a nonsingular matrix. Thus again we have a requirement which states that instruments should be correlated with the variables they "replace."

What is the set of all possible instruments? First, keeping the correlation requirement above in mind, instruments must be variables (or functions of variables) that actually appear in the system. This is so because if a variable exhibits sufficient correlation with an endogenous variable to warrant consideration as a possible instrument, then such a variable belongs in the model, if the latter is well specified. Second, the set of possible instruments cannot include the current endogenous variables of the system because of the requirement that instruments and disturbances be independent (or minimally uncorrelated), at least asymptotically.

This, of course, leaves us only with the predetermined variables, or functions thereof. We shall take the *class of potential instruments as being the class of all linear combinations of the predetermined variables of the system.*

Thus the class of instruments is given by

$$P = XA \tag{6.4.23}$$

where A is a suitable matrix. A choice of instruments is now tantamount to a choice of the matrix A. Thus in the future we shall drop the subscript on P when we consider alternative I.V. choices.

Let us now consider the problem of I.V. estimation of the parameters of the first structural equation. The I.V. estimator is given by

$$\tilde{\tilde{\delta}}_{\cdot 1} = (P' Z_1)^{-1} P' y_{\cdot 1} = \delta_{\cdot 1} + (P' Z_1)^{-1} P' u_{\cdot 1} \tag{6.4.24}$$

Using the techniques employed in Chapters 3 and 4, we can easily establish that, asymptotically,[6]

$$\sqrt{T}(\tilde{\tilde{\delta}}_{\cdot 1} - \delta_{\cdot 1}) \sim N\left[0, \sigma_{11} \plim_{T \to \infty} \left(\frac{P'Z_1}{T}\right)^{-1} \frac{P'P}{T} \left(\frac{Z_1'P}{T}\right)^{-1}\right] \tag{6.4.25}$$

Consider now the consistent estimator of the generalized variance in the asymptotic distribution of $\tilde{\tilde{\delta}}_{\cdot 1}$. It is given by

$$|\text{G.Var}\,(\tilde{\tilde{\delta}}_{\cdot 1})| = \tilde{\tilde{\delta}}_{11}^{G_1 + m_1} |(P'Z_1)^{-1} P'P(Z_1'P)^{-1}| \tag{6.4.26}$$

Again denoting by $r_{c(z_1, p)}$ the (sample) coefficient of vector correlation between the instruments and the variables they "replace," we have[7]

$$\text{G.Var}\,(\tilde{\tilde{\delta}}_{\cdot 1}) = \left(\frac{\tilde{\tilde{\delta}}_{11}^{G_1 + m_1}}{|Z_1'Z_1|}\right) \frac{1}{r_{c(z_1, p)}} \tag{6.4.27}$$

and obviously the generalized variance of the I.V. estimator $\tilde{\tilde{\delta}}_{\cdot 1}$ *is minimized if* $r_{c(z_1, p)}$ *is maximized.* Contrary to the situation encountered in (6.4.15), it is not apparent now what the upper bound of $r_{c(z_1, p)}$ is, for we cannot choose $P = Z_1$ by the requirements we place on instruments. Thus we must first determine the upper bound of the coefficient of vector correlation in (6.4.27). We shall now show that

$$r_{c(z_1, p)} \le r_{c(z_1, x)} \tag{6.4.28}$$

Hence if we find a matrix A for which this bound is attained, we would determine an optimal I.V. estimator.

By definition,

$$r_{c(z_1, x)} = (-1)^{m_1 + G_1} \frac{\begin{vmatrix} 0 & Z_1'X \\ X'Z_1 & X'X \end{vmatrix}}{|Z_1'Z_1| \, |X'X|} = \frac{|Z_1'X(X'X)^{-1}X'Z_1|}{|Z_1'Z_1|} \tag{6.4.29}$$

and

$$r_{c(z_1, p)} = (-1)^{m_1 + G_1} \frac{\begin{vmatrix} 0 & Z_1'P \\ P'Z_1 & P'P \end{vmatrix}}{|Z_1'Z_1| \, |P'P|} = \frac{|(Z_1'P)(P'P)^{-1}(P'Z_1)|}{|Z_1'Z_1|} \tag{6.4.30}$$

As a result of (6.4.23), we may write

$$Z_1'P(P'P)^{-1}P'Z_1 = Z_1'XA(A'X'XA)^{-1}A'X'Z_1 \tag{6.4.31}$$

---

[6] In discussing the asymptotic distribution of 2SLS estimators, we established a similar result under certain restrictive assumptions, the most notable of which was that the system contained no lagged endogenous among its predetermined variables.

[7] Of course, in all of this discussion we are assuming that variables are measured as deviations from their respective sample means.

Put

$$(A'X'XA)^{-1} = B \qquad (6.4.32)$$

and notice that (6.4.28) holds if and only if

$$|Z_1'XABA'X'Z_1| \le |Z'X(X'X)^{-1}X'Z_1| \qquad (6.4.33)$$

We shall demonstrate not only the validity of (6.4.33) but also that

$$(Z_1'XABA'X'Z_1)^{-1} - (Z_1'X(X'X)^{-1}X'Z_1)^{-1}$$

is a positive semidefinite matrix.

Consider the roots of ABA' in the metric of $(X'X)^{-1}$; thus consider the roots of

$$|\lambda(X'X)^{-1} - ABA'| = 0 \qquad (6.4.34)$$

But the roots of (6.4.34) are exactly those of

$$|\lambda I - ABA'X'X| = 0 \qquad (6.4.35)$$

and the nonzero roots of the latter are exactly those of

$$|\lambda I - BA'X'XA| = 0 \qquad (6.4.36)$$

Since

$$BA'X'XA = I_{G_1+m_1} \qquad (6.4.37)$$

we conclude that (6.4.34) has $G_1 + m_1$ roots equal to unity and $G - G_1 - m_1$ roots equal to zero. Let

$$M = \begin{bmatrix} I_{G_1+m_1} & 0 \\ 0 & 0 \end{bmatrix} \qquad (6.4.38)$$

Since $(X'X)^{-1}$ and ABA' are positive definite and semidefinite respectively, there exists a nonsingular matrix C such that

$$(X'X)^{-1} = CC' \qquad ABA' = CMC' \qquad (6.4.39)$$

Thus

$$Z_1'X(X'X)^{-1}X'Z_1 - Z_1'P(P'P)^{-1}P'Z_1 = Z_1'XC\begin{bmatrix} 0 & 0 \\ 0 & I_{G-G_1-m_1} \end{bmatrix}C'X'Z_1 \qquad (6.4.40)$$

But the right-hand member of (6.4.40) is a positive semidefinite matrix. Hence, in view of Corollary 7 (of the Mathematical Appendix), we conclude

$$|Z_1'P(P'P)^{-1}PZ| \le |Z_1'X(X'X)^{-1}X'Z_1| \qquad (6.4.41)$$

A slight modification of Corollary 6 (of the Appendix) will yield the additional conclusion that the matrix

$$S = (Z_1'P(P'P)^{-1}P'Z_1)^{-1} - (Z_1'X(X'X)^{-1}X'Z_1)^{-1} = S_1^{-1} - S_2^{-1} \qquad (6.4.42)$$

is positive semidefinite. Actually, the result in (6.4.42) can easily be established directly from (6.4.40).[8]

The preceding discussion has established certain bounds for the generalized variance and the covariance matrix of the asymptotic distribution of the I.V. estimator. It is interesting that these bounds are actually attained for the choice [in (6.4.23)]

$$A = (X'X)^{-1}X'Z_1 \tag{6.4.43}$$

When this choice is made, however, note that the resulting estimator is none other than the 2SLS estimator! Thus observe

$$P = XA = [X(X'X)^{-1}X'Y_1, \quad X(X'X)^{-1}X'X_1] = [X\tilde{\Pi}_1, X_1] \tag{6.4.44}$$

where, obviously,

$$\tilde{\Pi}_1 = (X'X)^{-1}X'Y_1 \tag{6.4.45}$$

is the OLS estimator of the reduced form parameters corresponding to the explanatory current endogenous variables actually appearing in the first structural equation. The reader may verify by direct substitution, that the bounds in (6.4.33) and (6.4.42) are actually attained and also that the I.V. estimator corresponding to the choice in (6.4.43) is actually the 2SLS estimator. Hence the latter dominates—in an asymptotic efficiency sense—the class of I.V. estimators as determined by (6.4.23).

Notice that

$$\left[\frac{Z_1'X}{T}\left(\frac{X'X}{T}\right)^{-1}\frac{X'Z_1}{T}\right]^{-1} \quad \text{and} \quad \left[\frac{Z_1'P}{T}\left(\frac{P'P}{T}\right)^{-1}\frac{P'Z_1}{T}\right]^{-1}$$

are proportional, respectively, to the consistent estimators of the covariance matrix of the asymptotic distribution of $\sqrt{T}(\tilde{\tilde{\delta}}_{\cdot 1} - \delta_{\cdot 1})$ and $\sqrt{T}(\tilde{\delta}_{\cdot 1} - \delta_{\cdot 1})$, $\tilde{\delta}_{\cdot 1}$ being the 2SLS estimator of $\delta_{\cdot 1}$.

Therefore we have proved the following

Theorem 2: Consider the structural system

$$y_{\cdot i} = Z_i \delta_{\cdot i} + u_{\cdot i} \quad Z_i = (Y_i, X_i) \qquad i = 1, 2, \ldots, m \tag{6.4.46}$$

subject to the conventions and hypotheses on its predetermined variables and errors terms as developed in the preceding discussion and more fully in Chapter 4.

Consider the set of all possible I.V. estimators of the parameters of, say, the first structural equation

$$\tilde{\tilde{\delta}}_{\cdot 1} = (P'Z_1)^{-1}P'y_{\cdot 1} \tag{6.4.47}$$

---

[8] *Hint*: Consider the roots of S_2 in the metric of S_1 and decompose S_1, S_2 simultaneously by $S_1 = D_1'D_1$, $S_2 = D_1' \Lambda D_1$, Λ being the diagonal matrix containing the (positive) roots of $|\lambda S_1 - S_2| = 0$. Since it is known that $S_2 - S_1$ is positive semidefinite, pre- and post-multiply, respectively, by $\Lambda^{-1/2}D_1'^{-1}$, $D_1^{-1}\Lambda^{-1/2}$ and complete the proof.

resulting from the choice of A in

$$P = XA \tag{6.4.48}$$

Let $C(A)$ be the covariance matrix of the asymptotic distribution of the I.V. estimator in (6.4.46). Let

$$\bar{A} = (X'X)^{-1}X'Z_1 \tag{6.4.49}$$

Then, for any A,

$$C(A) - C(\bar{A}) = C \tag{6.4.50}$$

is a positive semidefinite matrix,

$$|C(A)| \geq |C(\bar{A})| \tag{6.4.51}$$

and, moreover, the I.V. estimator corresponding to the choice of A, as in (6.4.49), is the 2SLS estimator.

6.5 RECURSIVE SYSTEMS

MOTIVATION AND GENERALITIES

When the problem of estimation in simultaneous equations systems (Chapter 4, Section 4.3) was first discussed, we noted that in certain instances OLS techniques applied to a structural equation will yield consistent estimators. In studying the identification problem in a previous section, we observed that under some circumstances restrictions on the probability structure of the error term of the system may induce identification.

Here we shall clarify these contentions and develop with some care the estimation theory in the context of recursive systems.

We begin with an example. Consider the equations

$$y_{t1} = \beta_{21} y_{t2} + \gamma_{11} x_{t1} + \gamma_{21} x_{t2} + u_{t1}$$
$$\phantom{y_{t2} = \beta_{12} y_{t1} + \gamma_{12} x_{t1} + \gamma_{22} x_{t2} + u_{t2}} \quad t = 1, 2, \ldots, T \tag{6.5.1}$$
$$y_{t2} = \beta_{12} y_{t1} + \gamma_{12} x_{t1} + \gamma_{22} x_{t2} + u_{t2}$$

As usual, we assert that the error terms are independent of (minimally uncorrelated with) the predetermined variables and

$$E(u_{ti}) = 0 \quad \mathrm{Cov}\,(u_{ti}, u_{t'j}) = \delta_{tt'} \sigma_{ij} \quad i, j = 1, 2, t; t' = 1, 2, \ldots, T \tag{6.5.2}$$

Clearly, the system as it stands is not identifiable, for the two equations cannot be adequately differentiated. Indeed, as the reader may easily verify, the order condition for identifiability fails for both equations!

How would the estimation problem be affected if we knew that

$$\beta_{21} = 0 \tag{6.5.3}$$

It is immediately apparent that the first equation is identified and that its parameters can be estimated efficiently by OLS techniques.

Obviously the condition in (6.5.3) does not affect the identifiability of the second equation, which thus remains not identified. The latter cannot be adequately differentiated from a convex combination of the two equations of the system given the assumptions in (6.5.2). In addition, note that if $\sigma_{12} \neq 0$, then even if $\gamma_{22} = 0$ so that the second equation is identified, OLS applied to the latter will *not yield consistent estimators* for its parameters. Why? The fact that y_{t1} is a linear function of u_{t1} and that the latter is correlated with u_{t2} imply *that y_{t1} is also correlated with u_{t2}*. Hence OLS applied to the second equation will yield inconsistent estimators for its parameters.

The issue involved in obtaining, at least, consistent OLS estimators for structural parameters will be clearly illustrated if we consider the reduced form of (6.5.1). Thus we obtain

$$y_{t1} = \frac{\gamma_{11} + \gamma_{12}\beta_{21}}{\beta} x_{t1} + \frac{\gamma_{21} + \gamma_{22}\beta_{21}}{\beta} x_{t2} + \frac{u_{t1} + \beta_{21}u_{t2}}{\beta}$$

$$y_{t2} = \frac{\gamma_{11}\beta_{12} + \gamma_{12}}{\beta} x_{t1} + \frac{\gamma_{21}\beta_{12} + \gamma_{22}}{\beta} x_{t2} + \frac{\beta_{12}u_{t1} + u_{t2}}{\beta} \tag{6.5.4}$$

where

$$\beta = \frac{1}{1 - \beta_{12}\beta_{21}} \tag{6.5.5}$$

If (6.5.3) holds, then *the structural and reduced forms of the first equation in* (6.5.1) *coincide.* In such a case, $\beta = 1$. Now, what is the covariance between y_{t1} and u_{t2}? It is simply

$$\text{Cov}(y_{t1}, u_{t2}) = \frac{1}{\beta}(\sigma_{12} + \beta_{21}\sigma_{22}) \tag{6.5.6}$$

If (6.5.3) holds and, in addition,

$$\sigma_{12} = 0 \tag{6.5.7}$$

then the covariance in (6.5.6) vanishes! But when this occurs, OLS applied to the second equation in (6.5.1) will yield consistent (indeed efficient) estimators for its parameters even though superficially it would appear that the second equation does not satisfy the order condition for identifiability. Hence here we have identifiability induced by the condition in (6.5.7), which is a condition on the probability structure of the error terms of the system! It certainly is not of the customary form of restrictions involving inclusion or exclusion of variables from certain equations.

We might ask: How can this be so? Do we not thereby invalidate the discussion of Sections 6.2 and 6.3? The development above actually points up the significance of Remark 8, Chapter 4, namely, that in classifying the variables of an equation into current endogenous and predetermined ones, what is important is not whether variables are determined by the system under consideration but whether they are independent of (or uncorrelated with) the relevant error term. If we take the latter point of view, then y_{t1} is predetermined in so far as the second equation is concerned, so that the order condition for identifiability is satisfied in the context of that equation. Hence not only do we obtain identifiability but OLS techniques yield consistent estimators for its parameters as well.

CONSISTENCY OF OLS FOR RECURSIVE SYSTEMS

What were the essential characteristics of the simple model above that permitted us to employ OLS in consistently estimating its structural parameters? The peculiar restrictions were

$$\beta_{21} = 0 \qquad \sigma_{12} = 0 \tag{6.5.8}$$

These imply that the matrix of coefficients of the variables whose behavior is explained by the system is *upper triangular* and that the covariance matrix of the system *is diagonal*.

It is interesting that this is exactly what we need in order to justify OLS estimation of parameters in a general structural system. The subsequent discussion will be facilitated if we introduce

Definition 1: The structural system

$$Y = YB + XC + U \tag{6.5.9}$$

is said to be *simply recursive* if the equations and variables of the system can be so numbered that the matrix B is *upper triangular* and the covariance matrix Σ, defined by

$$\text{Cov}(u'_t., u'_{t'}.) = \delta_{tt'}\Sigma \tag{6.5.10}$$

is *diagonal*, where $u_t. = (u_{t1}, u_{t2}, \ldots, u_{tm})$ is the (row) vector of the error terms in all equations of the system, at "time" t.

Notice that if B is upper triangular, then so is $I - B$. Upper triangularity for the latter matrix means that the first equation contains, in addition to y_{t1}, only predetermined variables (x's). The second equation contains, in addition to y_{t2}, at most only y_{t1} and predetermined variables (x's) and, in general, the kth equation contains, in addition to y_{tk}, at most only $y_{t1}, y_{t2}, \ldots, y_{t(k-1)}$ and predetermined variables (x's).

We shall now show that within the kth equation we can treat $y_{ti}, i = 1, 2, \ldots, k - 1$, as predetermined variables. Thus we have

Lemma 1: In the kth equation of a *simply recursive* system like (6.5.9), the variables $y_{t1}, y_{t2}, \ldots, y_{t(k-1)}$ are independent of (or minimally uncorrelated with) the error term u_{tk}.

PROOF: Consider the reduced form of the system in (6.5.9). We have

$$Y = XCD + UD \qquad (6.5.11)$$

where

$$D = (I - B)^{-1} \qquad (6.5.12)$$

Since $I - B$ is upper triangular, so is D, which means that if

$$D = (d_{ij}) \qquad (6.5.13)$$

then

$$d_{rj} = 0 \qquad \text{for } r > j \qquad (6.5.14)$$

What is the covariance between y_{ti} and u_{tk}, $i < k$? From the reduced form, we find

$$\text{Cov}\,(y_{ti}, u_{tk}) = E\left[\sum_{r=1}^{m}(u_{tr}\,d_{ri}\,u_{tk})\right] = \sum_{r=1}^{m} d_{ri}\,E(u_{tr}\,u_{tk})$$

$$= d_{ki}\,\sigma_{kk} \qquad (6.5.15)$$

The last equality follows from the fact that Σ is diagonal so that error terms in various equations are uncorrelated (if normally distributed, then they are also independent). However, since $k > i$, (6.5.14) implies that the covariance in (6.5.15) vanishes.   Q.E.D.

This leads to

Theorem 3: Consider the structural system

$$y_{.i} = Y_i\beta_{.i} + X_i\gamma_{.i} + u_{.i} \qquad i = 1, 2, \ldots, m \qquad (6.5.16)$$

where it is assumed that

$$E(u_t.\,X) = 0 \qquad E(u'_t.) = 0 \qquad (6.5.17)$$

X is the matrix of observations on all the predetermined variables in the system and

$$u_t. = (u_{t1}, u_{t2}, \ldots, u_{tm}) \qquad (6.5.18)$$

is the (row) vector of disturbances in (all) the equations of the system at "time" t.

Suppose, also, that variables and equations can be so renumbered that the system is simply recursive. Then the OLS estimator of the parameters in the kth structural equation is consistent.

PROOF: The kth structural equation is

$$._k = Y_k \beta._k + X_k \gamma._k + u._k \tag{6.5.19}$$

Here $u._k$ is the $(T \times 1)$ vector of "observations" on the error term of that equation and[9]

$$._k = (y._1, y._2, \ldots, y._{k-1})$$

Let

$$._k = (Y_k, X_k) \qquad \delta._k = \begin{pmatrix} \beta._k \\ \gamma._k \end{pmatrix} \tag{6.5.21}$$

The OLS estimator of $\delta._k$ is

$$._k = (Z_k' Z_k)^{-1} Z_k' y._k = \delta._k + (Z_k' Z_k)^{-1} Z_k' u._k \tag{6.5.22}$$

Thus

$$\lim (\tilde{\delta}._k - \delta._k) = \plim_{T \to \infty} \left(\frac{Z_k' Z_k}{T} \right)^{-1} \plim_{T \to \infty} \frac{Z_k' u._k}{T} \tag{6.5.23}$$

Under the standard assumptions for structural models (and as pointed out in Chapter 4), the first probability limit in the right-hand side of (6.5.23) exists as a nonstochastic matrix with finite elements. From Lemma 1 and (6.5.17) we conclude

$$\lim_{T \to \infty} \frac{Z_k' u._k}{T} = 0 \tag{6.5.24}$$

This, however, implies

$$\plim_{T \to \infty} \tilde{\delta}._k = \delta._k \qquad \text{Q.E.D.} \tag{6.5.25}$$

Corollary 2: Conditionally on Z_k, the estimator in (6.5.22) is best linear unbiased.

PROOF: From (6.5.22) we have

$$E(\tilde{\delta}._k - \delta._k) = (Z_k' Z_k)^{-1} Z_k' E(u._k) = 0 \tag{6.5.26}$$

---

[9] Actually, the fact that B is upper triangular does not imply that all the elements at or above its main diagonal are known to be nonzero. Indeed, by convention we take $\beta_{ii} = 0$. Similarly, some other elements may also be known to be zero. This would mean that Y_k of (6.5.19) may not contain *all* the variables $y_1, y_2, \ldots, y_{k-1}$. All that upper triangularity implies is that the elements below the main diagonal of B are known to be zero.

which shows unbiasedness conditionally on Z_k.[10] Now consider any other linear unbiased estimator of $\delta_{\cdot k}$, say,

$$\bar{\delta}_{\cdot k} = H y_{\cdot k} = H Z_k \delta_{\cdot k} + H u_{\cdot k} \tag{6.5.27}$$

By the requirement of unbiasedness, we conclude

$$H Z_k = I \tag{6.5.28}$$

Now, define a matrix K by

$$H = (Z_k' Z_k)^{-1} Z_k' + K \tag{6.5.29}$$

and notice that, conditionally on Z_k,

$$\text{Cov}(\bar{\delta}_{\cdot k}) = \text{Cov}(\tilde{\delta}_{\cdot k}) + \sigma_{kk} K K' \tag{6.5.30}$$

where $\tilde{\delta}_{\cdot k}$ is the estimator in (6.5.22). Since $\sigma_{kk} K K'$ is positive semidefinite, the conclusion of the corollary follows immediately.

BLOCK RECURSIVE SYSTEMS

Although the structure examined in the discussion above has considerable appeal due to the simplicity of the estimation procedure it entails, one seldom encounters the conditions of simple recursivity required there. On the other hand, it might well be that certain economic systems of interest can be decomposable into subsystems so that *conditions analogous to those required by simple recursivity hold among the subsystems.* To be precise, suppose it is possible to number the jointly dependent variables and the equations of the system so that the first subsystem (of s_1 equations) contains only the variables $y_1, y_2, \ldots, y_{s_1}$, the second subsystem (of the next s_2 equations) contains the variables $y_1, y_2, \ldots, y_{s_1}, y_{s_1+1}, \ldots, y_{s_1+s_2}$, and generally the rth subsystem (of s_r equations) contains, at most, the variables $y_1, y_2, \ldots, y_{s_1+s_2+\cdots+s_r}$.

Notice that the crucial aspect of the requirements above is that the rth subsystem *does not* contain the variables $y_{s_1+s_2+\cdots+s_r+1}, \ldots, y_m$. The requirement does not imply, for example, that all variables $y_1, y_2, \ldots, y_{s_1+s_2+\cdots+s_r}$ are present in the rth subsystem. Suppose, also, that the error terms in one subsystem are mutually independent of (or minimally uncorrelated with) the error terms in any other subsystem.

Although these are still restrictive assumptions, we are more likely to encounter models that may be so structured than models which are simply recursive in the sense of the preceding discussion. When such conditions are satisfied, certain important simplifications result in estimation. We shall facilitate our discussion if we introduce

---

[10] If the distribution of u_t is *multivariate normal* (the predetermined variables are independent of the error terms) and the expectation of $(Z_k' Z_k)^{-1}$ exists, then the result in (6.5.26) can be obtained directly, without first conditioning on Z_k.

Definition 2: Consider the structural model

$$Y = YB + XC + U \tag{6.5.31}$$

and suppose that by appropriate renumbering of equations and variables, if necessary, the system may be arranged so that B is an upper block triangular matrix of the form

$$B = \begin{bmatrix} B_{11} & B_{12} & \cdots & B_{1k} \\ 0 & B_{22} & \cdots & B_{2k} \\ \vdots & & \ddots & \\ 0 & \cdots\cdots\cdots & B_{kk} \end{bmatrix} \tag{6.5.32}$$

where B_{ii} is an $s_i \times s_i$ nonsingular (and not necessarily triangular) matrix. Let

$$u_{t\cdot} = (u_{t1}, \ldots, u_{tm}) \tag{6.5.33}$$

be the vector of the disturbance terms in all the equations of the system, at "time" t, and suppose that

$$E(u_t \cdot X) = 0 \quad E(u'_{t\cdot}) = 0 \quad \text{Cov}(u'_{t\cdot}, u'_{t\cdot}) = \delta_{tt'} \Sigma$$

$$\Sigma = \begin{bmatrix} \Sigma_{11} & 0 & \cdots & 0 \\ 0 & \Sigma_{22} & & \vdots \\ \vdots & & \ddots & \vdots \\ 0 \cdots 0 & & \cdots\cdots & \Sigma_{kk} \end{bmatrix} \tag{6.5.34}$$

where Σ_{ii} is an $s_i \times s_i$ positive definite (not necessarily diagonal) matrix. Then the system in (6.5.31) is said to be *block recursive*.

We observe that the salient characteristics of a *block recursive* system is that the matrix of coefficients of the system's jointly dependent variables is *upper block triangular* and that the covariance matrix of the error terms is *block diagonal. Both are essential, and either one separately does not constitute block recursivity nor does it induce significant estimation simplifications.* Finally, notice that the matrices B_{ij} are $s_i \times s_j$, that by convention the diagonal elements of B_{ii} are zero, and that $I - B$ is also *upper block triangular*.

Given the discussion of the previous section, one would surmise that in the rth subsystem, say, we may treat the variables $y_1, y_2, y_{s_1+s_2+\cdots+s_{r-1}}$ as predetermined. Indeed, this is so as is shown in

Lemma 2: The variables $y_1, y_2, \ldots, y_{s_1+s_2+\cdots+s_{r-1}}$ are uncorrelated with (or, in the case of normality, independent of) the error terms appearing in the rth subsystem.

PROOF: Partition the matrix Y by

$$Y = (Y^1, Y^2, \ldots, Y^k) \tag{6.5.35}$$

where

$$Y^r = (y_{\cdot s_1+s_2+\cdots+s_{r-1}+1}, y_{\cdot s_1+s_2+\cdots+s_{r-1}+2}, \ldots, y_{\cdot s_1+s_2+\cdots+s_r}) \tag{6.5.36}$$

Thus Y^r is $T \times s_r$ and is the matrix of observations on the s_r variables "explained" by the rth subsystem. Similarly, partition C by

$$C = (C^1, C^2, \ldots, C^k) \tag{6.5.37}$$

so that C^r is $G \times s_r$

and U by

$$U = (U^1, U^2, \ldots, U^k) \tag{6.5.38}$$

so that U^r is $T \times s_r$ and contains the error terms appearing in the rth subsystem. In this notation, the first subsystem consists of

$$Y^1 = Y^1 B_{11} + XC^1 + U^1 \tag{6.5.39}$$

and, in general, the rth subsystem consists of

$$Y^r = Y^r B_{rr} + \sum_{i=1}^{r-1} Y^i B_{ir} + XC^r + U^r \tag{6.5.40}$$

The reduced form of the system is

$$Y = X\Pi + V \tag{6.5.41}$$

where

$$\Pi = CD \quad V = UD \quad D = (I - B)^{-1} \tag{6.5.42}$$

Since $I - B$ is upper block triangular, then obviously so is D. Thus we may rewrite the latter as

$$D = \begin{pmatrix} D_{11} & D_{12} & \cdots & D_{1k} \\ 0 & D_{22} & \cdots & D_{2k} \\ \vdots & & \ddots & \\ 0 & \cdots\cdots\cdots\cdots & D_{kk} \end{pmatrix} \tag{6.5.43}$$

Let us now partition (the columns of) Π and V conformally with Y. Hence

$$\Pi = (\Pi^1, \Pi^2, \ldots, \Pi^k) \qquad V = (V^1, V^2, \ldots, V^k) \tag{6.5.44}$$

where Π^r is $G \times s_r$ and V^r is $T \times s_r$. Clearly

$$\Pi^r = \sum_{i=1}^{r} C^i D_{ir} \quad V^r = \sum_{i=1}^{r} U^i D_{ir} \qquad r = 1, 2, \ldots, k \tag{6.5.45}$$

Thus the reduced form corresponding to Y^r is given by

$$Y^r = X\Pi^r + V^r \tag{6.5.46}$$

Consider now

$$E[U^{r'} Y^j] = E[U^{r'} V^j] \qquad j = 1, 2, \ldots, r-1 \tag{6.5.47}$$

From (6.5.45) we have

$$E[U^{r'} V^j] = \sum_{i=1}^{j} E[U^{r'} U^i D_{ij}] \qquad j = 1, 2, \ldots, r-1 \tag{6.5.48}$$

ut in view of (6.5.34) we easily conclude

$$[U^{r'} Y^j] = 0 \qquad j = 1, 2, \ldots, r - 1 \qquad\qquad \text{Q.E.D.}$$

$$(6.5.49)$$

Remark 3: The import of the lemma is that the *variables in* $Y^1, Y^2, \ldots, Y^{r-1}$, *no less than the variables in* X, *may be considered as predetermined when we are dealing with the rth subsystem.* We would then surmise that each subsystem may *be dealt with in isolation and its parameters may be estimated by whatever technique appears appropriate in the context of that subsystem alone.*

To conclude this discussion we present

Theorem 4: Consider the structural model

$$Y = YB + XC + U \qquad\qquad (6.5.50)$$

together with the customary assumptions on the properties of its error terms. Suppose, also, that the model is *block recursive* and can be decomposed into k blocks, the ith block consisting of s_i equations. Then each block can be treated as if it were an autonomous simultaneous equations system.

In the rth block, the variables $y_1, y_2, \ldots, y_{s_1 + s_2 + \cdots + s_{r-1}}$ can be treated as predetermined and the parameters of this subsystem can be estimated without reference to the remainder of the system.

The proof of this theorem, although straightforward, is rather cumbersome and hence is omitted. The reader, however, may develop the proof rather easily by using of the result in Lemma 2.

Remark 4: Block recursivity may be of great value in coping with computational complexities in large, economy-wide econometric models such as the Brookings model. In effect, it allows us to treat each subsystem in isolation. The number of predetermined variables in a particular subsystem may be considerably smaller than the number of predetermined variables from the point of view of the system as a whole. Thus if block recursivity in fact holds, then for example, 2SLS estimators for the parameters of the system may be obtained block by block, while 2SLS estimators for the parameters of the system when the latter is viewed as an indecomposable unit may not exist due to the fact that the entire system may contain more predetermined variables than there are observations (see Chapter 5).

REFERENCES

1. Basmann, R. L., "On Finite Sample Distributions of GCL Identifiability Test Statistics," *Journal of the American Statistical Association*, vol. 55, 1960, pp. 650–659.
2. Basmann, R. L., "The Causal Interpretation of Nontriangular Systems of Economic Relations," *Econometrica*, vol. 31, 1963, pp. 439–448.

3. Basmann, R. L., "A Note on the Statistical Testability of 'Explicit Causal Chains' against the Class of 'Interdependent' Models," *Journal of the American Statistical Association* vol. 60, 1965, pp. 1080–1093.
4. Bentzel, R., and B. Hansen, "On Recursiveness and Interdependency in Economic Models," *Review of Economic Studies*, vol. 22, 1955, pp. 153–168.
5. Bergstrom, A. R., "Nonrecursive Models as Discrete Approximations to Systems of Stochastic Difference Equations," *Econometrica*, vol. 34, 1966, pp. 173–182.
6. Brown, T. M., "Simultaneous Least Squares: A Distribution Free Method of Equation System Structure Estimation," *International Economic Review*, vol. 1, 1960, pp. 173–191
7. Cragg, J. R., "On the Sensitivity of Simultaneous Equations Estimators to the Stochastic Assumptions of the Model," *Journal of the American Statistical Association*, vol. 61, 1966, pp. 136–151.
8. Fisher, F. M., "Generalization of the Rank and Order Conditions for Identifiability," *Econometrica*, vol. 27, 1959, pp. 431–447.
9. Fisher., F. M., "On the Cost of Approximate Specification in Simultaneous Equation Estimation," *Econometrica*, vol. 29, 1961, pp. 139–170.
10. Fisher, F. M., "Uncorrelated Disturbances and Identifiability Criteria," *International Economic Review*, vol. 4, 1963, pp. 134–152.
11. Fisher, F. M., "The Choice of Instrumental Variables in the Estimation of Economy-Wide Econometric Models," *International Economic Review*, vol. 6, 1965, pp. 245–274.
12. Fisher, F. M., *The Identification Problem in Econometrics*, New York, McGraw-Hill, 1966.
13. Fisher, F. M., "Approximate Specification and the Choice of a k-Class Estimator," *Journal of the American Statistical Association*, vol. 62, 1967, pp. 1265–1276.
14. Frisch, R., *Pitfalls in the Statistical Construction of Demand and Supply Curves*, Veroffentlichungen der Frankfurter Gesellschaft fur Konjukturforschung, Neue Folge, Heft 5, Hans Buske, Leipzig, 1933.
15. Geary, R. C., "Determination of Linear Relations Between Systematic Parts of Variables with Errors of Observation, the Variances of Which are Unknown," *Econometrica*, vol. 17, 1949, pp. 30–58.
16. Hurwicz, L., "Generalization of the Concept of Identification," Chapter 6 in *Statistical Inference in Dynamic Economic Models*, T. C. Koopmans (Ed.), New York, Wiley, 1950.
17. Klein, L. R., "Pitfalls in the Statistical Determination of the Investment Schedule," *Econometrica*, vol. 11, 1943, pp. 243–258.
18. Klein, L. R., *A Textbook of Econometrics*, Evanston, Illinois, Row Peterson, 1953.
19. Koopmans, T. C., "Identification Problems in Economic Model Construction," Chapter 2 in *Studies in Econometric Methods*, W. C. Hood and T. C. Koopmans, (Eds.), Cowles Foundation for Research in Economics, Monograph No. 14, New York, Wiley, 1953.
20. Liviatan, N., "Errors in Variables and Engle Curve Analysis," *Econometrica*, vol. 29, 1961, pp. 336–362.
21. Liu, T. C., "Underidentification, Structural Estimation and Forecasting," *Econometrica*, vol. 28, 1960, pp. 855–865.
22. Reiersol, O., "Confluence Analysis by Means of Instrumental Sets of Variables," *Arkiv for Mathematik, Astronomi och Fysik*, vol. 32, 1945.
23. Sargan, J. D., "The Estimation of Economic Relationships Using Instrumental Variables," *Econometrica*, vol. 26, 1958, pp. 393–415.
24. Schultz, H., *Theory and Measurement of Demand*, Chicago, University of Chicago Press, 1938.
25. Simon, H., "Causal Ordering and Identifiability," Chapter 3 in *Studies in Econometric Methods*, W. C. Hood and T. C. Koopmans (Eds.), Cowles Foundation for Research in Economics, Monograph No. 14, New York, Wiley, 1953.
26. Strotz, R. H., and H. Wold, "Recursive vs Nonrecursive Systems: An Attempt at Synthesis," *Econometrica*, vol. 28, 1960, pp. 417–427.
27. Strotz, R. H., and H. Wold, "The Causal Interpretability of Structural Parameters: A Reply," *Econometrica*, vol. 31, 1963, pp. 449–450.
28. Wald, A., "Note on the Identification of Economic Relations," in *Statistical Inference in Dynamic Economic Models*, T. C. Koopmans (Ed.), Cowles Foundation for Research in Economics, Monograph No. 10, New York, Wiley, 1950.

29. Wold, H., "Causal Inference from Observational Data: A Review of Ends and Means," *Journal of the Royal Statistical Society, Series A*, vol. 119, 1956, pp. 28–61.

30. Wold, H., "Ends and Means in Econometric Model Building," in *Probability and Statistics: The Harold Cramer Volume*, U. Grenander (Ed.), New York, Wiley, 1959.

31. Wold, H., "A Generalization of Causal Chain Models," *Econometrica*, vol. 28, 1960, pp. 443–463.

32. Wold, H., "Forecasting by Chain Principle." Chapter 1 in *Econometric Model Building: Essays on the Causal Chain Approach*, Contributions to Economic Analysis Series, Amsterdam, North Holland Publishing Co., 1964.

33. Working, E. J., "What do Statistical 'Demand Curves' Show?" *Quarterly Journal of Economics*, vol. 41, 1927, pp. 212–235.

MAXIMUM
LIKELIHOOD
METHODS

7

7.1 FORMULATION OF THE PROBLEM AND ASSUMPTIONS

In dealing with the problem of estimating the parameters of a *structural system of equations*, we had not, in previous chapters, explicitly stated the form of the density of the random terms appearing in the system. Indeed, the estimation aspects of classical least squares techniques and their generalization to systems of equations are distribution free, so that no explicit assumption need be made with respect to the distribution of the error terms. On the other hand, in considering various tests of significance on 2SLS or 3SLS estimated parameters of a structural system, we have occasionally found it convenient to assert (joint) normality of the structural error terms. Under this assumption, the derivation of the asymptotic distribution of such estimators is simplified considerably.

In this chapter we shall, explicitly and at the outset, make use of the normality assumption and thus derive structural parameter estimators using *maximum likelihood methods*.

Consider again the structural model

$$Y = YB^* + XC^* + U \tag{7.1.1}$$

where the starred coefficient matrices B^* and C^* *do not embody the a priori restrictions involving the absence of certain variables from certain equations.*[1]

---

[1] By convention, however, $\beta_{ii}^* = 0, i = 1, 2, \ldots, m.$

Thus in (7.1.1) Y, X are, respectively, the $T \times m$ and $T \times G$ matrices of current endogenous and predetermined variables; B^*, C^* are, respectively, $m \times m$ and $G \times m$ matrices of unknown parameters.

In addition, the *rows* of U, $u_t.$, have the properties

$$u_t'. \sim N(0, \Sigma) \quad E(u_t'. \, u_{t'}'.) = \delta_{tt'}\Sigma \qquad t, t' = 1, 2, \ldots, T \tag{7.1.2}$$

$\delta_{tt'}$ being the Kronecker delta and Σ a general positive definite matrix. Finally, we make the usual assumption

$$E(X'U) = 0 \qquad \text{rank} \, (X) = G \tag{7.1.3}$$

At the risk of being unduly repetitive, let us remind ourselves that the assumptions, in order of appearance, mean that, for any time t, the joint distribution of the error terms of the system is normal with mean 0 and covariance matrix Σ, that error terms may be *contemporaneously correlated* but are *intertemporally uncorrelated*, that the error terms are *uncorrelated* with the *predetermined variables of the system*, and that there is *no linear dependence* among the predetermined variables. In order that the current endogenous variables be uniquely determined in terms of the predetermined and random variables of the system, it is also necessary to assume that $I - B^*$ *is nonsingular.*

Given the stipulations above, the reduced form of the system becomes

$$Y = X\Pi + V \tag{7.1.4}$$

where

$$\Pi = C^*D^{-1} \quad V = UD^{-1} \quad D = I - B^* \tag{7.1.5}$$

We note that the tth row of V is given by

$$v_t. = u_t.D^{-1} \tag{7.1.6}$$

and thus

$$v_t'. \sim N(0, \Omega) \quad \Omega = D'^{-1}\Sigma D^{-1} \quad \text{Cov} \, (v_t'. \, , v_{t'}'.) = \delta_{tt'}\Omega \qquad t, t' = 1, 2, \ldots, T \tag{7.1.7}$$

Moreover,

$$E(X'V) = 0 \tag{7.1.8}$$

We see, therefore, that *the reduced form is completely* specified when we specify the conditional distribution of $y_t.$ given $x_t.$. The latter is, of course, given by

$$y_t'. \sim N(x_t.\Pi, \Omega) \quad \text{Cov} \, (y_t'. \, , y_{t'}'.) = \delta_{tt'}\Omega \qquad t, t' = 1, 2, \ldots, T \tag{7.1.9}$$

where $y_t.$ and $x_t.$ are, respectively, the tth rows of Y and X. From (7.1.9) it is apparent that the problem of estimating the reduced form, as ordinarily posed, is equivalent to the problem of estimating the conditional mean of the current endogenous *given* the predetermined variables of the system.

As pointed out earlier, the elements of the matrix Π may not be entirely unknown. In the process of estimation, some a priori restrictions will be imposed on the elements of the matrices B^* and C^*. Since Π is a well-defined function of these matrices, this would imply some restrictions on the elements of Π as well. Indeed, we have seen a form of such restrictions when we examined the identification problem briefly in the context of indirect least squares estimation.

7.2 REDUCED FORM (RF) AND FULL INFORMATION MAXIMUM LIKELIHOOD (FIML) ESTIMATION

GENERAL DISCUSSION

In the previous section we had set forth the model and the assumptions relating to the random and predetermined variables it contains.[2]

In estimating the parameters of the model, we can proceed in one of two basic ways: we can treat each equation (or perhaps a block of equations) in isolation as we did when discussing two stage least squares (2SLS) techniques, or we can estimate all the unknown structural parameters simultaneously as we did in the case of three stage least squares (3SLS).

The two approaches are referred to, respectively, in the context of maximum likelihood techniques as *limited information maximum likelihood* (LIML) and *full information maximum likelihood* (FIML).

Before considering the derivation of the FIML estimator, we shall give a brief account of the maximum likelihood estimator for the reduced form parameters. This will elucidate the nature of likelihood functions in the case of multiple equations systems and set forth, in a rather simple context, the notation and techniques to be employed in the more complex settings involved when we deal with FIML and particularly LIML estimation.

Thus our first task is to obtain the likelihood function with respect to the reduced form. Since the vectors $v_t.$ are the basic random variables of the reduced form, we must look to them in formulating the appropriate likelihood function.

In view of (7.1.7), the joint distribution (likelihood function) of such vectors is given by

$$p(v_{.1}, v_{.2}, \ldots, v_{.T}) = \prod_{t=1}^{T} [(2\pi)^{-m/2} |\Omega|^{-\frac{1}{2}} \exp(-\tfrac{1}{2} v_t. \Omega^{-1} v_t'.)] \tag{7.2.1}$$

Unfortunately, however, the form given in (7.2.1) is not a very useful one. First, it does not include all the parameters of interest; in particular, it does not contain the matrix Π. Second, it *does not contain any observable quantities*. It is

---

[2] Actually, certain other assumptions relating to the existence of second order moments and the nonsingularity of certain second moment matrices are also required. We shall invoke these when the occasion arises so as to indicate precisely the role these assumptions play.

clear, then, that it cannot possibly be used to make any inferences about—that is, estimate—the reduced form parameters of interest.

Yet this difficulty is easily removed by the simple transformation

$$v_t. = y_t. - x_t. \Pi \tag{7.2.2}$$

so that we no longer deal with the $v_t.$ but rather the $y_t..$ This transformation corrects the two deficiencies of the likelihood function as exhibited in (7.2.1). First, it introduces the reduced form parameter matrix Π and, second, in the place of the unobservable $v_t.$ it introduces the observable quantities $y_t.$ and $x_t..$

Since (7.2.1) is the joint density of the $v_t.$, and the Jacobian of the transformation in (7.2.2) is unity, then by Lemma 3 of Chapter 1 the joint density of the $y_t.$ is given by

$$\bar{L}(\Pi, \Omega; Y, X) = (2\pi)^{-mT/2} |\Omega|^{-T/2} \exp \left[-\frac{1}{2} \sum_{t=1}^{T} (y_t. - x_t. \Pi)\Omega^{-1}(y_t. - x_t. \Pi)' \right] \tag{7.2.3}$$

In view of the relations in (7.1.5), we see that the joint density of the current endogenous variables—conditioned on the predetermined ones—embodies all the information conveyed by the sample on the *entire set of parameters contained in the model*. It is important that this fact be clearly understood, as well as the fact that (7.2.3) is *the basic likelihood function* whether one treats of the problems of indirect least squares, FIML or LIML estimation.

Let us explain why this is so. First we note that as a matter of notation

$$\sum_{t=1}^{T} (y_t. - x_t. \Pi)\Omega^{-1}(y_t. - x_t. \Pi)' = \text{tr } (Y - X\Pi)\Omega^{-1}(Y - X\Pi)' \tag{7.2.4}$$

But from (7.1.5) we see that

$$\text{tr } (Y - X\Pi)\Omega^{-1}(Y - X\Pi)' = \text{tr } (YD - XC^*)\Sigma^{-1}(YD - XC^*)'$$
$$= \sum_{t=1}^{T} (y_t. D - x_t. C^*)\Sigma^{-1}(y_t. D - x_t. C^*)' \tag{7.2.5}$$

Furthermore,

$$|\Omega| = |D|^{-2}|\Sigma| \qquad |\Omega|^{-1} = |D|^2|\Sigma|^{-1} \tag{7.2.6}$$

Thus *as a matter of notational change only*, we can rewrite (7.2.3) as

$$\bar{L}(D, C^*, \Sigma; Y, X)$$
$$= (2\pi)^{-mT/2} |\Sigma|^{-T/2} |D|^T \exp \left[-\frac{1}{2} \sum_{t=1}^{T} (y_t. D - x_t. C^*)\Sigma^{-1}(y_t. D - x_t. C^*)' \right] \tag{7.2.7}$$

We can then verify by a rather simple computation that (7.2.7) is the likelihood function we shall obtain if we operate *directly* with the joint density of the structural disturbances and then effect the transformation

$$u_{t.} = y_t.D - x_t.C^* \tag{7.2.8}$$

noting that the Jacobian of this transformation is $|D|$.[3]

Two features of the likelihood function should be noted. First, notice that, as expressed in (7.2.7), the structural parameters enter in a highly nonlinear form through $|D|^T$. It is indeed this aspect that makes FIML estimation cumbersome. Second, observe that the parameters of the reduced form enter the likelihood function, as expressed in (7.2.3), in a rather simple manner. These observations partly motivate the two estimation procedures examined in this section. In indirect least squares (ILS), we seek to estimate the matrix Π—or some columns thereof—and through these estimators we seek to make inferences concerning the *structural parameters of interest*. Under this scheme, we operate with the likelihood function as exhibited in (7.2.3) and treat the elements of Π as free parameters. That is, we neglect the relations conveyed by (7.1.6) and the fact that a priori restrictions on B^* and C^* will, in general, imply some restrictions on Π.

In FIML we make use of all a priori restrictions, we operate with the likelihood function as exhibited in (7.2.7), and we seek *to estimate the unknown structural parameters by directly maximizing that function.*

Clearly, under some circumstances the two procedures are equivalent, but this will not always be so; *indeed, typically, it will not be.*

On the other hand, it is important to realize that ILS uses exactly the same likelihood function but deals instead with a *reparametrized* problem; that is, it deals with the estimation of Π. In the new parametric representation, we have to estimate the Gm elements of Π.

The original problem involves the estimation of the unknown structural parameters; according to our convention, there are $G_i + m_i$ unknown structural parameters in the ith equation. If the necessary conditions for identifiability are satisfied for all equations, then the number of unknown structural parameters in the system obeys

$$\sum_{i=1}^{m}(G_i + m_i) \leq Gm \tag{7.2.9}$$

---

[3] We should remark in this connection that what enters in (7.2.7) is not $|D|^T$ as exhibited there but rather the *absolute value* of $|D|$ raised to the Tth power. This follows immediately from (7.2.6), for what we have is really $\{|D|^2\}^{T/2}$ so that we are raising to the $(T/2)$th power the positive quantity $|D|^2$. To avoid cumber ome notation, we retain the symbol $|D|^T$ although this is always to be understood as a positive quantity. Finally notice that in previous chapters we termed D^{-1} what we here term D.

since for identifiability we need

$$G_i + m_i \leq G \qquad (7.2.10)$$

Thus we see that in the reparametrized problem dealt with by ILS, we are called upon to estimate a number of parameters that are a well-defined function of a *smaller number of structural parameters*. One does this because the new parametric representation makes the logarithm of the likelihood function *quadratic in Π*, and it is rather simple to maximize quadratic functions. The price paid for this is that we estimate a larger set of parameters than we need to, and *if just identifiability conditions do not hold, it is not possible to recover (uniquely) from reduced form estimators information concerning the structural parameters.*[4]

In the FIML scheme of estimation, we estimate the unknown structural parameters directly, but then we have to contend with a likelihood function, which, in its logarithmic form, contains the highly nonlinear term $\ln |D|$.

To conclude this preliminary exposition, ILS estimation of structural parameters purchases simplicity[5] at the cost of proliferating the number of parameters estimated; ILS cannot produce unique structural estimators unless the equations of the system are just identified.

On the other hand, FIML estimation economizes on the number of parameters to be estimated at the cost of dealing with a more complex form of the likelihood function. With these preliminaries aside, let us now obtain maximum likelihood estimators of the reduced form parameters.

In view of (7.2.3) and (7.2.4), we may write the logarithm of the likelihood function as

$$L(\Pi, \Omega; Y, X) = -\frac{mT}{2} \ln (2\pi) - \frac{T}{2} \ln |\Omega| - \frac{1}{2} \operatorname{tr} \Omega^{-1}(Y - X\Pi)'(Y - X\Pi)$$

$$(7.2.11)$$

Differentiating with respect to π_{rs}, $r = 1, 2, \ldots, G$, $s = 1, 2, \ldots, m$, we obtain the first-order conditions

$$\frac{\partial L}{\partial \Pi} = X'X\Pi\Omega^{-1} - X'Y\Omega^{-1} = 0 \qquad (7.2.12)$$

Since Ω is nonsingular, we conclude

$$\hat{\Pi} = (X'X)^{-1} X'Y \qquad (7.2.13)$$

That (7.2.13) is a maximum is ensured by the fact that L is a concave function of Π.

---

[4] This, of course, apart from any intrinsic interest one might have in the reduced form.
[5] We should stress that simplicity prevails only because we *ignore restrictions on* Π implied by the a priori restrictions on B^* and C^*; if the latter were taken into account, reduced form estimation may not be simpler than FIML estimation.

We see that $\hat{\Pi}$ of (7.2.13) is exactly the OLS estimator obtained in Chapter 4. This is, of course, not surprising, for it is apparent from the likelihood function that maximization of (7.2.11) is equivalent to *minimization* of

$$\sum_{t=1}^{T} (y_{t\cdot} - x_{t\cdot}\,\Pi)\Omega^{-1}(y_{t\cdot} - x_{t\cdot}\,\Pi)'$$

$$= \sum_{i=1}^{m} \sum_{j=1}^{m} \sum_{t=1}^{T} \left(y_{ti} - \sum_{s=1}^{G} x_{ts}\pi_{si}\right)\omega^{ij}\left(y_{tj} - \sum_{s=1}^{G} x_{ts}\pi_{sj}\right)$$

$$= \sum_{i=1}^{m} \sum_{j=1}^{m} (y_{\cdot i} - X\pi_{\cdot i})'\omega^{ij}(y_{\cdot j} - X\pi_{\cdot j})$$

$$= (y - X^*\pi^*)'\Phi^{-1}(y - X^*\pi^*) \tag{7.2.14}$$

where

$$y = \begin{pmatrix} y_{\cdot 1} \\ y_{\cdot 2} \\ \vdots \\ y_{\cdot m} \end{pmatrix} \quad X^* = I_m \otimes X \quad \pi^* = \begin{pmatrix} \pi_{\cdot 1} \\ \pi_{\cdot 2} \\ \vdots \\ \pi_{\cdot m} \end{pmatrix}$$

$$\Phi^{-1} = \Omega^{-1} \otimes I_T \qquad \Omega^{-1} = (\omega^{ij}) \tag{7.2.15}$$

$y_{\cdot i}$ and $\pi_{\cdot j}$ being, respectively, the ith and jth columns of Y and Π. But minimization of (7.2.14) with respect to the elements of π^* yields their *Aitken estimator* and thus the Aitken estimator of Π. As shown in Chapter 4, when all equations of a system of regression equations contain the same "explanatory" variables, then *Aitken and OLS* estimators coincide.

Since, as we see from (7.2.13), the maximum likelihood estimator of Π does not depend on Ω, it follows quite easily that an estimator of the latter can be obtained by maximizing the *concentrated* likelihood function

$$L(\Omega;\, Y,\, X) = -\frac{mT}{2}\ln(2\pi) + \frac{T}{2}\ln|\Omega^{-1}| - \frac{1}{2}\operatorname{tr}\Omega^{-1}S \tag{7.2.16}$$

where

$$(s_{ij}) = S = (Y - X\hat{\Pi})'(Y - X\hat{\Pi}) = Y'[I - X(X'X)^{-1}X']Y \tag{7.2.17}$$

We observe

$$\operatorname{tr}\Omega^{-1}S = \sum_{i=1}^{m} \sum_{j=1}^{m} \omega^{ij}s_{ji} \tag{7.2.18}$$

Now, since there is a unique relation between the elements of Ω and Ω^{-1}, it follows that if the maximizing values of the elements ω^{ij} of the latter, are given say by ω^{*ij}, then the values ω_{ij}^{*} corresponding to the ω^{*ij} will also maximize the function. In the case of (7.2.16), it is much simpler to maximize with respect to ω^{ij}. The first-order conditions of this maximization are

$$\frac{\partial L}{\partial \omega^{ij}} = \frac{T}{2} \frac{\Omega^{ij}}{|\Omega|} - \tfrac{1}{2}s_{ji} = 0 \qquad i, j = 1, 2, \ldots, m \tag{7.2.19}$$

where Ω^{ij} is *the cofactor* of the (i, j) element of Ω^{-1}. In matric form, the relations (7.2.19) read

$$\frac{T}{2}\Omega - \tfrac{1}{2}S' = 0 \tag{7.2.20}$$

Since S is symmetric, we conclude

$$\hat{\Omega} = \frac{S}{T} \tag{7.2.21}$$

which is, therefore, the maximum likelihood estimator of Ω.

To derive the covariance matrix of the reduced form estimator, it is perhaps most convenient to revert to the notation of (7.2.15). Thus

$$\hat{\pi}^* = (X^{*\prime}X^*)^{-1}X^{*\prime}y = \pi^* + (X^{*\prime}X^*)^{-1}X^{*\prime}v \tag{7.2.22}$$

where we have expressed the reduced form as

$$y = X^*\pi^* + v \qquad v = \begin{pmatrix} v_{.1} \\ v_{.2} \\ \vdots \\ v_{.m} \end{pmatrix} \tag{7.2.23}$$

$v_{.i}$ being the ith column of V as given in (7.1.4) and (7.1.5). From (7.1.7) and (7.2.22), we conclude[6]

$$\hat{\pi}^* \sim N[\pi^*, \Omega \otimes (X'X)^{-1}] \tag{7.2.24}$$

It follows then from (7.2.21) that the maximum likelihood estimator of the covariance matrix of π^* is given by

$$\text{Cov}(\hat{\pi}^*) = \frac{S}{T} \otimes (X'X)^{-1} \tag{7.2.25}$$

Moreover, since

$$S = Y'[I - X(X'X)^{-1}X']Y = V'(I - N)V \qquad N = X(X'X)^{-1}X' \tag{7.2.26}$$

we note that it follows from the discussion in Chapter 1 that

$$S \sim W(\Omega, T - G, m) \tag{7.2.27}$$

---

[6] Notice that

$$\text{Cov}(\hat{\pi}^*) = E[(X^{*\prime}X^*)^{-1}X^{*\prime}vv'X^*(X^{*\prime}X^*)^{-1}] = (X^{*\prime}X^*)^{-1}X^{*\prime}\Phi X^*(X^{*\prime}X^*)^{-1}$$
$$= (I_m \otimes X'X)^{-1}(\Omega \otimes X'X)(I_m \otimes X'X)^{-1} = \Omega \otimes (X'X)^{-1}$$

Furthermore, the marginal distribution of the ith subvector of $\hat{\pi}^*$—and hence the marginal distribution of the parameters in the ith equation of the reduced form—is given by

$$\hat{\pi}._{\cdot i} \sim N[\pi._{\cdot i}, \omega_{ii}(X'X)^{-1}] \qquad (7.2.28)$$

From (7.2.28) it follows that the usual t and F tests of significance can be carried out on the estimators of the parameters of the reduced form. Thus there is a complete equivalence between the results derived here and those obtained when we studied the simple general linear model (single equation OLS). It is also apparent from the discussion in Chapter 6 that having obtained an estimator for π^* (or Π), we can, under certain circumstances, recover estimators for the structural parameters by ILS (here indirect maximum likelihood estimation) methods. Since it is quite unnecessary to repeat that discussion here, we now turn to the problem of estimating the structural parameters of the system by maximizing directly the likelihood function as exhibited in (7.2.7).

The logarithm of that function is given by

$$L(B, C, \Sigma; Y, X) = -\frac{mT}{2} \ln (2\pi) - \frac{T}{2} \ln |\Sigma| + T \ln |I - B|$$

$$-\frac{1}{2} \sum_{t=1}^{T} [y_t._{\cdot}(I - B) - x_t._{\cdot} C]\Sigma^{-1}[y_t._{\cdot}(I - B) - x_t._{\cdot} C]' \qquad (7.2.29)$$

As a matter of notation, we have

$$\sum_{t=1}^{T} [y_t._{\cdot}(I - B) - x_t._{\cdot} C]\Sigma^{-1}[y_t._{\cdot}(I - B) - x_t._{\cdot} C]'$$
$$= \operatorname{tr}(Z A\Sigma^{-1}A'Z') = T \operatorname{tr} \Sigma^{-1}A'MA \qquad (7.2.30)$$

where

$$M = \frac{1}{T}Z'Z \qquad A = \begin{pmatrix} I - B \\ -C \end{pmatrix} \qquad Z = (Y, X) \qquad (7.2.31)$$

and the removal of asterisks from B and C *indicates that the a priori restrictions on the elements of B^* and C^* have now been imposed so that B and C have some elements that are known to be zero.*

Thus (7.2.29) can be written more conveniently as

$$L(B, C, \Sigma; Y, X) = -\frac{mT}{2} \ln (2\pi) - \frac{T}{2} \ln |\Sigma| + T \ln |I - B| - \frac{T}{2} \operatorname{tr} \Sigma^{-1}A'MA$$

$$(7.2.32)$$

To maximize L with respect to the *unknown elements* of B, C and with respect to Σ, we proceed stepwise; we first obtain an estimator for Σ^7 *in terms of the unknown* parameters of A. Inserting this maximizing value of Σ in (7.2.32), we obtain the "concentrated" likelihood function, which is now solely a function of A. The final step consists in maximizing the "concentrated" likelihood function with respect to A.

Let us now see what this procedure involves. Proceeding exactly as we did just prior to (7.2.19) above, we find that maximizing (7.2.32) with respect to σ^{ij}, $i, j = 1, 2, \ldots, m$, yields

$$\hat{\Sigma} = A'MA \qquad (7.2.33)$$

Inserting (7.2.33) in (7.2.32), we find the "concentrated" likelihood function

$$L(B, C; Y, X) = -\frac{mT}{2}\left[\ln(2\pi) + 1\right] + T\ln|I - B| - \frac{T}{2}\ln|A'MA| \qquad (7.2.34)$$

which is now to be maximized with respect to the unknown elements of B and C. It is apparent from (7.2.34) that the unknown parameters enter the likelihood function in a highly nonlinear fashion. This precludes our finding an explicit expression for the estimators of B and C; indeed, at best we can only give an algorithm for obtaining such estimators. Suitable algorithms are available, for example, in [6] and [13].

Now, assuming that such estimators can be obtained, what are their statistical properties?

From the results of Chapter 3, we know that, in a simpler context at least, maximum likelihood estimators are asymptotically efficient, in the MVB sense. Moverover, their asymptotic distribution is normal. If we put

$$\delta = \begin{pmatrix} \beta_{\cdot 1} \\ \gamma_{\cdot 1} \\ \beta_{\cdot 2} \\ \gamma_{\cdot 2} \\ \vdots \\ \beta_{\cdot m} \\ \gamma_{\cdot m} \end{pmatrix} \qquad (7.2.35)$$

where $\beta_{\cdot i}$ and $\gamma_{\cdot i}$ represent the (unknown) structural coefficients of the ith equation, it can be shown that, asymptotically,

$$T^{\frac{1}{2}}(\hat{\delta} - \delta) \sim N(0, \psi) \qquad (7.2.36)$$

where

$$\psi = -\left[\lim_{T \to \infty} E\left(\frac{1}{T}\frac{\partial^2 L}{\partial \delta\,\partial \delta}\right)\right]^{-1} \qquad (7.2.37)$$

---

[7] We remind the reader that in this context one does not suppose any a priori knowledge concerning the σ_{ij} so that all that is asserted about Σ is that it is a positive definite symmetric matrix.

and $\hat{\delta}$ is the FIML estimator of δ. We shall not prove the validity of (7.2.36) and (7.2.37), for the proof will not particularly illuminate the issues. The interested reader may find an excellent discussion of this problem in [21], [22].

SIMPLIFIED FIML ESTIMATORS

Although the preceding discussion has dealt with the problem in complete generality, it is clear that the FIML estimator will be extremely difficult to obtain in practice. Consequently, we shall deal here with certain simplifications that involve a judicious degree of approximation. As we shall see in subsequent chapters, the 3SLS estimator may also be viewed as an approximation to FIML.

For notational simplicity, and in the following discussion only, let

$$B^* = I - B \tag{7.2.38}$$

and write the concentrated likelihood function of (7.2.34) in the equivalent form

$$L(B, C; Y, X) = -\frac{mT}{2} [\ln (2\pi) + 1] - \frac{T}{2} \ln |M_{yy}|$$

$$+ \frac{T}{2} \ln |B^{*\prime} M_{yy} B^*| - \frac{T}{2} \ln |\hat{\Sigma}| \tag{7.2.39}$$

where, of course,

$$M_{yy} = \frac{1}{T} Y'Y \qquad \hat{\Sigma} = A'MA \tag{7.2.40}$$

Notice that

$$P = B^{*\prime} M_{yy} B^* \tag{7.2.41}$$

is the leading term in the sum defining $\hat{\Sigma}$.

If p_{ij} and s_{ij} are the (i, j) elements of P and $\hat{\Sigma}$ respectively, we see that

$$p_{ij} = \frac{1}{T} (y_{\cdot i} - Y_i \beta_{\cdot i})'(y_{\cdot j} - Y_j \beta_{\cdot j})$$

$$s_{ij} = \frac{1}{T} (y_{\cdot i} - Z_i \delta_{\cdot i})'(y_{\cdot j} - Z_j \delta_{\cdot j}) \tag{7.2.42}$$

and that $\beta_{\cdot i}$ appears only in the ith row and column of P and $\delta_{\cdot i}$ only in the ith row and column of $\hat{\Sigma}$. To obtain FIML estimators for the vectors $\delta_{\cdot i}$, $i = 1, 2, \ldots, m$, we must solve the following normal equations:

$$\frac{\partial L}{\partial \delta_{\cdot i}} = \frac{T}{2} \frac{1}{|P|} \frac{\partial |P|}{\partial \delta_{\cdot i}} - \frac{T}{2} \frac{1}{|\hat{\Sigma}|} \frac{\partial |\hat{\Sigma}|}{\partial \delta_{\cdot i}} = 0 \qquad i = 1, 2, \ldots, m \tag{7.2.43}$$

But

$$\frac{\partial |P|}{\partial \delta_{\cdot i}} = \begin{pmatrix} \dfrac{\partial |P|}{\partial \beta_{\cdot i}} \\ 0 \end{pmatrix} \tag{7.2.44}$$

since P does not depend on the vectors $\gamma_{\cdot i}$. If we denote the *cofactor* of the element p_{kj} by P_{kj}, we have

$$|P| = \frac{1}{m} \sum_{k=1}^{m} \sum_{j=1}^{m} p_{kj} P_{kj} \tag{7.2.45}$$

Thus

$$\frac{\partial |P|}{\partial \beta_{\cdot i}} = \frac{1}{m} \sum_{j=1}^{m} P_{ij} \frac{\partial p_{ij}}{\partial \beta_{\cdot i}} \tag{7.2.46}$$

$$\frac{\partial p_{ij}}{\partial \beta_{\cdot i}} = Y_i' Y_j \beta_{\cdot j} - Y_i' y_{\cdot j} \tag{7.2.47}$$

Hence

$$\frac{\partial \ln |P|}{\partial \beta_{\cdot i}} = \frac{1}{m} \sum_{j=1}^{m} p^{ij} (Y_i' Y_j \beta_{\cdot j} - Y_i' y_{\cdot j}) \qquad i = 1, 2, \ldots, m \tag{7.2.48}$$

where, according to our long-established convention, the ith structural equation is given by

$$y_{\cdot i} = Y_i \beta_{\cdot i} + X_i \gamma_{\cdot i} + u_{\cdot i} \qquad i = 1, 2, \ldots, m \tag{7.2.49}$$

so that Y_i, X_i are, respectively, the submatrices of Y, X containing the observations on the jointly dependent and predetermined variables appearing in the right-hand side of the ith structural equation. In (7.2.48) p^{ij} is the (i, j) element of P^{-1}. A similar argument easily establishes that

$$\frac{|\partial \hat{\Sigma}|}{\partial \delta_{\cdot i}} = \frac{1}{m} \sum_{j=1}^{m} S_{ij} \frac{\partial s_{ij}}{\partial \delta_{\cdot i}} \tag{7.2.50}$$

where S_{ij} is the *cofactor* of s_{ij}. Now

$$\frac{\partial s_{ij}}{\partial \delta_{\cdot i}} = Z_i' Z_j \delta_{\cdot j} - Z_i' y_{\cdot j} \tag{7.2.51}$$

Thus

$$\frac{\partial \ln |\hat{\Sigma}|}{\partial \delta_{\cdot i}} = \frac{1}{m} \sum_{j=1}^{m} s^{ij} (Z_i' Z_j \delta_{\cdot j} - Z_i' y_{\cdot j}) \tag{7.2.52}$$

where s^{ij} is the (i, j) element of $\hat{\Sigma}^{-1}$. The normal equations in (7.2.43) are therefore

$$\sum_{j=1}^{m} s^{ij}(Z_i'Z_j\delta_{.j} - Z_i'y_{.j}) - \sum_{j=1}^{m} p^{ij}(Y_i'Y_j\beta_{.j} - Y_i'y_{.j}) = 0 \qquad i = 1, 2, \ldots, m$$

(7.2.53)

Putting

$$y = \begin{pmatrix} y_{.1} \\ y_{.2} \\ \vdots \\ y_{.m} \end{pmatrix} \qquad \begin{matrix} Z^* = \operatorname{diag}(Z_1, Z_2, \ldots, Z_m) \\ \bar{Z}^* = \operatorname{diag}(\bar{Z}_1, \bar{Z}_2, \ldots, \bar{Z}_m) \end{matrix}$$

(7.2.54)

where

$$Z_i = (Y_i, X_i) \qquad \bar{Z}_i = (Y_i, 0)$$

(7.2.55)

and the zero matrix in $\bar{Z}_i$ is of the same dimension as X_i, we see that the normal equations may be written compactly as

$$[Z^{*\prime}(\hat{\Sigma}^{-1} \otimes I_T)Z^* - \bar{Z}^{*\prime}(P^{-1} \otimes I_T)\bar{Z}^*]\hat{\delta} = [Z^{*\prime}(\hat{\Sigma}^{-1} \otimes I_T) - \bar{Z}^{*\prime}(P^{-1} \otimes I_T)]y$$

(7.2.56)

$\hat{\delta}$ being the FIML estimator of δ as defined in (7.2.35). In general, since $\hat{\Sigma}$ and P contain δ, the system in (7.2.56) can only be solved by iteration, as we remarked in the previous section. It has been suggested by Chow [8], by analogy with 3SLS, that we obtain a modified (linearized) FIML estimator from (7.2.56) by substituting a consistent estimator of δ in the expressions for Σ and P. Then these matrices will be completely determined and the modified FIML estimator will be easily obtained by inversion of the matrix in the left-hand member of (7.2.56), provided that the matrix is *nonsingular*. This is an entirely feasible scheme; thus we may take, for example,

$$s_{ij} = \frac{1}{T} [(y_{.i} - Z_i\tilde{\delta}_{.i})'(y_{.j} - Z_j\tilde{\delta}_{.j})]$$

$$p_{ij} = \frac{1}{T} (y_{.i} - Y_i\tilde{\beta}_{.i})'(y_{.j} - Y_j\tilde{\beta}_{.j})$$

(7.2.57)

$\tilde{\delta}_{.j}$ being the 2SLS estimator of $\delta_{.j}$.

As an exercise, the reader may ask himself: What is the connection, if any, between the estimator just suggested and the 3SLS estimator?

A second simplification may be based on the method of scoring. Before we examine it, perhaps a few words of explanation are in order regarding the method of scoring.

If $L(\theta; X)$ is $1/T$ times the (log of) the likelihood function of the observations given by the matrix X and characterized by the parameter vector θ, then the maximum likelihood estimator of θ is obtained by solving the normal equations

$$\frac{\partial L}{\partial \theta} = 0 \qquad (7.2.58)$$

Typically θ is constrained to belong to some well-defined set of admissible parameter vectors, but we shall neglect this minor refinement in our subsequent discussion.

Now the equation in (7.2.58) will often be highly nonlinear so that an explicit solution may not be possible. In such a case, it has been suggested by Fisher [15] and Rao [25] that we may proceed as follows:

Let θ^0 be an admissible parameter vector and expand $\partial L/\partial \theta$ by Taylor series about θ^0 retaining only the first term. Thus we have, in a small neighborhood about θ^0,

$$\frac{\partial L(\theta)}{\partial \theta} \approx \frac{\partial L(\theta^0)}{\partial \theta} + \frac{\partial^2 L(\theta^0)}{\partial \theta \, \partial \theta} (\theta - \theta^0) \qquad (7.2.59)$$

where the notation $\partial L(\theta^0)/\partial \theta$, for example, means the gradient (vector of first derivatives) of the (log of the) likelihood function evaluated at the point $\theta = \theta^0$. Now the maximum likelihood estimator, say $\hat{\theta}$, has the property that $\partial L(\hat{\theta})/\partial \theta = 0$. The elements $\partial L/\partial \theta_i$ of the gradient are said to be the *efficient scores* (hence the term method of scoring) and thus the maximum likelihood estimator is obtained by the condition that the efficient scores vanish. Suppose that we set the left-hand side of (7.2.59) equal to zero to obtain the correction

$$\theta = \theta^0 - \left[\frac{\partial^2 L(\theta^0)}{\partial \theta \, \partial \theta} \right]^{-1} \frac{\partial L(\theta^0)}{\partial \theta} \qquad (7.2.60)$$

If we call this quantity θ^1, we may repeat this procedure until we converge, that is, until, say, at the kth iteration we have

$$\theta^k - \theta^{k-1} = - \left[\frac{\partial^2 L(\theta^{k-1})}{\partial \theta \, \partial \theta} \right]^{-1} \frac{\partial L(\theta^{k-1})}{\partial \theta} \approx 0 \qquad (7.2.61)$$

Let

$$\hat{\theta} = \theta^{k-1} \approx \theta^k \qquad (7.2.62)$$

then for this $\hat{\theta}$ we see that the condition

$$\frac{\partial L(\hat{\theta})}{\partial \theta} = 0 \qquad (7.2.63)$$

holds. Thus $\hat{\theta}$ satisfies the normal equations of the maximum likelihood estimator.

It is frequently suggested in this context that the quantity $\partial^2 L/\partial\theta \, \partial\theta$ be replaced by $E[\partial^2 L/\partial\theta \, \partial\theta]$ in the iterations. The advantage is that if convergence is obtained, the matrix inverted at the kth iteration is also the covariance matrix of the asymptotic distribution of the maximum likelihood estimator, as pointed out in Chapter 3.

It is immediately seen that this method applies to the problem of obtaining FIML estimators. It has been suggested by Rothenberg and Leenders [26] that we proceed as follows:

In the concentrated likelihood function of (7.2.39), consider the relation

$$\frac{\partial L(\hat{\delta})}{\partial \delta} \approx \frac{\partial L(\tilde{\delta})}{\partial \delta} + \left[\frac{\partial^2 L(\tilde{\delta})}{\partial \delta \, \partial \delta}\right](\hat{\delta} - \tilde{\delta}) \qquad (7.2.64)$$

Setting the right-hand side equal to zero and solving, we find

$$\hat{\delta} = \tilde{\delta} - \left[\frac{\partial^2 L(\tilde{\delta})}{\partial \delta \, \partial \delta}\right]^{-1} \frac{\partial L(\tilde{\delta})}{\partial \delta} \qquad (7.2.65)$$

where δ is the vector of the structural parameters as defined in (7.2.35), $\tilde{\delta}$ is a consistent estimator of δ, say the 2SLS estimator, and $\hat{\delta}$ is the proposed modified FIML estimator. Rothenberg and Leenders have called this the linearized maximum likelihood estimator. From the preceding discussion, this is similar to the first round estimator obtained by the method of scoring. The only difference is that in (7.2.64) one evaluates the derivatives of the likelihood function at $\tilde{\delta}$ which is a *consistent* estimator of δ, while in the method of scoring one begins with an arbitrary point $\delta°$. Of course, there is no reason why one can't take $\delta° = \tilde{\delta}$.

Finally, it should be noted that the asymptotic distribution of the estimator in (7.2.65) is exactly that of the FIML estimator, and thus nothing will be gained in terms of asymptotic properties by carrying out the method of scoring until convergence is obtained.

7.3 LIMITED INFORMATION (LIML) ESTIMATION

THE "CONCENTRATED" LIKELIHOOD FUNCTION FOR A SUBSET OF m^* STRUCTURAL EQUATIONS

As we pointed out in Section 7.2, LIML is an estimation procedure that uses a priori information pertaining *only* to the equation (or equations) whose parameters we are interested in estimating. A priori restrictions on the parameters of the remaining equations are completely ignored.

Because LIML is a relatively complex procedure, let us give an outline of the estimation strategy before actually deriving the LIML estimator.

Now suppose that we are interested in estimating the parameters of a subset of m^* $(\leq m)$ equations. Or, alternatively, because of the cumbersome nature of the system we must solve in order to obtain FIML estimators, suppose that we wish to break up the system into small subsystems, thus reducing the computational complexity involved and estimating the parameters of each subsystem separately. Obviously, in doing so we cannot, of course, ignore the remainder of the system. On the other hand, we cannot handle all equations symmetrically as we do with FIML, for then no computational economy arises. The strategy is to concentrate on the parameters of the subsystem of interest without being forced to ignore a great deal of information in the process. How can this be done? We could eliminate the parameters of the remainder of the system by partially maximizing the likelihood function with respect to them. Of course, then *we shall ignore all a priori restrictions on such parameters*. This last remark is essential. First, it greatly simplifies the process of maximization and, second, it constitutes the essential distinction between FIML and LIML.

Having expressed the likelihood function in "concentrated" form, that is, in a form involving *only* the parameters of the subsystem of interest, we proceed to obtain maximum likelihood estimators in much the same way as in FIML. We maximize the "concentrated" likelihood function with respect to the unknown parameters it contains, *taking the a priori restrictions on the subsystem in question fully into account*.

Let us give a formal account of the procedure. As before, suppose that we are interested in the parameters of the first $m^*(\leq m)$ equations. Thus partition the covariance matrix of the error terms of the system by

$$\Sigma \doteq \begin{bmatrix} \Sigma_{11} & \Sigma_{12} \\ \Sigma_{21} & \Sigma_{22} \end{bmatrix} \tag{7.3.1}$$

where Σ_{11} is the covariance matrix of the error terms appearing in the first m^* equations, Σ_{22} is the covariance matrix corresponding to the error terms appearing the remaining $(m - m^*)$ equations, and Σ_{12}, Σ_{21} are the appropriate "cross covariance" matrices.

We wish to transform the system in such a way that

i. the two subsystems are mutually independent.
ii. we do not disturb the parameters of the subsystem of interest.

If condition i is satisfied, then, since the second subsystem is unrelated (stochastically) to the first, the information "lost" by not explicitly taking it into account is "minimized." If ii is also satisfied, then it is possible to obtain estimators for the parameters of interest directly.

Of course, we should point out that a price is still being paid for this simplification. The price is that the maximizing values of the parameters of the second subsystem *do not necessarily satisfy the a priori restrictions on them*. Thus when used to obtain the concentrated likelihood function, these values entail LIML estimators that will generally be different from what they would have been if all a priori restrictions were respected in the estimation scheme. If the latter holds, we are, of course, reduced to FIML estimation.

Let us see whether a transformation that accomplishes i and ii above actually exists.

Consequently, recall that

$$A = \begin{pmatrix} I - B \\ -C \end{pmatrix} \tag{7.3.2}$$

and partition A by

$$A = (\alpha_0, A_0) \tag{7.3.3}$$

so that α_0 contains the parameters of the first m^* equations of interest; that is, it consists of the first m^* columns of A. If H is the transforming matrix, and if it is to accomplish our objectives under conditions i and ii above, then we must have

$$H = \begin{bmatrix} H_{11} & H_{12} \\ H_{21} & H_{22} \end{bmatrix} \quad H'\Sigma H = \begin{bmatrix} \Sigma_{11} & 0 \\ 0 & P \end{bmatrix} \quad AH = (\alpha_0, A_0^*) \tag{7.3.4}$$

To make the requirements on H perfectly transparent, we note that the sample on the structural model can be written as

$$ZA = U \quad Z = (Y, X) \tag{7.3.5}$$

Transforming by H on the right, we find[8]

$$ZAH = UH \tag{7.3.6}$$

The transformed coefficient matrix is thus

$$(\alpha_0, A_0)\begin{bmatrix} H_{11} & H_{12} \\ H_{21} & H_{22} \end{bmatrix} = (\alpha_0 H_{11} + A_0 H_{21}, \alpha_0 H_{12} + A_0 H_{22}) \tag{7.3.7}$$

Since we wish α_0 to remain undisturbed, we find we can accomplish this by taking

$$H_{11} = I \quad H_{21} = 0 \tag{7.3.8}$$

If equations (7.3.8) are satisfied, then

$$(\alpha_0, A_0)H = (\alpha_0, A_0^*) \quad A_0^* = \alpha_0 H_{12} + A_0 H_{22} \tag{7.3.9}$$

Next we ask: What is the distribution of the transformed error vector? We note that the tth row of UH is given by $u_t. H$. Since H is a constant matrix, then from (7.1.2) of Section 7.1, we conclude immediately

$$u_t. H \sim N(0, H' \Sigma H) \tag{7.3.10}$$

---

[8] As an exercise, the reader might ask himself: Why transform on the right and not, for example, on the left? *Hint*: Recall that we are dealing with observations on the vectors $z_t. A = u_t..$

Since H has to satisfy (7.3.8), we see that
$$H'\Sigma H =$$
$$\begin{bmatrix} \Sigma_{11} & \Sigma_{11}H_{12} + \Sigma_{12}H_{22} \\ H'_{12}\Sigma_{11} + H'_{22}\Sigma_{21} & H'_{12}\Sigma_{11}H_{12} + H'_{22}\Sigma_{21}H_{12} + H'_{12}\Sigma_{12}H_{22} + H'_{22}\Sigma_{22}H_{22} \end{bmatrix}$$
$$(7.3.11)$$

By the requirements of (7.3.4), we see that (7.3.11) implies that H_{12} must be chosen so that

$$\Sigma_{11}H_{12} + \Sigma_{12}H_{22} = 0 \qquad (7.3.12)$$

But this means

$$H_{12} = -\Sigma_{11}^{-1}\Sigma_{12}H_{22} \qquad (7.3.13)$$

Finally, substituting (7.3.13) in the lower right-hand block of (7.3.11), we find

$$H'_{12}(\Sigma_{11}H_{12} + \Sigma_{12}H_{22}) + H'_{22}(\Sigma_{21}H_{12} + \Sigma_{22}H_{22})$$
$$= H'_{22}(\Sigma_{22} - \Sigma_{21}\Sigma_{11}^{-1}\Sigma_{12})H_{22} \qquad (7.3.14)$$

Since Σ is positive definite, so is $\Sigma_{22} - \Sigma_{21}\Sigma_{11}^{-1}\Sigma_{12}$. Thus there exists a matrix, say H_{22}^{-1}, such that

$$H_{22}'^{-1}H_{22}^{-1} = \Sigma_{22} - \Sigma_{21}\Sigma_{11}^{-1}\Sigma_{12} \qquad (7.3.15)$$

and we may indeed choose H_{22} so that the second equation in (7.3.4) is satisfied with

$$P = I \qquad (7.3.16)$$

simply by choosing H_{22} so as to satisfy (7.3.15). We see, then, that there exists a matrix H satisfying the conditions i and ii above. The form of H is given by

$$H = \begin{bmatrix} I & -\Sigma_{11}^{-1}\Sigma_{12}H_{22} \\ 0 & H_{22} \end{bmatrix} \qquad (7.3.17)$$

and H_{22} is chosen so that

$$H'_{22}(\Sigma_{22} - \Sigma_{21}\Sigma_{11}^{-1}\Sigma_{12})H_{22} = I \qquad (7.3.18)$$

Now, what is the (log) likelihood function of the transformed system? Because of the mutual independence of the vectors $u_{t\cdot}$, we have

$$\text{Cov}(u_{t\cdot}H, u_{t'\cdot}H) = H'E(u'_{t\cdot}u_{t'\cdot})H = \delta_{tt'}H'\Sigma H \qquad t, t' = 1, 2, \ldots, T \quad (7.3.19)$$

From (7.3.10) we conclude that the vectors $u_{t\cdot}H$ are mutually independent. Now the joint density of these vectors is

$$p(u_{1\cdot}H, \ldots, u_{T\cdot}H)$$
$$= (2\pi)^{-mT/2}|H'\Sigma H|^{-T/2}\exp\left[-\frac{1}{2}\sum_{t=1}^{T}(u_{t\cdot}H)(H^{-1}\Sigma^{-1}H'^{-1})(u_{t\cdot}H)'\right]$$
$$(7.3.20)$$

Consider now the transformation

$$u_t.H = y_t.(I - B)H - x_t.CH \tag{7.3.21}$$

and note that the Jacobian of the transformation *from* $u_t.H$ *to* $y_t.$ is given by

$$J = |(I - B)H| \tag{7.3.22}$$

Hence the (log) likelihood function of the current endogenous variables in the context of the transformation above is

$$L(A, H, \Sigma; Y, X) = -\frac{mT}{2} \ln (2\pi) - \frac{T}{2} \ln |H'\Sigma H| + T \ln |(I - B)H|$$

$$-\frac{1}{2} \sum_{t=1}^{T} (z_t. AH)(H'\Sigma H)^{-1}(z_t. AH)' \tag{7.3.23}$$

where

$$z_t. = (y_t., x_t.) \tag{7.3.24}$$

Using the notation in (7.3.5), we can rewrite the last term of the right-hand side of (7.3.23) as

$$\sum_{t=1}^{T} (z_t. AH)(H'\Sigma H)^{-1}(z_t. AH)' = \text{tr } (ZAH)(H'\Sigma H)^{-1}(ZAH)' \tag{7.3.25}$$

Our next step is to use the properties of the transforming matrix H so as to derive a notation that separates, as far as possible, the parameters of interest from those in which we have no interest.

Thus partition

$$AH = \begin{bmatrix} (I - B)H \\ -CH \end{bmatrix} = \begin{bmatrix} B_\text{I} & B_\text{II} \\ C_\text{I} & C_\text{II} \end{bmatrix} = (\alpha_0, A_0^*) \tag{7.3.26}$$

The obvious meaning is that

$$(I - B)H = (B_\text{I}, B_\text{II}) \quad \alpha_0 = \begin{pmatrix} B_\text{I} \\ C_\text{I} \end{pmatrix} \quad -CH = (C_\text{I}, C_\text{II}) \quad A_0^* = \begin{pmatrix} B_\text{II} \\ C_\text{II} \end{pmatrix} \tag{7.3.27}$$

We have, therefore,

$$\text{tr } (ZAH)(H'\Sigma H)^{-1}(ZAH)' = T \text{ tr } \left\{ \begin{bmatrix} \Sigma_{11}^{-1} & 0 \\ 0 & I \end{bmatrix} \begin{pmatrix} \alpha_0' \\ A_0^{*'} \end{pmatrix} M(\alpha_0, A_0^*) \right\}$$

$$= T \text{ tr } (\Sigma_{11}^{-1}\alpha_0' M\alpha_0) + T \text{ tr } (A_0^{*'} M A_0^*) \tag{7.3.28}$$

where M is as defined in (7.2.31).

In view of the above, (7.3.23) can be written in the notationally more convenient form

$$L(\alpha_0, \Sigma_{11}, A_0^*; Y, X) = -\frac{mT}{2} \ln (2\pi) - \frac{T}{2} \ln |\Sigma_{11}| + T \ln |B_\text{I}, B_\text{II}|$$

$$-\frac{T}{2} \text{ tr } (\Sigma_{11}^{-1}\alpha_0' M\alpha_0) - \frac{T}{2} \text{ tr } (A_0^{*'} M A_0^*) \tag{7.3.29}$$

We observe that the transformation has simplified matters considerably; the parameters of interest, (α_0, Σ_{11}) seem almost completely segregated from those in which we have no interest, namely, A_0^*. We still face a problem, however, in the term $T \ln |B_{\mathrm{I}}, B_{\mathrm{II}}|$, which contains a submatrix of α_0—B_{I}—and a submatrix of A_0^*—B_{II}.

Our next step is to eliminate the nuisance parameters in A_0^* by partially maximizing (7.3.29) with respect to them and substituting therein their maximizing values. We stress again that in maximizing with respect to A_0^* *we neglect all a priori restrictions* on its elements thus rendering the procedure somewhat inefficient. Unfortunately, this is the price to be paid for the second aspect of LIML which is that we now have to deal with a smaller and perhaps simpler system of equations in obtaining an estimator for α_0.

The first-order conditions for partial maximization with respect to A_0^* are[9]

$$\frac{\partial L}{\partial A_0^*} = T \frac{\partial \ln |B_{\mathrm{I}} B_{\mathrm{II}}|}{\partial A_0^*} - \frac{T}{2} \frac{d}{dA_0^*} \operatorname{tr}(A_0^{*\prime} M A_0^*) = 0 \tag{7.3.30}$$

In view of the symmetry of M,

$$\frac{d}{dA_0^*} \operatorname{tr}(A_0^{*\prime} M A_0^*) = 2 M A_0^* \tag{7.3.31}$$

Moreover, by definition,

$$\frac{\partial \ln |B_{\mathrm{I}}, B_{\mathrm{II}}|}{\partial A_0^*} = \begin{bmatrix} \dfrac{\partial \ln |B_{\mathrm{I}}, B_{\mathrm{II}}|}{\partial B_{\mathrm{II}}} \\[2mm] \dfrac{\partial \ln |B_{\mathrm{I}}, B_{\mathrm{II}}|}{\partial C_{\mathrm{II}}} \end{bmatrix} \tag{7.3.32}$$

It is obvious that the lower block of the matrix in the right-hand side of (7.3.32) is zero. Thus we need only be concerned about finding an expression for the upper block. Now, by definition,

$$\frac{d \ln |B_{\mathrm{I}}, B_{\mathrm{II}}|}{d(B_{\mathrm{I}}, B_{\mathrm{II}})} = \begin{bmatrix} \dfrac{\partial \ln |B_{\mathrm{I}}, B_{\mathrm{II}}|}{\partial B_{\mathrm{I}}} & \dfrac{\partial \ln |B_{\mathrm{I}}, B_{\mathrm{II}}|}{\partial B_{\mathrm{II}}} \end{bmatrix} \tag{7.3.33}$$

By the usual rules of differentiation, we conclude that

$$\frac{\partial \ln |B_{\mathrm{I}}, B_{\mathrm{II}}|}{\partial B_{\mathrm{II}}} = S_2 \tag{7.3.34}$$

where

$$\begin{pmatrix} B_{\mathrm{I}}' \\ B_{\mathrm{II}}' \end{pmatrix}^{-1} = S = (S_1, S_2) \qquad S_2 = (S_1, S_2)\begin{pmatrix} 0 \\ I_{m-m^*} \end{pmatrix} \tag{7.3.35}$$

---

[9] We use the partial differential symbol ∂ in the first term of the right-hand side of (7.3.30) because $\ln |B_{\mathrm{I}}, B_{\mathrm{II}}|$ is not solely a function of A_0^*; Similarly, we use the symbol d in the second term because, for given Y, X, $\operatorname{tr}(A_0^* M A_0^*)$ is solely a function of A_0^*.

that is, S_2 consists of the last $m - m^*$ columns of $(B_I, B_{II})'^{-1}$. We find, therefore, that (7.3.30) implies [10]

$$\begin{pmatrix} S_2 \\ 0 \end{pmatrix} - MA_0^* = 0 \tag{7.3.36}$$

Let us partition M by

$$M = \frac{1}{T} \begin{bmatrix} Y'Y & Y'X \\ X'Y & X'X \end{bmatrix} = \begin{bmatrix} M_{yy} & M_{yx} \\ M_{xy} & M_{xx} \end{bmatrix} \tag{7.3.37}$$

and note that

$$MA_0^* = \begin{bmatrix} M_{yy} B_{II} + M_{yx} C_{II} \\ M_{xy} B_{II} + M_{xx} C_{II} \end{bmatrix} \tag{7.3.38}$$

Hence (7.3.36) merely states that

$$S_2 = M_{yy} B_{II} + M_{yx} C_{II}$$
$$0 = M_{xy} B_{II} + M_{xx} C_{II} \tag{7.3.39}$$

Eliminating C_{II} from (7.3.39), we find [11]

$$S_2 = W B_{II} \qquad W = M_{yy} - M_{yx} M_{xx}^{-1} M_{xy} \tag{7.3.40}$$

Morever, it will be extremely difficult to find an explicit expression for the elements of A_0^* in terms of the data and the elements of α_0. Fortunately, we do not need that at all; we only need to determine the maximizing value of $\mathrm{tr}\,(A_0^{*'} M A_0^*)$ and $\ln |B_I, B_{II}|$, since that is all that is required in order to obtain the "concentrated" likelihood function.

But from (7.3.27), (7.3.35), and (7.3.36), we have

$$A_0^{*'} M A_0^* = (B_{II}', C_{II}') \begin{pmatrix} S_2 \\ 0 \end{pmatrix} = B_{II}' S_2 \tag{7.3.41}$$

Furthermore,

$$B_{II}' S_2 = (0, I_{m\ m^*}) \begin{pmatrix} B_I' \\ B_{II}' \end{pmatrix} \begin{pmatrix} B_I' \\ B_{II}' \end{pmatrix}^{-1} \begin{pmatrix} 0 \\ I_{m-m^*} \end{pmatrix} = I_{m-m^*} \tag{7.3.42}$$

Thus

$$\mathrm{tr}\,(A_0^{*'} M A_0^*) = \mathrm{tr}\,(I_{m-m^*}) = m - m^* \tag{7.3.43}$$

To obtain the maximizing value of $\ln |B_I, B_{II}|$, we note

$$|(B_I, B_{II})' W (B_I, B_{II})| = |B_I, B_{II}|^2 |W| \tag{7.3.44}$$

---

[10] That this indeed represents a maximum is implied by the concavity of (7.3.29) in the parameters A_0^*.

[11] Notice, incidentally, that W is the second moment matrix of residuals of the OLS estimated reduced form of the (entire) system.

However,

$$(B_{\mathrm{I}}, B_{\mathrm{II}})' W (B_{\mathrm{I}}, B_{\mathrm{II}}) = \begin{bmatrix} B_{\mathrm{I}}' W B_{\mathrm{I}} & B_{\mathrm{I}}' W B_{\mathrm{II}} \\ B_{\mathrm{II}}' W B_{\mathrm{I}} & B_{\mathrm{II}}' W B_{\mathrm{II}} \end{bmatrix} \tag{7.3.45}$$

In addition, due to (7.3.35), (7.3.40), and (7.3.42), we find

$$B_{\mathrm{I}}' W B_{\mathrm{II}} = (I_{m^*}, 0)\begin{pmatrix} B_{\mathrm{I}}' \\ B_{\mathrm{II}}' \end{pmatrix}\begin{pmatrix} B_{\mathrm{I}}' \\ B_{\mathrm{II}}' \end{pmatrix}^{-1}\begin{pmatrix} 0 \\ I_{m-m^*} \end{pmatrix} = 0 \tag{7.3.46}$$

$$B_{\mathrm{II}}' W B_{\mathrm{II}} = (0, I_{m-m^*})\begin{pmatrix} B_{\mathrm{I}}' \\ B_{\mathrm{II}}' \end{pmatrix}\begin{pmatrix} B_{\mathrm{I}}' \\ B_{\mathrm{II}}' \end{pmatrix}^{-1}\begin{pmatrix} 0 \\ I_{m-m^*} \end{pmatrix} = I_{m-m^*} \tag{7.3.47}$$

Finally, from (7.3.44), (7.3.45), (7.3.46), and (7.3.47), we conclude

$$\ln |B_{\mathrm{I}}, B_{\mathrm{II}}| = \frac{1}{2} \ln |B_{\mathrm{I}}' W B_{\mathrm{I}}| - \frac{1}{2} \ln |W| \tag{7.3.48}$$

Inserting the maximizing values of (7.3.43) and (7.3.48) into (7.3.29), we obtain the "concentrated" likelihood function

$$L(\alpha_0, \Sigma_{11}; Y, X) = -\frac{mT}{2}[\ln (2\pi) + 1] + \frac{T}{2} m^* - \frac{T}{2} \ln |W| - \frac{T}{2} \ln |\Sigma_{11}|$$

$$+ \frac{T}{2} \ln |B_{\mathrm{I}}' W B_{\mathrm{I}}| - \frac{T}{2} \operatorname{tr}(\Sigma_{11}^{-1}\alpha_0' M \alpha_0) \tag{7.3.49}$$

This essentially accomplishes the task of LIML estimation. Now, as in FIML, we make use of all a priori restrictions[12] on α_0 and maximize (7.3.49) with respect to the unknown parameters of α_0 and Σ_{11}. As in the case of FIML, it is not easy to give an explicit expression for the LIML estimator of α_0. However, the same remarks concerning algorithms for obtaining FIML estimators apply here as well. Moreover, it can be shown that the asymptotic distribution of the LIML estimator of α_0 is, *mutatis mutandis*, of exactly the same form as that for the FIML estimator shown in Section 7.2—equations (7.2.36) and (7.2.37).

THE LIML ESTIMATOR FOR A SINGLE STRUCTURAL EQUATION

Here we examine in considerable detail the nature of the LIML estimator when the subsystem of interest consists of a single equation, say the first. In terms of the notation of the earlier discussion, we are dealing with

$$m^* = 1 \quad \alpha_0 = \begin{pmatrix} 1 \\ -\beta_{\cdot 1} \\ 0 \\ -\gamma_{\cdot 1} \\ 0 \end{pmatrix} \quad B_{\mathrm{I}} = \begin{pmatrix} 1 \\ -\beta_{\cdot 1} \\ 0 \end{pmatrix} \quad C_{\mathrm{I}} = \begin{pmatrix} -\gamma_{\cdot 1} \\ 0 \end{pmatrix} \quad \Sigma_{11} = \sigma_{11} \tag{7.3.50}$$

---

[12] There may well be a priori restrictions on Σ_{11} as well, and such restrictions, of course, must be used. Typically, however, we do not assert that we know more about Σ_{11} beyond the fact that it is positive definite.

where $\beta._1$ and $\gamma._1$ are the coefficients of the current endogenous and predetermined variables that enter as *explanatory variables in the first structural equation*.

As in previous chapters, we adhere to the convention that it is known a priori that only m_i current endogenous and G_i predetermined variables enter in the right-hand side of the ith structural equation. Thus, in the context above, $\beta._1$ is $m_1 \times 1$ and $\gamma._1$ is $G_1 \times 1$.

In what follows, it will be convenient if we do not impose a normalization on our system, that is, if we do not assert *ab initio* that the coefficient of y_i in the ith equation is unity. For this purpose, we shall introduce the notation

$$\beta^0._1 = \begin{pmatrix} 1 \\ -\beta._1 \end{pmatrix} \tag{7.3.51}$$

and we shall treat $\beta^0._1$ as if all its elements are unknown. We shall see below that LIML estimation is rather flexible regarding the specific normalization to be employed, which partly accounts for the slightly different notational schemes encountered in 2SLS and LIML estimation discussions.

In 2SLS and 3SLS estimation discussions, one finds the notation

$$y_{ti} = \sum_{j=1}^{m} \beta_{ji} y_{tj} + \sum_{s=1}^{G} \gamma_{si} x_{ts} + u_{ti} \qquad \begin{array}{l} i = 1, 2, \ldots, m \\ t = 1, 2, \ldots, T \end{array} \tag{7.3.52}$$

with the understanding that *only m_i of the β_{ji} and G_i of the γ_{si} are not known to be zero*. In particular, one always assumes $\beta_{ii} = 0$, all i. In FIML and LIML discussions, one is likely to encounter the notation

$$\sum_{j=1}^{m} \beta^0_{ji} y_{tj} = \sum_{s=1}^{G} \gamma_{si} x_{ts} + u_{ti} \qquad \begin{array}{l} i = 1, 2, \ldots, m \\ t = 1, 2, \ldots, T \end{array} \tag{7.3.53}$$

with the understanding, again, that only $m_i + 1$ *of the β^0_{ji} and G_i of the γ_{si} are not known to be zero*. Of course, the two notational schemes are perfectly equivalent if in (7.3.53) we agree to take the *coefficient of the y_{ti} to be unity*. Then we shall obviously have

$$\beta^0_{ji} = -\beta_{ji} \qquad j \neq i \tag{7.3.54}$$

As we shall see below, *it is not possible to estimate by LIML techniques all the elements of $\beta^0._1$. In fact, there is one degree of arbitrariness*; this may be removed by imposing some normalization scheme on them. In 2SLS we impose *ab initio* the normalization $\beta^0_{11} = 1$. In LIML estimation we are a little more flexible. Instead of elaborating at this point, we shall wait until the matter arises naturally in the discussion.

Let us return to the development of our argument and partition M conformally with α_0 as shown in (7.3.50), remembering (7.3.51) and the convention adhering to it. Thus

$$M = \begin{bmatrix} M_{11} & M_{12} & M_{13} & M_{14} \\ M_{21} & M_{22} & M_{23} & M_{24} \\ M_{31} & M_{32} & M_{33} & M_{34} \\ M_{41} & M_{42} & M_{43} & M_{44} \end{bmatrix} \tag{7.3.55}$$

From the discussion above, note that M_{11} is $(m_1 + 1) \times (m_1 + 1)$. Furthermore, partition W conformally with $\begin{pmatrix} \beta^0_{\cdot 1} \\ 0 \end{pmatrix}$ to obtain

$$W = \begin{bmatrix} W_{11} & W_{12} \\ W_{21} & W_{22} \end{bmatrix} \tag{7.3.56}$$

In this notation we have

$$\alpha'_0 M \alpha_0 = \beta^{0\prime}_{\cdot 1} M_{11} \beta^0_{\cdot 1} - 2\gamma'_{\cdot 1} M_{31} \beta^0_{\cdot 1} + \gamma_{\cdot 1} M_{33} \gamma_{\cdot 1}$$
$$B'_1 W B_1 = \beta^{0\prime}_{\cdot 1} W_{11} \beta^0_{\cdot 1} \tag{7.3.57}$$

From (7.3.50) and (7.3.57), the concentrated likelihood function of (7.3.49) in the *special case* of the *first structural equation* may be written as

$$L(\beta^0_{\cdot 1}, \gamma_{\cdot 1}, \sigma_{11}; Y, X) = c_0 - \frac{T}{2} \ln \sigma_{11} + \frac{T}{2} \ln (\beta^{0\prime}_{\cdot 1} W_{11} \beta^0_{\cdot 1})$$

$$- \frac{T}{2} \frac{1}{\sigma_{11}} (\beta^{0\prime}_{\cdot 1} M_{11} \beta^0_{\cdot 1} - 2\gamma'_{\cdot 1} M_{31} \beta^0_{\cdot 1} + \gamma'_{\cdot 1} M_{33} \gamma_{\cdot 1})$$

$$\tag{7.3.58}$$

where

$$c_0 = -\frac{mT}{2} [\ln (2\pi) + 1] + \frac{T}{2} (1 - \ln |W|) \tag{7.3.59}$$

This is now to be maximized with respect to $\beta^0_{\cdot 1}$, $\gamma_{\cdot 1}$, and σ_{11}. We again follow a stepwise maximization procedure.[13]

Maximizing first with respect to $\gamma_{\cdot 1}$, we obtain

$$\frac{\partial L}{\partial \gamma_{\cdot 1}} = -\frac{T}{2} \frac{1}{\sigma_{11}} (-2M_{31}\beta^0_{\cdot 1} + 2M_{33}\gamma_{\cdot 1}) = 0 \tag{7.3.60}$$

---

[13] It should be noted that whether we proceed stepwise or simultaneously, we obtain exactly the same set of equations. Thus simultaneously maximizing, we obtain

$$\frac{\partial L}{\partial \gamma_{\cdot 1}} = -\frac{T}{2} \frac{1}{\sigma_{11}} (-2M_{31}\beta^0_{\cdot 1} + 2M_{33}\gamma_{\cdot 1}) = 0$$

$$\frac{\partial L}{\partial \sigma_{11}} = -\frac{T}{2} \frac{1}{\sigma_{11}} + \frac{T}{2} \frac{1}{\sigma_{11}^2} (\beta^{0\prime}_{\cdot 1} M_{11} \beta^0_{\cdot 1} - 2\beta_{\cdot 1} M_{13} \gamma_{\cdot 1} + \gamma'_{\cdot 1} M_{33} \gamma_{\cdot 1}) = 0$$

$$\frac{\partial L}{\partial \beta^0_{\cdot 1}} = \frac{T}{2} \frac{2W_{11}\beta^0_{\cdot 1}}{\beta^0_{\cdot 1} W_{11} \beta^0_{\cdot 1}} - \frac{T}{2} \frac{1}{\sigma_{11}} (2M_{11}\beta^0_{\cdot 1} - 2M_{13}\gamma_{\cdot 1}) = 0$$

From the first and second equations, we easily obtain (7.3.61) and (7.3.63). Substituting these values in the third equation above, we obtain exactly the first-order conditions implied by the maximization of (7.3.64) with respect to $\beta^0_{\cdot 1}$. This demonstrates, in the present special case, the equivalence of stepwise and simultaneous maximization; this equivalence can also be established quite generally.

which implies

$$\gamma_{\cdot 1} = M_{33}^{-1} M_{31} \beta^0_{\cdot 1} \tag{7.3.61}$$

It is, of course, apparent that for given $\beta^0_{\cdot 1}$ and σ_{11}, $\gamma_{\cdot 1}$ of (7.3.61) globally maximizes (7.3.58).

Inserting (7.3.61) into (7.3.58) and maximizing with respect to σ_{11}, we find

$$\frac{\partial L}{\partial \sigma_{11}} = -\frac{T}{2}\frac{1}{\sigma_{11}} + \frac{T}{2}\frac{1}{\sigma_{11}^2}[\beta^{0\prime}_{\cdot 1}(M_{11} - M_{13}M_{33}^{-1}M_{31})\beta^0_{\cdot 1}] = 0 \tag{7.3.62}$$

which implies

$$\tilde\sigma_{11} = \beta^{0\prime}_{\cdot 1}(M_{11} - M_{13}M_{33}^{-1}M_{31})\beta^0_{\cdot 1} \tag{7.3.63}$$

It can be verified that this represents a maximum for given $\beta^0_{\cdot 1}$ by noting that for σ_{11} as in (7.3.63)

$$\frac{\partial^2 L}{\partial \sigma_{11}^2} < 0$$

Now inserting (7.3.63) and (7.3.61) into (7.3.58), we have

$$L(\beta^0_{\cdot 1}; Y, X) = c_0 - \frac{T}{2} - \frac{T}{2}\ln\left(\frac{\beta^{0\prime}_{\cdot 1}W^*_{11}\beta^0_{\cdot 1}}{\beta^{0\prime}_{\cdot 1}W_{11}\beta^0_{\cdot 1}}\right) \tag{7.3.64}$$

where

$$W^*_{11} = M_{11} - M_{13}M_{33}^{-1}M_{31} \tag{7.3.65}$$

To maximize (7.3.64), it is simpler to use an alternative to the straightforward differentiation process. We first note that maximizing (7.3.64) is equivalent to *minimizing*

$$\ell(\beta^0_{\cdot 1}) = \frac{\beta^{0\prime}_{\cdot 1}W^*_{11}\beta^0_{\cdot 1}}{\beta^{0\prime}_{\cdot 1}W_{11}\beta^0_{\cdot 1}} \tag{7.3.66}$$

It is clear from (7.3.66) that $\ell(\beta^0_{\cdot 1})$ is *homogeneous of degree zero in* $\beta^0_{\cdot 1}$. Thus the minimizing value of $\beta^0_{\cdot 1}$, if it exists, will not be unique. Indeed, if $\beta^0_{\cdot 1}$ is such a value, then $c\beta^0_{\cdot 1}$, where c is any scalar, will be a minimizing value as well. This is the nature of the indeterminacy we referred to above with respect to the elements of $\beta^0_{\cdot 1}$. On the other hand, if we require the first element of $\beta^0_{\cdot 1}$ *to be unity*, then this indeterminacy disappears. In fact, this is the type of *normalization* employed in the context of 2SLS estimation. However, in the present context, this type of normalization *is not an integral part of the estimation procedure*; any other type of normalization will do as well. We may, for example, require that $\beta^{0\prime}_{\cdot 1}\beta^0_{\cdot 1} = 1$ or, more commonly, that

$$\beta^{0\prime}_{\cdot 1}W_{11}\beta^0_{\cdot 1} = 1 \tag{7.3.67}$$

For the moment, however, let us not commit ourselves to any specific type of normalization; let us instead proceed with the formal aspects of minimizing (7.3.66).

Now, since W_{11} and W_{11}^* [14] are both positive definite matrices, we can simultaneously decompose them by

$$W_{11} = F'F \qquad W_{11}^* = F'\Lambda F \tag{7.3.68}$$

where F is a nonsingular matrix and Λ is the (diagonal) matrix of the characteristic roots of W_{11}^* in the metric of W_{11}, that is, its diagonal elements are the solutions of

$$|\lambda W_{11} - W_{11}^*| = 0 \tag{7.3.69}$$

Thus the ratio in (7.3.66) may be written, because of (7.3.68), as

$$\ell(\beta_{\cdot 1}^0) = \frac{\beta_{\cdot 1}^{0\prime} F'\Lambda F \beta_{\cdot 1}^0}{\beta_{\cdot 1}^{0\prime} F'F \beta_{\cdot 1}^0} = \frac{\zeta'\Lambda\zeta}{\zeta'\zeta} \tag{7.3.70}$$

where

$$\zeta = F\beta_{\cdot 1}^0 \tag{7.3.71}$$

Thus

$$\ell(\beta_{\cdot 1}^0) = \sum_{i=1}^{m_1+1} \lambda_i \left(\frac{\zeta_i^2}{\sum_{j=1}^{m_1+1} \zeta_i^2} \right) \tag{7.3.72}$$

Since the coefficients of λ_i are positive and since $\lambda_i \geq 0$, we conclude

$$\operatorname*{Min}_i \lambda_i \leq \ell(\beta_{\cdot 1}^0) \leq \operatorname*{Max}_i \lambda_i \tag{7.3.73}$$

Let

$$\hat{\lambda} = \operatorname*{Min}_i \lambda_i \tag{7.3.74}$$

To complete the solution of the problem, we need to determine the estimator of $\beta_{\cdot 1}^0$. Hence let $\hat{\beta}_{\cdot 1}^0$ be the characteristic vector of W_{11}^* (in the metric of W_{11}) corresponding to the smallest characteristic root $\hat{\lambda}$. Then we have

$$W_{11}^* \hat{\beta}_{\cdot 1}^0 = \hat{\lambda} W_{11} \hat{\beta}_{\cdot 1}^0 \tag{7.3.75}$$

Premultiplying by $\hat{\beta}_{\cdot 1}^0$, we obtain

$$\hat{\lambda} = \frac{\hat{\beta}_{\cdot 1}^{0\prime} W_{11}^* \hat{\beta}_{\cdot 1}^0}{\hat{\beta}_{\cdot 1}^{0\prime} W_{11} \hat{\beta}_{\cdot 1}^0} \tag{7.3.76}$$

---

[14] Note that W_{11} is the second moment matrix of residuals from the regression of $Y_I = (y_{\cdot 1}, y_{\cdot 2}, \ldots, y_{\cdot m+1})$ on X and W_{11}^* is the second moment matrix of residuals from the regression of Y_I on X_1. We stress that X is the matrix of observations on all the predetermined variables of the system, while X_1 is the matrix of observations on the predetermined variables actually appearing in the first structural equation.

We see from (7.3.73) that $\hat{\beta}^0_{\cdot 1}$ minimizes the ratio $\ell(\beta^0_{\cdot 1})$. But now our estimation problem is complete, for having determined $\beta^0_{\cdot 1}$, we can substitute in (7.3.61) and (7.3.63) to obtain estimators for $\gamma_{\cdot 1}$ and σ_{11} respectively.

To obtain unique estimators, we have to impose on $\beta^0_{\cdot 1}$ some normalization scheme. In this context, let us take the first element of $\hat{\beta}^0_{\cdot 1}$ to be unity; such convention renders the LIML estimator directly comparable with the 2SLS estimator. At any rate, if this convention is adopted, then the only relevant subvector of $\hat{\beta}^0_{\cdot 1}$ is $\hat{\beta}_{\cdot 1}$ and we may establish the following result, holding asymptotically, X_2 being defined by $X = (X_1, X_2)$

$$\sqrt{T}\begin{pmatrix} \hat{\beta}_{\cdot 1} - \beta_{\cdot 1} \\ \hat{\gamma}_{\cdot 1} - \gamma_{\cdot 1} \end{pmatrix} = \sqrt{T}(\hat{\delta}_{\cdot 1} - \delta_{\cdot 1}) \sim N(0, \sigma_{11}\Psi) \tag{7.3.77}$$

where

$$\Psi = \begin{bmatrix} \Psi_{11} & \Psi_{12} \\ \Psi_{21} & \Psi_{22} \end{bmatrix} \qquad \sigma_{11} = E(u_{t1}^2) \qquad \text{all } t \tag{7.3.78}$$

$$\Psi_{11} = \left\{ \Pi'_{G*1} \plim_{T\to\infty} \left[\frac{X'_2 X_2}{T} - \frac{X'_2 X_1}{T}\left(\frac{X'_1 X_1}{T}\right)^{-1}\frac{X'_1 X_2}{T}\right]\Pi_{G*1} \right\}^{-1} \tag{7.3.79}$$

$$\Psi_{12} = -\Psi_{11}\overline{\Pi}'_{G_1 1} \qquad \Psi_{21} = \Psi'_{12} \tag{7.3.80}$$

$$\overline{\Pi}_{G_1 1} = \Pi_{G_1 1} + \left[\plim_{T\to\infty}\left(\frac{X'_1 X_1}{T}\right)^{-1}\frac{X'_1 X_2}{T}\right]\Pi_{G*1} \tag{7.3.81}$$

$$\Psi_{22} = \overline{\Pi}_{G_1 1}\Psi_{11}\overline{\Pi}'_{G_1 1} + \plim_{T\to\infty}\left(\frac{X'_1 X_1}{T}\right)^{-1} \tag{7.3.82}$$

In the above equations we have partitioned the matrix of the reduced form of the system by

$$\Pi = (\pi_{\cdot 1}, \Pi_1, \Pi_*) \qquad \Pi_1 = \begin{pmatrix} \Pi_{G_1 1} \\ \Pi_{G*1} \end{pmatrix} \tag{7.3.83}$$

where $\pi_{\cdot 1}, \Pi_1, \Pi_*$ consist, respectively, of the first column, next m_1 columns, and last $m - m_1 - 1$ columns of Π. Finally, $\Pi_{G_1 1}$ consists of the first G_1 rows of Π_1, and Π_{G*1} consists of the last $G - G_1$ rows of Π_1.

The foregoing assertions will not be proved; the proofs are rather cumbersome and offer little useful insight into the nature of the problems. The interested reader may find an exhaustive discussion of these matters in Anderson and Rubin [2, 3].[15]

---

[15] The asymptotic covariance matrix of

$$\begin{pmatrix} \hat{\beta}^0_{\cdot 1} \\ \hat{\gamma}_{\cdot 1} \end{pmatrix}$$

for alternative normalizations on the elements of $\beta^0_{\cdot 1}$ is also discussed in Anderson and Rubin [2, 3].

The preceding discussion has served to prove the following

Theorem 1: Consider the system of structural equations

$$\sum_{j=1}^{m} \beta_{ji}^{*} y_{tj} = \sum_{s=1}^{G} \gamma_{si}^{*} x_{ts} + u_{ti} \qquad \begin{array}{l} t = 1, 2, \ldots, T \\ i = 1, 2, \ldots, m \end{array} \qquad (7.3.84)$$

where β_{ji}^{*}, γ_{si}^{*} are the *unrestricted structural parameters* and the u_{ti} are random variables having the properties

$$u_{t\cdot}' \sim N(0, \Sigma) \quad \text{Cov}(u_{t\cdot}, u_{t'\cdot}') = \delta_{tt'}\Sigma \quad E(u_{t\cdot}.X) = 0 \qquad t, t' = 1, 2, \ldots, T \tag{7.3.85}$$

$\delta_{tt'}$, being the Kronecker delta. In (7.3.85) $u_{t\cdot}$ is the (row) vector of error terms appearing in all the (m) equations of the system at "time" t and X is the $(T \times G)$ matrix of observations on all the predetermined variables of the system. Similarly, let Y be the $(T \times m)$ matrix of observations on all the current endogenous variables of the system. Then the LIML estimator of the parameters of the first m^* ($\leq m$) (structural) equations is obtained by maximizing the "concentrated" likelihood function

$$L(\alpha_0, \Sigma_{11}; Y, X) = c - \frac{T}{2} \ln |\Sigma_{11}| + \frac{T}{2} \ln |B_1' W B_1| - \frac{T}{2} \operatorname{tr}(\Sigma_{11}^{-1} \alpha_0' M \alpha_0) \tag{7.3.86}$$

where

$$c = -\frac{mT}{2}[\ln(2\pi) + 1] + \frac{T}{2} m^* - \frac{T}{2} \ln |W| \qquad W = M_{yy} - M_{yx} M_{xx}^{-1} M_{xy} \tag{7.3.87}$$

$$M = \frac{1}{T}\begin{bmatrix} Y'Y & Y'X \\ X'Y & X'X \end{bmatrix} = \begin{bmatrix} M_{yy} & M_{yx} \\ M_{xy} & M_{xx} \end{bmatrix} \qquad \Sigma = \begin{bmatrix} \Sigma_{11} & \Sigma_{12} \\ \Sigma_{21} & \Sigma_{22} \end{bmatrix} \tag{7.3.88}$$

Here Σ_{11} is the covariance matrix of the error terms appearing in the first m^* equations, Σ_{22} is the covariance matrix of the error terms appearing in the remaining $m - m^*$ equations, and Σ_{12}, Σ_{21} are the appropriate "cross covariance" matrices.

In addition,

$$\alpha_0 = \begin{pmatrix} B_{\mathrm{I}} \\ C_{\mathrm{I}} \end{pmatrix} \tag{7.3.89}$$

B_{I}, C_{I} being, respectively, the matrices of coefficients of the current endogenous and predetermined variables actually appearing in the first m^* equations, that is, *after all a priori information (restrictions) has been used.*

Remark 1: Notice that W is simply the second moment matrix of the residuals of the (set of) regressions of Y on X. That is, it is the second moment matrix of *reduced form residuals.* We have also proved

Theorem 2: Let the model be as specified in Theorem 1 and suppose we are interested in the parameters of only one structural equation, say the first. Suppose, also, that we employ the numbering convention that the variables *actually appearing* in that equation are $y_1, y_2, \ldots, y_{m_1+1}, x_1, x_2 \ldots, x_{G_1}$. Let

$$Y_I = (y_{\cdot 1}, y_{\cdot 2}, \ldots, y_{\cdot m_1+1}) \qquad X_1 = (x_{\cdot 1}, x_{\cdot 2}, \ldots, x_{\cdot G_1}) \tag{7.3.90}$$

where $y_{\cdot i}$ and $x_{\cdot j}$ are, respectively, the vectors of (T) observations on the variables y_i and x_j.

Let the vector of unknown coefficients, once restrictions have been imposed, be denoted by

$$\alpha_0 = \begin{pmatrix} \beta^0_{\cdot 1} \\ 0 \\ \gamma_{\cdot 1} \\ 0 \end{pmatrix} \tag{7.3.91}$$

where $\beta^0_{\cdot 1}$ is $(m_1 + 1) \times 1$, $\gamma_{\cdot 1}$ is $G_1 \times 1$, and the zero vectors are, respectively, $(m - m_1 - 1) \times 1$ and $(G - G_1) \times 1$.

Then the LIML estimator of σ_{11} and $\delta_{\cdot 1} = \begin{pmatrix} \beta^0_{\cdot 1} \\ \gamma_{\cdot 1} \end{pmatrix}$ is obtained by maximizing the "concentrated" likelihood function

$$L(\alpha_0, \sigma_{11}; Y, X) = c_0 - \frac{T}{2} \ln \sigma_{11} + \frac{T}{2} \ln (\beta^{0\prime}_{\cdot 1} W_{11} \beta^0_{\cdot 1})$$

$$- \frac{T}{2} \frac{1}{\sigma_{11}} (\beta^{0\prime}_{\cdot 1} M_{11} \beta^0_{\cdot 1} + 2\gamma'_{\cdot 1} M_{31} \beta^0_{\cdot 1} + \gamma'_{\cdot 1} M_{33} \gamma_{\cdot 1}) \tag{7.3.92}$$

where

$$c_0 = -\frac{mT}{2} [\ln (2\pi) + 1] + \frac{T}{2} (1 - \ln |W|) \tag{7.3.93}$$

$$M_{11} = \frac{1}{T} (Y_I' Y_I) \quad M_{31} = \frac{1}{T} (X_1' Y_I) \quad M_{33} = \frac{1}{T} (X_1' X_1) \tag{7.3.94}$$

and, in general, M and W have been partitioned as in (7.3.55) and (7.3.56). Specifically, the LIML estimator is given by

$$\hat{\gamma}_{\cdot 1} = -M_{33}^{-1} M_{31} \hat{\beta}^0_{\cdot 1} \quad \hat{\sigma}_{11} = \hat{\beta}^{0\prime}_{\cdot 1} W^*_{11} \hat{\beta}^0_{\cdot 1} \quad W^*_{11} = M_{11} - M_{13} M_{33}^{-1} M_{31} \tag{7.3.95}$$

where $\hat{\beta}^0_{\cdot 1}$ is the characteristic vector corresponding to the *smallest characteristic root of W^*_{11} in the metric of W_{11}*. Thus if $\hat{\lambda}$ is the smallest root of

$$|\lambda W_{11} - W^*_{11}| = 0 \tag{7.3.96}$$

then $\hat{\beta}^0_{.1}$ obeys

$$W^*_{11}\hat{\beta}^0_{.1} = \hat{\lambda}W_{11}\hat{\beta}^0_{.1} \tag{7.3.97}$$

Clearly $\hat{\beta}^0_{.1}$—and hence $\hat{\gamma}_{.1}$ and $\hat{\sigma}_{11}$—is not unique, for a characteristic vector is arbitrary within a scalar multiplication. This arbitrariness may be removed by a normalization of its elements. If the normalization

$$\hat{\beta}^{0\prime}_{.1}W_{11}\hat{\beta}^0_{.1} = 1 \tag{7.3.98}$$

is imposed, then we observe that

$$\hat{\sigma}_{11} = \hat{\lambda} \tag{7.3.99}$$

If the normalization is imposed that the first element of $\hat{\beta}^0_{.1}$ is unity [16] and thus if we write

$$\hat{\beta}^0_{.1} = \begin{pmatrix} 1 \\ -\hat{\beta}_{.1} \end{pmatrix} \qquad \hat{\delta}_{.1} = \begin{pmatrix} \hat{\beta}_{.1} \\ \hat{\gamma}_{.1} \end{pmatrix} \tag{7.3.100}$$

then the asymptotic distribution of $\hat{\delta}_{.1}$ is given by

$$\sqrt{T}(\hat{\delta}_{.1} - \delta_{.1}) \sim N(0, \sigma_{11}\Psi) \tag{7.3.101}$$

where Ψ and σ_{11} are as defined in (7.3.78) through (7.3.82).

Remark 2: In view of our convention regarding the numbering of variables and the nature of the partition of W, we note that

$$W_{11} = M_{y_I y_I} - M_{y_I x} M^{-1}_{xx} M_{x y_I} \tag{7.3.102}$$

so that it is the second moment matrix of residuals in the regression of Y_I—the current endogenous variables *actually appearing* in the first structural equation—on X, that is, *on all the predetermined variables of the system.*
On the other hand,

$$W^*_{11} = M_{y_I y_I} - M_{y_I x_1} M^{-1}_{x_1 x_1} M_{x_1 y_I} \tag{7.3.103}$$

so that it is the *second moment matrix of residuals in the regression of Y_I on X_1, that is, on those predetermined variables actually appearing in the first structural equation.* Finally, it should be noted that although Theorem 2 refers to the first structural equation, the results are not confined to that equation alone. Obviously, if we are dealing with the ith equation, then we replace σ_{11} by σ_{ii} and define Y_I, X_1 to refer, respectively, to the current endogenous and predetermined variables actually appearing in the ith equation. Furthermore, in (7.3.83) we define Π_1 to refer to the reduced form parameters corresponding to Y_I as defined above, that is, to the current endogenous variables actually appearing in the ith structural equation, and partition it conformally with the partition of X.

---

[16] We shall call this the *standard normalization*.

Remark 3: It is apparent that the covariance matrix of asymptotic distribution of the LIML estimator as given in (7.3.101) may be estimated by

$$\hat{\sigma}_{11}\hat{\Psi} = \hat{\sigma}_{11}\begin{bmatrix} \hat{\Psi}_{11} & \hat{\Psi}_{12} \\ \hat{\Psi}_{21} & \hat{\Psi}_{22} \end{bmatrix} \tag{7.3.104}$$

where

$$\hat{\sigma}_{11} = (1/T)(y_{\cdot 1} - Y_1\hat{\beta}_{\cdot 1} - X_1\hat{\gamma}_{\cdot 1})'\,(y_{\cdot 1} - Y_1\hat{\beta}_{\cdot 1} - X_1\hat{\gamma}_{\cdot 1})$$

$$\hat{\Psi}_{11} = \left\{\hat{\Pi}'_{G*1}\left[\frac{X'_2 X_2}{T} - \frac{X'_2 X_1}{T}\left(\frac{X'_1 X_1}{T}\right)^{-1}\frac{X'_1 X_2}{T}\right]\hat{\Pi}_{G*1}\right\}^{-1} \tag{7.3.105}$$

$$\hat{\Psi}_{12} = -\hat{\Psi}_{11}\hat{\Pi}_{G_11} \quad \hat{\Psi}_{21} = \hat{\Psi}'_{12} \tag{7.3.106}$$

$$\hat{\Psi}_{22} = \hat{\Pi}_{G_11}\hat{\Psi}_{11}\hat{\Pi}'_{G_11} + \left(\frac{X'_1 X_1}{T}\right)^{-1} \tag{7.3.107}$$

$$\hat{\Pi}_{G_11} = \hat{\Pi}_{G_11} + \left(\frac{X'_1 X_1}{T}\right)^{-1}\frac{X'_1 X_2}{T}\hat{\Pi}_{G*1} \tag{7.3.108}$$

and $\hat{\Pi}_{G_11}$, $\hat{\Pi}_{G*1}$ are appropriate submatrices of

$$\hat{\Pi}_1 = (X'X)^{-1}X'Y_1 \tag{7.3.109}$$

partitioned as in (7.3.83)

AN INTERESTING INTERPRETATION OF
THE SINGLE EQUATION LIML ESTIMATOR

Before proceeding to another topic it will be instructive to exploit certain relationships established in deriving the LIML estimator in order to gain a firmer intuitive grasp of the procedure.

First recall the interpretation given to the matrices W_{11} and W^*_{11} in Remark 2. This interpretation discloses the connection between LIML estimation and the reduced form of the system quite strikingly. As in (7.3.90), let Y_I be the matrix of observations on the current endogenous variables appearing in the first structural equation. The reduced form corresponding to these variables is

$$Y_I = X\Pi_I + V_I \tag{7.3.110}$$

where V_I is the corresponding submatrix of reduced form errors. The OLS estimator for Π_I is

$$\hat{\Pi}_I = (X'X)^{-1}X'Y_I \tag{7.3.111}$$

and thus we may write

$$Y_I = X\hat{\Pi}_I + \hat{V}_I \tag{7.3.112}$$

where $\hat{V}_I$ is the corresponding matrix of reduced form residuals. We obviously have

$$W_{11} = \frac{1}{T} \hat{V}_I' \hat{V}_I \tag{7.3.113}$$

Similarly, define

$$P_I = (X_1' X_1)^{-1} X_1' Y_I \tag{7.3.114}$$

where X_1 is the $(T \times G_1)$ matrix of observations on the predetermined variables appearing in the first structural equation. Thus we may write

$$Y_I = X_1 P_I + \hat{V}_I^* \tag{7.3.115}$$

where $\hat{V}_I^*$ is the matrix of residuals in the regression of Y_I on X_1. We obviously have

$$W_{11}^* = \frac{1}{T} \hat{V}_I^{*\prime} \hat{V}_I^* \tag{7.3.116}$$

Now, recall from (7.1.7) that the reduced form errors obey

$$v_{t\cdot}' \sim N(0, \Omega) \qquad t = 1, 2, \ldots, T \tag{7.3.117}$$

The (marginal) covariance matrix of the reduced form errors appearing in the equations corresponding to Y_I is given by the upper left block of

$$\Omega = \begin{bmatrix} \Omega_{11} & \Omega_{12} \\ \Omega_{21} & \Omega_{22} \end{bmatrix} \tag{7.3.118}$$

Hence Ω_{11} is $(m_1 + 1) \times (m_1 + 1)$ and Ω_{22} is $(m - m_1 - 1) \times (m - m_1 - 1)$. It is clear, then, from the preceding that W_{11} is an estimator of Ω_{11} under the hypothesis *that Y_I depends on X*, whereas W_{11}^* is an estimator of Ω_{11} under the hypothesis *that Y_I only depends on X_1*. Both, of course, are maximum likelihood estimators under their respective hypotheses.

Let s be any $(m_1 + 1) \times 1$ nonnull vector and consider the "synthetic" variable

$$\tilde{y} = Y_I s \tag{7.3.119}$$

From (7.3.110) we have

$$\tilde{y} = X \Pi_I s + V_I s \tag{7.3.120}$$

What is the covariance matrix of $V_I s$? It is

$$\text{Cov}(V_I s) = (s' \Omega_{11} s) I \tag{7.3.121}$$

It follows, then, that $s' W_{11} s$ is the maximum likelihood estimator of the (common) variance of the elements of $V_I s$ under the hypothesis that $\tilde{y}$ depends on X, that is, *that $\tilde{y}$ depends on all the predetermined variables of the system.* Following a similar line of argument, we can show that $s'W_{11}^* s$ is the maximum likelihood estimator of $s'\Omega_{11}s$, under the hypothesis that $\tilde{y}$ depends on X_1, that is, *that $\tilde{y}$ depends only on the predetermined variables appearing in the first structural equation.*

Since by introducing more variables in a regression we can explain the variation in the dependent variable at least as well as with fewer variables, we conclude

$$s'W_{11}^* s \geq s'W_{11}s \tag{7.3.122}$$

The preceding discussion has pointed out two things: First, the LIML estimator can be interpreted as minimizing

$$\ell(s) = \frac{s'W_{11}^* s}{s'W_{11}s} \tag{7.3.123}$$

which is the quotient of two residual variances. Hence the LIML estimator is also referred to as a *least variance ratio estimator*, and the estimation procedure leading to it is referred to as the *least variance ratio* procedure or principle.

Second, we have also shown that

$$\ell(s) \geq 1 \tag{7.3.124}$$

In view of Theorem 2, we further conclude that the smallest root, $\hat{\lambda}$, of

$$|\lambda W_{11} - W_{11}^*| = 0 \tag{7.3.125}$$

obeys

$$\hat{\lambda} \geq 1 \tag{7.3.126}$$

It would be interesting to ask: Under what circumstances does $\hat{\lambda}$ assume its minimum (for finite samples), that is, under what circumstances do we have

$$\hat{\lambda} = 1 \tag{7.3.127}$$

First, notice that we may partition the reduced form subsystem of (7.3.110) as follows:

$$Y_I = (X_1, X_2)\binom{\Pi_{G_1 I}}{\Pi_{G*I}} + V_I = X_1\Pi_{G_1 I} + X_2\Pi_{G*I} + V_I \tag{7.3.128}$$

where, as before, X_1 is the $(T \times G_1)$ matrix of predetermined variables actually appearing in the first structural equation; obviously $\Pi_{G_1 I}$ is $G_1 \times (m_1 + 1)$ and Π_{G*I} is $(G - G_1) \times (m_1 + 1)$. Now, observe that

$$\tilde{y} = Y_I s = X_1\Pi_{G_1 I}s + X_2\Pi_{G*I}s + V_I s \tag{7.3.129}$$

On the other hand, the first structural equation reads

$$Y_I \beta_{\cdot 1}^0 = X_1\gamma_{\cdot 1} + u_{\cdot 1} \tag{7.3.130}$$

Comparing (7.3.129) to (7.3.130) for $s = \beta^0_{.1}$, we conclude that

$$\Pi_{G*I}\,\beta^0_{.1} = 0 \qquad (7.3.131)$$

A necessary and sufficient condition for (7.3.131) to be satisfied uniquely under the standard normalization rule for $\beta^0_{.1}$ is that

$$\text{rank}\,(\Pi_{G\,*I}) = m_1 \qquad G^* = m_1 \qquad (7.3.132)$$

We recall that these are the conditions for *just identifiability*, and also that if such conditions are satisfied, then there exist unique indirect least squares (ILS) estimators for $\beta^0_{.1}$ and $\gamma_{.1}$. However, in the present case, that is, in order to obtain conditions for the validity of (7.3.127), we need concern ourselves with the question of whether or not

$$\hat{V}_I = \hat{V}^*_I \qquad (7.3.133)$$

holds. This entails our consideration of the (OLS and ML) estimators of $\Pi_{G\,*I}$ and $\Pi_{G_1 I}$, which we denote by $\hat{\Pi}_{G\,*I}$ and $\hat{\Pi}_{G_1 I}$ respectively. Clearly, for (7.3.133) to be satisfied, there must exist an estimator $\hat{\beta}^0_{.1}$ such that

$$\hat{\Pi}_{G*I}\,\hat{\beta}^0_{.1} = 0 \qquad (7.3.134)$$

Of course, $\hat{\beta}^0_{.1} = 0$ satisfies (7.3.134), but this an irrelevant case because then $\ell(\hat{\beta}^0_{.1})$ is not defined.

Clearly, a necessary and sufficient condition for (7.3.134) to admit a unique nontrivial solution $\hat{\beta}^0_{.1}$ obeying the standard normalization rule is that

$$\text{rank}\,(\hat{\Pi}_{G\,*I}) = m_1 \qquad G^* = m_1 \qquad (7.3.135)$$

In this case, of course, $\hat{V}^*_I = \hat{V}_I$ and thus

$$\ell(\hat{\beta}^0_{.1}) = 1 \qquad (7.3.136)$$

We conclude, therefore, that when the condition for just identifiability, (7.3.132), holds, then ILS and LIML estimators coincide, and moreover, (7.3.127) is also satisfied. Suppose, however, that

$$G^* = m_1 + 1 \qquad (7.3.137)$$

Then the equation is overidentified and with finite probability we would have

$$\text{rank}\,(\hat{\Pi}_{G\,*I}) = m_1 + 1 \qquad (7.3.138)$$

In this case, a nontrivial vector obeying the standard normalization rule and satisfying (7.3.134) does not exist. In addition, the necessary and sufficient conditions (7.3.132) are violated and thus

$$\ell(\hat{\beta}^0_{.1}) > 1 \qquad \hat{\lambda} > 1 \qquad (7.3.139)$$

where $\hat{\beta}^0_{\cdot 1}$ is the LIML estimator. We also note that we do not have a *unique* ILS estimator[17] in this overidentified case. Hence we have proved the following useful

Proposition 1: Let the conditions of Theorems 1 and 2 hold. Then the LIML estimator of the parameters of, say, the first structural equation may be thought of as minimizing the (residual) variance ratio

$$\ell(s) = \frac{s'W_{11}^* s}{s'W_{11}s} \tag{7.3.140}$$

of the regressions

$$\tilde{y} = Y_I s = X_1 \Pi_{G_1 I} s + X_2 \Pi_{G*I} s + V_I s \tag{7.3.141}$$

$$\tilde{y} = Y_I \beta^0_{\cdot 1} = X_1 \gamma_{\cdot 1} + u_{\cdot 1} \tag{7.3.142}$$

where W_{11}^* and W_{11} are as defined in (7.3.103) and (7.3.102). The LIML estimator $\hat{\beta}^0_{\cdot 1}$ of $\beta^0_{\cdot 1}$, subject to the standard normalization, obeys

$$\ell(\hat{\beta}^0_{\cdot 1}) = \underset{s}{\mathrm{Min}} \; \ell(s) \qquad \ell(\hat{\beta}^0_{\cdot 1}) \geq 1 \tag{7.3.143}$$

If the equation in question satisfies the condition for just identifiability, then with probability one

$$\ell(\hat{\beta}^0_{\cdot 1}) = 1 \tag{7.3.144}$$

If the equation is overidentified, then

$$\ell(\hat{\beta}^0_{\cdot 1}) > 1 \tag{7.3.145}$$

SOME INTERESTING PROPERTIES OF THE LIML SINGLE EQUATION ESTIMATOR

The estimator developed above can easily be shown to be consistent and asymptotically efficient within the class of estimators making use of the same information. Instead of proving this assertion directly, we shall demonstrate the following statements:

i. LIML is a k-class estimator with k equal to $\hat{\lambda}$ of the discussion above.
ii. The asymptotic distribution of LIML and 2SLS estimators is identical.
iii. $\underset{T \to \infty}{\mathrm{plim}} \; \hat{\lambda} = 1$. This, of course, easily follows from i and ii.

We first prove

---

[17] Of course, if from (7.3.134) we suppress $G^* - m_1$ equations, we will in general find a vector obeying the standard normalization rule and (7.3.134). But we shall have a multiplicity of such vectors, depending on which equations we suppress. At any rate, no vector exists that, suitably normalized, satifies *all* equations of (7.3.134).

Proposition 2: The LIML estimator of an identifiable structural equation, as established in Theorems 1 and 2, is a k-class estimator, where

$$k = \hat{\lambda} \tag{7.3.146}$$

$\hat{\lambda}$ is the smallest characteristic root of (7.3.96) and the standard normalization has been imposed on the vector of parameters to be estimated.

PROOF: For definiteness, we shall deal with the first structural equation, which we shall assume to be identified. Imposing the standard normalization, we have

$$\beta^0_{\cdot 1} = \begin{pmatrix} 1 \\ -\beta_{\cdot 1} \end{pmatrix} \tag{7.3.147}$$

The equations defining the k-class estimator of $\begin{pmatrix} \beta_{\cdot 1} \\ \gamma_{\cdot 1} \end{pmatrix}$ are given by

$$\begin{bmatrix} Y'_1 Y_1 - k\tilde{V}'_1 \tilde{V}_1 & Y'_1 X_1 \\ X'_1 Y_1 & X'_1 X_1 \end{bmatrix} \begin{bmatrix} \tilde{\beta}_{\cdot 1} \\ \tilde{\gamma}_{\cdot 1} \end{bmatrix} = \begin{bmatrix} Y'_1 y_{\cdot 1} - k\tilde{V}_1 y_{\cdot 1} \\ X'_1 y_{\cdot 1} \end{bmatrix} \tag{7.3.148}$$

where

$$\tilde{V}_1 = N Y_1 \qquad N = I - X(X'X)^{-1}X' \tag{7.3.149}$$

The equations defining the LIML estimator of the same parameters are

$$(\hat{\lambda} W_{11} - W^*_{11})\beta^0_{\cdot 1} = 0$$
$$M_{31}\beta^0_{\cdot 1} + M_{33}\hat{\gamma}_{\cdot 1} = 0 \tag{7.3.150}$$

Observe that

$$Y_I = (y_{\cdot 1}, Y_1) \tag{7.3.151}$$

and thus

$$W_{11} = \frac{1}{T}\begin{pmatrix} y'_{\cdot 1} \\ Y'_1 \end{pmatrix} N(y_{\cdot 1}, Y_1) = \frac{1}{T}\begin{bmatrix} y'_{\cdot 1} N y_{\cdot 1} & y'_{\cdot 1} N Y_1 \\ Y'_1 N y_{\cdot 1} & Y'_1 N Y_1 \end{bmatrix} \tag{7.3.152}$$

$$W^*_{11} = \frac{1}{T}\begin{pmatrix} y'_{\cdot 1} \\ Y'_1 \end{pmatrix} N_1(y_{\cdot 1}, Y_1) = \frac{1}{T}\begin{bmatrix} y'_{\cdot 1} N_1 y_{\cdot 1} & y'_{\cdot 1} N_1 Y_1 \\ Y'_1 N_1 y_{\cdot 1} & Y'_1 N_1 Y_1 \end{bmatrix} \tag{7.3.153}$$

where

$$N_1 = I - X_1(X'_1 X_1)^{-1}X'_1 \tag{7.3.154}$$

Making use of (7.3.147), (7.3.152) and (7.3.153), we can rewrite (7.3.150) as

$$y'_{\cdot 1}(N_1 - \hat{\lambda}N)Y_1\beta_{\cdot 1} = y'_1(N_1 - \hat{\lambda}N)y_{\cdot 1}$$
$$Y'_1(N_1 - \hat{\lambda}N)Y_1\beta_{\cdot 1} = Y'_1(N_1 - \hat{\lambda}N)y_{\cdot 1}$$
$$X'_1 Y_1\beta_{\cdot 1} + X'_1 X_1\hat{\gamma}_{\cdot 1} = X'_1 y_{\cdot 1} \tag{7.3.155}$$

We see that $Y_1'(N_1 - \hat{\lambda}N)Y_1$ is the $m_1 \times m_1$ principal submatrix of $W_{11}^* - \hat{\lambda}W_{11}$ appearing in the lower right-hand block of the partition as exhibited in (7.3.152) and (7.3.153). Now, for any vector x, $x'W_{11}^*x/x'W_{11}x \geq \hat{\lambda}$; thus $W_{11}^* - \hat{\lambda}W_{11}$ is a *positive semidefinite matrix*. If $\hat{\lambda}$ is a simple root, as will ordinarily be the case, then $W_{11}^* - \hat{\lambda}W_{11}$ is of rank m_1. Since this is so, then at least one of its $m_1 \times m_1$ principal submatrices must be of rank m_1. With little loss of relevance, we may assume that $Y_1'(N_1 - \hat{\lambda}N)Y_1$ is nonsingular. If this is so, then from the second equation of (7.3.155) we determine $\hat{\beta}._1$ uniquely, and from the third equation we thus determine $\hat{\gamma}._1$. We shall next show that $\hat{\beta}._1$ so determined satisfies the first equation as well. For notational simplicity, let us put

$$W_{11}^* - \hat{\lambda}W_{11} = \begin{bmatrix} C_{00} & C_{01} \\ C_{10} & C_{11} \end{bmatrix} \tag{7.3.156}$$

where the partition is identical with that exhibited in (7.3.152) and (7.3.153). Thus

$$\begin{aligned} C_{11} &= Y_1'(N_1 - \hat{\lambda}N)Y_1 & C_{00} &= y_1'(N_1 - \hat{\lambda}N)y._1 \\ C_{01} &= y'._1(N_1 - \hat{\lambda}N)Y_1 & C_{10} &= C_{10}' \end{aligned} \tag{7.3.157}$$

In view of (7.3.157) and (7.3.155), we have

$$\hat{\beta}._1 = C_{11}^{-1}C_{10} \tag{7.3.158}$$

Substituting in the first equation of (7.3.155), we obtain

$$C_{01}C_{11}^{-1}C_{10} - C_{00} = 0 \tag{7.3.159}$$

Now, since by assumption C_{11} is nonsingular,

$$|W_{11}^* - \hat{\lambda}W_{11}| = |C_{11}||C_{00} - C_{01}C_{11}^{-1}C_{10}| \tag{7.3.160}$$

But $W_{11}^* - \hat{\lambda}W_{11}$ is a singular matrix; because of the nonsingularity of C_{11}, we conclude

$$C_{00} - C_{01}C_{11}^{-1}C_{10} = 0^{18} \tag{7.3.161}$$

This means that the first equation in (7.3.155) is redundant, for if $\hat{\beta}._1$ satisfies the the second equation, then it satisfies the first as well.

After some rearrangement, the system in (7.3.155) can be written as

$$Y_1'(I - \hat{\lambda}N)Y_1\hat{\beta}._1 - Y_1'X_1(X_1'X_1)^{-1}X_1'Y_1\hat{\beta}._1$$
$$= Y_1'(I - \hat{\lambda}N)y._1 - Y_1'X_1(X_1'X_1)^{-1}X_1'y._1$$
$$X_1'Y_1\hat{\beta}._1 + X_1'X_1\hat{\gamma}._1 = X_1'y._1 \tag{7.3.162}$$

Premultiplying the last equation above by $Y_1'X_1(X_1'X_1)^{-1}$ and adding to the first, we obtain the equivalent system

---

[18] We have removed the bars, for $C_{00} - C_{10}C_{11}^{-1}C_{10}$ is a scalar.

$$Y_1'(I - \hat{\lambda}N)Y_1\hat{\beta}_{.1} + Y_1'X_1\hat{\gamma}_{.1} = Y_1'(I - \hat{\lambda}N)y_{.1}$$
$$X_1'Y_1\hat{\beta}_{.1} + X_1'X_1\hat{\gamma}_{.1} = X_1'y_{.1} \tag{7.3.163}$$

But from (7.3.149) we have

$$Y_1'Y_1 - k\tilde{V}_1'\tilde{V}_1 = Y_1'(I - kN)Y_1 \tag{7.3.164}$$

$$Y_1'y_{.1} - k\tilde{V}_1'y_{.1} = Y_1'(I - kN)y_{.1} \tag{7.3.165}$$

Using the relations above and comparing (7.3.148) with (7.3.163), we conclude that k-class and LIML estimators are identical, under the standard normalization, for the choice

$$k = \hat{\lambda} \qquad\qquad\qquad\qquad \text{Q.E.D.}$$
$$\tag{7.3.166}$$

We shall next show that under the standard normalization the asymptotic distribution of the LIML estimator is identical to that of the 2SLS estimator. Thus we have

Proposition 3: The asymptotic distribution of the LIML estimator of an identifiable structural equation as exhibited in Theorems 1 and 2 is identical with that of the 2SLS estimator.

PROOF: Again, for definiteness, we deal with the first structural equation, which is assumed to be identifiable. The asymptotic distribution of the 2SLS estimator $\tilde{\delta}_{.1}$, of $\delta_{.1}$, was obtained in Section 4.5 of Chapter 4. There we had established that

$$\sqrt{T}(\tilde{\delta}_{.1} - \delta_{.1}) \sim N(0, C) \tag{7.3.167}$$

where

$$C = \sigma_{11} \underset{T \to \infty}{\text{plim}} \begin{bmatrix} \Pi_1' \dfrac{X'X}{T} \Pi_1 & \Pi_1' \dfrac{X'X_1}{T} \\[2ex] \dfrac{X_1'X}{T} \Pi_1 & \dfrac{X_1'X_1}{T} \end{bmatrix}^{-1} \tag{7.3.168}$$

The asymptotic distribution of the LIML estimator was given in equations (7.3.77) through (7.3.82). Thus to establish the validity of the proposition, it is sufficient to show that the inverse of the matrix in (7.3.168), multiplied by Ψ of (7.3.78) yields the identity matrix. In the process we shall, for notational convenience, dispense with the $\text{plim}_{T \to \infty}$ operator and employ the notation

$$M_{y_1x} = \frac{1}{T}Y_1'X \quad M_{y_1x_1} = \frac{1}{T}Y_1'X_1 \quad X = (X_1, X_2)$$

$$M_{xx} = \frac{1}{T}X'X = \begin{pmatrix} M_{x_1x_1} & M_{x_1x_2} \\ M_{x_2x_1} & M_{x_2x_2} \end{pmatrix} \tag{7.3.169}$$

where, as before, X_1 is the $T \times G_1$ matrix of observations on the G_1 predetermined variables actually appearing in the first equation.

Let us again partition

$$\Pi_1 = \begin{pmatrix} \Pi_{G_1 1} \\ \Pi_{G*1} \end{pmatrix} \tag{7.3.170}$$

in exactly the same way as in (7.3.83). Then we have

$$\Pi_1' \frac{X'X}{T} \Pi_1 = \Pi_{G_1 1}' M_{x_1 x_1} \Pi_{G_1 1} + \Pi_{G_1 1}' M_{x_1 x_2} \Pi_{G*1} + \Pi_{G*1}' M_{x_2 x_1} \Pi_{G_1 1}$$
$$+ \Pi_{G*1}' M_{x_2 x_2} \Pi_{G*1} \tag{7.3.171}$$

$$\Pi_1' \frac{X'X_1}{T} = \Pi_{G_1 1}' M_{x_1 x_1} + \Pi_{G*1}' M_{x_2 x_1} \tag{7.3.172}$$

We must now show that

$$\Psi \, \underset{T \to \infty}{\text{plim}} \begin{bmatrix} \Pi_1' \dfrac{X'X}{T} \Pi_1 & \Pi_1' \dfrac{X'X_1}{T} \\ \dfrac{X_1'X}{T} \Pi_1 & \dfrac{X_1'X_1}{T} \end{bmatrix} = \begin{bmatrix} I_{m_1} & 0 \\ 0 & I_{G_1} \end{bmatrix} \tag{7.3.173}$$

For simplicity, let us put

$$S_{11} = [\Pi_{G*1}'(M_{x_2 x_2} - M_{x_2 x_1} M_{x_1 x_1}^{-1} M_{x_1 x_2})\Pi_{G*1}]^{-1}$$
$$S_{12} = -S_{11}\overline{\Pi}_{G_1 1}'$$
$$\overline{\Pi}_{G_1 1} = \Pi_{G_1 1} + M_{x_1 x_1}^{-1} M_{x_1 x_2} \Pi_{G*1} \qquad S_{22} = \overline{\Pi}_{G_1 1} S_{11} \overline{\Pi}_{G_1 1}' + M_{x_1 x_1}^{-1}$$
$$S_{21} = S_{12}' \tag{7.3.174}$$

We then have

$$\begin{bmatrix} S_{11} & S_{12} \\ S_{21} & S_{22} \end{bmatrix} \begin{bmatrix} \Pi_1' \dfrac{X'X}{T} \Pi_1 & \Pi_1' \dfrac{X'X_1}{T} \\ \dfrac{X_1'X}{T} \Pi_1 & \dfrac{X_1'X_1}{T} \end{bmatrix} = \begin{bmatrix} R_{11} & R_{12} \\ R_{21} & R_{22} \end{bmatrix} \tag{7.3.175}$$

and

$$R_{11} = S_{11}[S_{11}^{-1} + \Pi_{G_1 1}' M_{x_1 x_1} \Pi_{G_1 1} + \Pi_{G_1 1}' M_{x_1 x_2} \Pi_{G*1} + \Pi_{G*1}' M_{x_2 x_1} \Pi_{G_1 1}$$
$$+ \Pi_{G*1}' M_{x_2 x_1} M_{x_1 x_1}^{-1} M_{x_1 x_2} \Pi_{G*1}]$$
$$- S_{11}(\Pi_{G_1 1}' + \Pi_{G*1}' M_{x_2 x_1} M_{x_1 x_1}^{-1})(M_{x_1 x_1} \Pi_{G_1 1} + M_{x_1 x_2} \Pi_{G*1}) = I_{m_1} \tag{7.3.176}$$

$$R_{21} = R_{12}' = 0 \tag{7.3.177}$$

$$R_{22} = -\overline{\Pi}_{G_1 1} S_{11} \overline{\Pi}_{G_1 1}' M_{x_1 x_1} + \overline{\Pi}_{G_1 1} S_{11} \overline{\Pi}_{G_1}' M_{x_1 x_1} + I_{G_1} = I_{G_1} \tag{7.3.178}$$

Since

$$\text{plim}_{T \to \infty} \left\{ S \begin{bmatrix} \Pi_1' \dfrac{X'X}{T} \Pi_1 & \Pi_1' \dfrac{X'X_1}{T} \\[2mm] \dfrac{X_1'X}{T} \Pi_1 & \dfrac{X_1'X_1}{T} \end{bmatrix} \right\} = \Psi \, \text{plim}_{T \to \infty} \begin{bmatrix} \Pi_1' \dfrac{X'X}{T} \Pi_1 & \Pi_1' \dfrac{X'X_1}{T} \\[2mm] \dfrac{X_1'X}{T} \Pi_1 & \dfrac{X_1'X_1}{T} \end{bmatrix}$$

$$(7.3.179)$$

the proof of the proposition is now complete.

We may now prove

Proposition 4: Let $\hat{\lambda}$ be the smallest root of

$$|\lambda W_{11} - W_{11}^*| = 0 \tag{7.3.180}$$

where W_{11}^* and W_{11} have the meaning given them in Theorems 1 and 2 and the conditions of Proposition 2 hold. Then

$$\text{plim}_{T \to \infty} \hat{\lambda} = 1 \tag{7.3.181}$$

PROOF: We observe that since the (characteristic) roots of (7.3.180) are rational functions of the elements of W_{11} and W_{11}^*, then if λ_i is the ith largest root of (7.3.180) $\text{plim}_{T \to \infty} \lambda_i$ is the ith largest root of

$$|\lambda \overline{W}_{11} - \overline{W}_{11}^*| = 0 \tag{7.3.182}$$

where

$$\overline{W}_{11} = \text{plim}_{T \to \infty} W_{11} \qquad \overline{W}_{11}^* = \text{plim}_{T \to \infty} W_{11}^* \tag{7.3.183}$$

Thus to demonstrate the validity of (7.3.181), it is sufficient to prove that the smallest root of (7.3.182) is unity. But this is also equivalent to showing that one and only one of the roots of

$$|\mu \overline{W}_{11} - (\overline{W}_{11}^* - \overline{W}_{11})| = 0 \tag{7.3.184}$$

is zero, the others being positive. In (7.3.184) we have, of course,

$$\mu = \lambda - 1 \tag{7.3.185}$$

Now, for every sample of size T, $W_{11}^* - W_{11}$ is positive semidefinite. Thus we have that

$$\overline{W}_{11}^* - \overline{W}_{11} = \text{plim}_{T \to \infty} (W_{11}^* - W_{11}) \tag{7.3.186}$$

is also positive semidefinite. Moreover, $\overline{W}_{11}$ is positive definite, for it is simply a principal submatrix of the covariance matrix of the reduced form error terms. It follows, therefore, that the roots of (7.3.184) are nonnegative.

The next step is to show that the identifiability condition implies that

$\overline{W}_{11}^* - \overline{W}_{11}$ is of rank m_1. Since the matrix is $(m_1 + 1) \times (m_1 + 1)$, this will obviously imply that one and only one of its roots is zero, the others being positive. Now, using the notation of equations (7.3.110) through (7.3.116), we have

$$W_{11}^* - W_{11} = \Pi_I' \frac{X'X}{T} \hat{\Pi}_I + \frac{V_I'X}{T} \hat{\Pi}_I - \Pi_I' \frac{X'X_1}{T} P_I - \frac{V_I'X_1}{T} P_I \qquad (7.3.187)$$

where, we repeat,

$$P_I = (X_1'X_1)^{-1}X_1'Y_I \quad \hat{\Pi}_I = (X'X)^{-1}X'Y_I \quad Y_I = X\Pi_I + V_I \qquad (7.3.188)$$

so that Y_I is the matrix of current endogenous variables appearing in the first equation ($m_1 + 1$ in number) and X_1 is the matrix of predetermined variables appearing there (G_1 in number).

Because of the consistency of $\hat{\Pi}_I$ as an estimator of Π_I and the absence of correlation between the elements of X and V_I, we conclude

$$\underset{T\to\infty}{\text{plim}} \; \hat{\Pi}_I = \Pi_I \qquad \underset{T\to\infty}{\text{plim}} \; P_I = \underset{T\to\infty}{\text{plim}} \left[I_{G_1}, \; \left(\frac{X_1'X_1}{T}\right)^{-1} \frac{X_1'X_2}{T} \right] \Pi_I$$

$$\underset{T\to\infty}{\text{plim}} \; \frac{V_I'X}{T} = 0 \qquad (7.3.189)$$

$$\underset{T\to\infty}{\text{plim}} \; (W_{11}^* - W_{11}) = \overline{W}_{11}^* - \overline{W}_{11} = \Pi_{G*I}' \left(\underset{T\to\infty}{\text{plim}} \; \frac{X_2^{*\prime}X_2^*}{T} \right) \Pi_{G*I}$$

$$X_2^* = X_2 - X_1(X_1'X_1)^{-1}X_2 \qquad (7.3.190)$$

where we have partitioned

$$X = (X_1, X_2) \qquad \Pi_I = \begin{pmatrix} \Pi_{G_1 I} \\ \Pi_{G*I} \end{pmatrix} \qquad (7.3.191)$$

so that X_1 is $T \times G_1$, X_2 is $T \times (G - G_1)$, $\Pi_{G_1 I}$ is $G_1 \times (m_1 + 1)$, and Π_{G*I} is $(G - G_1) \times (m_1 + 1)$.

Since, by hypothesis, $\text{plim}_{T\to\infty}(X'X/T)$ (or $\lim_{T\to\infty}(X'X/T)$ as the case may be) is assumed to be nonsingular and thus positive definite, it follows that $\text{plim}_{T\to\infty}(X_2^{*\prime}X_2^*/T)$ is also positive definite. From (7.3.190) we then conclude

$$\text{rank} \; (\overline{W}_{11}^* - \overline{W}_{11}) = \text{rank} \; (\Pi_{G*I}) \qquad (7.3.192)$$

From the conditions of identifiability, we have

$$\text{rank} \; (\Pi_{G*I}) = m_1 \qquad (7.3.193)$$

Since $\overline{W}_{11}^* - \overline{W}_{11}$ is $(m_1 + 1) \times (m_1 + 1)$, we conclude that *exactly one of its roots is zero*, the others being positive. However, this means that exactly one of the roots of (7.3.184) is zero, the others being positive, which implies

$$\underset{T\to\infty}{\text{plim}} \; \hat{\lambda} = 1 \qquad \text{Q.E.D.}$$

$$(7.3.194)$$

Remark 4: The import of Propositions 2, 3, and 4 is that the LIML estimator is asymptotically equivalent to the 2SLS estimator. Since most of the properties established and the tests of hypotheses formulated are large sample ones, it follows that whatever properties and tests we had established for 2SLS estimators are fully applicable here as well.

Remark 5: It is interesting that one can conduct a test of the hypothesis that the equation under consideration is identifiable. Two such tests are available; both originate with the likelihood ratio principle.

The likelihood ratio of the null hypothesis

$$H_0: \text{rank } (\Pi_{G*I}) = m_1 \qquad (7.3.195)$$

as against

$$H_1: \text{rank } (\Pi_{G*I}) \geq m_1 + 1 \qquad (7.3.196)$$

is given by $\hat{\lambda}^{-\frac{1}{2}T}$.

Moreover, Anderson and Rubin [2, 3], to whom this development is due, show that, asymptotically,

$$T \ln \hat{\lambda} \sim \chi^2_{G*-m_1} \qquad (7.3.197)$$

This is a test of the hypothesis that there are G_1 predetermined variables in the equation under consideration as against the alternative that there are *more than* G_1.

Another test proposed by Koopmans and Hood [20] is again based on the likelihood ratio principle and involves the null hypothesis

$$H_0: \text{rank } (\Pi_{G*I}) \leq m_1 - 1 \qquad (7.3.198)$$

as against the alternative

$$H_1: \text{rank } (\Pi_{G*I}) = m_1 \qquad (7.3.199)$$

The test statistic obtained is shown to obey, asymptotically,

$$T[\ln \hat{\lambda} + \ln \lambda^*] \sim \chi^2_{G*-m_1-1} \qquad (7.3.200)$$

where λ^* is the *second smallest root* of (7.3.125).

Strictly speaking, this is a test of the hypothesis that the *equation under consideration is not identifiable* and is best termed a *test of underidentifiability*.

Remark 6: It should be observed that the two test statistics above are defined only if

$$G - G_1 - m_1 > 0 \qquad G - G_1 - m_1 - 1 > 0 \qquad (7.3.201)$$

respectively. In either case, we must have

$$G > G_1 + m_1 \qquad (7.3.202)$$

That is, the equation under consideration should satisfy at least an order condition for overidentifiability in the sense that it must exclude more predetermined variables than there are current endogenous variable coefficients to be estimated. It should also be recalled that, for an apparently overidentified equation, we had derived, (Chapter 5) an asymptotic test of significance for 2SLS estimated parameters and, moreover, that the test was based on the t distribution with $G^* - m_1$ degrees of freedom. This parameter is identical with that of the statistic in (7.3.197).

REFERENCES

1. Anderson, T. W., "Estimation of the Parameters of a Single Equation by the Limited Information Maximum Likelihood Method," Chapter 9 in *Statistical Inference in Dynamic Economic Models*, T. C. Koopmans (Ed.). Cowles Foundation for Research in Economics, Monograph No. 10, New York, Wiley, 1950.
2. Anderson, T. W., and H. Rubin, "Estimation of the Parameters of a Single Equation in a Complete System of Stochastic Equations," *Annals of Mathematical Statistics*, vol. 20, 1949, pp. 46–63.
3. Anderson, T. W., and H. Rubin, "The Asymptotic Properties of Estimates of the Parameters of a Single Equation in a Complete System of Stochastic Equations," *Annals of Mathematical Statistics*, vol. 20, 1950. pp. 570–582.
4. Bellman, R., *A Survey of the Boundedness, Stability, and Asymptotic Behavior of Solutions to Linear and Nonlinear Differential and Difference Equations*. Contract NC ori-105 Task-order V, Washington, D.C., Office of Naval Research, Dept. of the Navy, 1949.
5. Brown, T. M., "Simplified Full Maximum Likelihood and Comparative Structural Estimates," *Econometrica*, vol. 27, 1959, pp. 638–653.
6. Chernoff, H., and N. Divinsky, "The Computation of Maximum Likelihood Estimates of Linear Structural Equations," in *Studies in Econometric Methods*, W. C. Hood and T. C. Koopmans (Eds.), New York, Wiley, 1953.
7. Chernoff, H., and H. Rubin, "Asymptotic Properties of Limited Information Estimates Under Generalized Conditions," in *Studies in Econometric Methods*, W. C. Hood and T. C. Koopmans (Eds.), New York, Wiley, 1953.
8. Chow, G. C., "Two Methods of Computing Full Information Maximum Likelihood Estimates in Simultaneous Stochastic Equations," *International Economic Review*, vol. 9, 1968, pp. 100–112.
9. Court, R. H., "Utility Maximization and the Demand for New Zealand Meats," *Econometrica*, vol. 35, 1967, pp. 424–446.
10. Cramer, H., *Mathematical Methods of Statistics*, Princeton, N.J., Princeton University Press, 1946.
11. Durbin, J., "Maximum Likelihood Estimation of the Parameters of a System of Simultaneous Regression Equations." Paper presented at the meetings of the Econometric Society, Copenhagen, 1963.
12. Eisenpress, H., "Note on the Computation of Full Information Maximum Likelihood Estimates of Coefficients of a Simultaneous System," *Econometrica*, vol. 30, 1962, pp. 343–348.
13. Eisenpress, H., and J. Greenstadt, "The Estimation of Nonlinear Econometric Systems," *Econometrica*, vol. 34, 1966, pp. 851–861.
14. Fisher, F. M., "Identifiability Criteria in Nonlinear Systems," *Econometrica*, vol. 29, 1961, pp. 574–590.
15. Fisher, R. A., *Statistical Methods for Research Workers*, Edinburgh, Oliver and Boyd, 1954.

16. Haavelmo, T., "The Statistical Implications of a System of Simultaneous Equations," *Econometrica*, vol. 11, 1943, pp. 1–12.
17. Hood, W. C., and T. C. Koopmans (Eds.), *Studies in Econometric Methods*, Cowles Foundation for Research in Economics, Monograph No. 14, New York, Wiley, 1953.
18. Klein, L. R., *A Textbook of Econometrics*, Englewood Cliffs, N.J., Prentice-Hall, 1953.
19. Koopmans, T. C., "The Equivalence of Maximum Likelihood and Least Squares Estimates of Regression Coefficients," Chapter 7 in *Statistical Inference in Dynamic Economic Models*. T. C. Koopmans (Ed.) Cowles Foundation for Research in Economics, Monograph No. 10, New York, Wiley, 1950.
20. Koopmans, T. C., and W. C. Hood, "The Estimation of Simultaneous Economic Relationships," in *Studies in Econometric Methods*, W. C. Hood and T. C. Koopmans (Eds.), New York, Wiley, 1953.
21. Koopmans, T. C., H. Rubin, and R. B. Leipnik, "Measuring the Equation Systems of Dynamic Economics," Chapter 2 in *Statistical Inference in Dynamic Economic Models*, T. C. Koopmans (Ed.), New York, Wiley, 1950.
22. Mann, H. B., and A. Wald, "On the Statistical Treatment of Linear Stochastic Difference Equations," *Econometrica*, vol. 11, 1943, pp. 173–220.
23. Marschak, J., "Economic Interdependence and Statistical Analysis," in *Studies in Mathematical Economics and Econometrics, in Memory of Henry Schultz*, O. Lange, F. McIntyre, and T. O. Yntema (Eds.), Chicago, University of Chicago Press, 1942.
24. Meyer, J. R., and H. L. Miller, Jr., "Some Comments on the 'Simultaneous Equations Approach'," *Review of Economics and Statistics*, vol. 36, 1954, pp. 88–92.
25. Rao, C. R., *Advanced Statistical Methods in Biometric Research*, New York, Wiley, 1952.
26. Rothenberg, T. J., and C. T. Leenders, "Efficient Estimation of Simultaneous Equation Systems," *Econometrica*, vol. 32, 1964, pp. 57–76.
27. Sargan, J. D., "The Maximum Likelihood Estimation of Economic Relationships with Autoregressive Residuals," *Econometrica*, vol. 29, 1961, pp. 414–426.
28. Tinbergen, J., "Econometric Business Cycle Research," *Review of Economic Studies*, vol. 7, 1940, pp. 73–90.
29. Tintner, G., "Multiple Regression for Systems of Equations," *Econometrica*, vol. 14, 1946, pp. 5 32.
30. Wold, H., "Statistical Estimation of Economic Relationships," *Econometrica*, supplement, vol. 17, 1949, pp. 1–22.

RELATIONS
AMONG ESTIMATORS;
MONTE CARLO METHODS

8

8.1 INTRODUCTION

In previous chapters we have examined several estimators for the parameters of the standard (structural) simultaneous equations model.

It would be appropriate for us to determine what, if any, relations hold among such estimators. We had done so to some extent in Chapters 6 and 7, where we established that 2SLS has an interpretation as an optimal I.V. estimator and the LIML as well as 2SLS were k-class estimators. Here we shall approach the problem systematically.

In addition, in previous chapters the distributional aspects of all estimators were dealt with from an asymptotic (large sample) point of view. In general, their small sample properties have not been satisfactorily established analytically, although in certain special cases exact results have been recently obtained [1, 2, 10, 11, 18, 23]. No doubt it is extremely important to determine the small sample properties and performance of alternative estimators. If analytical techniques fail, then an alternative approach to the small sample problem has to be developed.

This may be done by constructing an artificial model and using it to generate (artificial) data obeying exactly the relations of the model. Thus we ensure that no misspecification is present. Having obtained such data, we then apply the various estimation techniques to them. If we generate N samples of size T, then from each we can obtain an estimate corresponding to the estimation procedure(s) we wish to study. We may think of such estimates as "observations" on the size T sampling distribution of the relevant estimator. We may then process these "observations" in exactly the same fashion as we process bona fide data and thus make inferences regarding the sampling distribution.

This is the theoretical framework of *Monte Carlo experiments*. We shall discuss this method briefly below and give some results concerning various estimators of structural parameters.

8.2 RELATIONS AMONG DOUBLE k-CLASS ESTIMATORS

In this section we shall establish an interesting identity connecting the 2SLS and general double k-class estimators.

First, however, the following useful result from misspecification theory will be required.

Lemma 1: Consider the general linear model

$$y = X\beta + u \tag{8.2.1}$$

subject to the classical assumptions. Here y is $T \times 1$, X is $T \times G$, u is $T \times 1$, β is $G \times 1$, and they represent, respectively, the dependent and explanatory variables, the error terms, and the unknown parameters of the problem.

Partition X by

$$X = (X_1, X_2) \tag{8.2.2}$$

so that X_1 is $T \times G_1$, X_2 is $T \times G_2$, $G_1 + G_2 = G$.

Partition β conformally; thus

$$\beta = \begin{pmatrix} \beta_1 \\ \beta_2 \end{pmatrix} \tag{8.2.3}$$

and denote by

$$\hat{\beta} = (X'X)^{-1}X'y \tag{8.2.4}$$

the OLS estimator of β.
Let

$$\tilde{\beta}_1 = (X_1'X_1)^{-1}X_1'y \tag{8.2.5}$$

Then

$$\tilde{\beta}_1 = \hat{\beta}_1 + S_{12}\hat{\beta}_2 \tag{8.2.6}$$

where $\hat{\beta}_i$, $i = 1, 2$, are the appropriate subvectors of $\hat{\beta}$ in (8.2.4) and

$$S_{12} = (X_1' X_1)^{-1} X_1' X_2 \tag{8.2.7}$$

PROOF: Using the partitions in (8.2.2) and (8.2.3), we see that $\hat{\beta}$ of (8.2.4) obeys

$$X_1' X_1 \hat{\beta}_1 + X_1' X_2 \hat{\beta}_2 = X_1' y$$
$$X_2' X_1 \hat{\beta}_1 + X_2' X_2 \hat{\beta}_2 = X_2' y \tag{8.2.8}$$

From (8.2.5) we have

$$X_1' X_1 \tilde{\beta}_1 = X_1' y \tag{8.2.9}$$

Solving the second set of equations in (8.2.8) for $\hat{\beta}_2$, we find

$$\hat{\beta}_2 = (X_2' X_2)^{-1} X_2' y - (X_2' X_2)^{-1} X_2' X_1 \hat{\beta}_1 \tag{8.2.10}$$

Substituting (8.2.9) and (8.2.10) in the first set of equations in (8.2.8), we have

$$X_1' X_1 \hat{\beta}_1 - X_1' X_2 (X_2' X_2)^{-1} X_2' X_1 \hat{\beta}_1 = X_1' X_1 \tilde{\beta}_1 - (X_1' X_2)(X_2' X_2)^{-1} X_2' y$$
$$\tag{8.2.11}$$

Premultiplying by $(X_1' X_1)^{-1}$ and rearranging, we obtain

$$\tilde{\beta}_1 = \hat{\beta}_1 + S_{12}[(X_2' X_2)^{-1} X_2' y - (X_2' X_2)^{-1} X_2' X_1 \hat{\beta}_1] \tag{8.2.12}$$

Substituting from (8.2.10), we finally have

$$\tilde{\beta}_1 = \hat{\beta}_1 + S_{12} \hat{\beta}_2 \qquad\qquad \text{Q.E.D.}$$
$$\tag{8.2.13}$$

Remark 1: The lemma above establishes a result not obtained in our discussion of misspecification errors in Chapter 5. There we were interested in the bias and inconsistency properties of coefficient estimators obtained from a misspecified relation. Here we have established an *identity* between the OLS estimator of parameters in a *misspecified relation* and the OLS estimator of parameters in the *correctly specified relation*. If the misspecification consists of omitting certain variables, then the *OLS estimator of parameters in the misspecified relation is a linear combination of the elements of the OLS estimator of parameters in the correctly specified relation*, the matrix of this linear combination being

$$A = [I, S_{12}] \tag{8.2.14}$$

Here, S_{12} *is the matrix of "regression" coefficients in the regression of the omitted on the included variables.* The reader may easily obtain the bias and inconsistency properties of $\tilde{\beta}_1$ by using (8.2.13) directly. He will then obtain exactly the results of Chapter 5. On the other hand, it is important to realize that while those results depend on the assumptions made regarding the error terms of the system, the relation in (8.2.13) is a mathematical identity that holds irrespective of the properties of error terms. The only requisite for its validity is that the matrix $X'X$ be nonsingular—and thus positive definite.

Now, what is the relevance of the lemma to the topic of this section? Interestingly, we shall establish an identity such as the one in (8.2.13) between the 2SLS and the general double k-class estimators.

To this effect, consider again the structural model

$$y_{\cdot i} = Y_i \beta_{\cdot i} + X_i \gamma_{\cdot i} + u_{\cdot i} \qquad i = 1, 2, \ldots, m \tag{8.2.15}$$

with the usual conventions and assumptions.[1] Associated with the system in (8.2.15), which may be written more compactly as

$$Y = YB + XC + U \tag{8.2.16}$$

is its reduced form

$$Y = X\Pi + V \tag{8.2.17}$$

where

$$\Pi = CD \quad V = UD \quad D = (I - B)^{-1} \tag{8.2.18}$$

For definiteness, let us concentrate on the first structural equation and note that the reduced form corresponding to the jointly dependent variables it contains is

$$Y_1 = X\Pi_1 + V_1 \qquad y_{\cdot 1} = X\pi_{\cdot 1} + v_{\cdot 1} \tag{8.2.19}$$

where, evidently, $\pi_{\cdot 1}$ is the first column of Π and Π_1 is the submatrix of the latter formed by its next m_1 columns (i.e., formed by columns $2, 3, \ldots, m_1 + 1$); similarly, $v_{\cdot 1}$ and V_1 bear the same relation to V.

Let the OLS estimators of $\pi_{\cdot 1}$ and Π_1 be denoted by

$$\tilde{\pi}_{\cdot 1} = (X'X)^{-1}X'y_{\cdot 1} \qquad \tilde{\Pi}_1 = (X'X)^{-1}X'Y_1 \tag{8.2.20}$$

Let the OLS (reduced form) residuals be denoted by

$$\tilde{v}_{\cdot 1} = y_{\cdot 1} - X\tilde{\pi}_{\cdot 1} \qquad \tilde{V}_1 = Y_1 - X\tilde{\Pi}_1 \tag{8.2.21}$$

and observe that

$$\tilde{V}_1'X = 0 \qquad \tilde{v}_{\cdot 1}'X = 0 \tag{8.2.22}$$

Finally, define

$$\tilde{Y}_1 = X\tilde{\Pi}_1 \quad \tilde{W}_1 = h_1\tilde{V}_1 \quad \tilde{w}_{\cdot 1} = h_2\tilde{v}_{\cdot 1} \tag{8.2.23}$$

---

[1] In the interest of brevity we shall not repeat these assumptions and conventions here. They have been discussed extensively in Chapters 4, 5, and 6.

where h_1, h_2 are appropriate constants whose variation, as we shall see presently, determines the type of estimator with which we are dealing.

We then obtain

Lemma 2: The 2SLS estimator of the parameters of the first structural equation in (8.2.15), denoted by $\tilde{\beta}._1$, $\tilde{\gamma}._1$ is the OLS estimator of the coefficient vectors of $(\tilde{Y}_1 + \tilde{W}_1)$ and X_1, respectively, in the relation

$$y._1 + \tilde{w}._1 = (\tilde{Y}_1 + \tilde{W}_1)\beta._1 + X_1\gamma._1 + \tilde{W}_1 d._1 + \text{error} \tag{8.2.24}$$

PROOF: The OLS estimator of the parameters in (8.2.24) is defined by the equations

$$(\tilde{Y}'_1\tilde{Y}_1 + \tilde{W}'_1\tilde{W}_1)\tilde{\beta}._1 + Y'_1X_1\tilde{\gamma}._1 + \tilde{W}'_1\tilde{W}_1\tilde{d}._1 = (\tilde{Y}'_1 + \tilde{W}'_1)(y._1 + \tilde{w}._1)$$
$$X'_1Y_1\tilde{\beta}._1 + X'_1X_1\tilde{\gamma}._1 \qquad\qquad = X'_1y._1$$
$$\tilde{W}'_1\tilde{W}_1\tilde{\beta}._1 \qquad\qquad + \tilde{W}'_1\tilde{W}_1\tilde{d}._1 = \tilde{W}'_1(y._1 + \tilde{w}._1) \tag{8.2.25}$$

Subtracting the last from the first set of equations in (8.2.25), we obtain the *equivalent system*

$$\tilde{Y}'_1\tilde{Y}_1\tilde{\beta}._1 + Y'_1X_1\tilde{\gamma}._1 \qquad\qquad = \tilde{Y}'_1y._1$$
$$X'_1Y_1\tilde{\beta}._1 + X'_1X_1\tilde{\gamma}._1 \qquad\qquad = X'_1y._1$$
$$\tilde{W}'_1\tilde{W}_1\tilde{\beta}._1 \qquad\qquad + \tilde{W}'_1\tilde{W}_1\tilde{d}._1 = \tilde{W}'_1(y._1 + \tilde{w}._1) \tag{8.2.26}$$

We are, therefore, dealing with a recursive system in which $\tilde{\beta}._1$, $\tilde{\gamma}._1$ can be solely determined from the first two sets of equations in (8.2.26). But these are exactly the equations that define the 2SLS estimator of $\beta._1$ and $\gamma._1$. Q.E.D.

Remark 2: In fact, (8.2.26) justifies the use of the symbols $\tilde{\beta}._1$, $\tilde{\gamma}._1$ for the OLS estimator of the coefficient vectors of $(\tilde{Y}_1 + \tilde{W}_1)$ and X_1 in (8.2.24). Furthermore, notice that from the last set of equations in (8.2.26) we obtain, in view of the definitions in (8.2.23),

$$\tilde{d}._1 = \left(\frac{1 + h_2}{h_1}\right)(\tilde{V}'_1\tilde{V}_1)^{-1}\tilde{V}'_1\tilde{v}._1 - \tilde{\beta}._1 \tag{8.2.27}$$

The reader is entitled to ask: Why did we go to the trouble of deriving the result in Lemma 2? A partial answer is provided by

Lemma 3: The double k-class estimator of the parameters of the first structural equation in (8.2.15) is the OLS estimator of the parameters in

$$y._1 + \tilde{w}._1 = (\tilde{Y}_1 + \tilde{W}_1)\beta._1 + X_1\gamma._1 + \text{error} \tag{8.2.28}$$

PROOF: Denote the OLS estimator of $\beta._1, \gamma._1$ in (8.2.28) by $\tilde{\beta}._1(h_1, h_2)$, $\tilde{\gamma}._1(h_1, h_2)$, and note that it is given by

$$\begin{bmatrix} \tilde{\beta}._1(h_1, h_2) \\ \tilde{\gamma}._1(h_1, h_2) \end{bmatrix} = \begin{bmatrix} \tilde{Y}'_1\tilde{Y}_1 + \tilde{W}'_1\tilde{W}_1 & Y'_1X_1 \\ X'_1Y_1 & X'_1X_1 \end{bmatrix}^{-1} \begin{bmatrix} (\tilde{Y}'_1 + \tilde{W}'_1)(y._1 + \tilde{w}._1) \\ X'_1y._1 \end{bmatrix} \tag{8.2.29}$$

Notice, also, that

$$\tilde{Y}_1'\tilde{Y}_1 + \tilde{W}_1'\tilde{W}_1 = Y_1'Y_1 - (1 - h_1^2)\tilde{V}_1'\tilde{V}_1 \tag{8.2.30}$$

$$(\tilde{Y}_1' + \tilde{W}_1')(y_{.1} + \tilde{w}_{.1}) = \{Y_1' - [1 - h_1(1 + h_2)]\tilde{V}_1'\}y_{.1} \tag{8.2.31}$$

Making the identification

$$k_1 = 1 - h_1^2 \qquad k_2 = 1 - h_1(1 + h_2) \tag{8.2.32}$$

and comparing with the results of Chapter 4 (Section 4.6), we conclude that the estimator in (8.2.29) is indeed exactly the double k-class estimator of $\beta_{.1}$ and $\gamma_{.1}$.   Q.E.D.

Remark 3: It should now become clear to the reader why Lemmas 1, 2, and 3 were needed. From Lemmas 2 and 3 we see that the 2SLS and double k-class estimators differ in that the equation from which the latter is defined is a "mis-specified" version of the relation from which we derive the former. Furthermore, Lemma 1 establishes an identity connecting regression coefficient estimates in such cases.

The discussion above implies

Theorem 1: Consider the general (structural) simultaneous equations model in (8.2.15). Then the 2SLS and double k-class estimators of the para-meters, say, of the first structural equation are connected by the identity

$$\begin{bmatrix} \tilde{\beta}_{.1}(h_1, h_2) \\ \tilde{\gamma}_{.1}(h_1, h_2) \end{bmatrix} = \begin{bmatrix} \tilde{\beta}_{.1} \\ \tilde{\gamma}_{.1} \end{bmatrix} + S_{12}\tilde{d}_{.1} \tag{8.2.33}$$

where

$$S_{12} = \begin{bmatrix} Y_1'Y_1 - (1 - h_2^2)\tilde{V}_1'\tilde{V}_1 & Y_1'X_1 \\ X_1'Y_1 & X_1'X_1 \end{bmatrix}^{-1} \begin{bmatrix} h_1^2\tilde{V}_1'\tilde{V}_1 \\ 0 \end{bmatrix} \tag{8.2.34}$$

$\tilde{d}_{.1}$ is as defined in (8.2.27), and $\tilde{\beta}_{.1}, \tilde{\gamma}_{.1}$ are the 2SLS estimators, respectively, of $\beta_{.1}, \gamma_{.1}$.

PROOF: Lemmas 1, 2, and 3.

Remark 4: Notice that, when written out explicitly, the identity in (8.2.33) assumes the form

$$\begin{bmatrix} \tilde{\beta}_{.1}(h_1, h_2) \\ \tilde{\gamma}_{.1}(h_1, h_2) \end{bmatrix} = \begin{bmatrix} \tilde{\beta}_{.1} \\ \tilde{\gamma}_{.1} \end{bmatrix} + \begin{bmatrix} Y_1'Y_1 - (1 - h_1^2)\tilde{V}_1'\tilde{V}_1 & Y_1'X_1 \\ X_1'Y_1 & X_1'X_1 \end{bmatrix}^{-1}$$
$$\times \begin{bmatrix} h_1(1 + h_2)\tilde{V}_1'\tilde{v}_{.1} - h_1^2\tilde{V}_1'\tilde{V}_1\tilde{\beta}_{.1} \\ 0 \end{bmatrix} \tag{8.2.35}$$

It is clear, therefore, that given the data and the 2SLS estimator, any member of the double k-class can be generated from (8.2.35) by appropriate variation of h_1 and h_2. In particular, notice that if

$$h_1 = 0 \tag{8.2.36}$$

$$\begin{bmatrix} \tilde{\beta}_{.1}(0, h_2) \\ \tilde{\gamma}_{.1}(0, h_2) \end{bmatrix} = \begin{bmatrix} \tilde{\beta}_{.1} \\ \tilde{\gamma}_{.1} \end{bmatrix} \tag{8.2.37}$$

so that the choice in (8.2.36) yields the 2SLS estimator. If

$$h_2 = h_1 - 1 \tag{8.2.38}$$

then the left-hand side of (8.2.35) yields the general k-class estimator. If (8.2.38) holds and, in addition, h_1 is *pure imaginary*, then we obtain the LIML estimator of the previous chapter, for it was shown there that the latter is a k-class estimator with $k \geq 1$.

If

$$h_2 = 0 \tag{8.2.39}$$

then the left-hand side of (8.2.35) yields the h-class estimator of Chapter 4. Finally, if

$$h_2 = 0 \qquad h_1 = 1 \text{ (or } h_1 = -1 \quad h_2 = -2) \tag{8.2.40}$$

then we obtain the OLS estimator.

Since we had shown in Chapter 6 that 2SLS is an optimal I.V. estimator—when the set of admissible instruments is the set of all linear combinations of the predetermined variables of the system—we conclude that (8.2.35) provides an explicit relation among nearly all limited information estimators of structural parameters studied in this book.

8.3 I.V., ILS, AND DOUBLE k-CLASS ESTIMATORS

It is perhaps easily inferred from the discussion of Chapters 4 and 6 that the general k-class estimator has a straightforward I.V. interpretation. To this effect, notice that in the context of the model in (8.2.15), the general k-class estimator of, say, the first structural equation, is, in view of (8.2.29) and Remark 4,

$$\begin{bmatrix} \hat{\beta}_{\cdot 1}(h_1, h_1 - 1) \\ \hat{\gamma}_{\cdot 1}(h_1, h_1 - 1) \end{bmatrix} = \begin{bmatrix} Y_1'Y_1 - (1 - h_1^2)\tilde{V}_1'\tilde{V}_1 & Y_1'X_1 \\ X_1'Y_1 & X_1'X_1 \end{bmatrix}^{-1} \begin{bmatrix} (Y_1' - (1 - h_1^2)\tilde{V}_1')y_{\cdot 1} \\ X_1'y_{\cdot 1} \end{bmatrix} \tag{8.3.1}$$

If P is the matrix of instrumental variables and if P is chosen as

$$P = [Y_1 - (1 - h_1^2)\tilde{V}_1, X_1] \tag{8.3.2}$$

it is easily seen that (8.3.1) has an interpretation as an I.V. estimator.

What is not frequently realized, however, is that ILS also represents an attempt at I.V. estimation. Recall Theorem 1 of Chapter 6 and the equations defining the ILS estimator of the parameters of, say, the first structural equation. They are of the form

$$\begin{bmatrix} \tilde{\Pi}_{G_1 m_1} & I \\ \tilde{\Pi}_{G^* m_1} & 0 \end{bmatrix} \begin{bmatrix} \hat{\beta}_{\cdot 1} \\ \hat{\gamma}_{\cdot 1} \end{bmatrix} = \begin{bmatrix} \tilde{\pi}_{G_1 1} \\ \tilde{\pi}_{G^* 1} \end{bmatrix} \tag{8.3.3}$$

$\hat{\beta}_{.1}, \hat{\gamma}_{.1}$ being the ILS estimators of $\beta_{.1}$ and $\gamma_{.1}$ respectively. But the matrix in the left member of (8.3.3) is simply

$$\begin{bmatrix} \tilde{\Pi}_{G_1 m_1} & I \\ \tilde{\Pi}_{G*m_1} & 0 \end{bmatrix} = [(X'X)^{-1}X'Y_1, C] = (X'X)^{-1}[X'Y_1, X'XC] \qquad (8.3.4)$$

where

$$C = \begin{bmatrix} I \\ 0 \end{bmatrix} \qquad (8.3.5)$$

But

$$X'XC = \begin{bmatrix} X_1'X_1 & X_1'X_2 \\ X_2'X_1 & X_2'X_2 \end{bmatrix} \begin{bmatrix} I \\ 0 \end{bmatrix} = X'X_1 \qquad (8.3.6)$$

On the other hand,

$$\begin{bmatrix} \tilde{\pi}_{G_1 1} \\ \tilde{\pi}_{G*1} \end{bmatrix} = (X'X)^{-1}X'y_{.1} \qquad (8.3.7)$$

Thus the equation in (8.3.3) can be written as

$$(X'X)^{-1}X'(Y_1, X_1)\hat{\delta}_{.1} = (X'X)^{-1}X'y_{.1} \qquad (8.3.8)$$

which is equivalent to

$$X'Z_1\hat{\delta}_{.1} = X'y_{.1} \qquad (8.3.9)$$

where, of course,

$$Z_1 = (Y_1, X_1) \qquad \hat{\delta}_{.1} = \begin{bmatrix} \hat{\beta}_{.1} \\ \hat{\gamma}_{.1} \end{bmatrix} \qquad (8.3.10)$$

But (8.3.9) represents exactly the equations defining the I.V. estimator when the matrix of instrumental variables is taken to be X.

If the equation under consideration is *just identified*, the matrix $X'Z_1$ would be nonsingular and thus we shall obtain a unique ILS estimator. This will be exactly the I.V. estimator. On the other hand, when the equation is *overidentified*, ILS may be interpreted as attempting to use "too many" instruments in estimating structural parameters. Consequently, it fails to yield unique estimators.

8.4 LIMITED INFORMATION ESTIMATORS AND JUST IDENTIFICATION

In past discussions we had considered two broad classes of estimators: those that make use of a priori information in all equations of the system and those that make use of a priori information relative to a certain subsystem only. In this book the subsystem was typically taken to consist of a *single equation*.

Estimators belonging to the first class are termed *full information*, while those belonging to the second class are termed *limited information estimators*. We had considered four basic types of limited information estimators, namely, 2SLS, I.V., ILS, and LIML estimators. This is so because when considering the k-, h- and double k-class estimators we observed that if such estimators are to be consistent, then they must (asymptotically) converge to the 2SLS estimator.

In this section we shall show that when we deal with the *just identified case*, all *four basic limited information estimators coincide*.

Thus consider again the general (structural) simultaneous equations model of Section 8.2 and, for definiteness, concentrate on the first equation,

$$y_{\cdot 1} = Z_1 \delta_{\cdot 1} + u_{\cdot 1} \tag{8.4.1}$$

where the symbols are as defined in (8.3.10). From Chapter 4 we recall that the 2SLS estimator of $\delta_{\cdot 1}$ is given by

$$\tilde{\delta}_{\cdot 1} = (Q_1' Q_1)^{-1} Q_1' w_{\cdot 1} \tag{8.4.2}$$

where

$$Q_1 = R^{-1} X' Z_1 \quad X'X = RR' \quad w_{\cdot 1} = R^{-1} X' y_{\cdot 1} \tag{8.4.3}$$

In the *just identified* case $X'Z_1$ would ordinarily be nonsingular and thus Q_1^{-1} will exist. Hence (8.4.2) will reduce to

$$\tilde{\delta}_{\cdot 1} = Q_1^{-1} w_{\cdot 1} = (X'Z_1)^{-1} X' y_{\cdot 1}' \tag{8.4.4}$$

Comparing with (8.3.9), we see that 2SLS, ILS, and I.V. estimators are equivalent even when the set of possible instruments is restricted to that of the predetermined variables of the model.

Finally, we recall that in Chapter 7 we had demonstrated that in the case of just identifiability, ILS and LIML estimators are equivalent. Thus our task is complete.

The discussion above is summarized in

Theorem 2: Consider the standard general structural model

$$y_{\cdot i} = Z_i \delta_{\cdot i} + u_{\cdot i} \quad i = 1, 2, \ldots, m \tag{8.4.5}$$

where

$$Z_i = (Y_i, X_i) \quad \delta_{\cdot i} = \begin{pmatrix} \beta_{\cdot i} \\ \gamma_{\cdot i} \end{pmatrix} \quad i = 1, 2, \ldots, m \tag{8.4.6}$$

and suppose that the ith structural equation is just identified. Then the 2SLS, LIML, ILS, and I.V. estimators of its parameters are equivalent (identical).

Remark 5: It should be noted, of course, that for the LIML estimator to have the property ascribed to it above, the joint distribution of the disturbances of the system must be normal.

8.5 RELATIONSHIPS AMONG FULL INFORMATION ESTIMATORS

In this section we shall explore the relation between the two full information estimators considered in this book, namely, 3SLS and FIML.

Consider again the standard general structural model as given, for example, in (8.2.16). In addition, assume that the model contains no identities, that every equation is identified, and that

$$u'_t. \sim N(0, \Sigma) \quad \text{Cov}(u'_t., u'_{t'}.) = \delta_{tt'} \Sigma \quad E(u_t. X) = 0 \qquad (8.5.1)$$

all t, t', where $\delta_{tt'}$ is the Kronecker delta, Σ a general positive definite matrix, and

$$u_t. = (u_{t1}, u_{t2}, \ldots, u_{tm}) \qquad (8.5.2)$$

is the vector of disturbances in *all* the equations of the system at time t.

Under these assumptions, we have shown in Chapter 7 that the (logarithm of the) likelihood function of the observations is given by

$$L(A, \Sigma; Y, X) = -\frac{mT}{2} \ln(2\pi) - \frac{T}{2} \ln |\Sigma| + \frac{T}{2} \ln |B^{*\prime}B^*| - \frac{1}{2} \text{tr}\{\Sigma^{-1} A'Z'ZA\}$$

$$(8.5.3)$$

where

$$B^* = I - B \quad A = \begin{pmatrix} B^* \\ -C \end{pmatrix} \quad Z = (Y, X) \qquad (8.5.4)$$

Of course, in all such discussions it is always assumed that $Z'Z/T$ and $\text{plim}(Z'Z/T)$ are positive definite matrices, the latter with nonstochastic elements.

Now define

$$\tilde{Z} = (\tilde{Y}, X) \qquad \tilde{Y} = X(X'X)^{-1}X'Y \qquad (8.5.5)$$

and notice that

$$Z = \tilde{Z} + (\tilde{V}, 0) \qquad \tilde{V} = Y - \tilde{Y} \qquad (8.5.6)$$

In (8.5.6), $\tilde{V}$ is the matrix of the system's reduced form residuals and as such it obeys

$$X'\tilde{V} = 0 \qquad \tilde{Y}'\tilde{V} = 0 \qquad (8.5.7)$$

Hence we can write

$$Z'Z = \tilde{Z}'\tilde{Z} + \begin{bmatrix} \tilde{V}'\tilde{V} & 0 \\ 0 & 0 \end{bmatrix} \qquad (8.5.8)$$

Thus the likelihood function in (8.5.3) may be expressed more conveniently as

$$L(A, \Sigma; Y, X) = L_1(A, \Sigma; Y, X) + L_2(\Sigma; U, X) \qquad (8.5.9)$$

where

$$L_1(A, \Sigma; Y, X) = -\frac{mT}{2}(\ln(2\pi) + 1) - \frac{T}{2}\ln\left|\frac{\tilde{V}'\tilde{V}}{T}\right| - \frac{1}{2}\operatorname{tr}(\Sigma^{-1}A'\tilde{Z}'\tilde{Z}A)$$

(8.5.10)

$$L_2(\Sigma; U, X) = \frac{T}{2}\ln\left|\frac{B^{*'}\tilde{V}'\tilde{V}B^*}{T}\right| - \frac{T}{2}\ln|\Sigma| - \frac{T}{2}\operatorname{tr}\left\{\Sigma^{-1}\frac{B^{*'}\tilde{V}'\tilde{V}B^*}{T}\right\} + \frac{mT}{2}$$

(8.5.11)

Let us now justify the notation $L_2(\Sigma; U, X)$, which implies that the term in question does not contain any parameter other than Σ. Notice that, by definition,

$$\tilde{V} = Y - X(X'X)^{-1}X'Y = (I - N)V \qquad N = X(X'X)^{-1}X' \tag{8.5.12}$$

where V is the matrix of reduced form disturbances given by

$$V = UB^{*-1} \tag{8.5.13}$$

in view of (8.5.4).

Hence

$$B^{*'}\tilde{V}'\tilde{V}B^* = B^{*'}V'(I - N)VB^* = U'(I - N)U \tag{8.5.14}$$

Thus (8.5.11) can also be written as

$$L_2(\Sigma; U, X) = \frac{T}{2}\ln\left|\frac{U'(I - N)U}{T}\right| - \frac{T}{2}\operatorname{tr}\left\{\Sigma^{-1}\frac{U'(I - N)U}{T}\right\} - \frac{T}{2}\ln|\Sigma| + \frac{mT}{2}$$

(8.5.15)

and we see that the notation is fully justified. Indeed, it may be readily seen that

$$\operatorname*{plim}_{T \to \infty} \frac{1}{T}L_2 = 0 \tag{8.5.16}$$

This is so since

$$\operatorname*{plim}_{T \to \infty} \frac{U'(I - N)U}{T} = \operatorname*{plim}_{T \to \infty} \frac{U'U}{T} - \operatorname*{plim}_{T \to \infty} \frac{U'NU}{T} = \Sigma \tag{8.5.17}$$

The preceding suggests that, if we are not interested in Σ, L_2 may be neglected in the maximization process. However, one may object to the procedure above, pointing out that although the argument with respect to L_2 is certainly suggestive, it is not entirely admissible, for we should not be dealing with nonobservables in the likelihood function. Or, alternatively, that if U is expressed in terms of A and Z, we indeed have other parameters entering L_2. Thus let us give a fuller, if more tedious, argument about the informational content of L_2.

As pointed out in Chapter 7, to obtain the FIML estimator of A, Σ, we maximize (8.5.3), partially, with respect to Σ, substitute the resulting expression therein, thus obtaining the "concentrated" likelihood function which is finally maximized with respect to A. As we had also determined in Chapter 7, the estimator of Σ thus obtained is

$$\hat{\Sigma} = \frac{A'Z'ZA}{T} \tag{8.5.18}$$

which may also be written as

$$\hat{\Sigma} = \frac{A'\tilde{Z}'\tilde{Z}A}{T} + \frac{B^{*\prime}\tilde{V}'\tilde{V}B^*}{T} \tag{8.5.19}$$

It is interesting to note that

$$\operatorname*{plim}_{T\to\infty} \frac{A'\tilde{Z}'\tilde{Z}A}{T} = 2\operatorname*{plim}_{T\to\infty} \left[\frac{C'X'XC}{T} - \frac{C'X'XC}{T}\right] = 0 \tag{8.5.20}$$

and thus, for large T, we have approximately

$$\hat{\Sigma} \approx \frac{B^{*\prime}\tilde{V}'\tilde{V}B^*}{T} \tag{8.5.21}$$

Substituting this in (8.5.11), we find

$$L_2 \approx \frac{T}{2}\ln\left|\frac{B^{*\prime}\tilde{V}'\tilde{V}B^*}{T}\right| - \frac{T}{2}\ln\left|\frac{B^{*\prime}\tilde{V}'\tilde{V}B^*}{T}\right| - \frac{T}{2}\operatorname{tr}\left\{\hat{\Sigma}^{-1}\frac{B^{*\prime}\tilde{V}'\tilde{V}B^*}{T}\right\} + \frac{mT}{2} = 0 \tag{8.5.22}$$

Thus the concentrated likelihood function is, approximately,

$$L(A;\ Y,\ X) \approx -\frac{mT}{2}(\ln(2\pi) + 1) - \frac{T}{2}\ln\left|\frac{\tilde{V}'\tilde{V}}{T}\right| - \frac{1}{2}\operatorname{tr}(\hat{\Sigma}^{-1}A'\tilde{Z}'\tilde{Z}A) \tag{8.5.23}$$

The preceding discussion has shown that, asymptotically, L_2 is a constant not depending on any unknown parameters and thus, asymptotically, FIML obtains an estimator for A by maximizing essentially L_1 in which the specific estimator $\hat{\Sigma}$ of (8.5.18) has been substituted for Σ.

We are now in a position to establish the relation between the 3SLS and FIML estimators clearly. Thus recall from Chapter 4 that we had obtained the 3SLS estimator by minimizing, in the notation of that chapter,

$$(w - Q\delta)'\Phi^{-1}(w - Q\delta)$$

conditionally on

$$\Phi = \Sigma \otimes I_G \tag{8.5.24}$$

We shall now show that

$$(w - Q\delta)'\Phi^{-1}(w - Q\delta) = \text{tr } \{\Sigma^{-1}A'\tilde{Z}'\tilde{Z}A\}^2 \tag{8.5.25}$$

Consider the transform of the system in (8.2.16)

$$R^{-1}X'Y = R^{-1}X'YB + R^{-1}X'XC + R^{-1}X'U \tag{8.5.26}$$

where R is a nonsingular matrix defined by

$$X'X = RR' \tag{8.5.27}$$

We may write (8.5.26) more conveniently as

$$R^{-1}X'ZA = R^{-1}X'U \tag{8.5.28}$$

We notice that the ith column in the left member of (8.5.28) is simply $w_{\cdot i} - Q_i\delta_{\cdot i}$, where, we remind the reader,

$$w_{\cdot i} = R^{-1}X'y_{\cdot i} \quad Q_i = R^{-1}X'Z \quad \delta_{\cdot i} = \begin{pmatrix} \beta_{\cdot i} \\ \gamma_{\cdot i} \end{pmatrix} \tag{8.5.29}$$

and

$$w = \begin{pmatrix} w_{\cdot 1} \\ w_{\cdot 2} \\ \vdots \\ w_{\cdot m} \end{pmatrix} \quad \delta = \begin{pmatrix} \delta_{\cdot 1} \\ \delta_{\cdot 2} \\ \vdots \\ \delta_{\cdot m} \end{pmatrix} \quad Q = \text{diag } (Q_1, Q_2, \ldots, Q_m) \tag{8.5.30}$$

To prove the assertion in (8.5.25), we recall from Chapter 7 [in particular, equation (7.2.14)] that if P, S are, respectively, $m \times n$ and $n \times n$ matrices, then

$$\text{tr } (PSP') = p'(S \otimes I_m)p \tag{8.5.31}$$

where p is defined by

$$p = \begin{pmatrix} p_{\cdot 1} \\ p_{\cdot 2} \\ \vdots \\ p_{\cdot m} \end{pmatrix} \quad P = (p_{\cdot 1}, p_{\cdot 2}, \ldots, p_{\cdot m}) \tag{8.5.32}$$

each $p_{\cdot i}$ being an n-element column vector.

In view of the relation in (8.5.31) and the fact that $w_{\cdot i} - Q_i\delta_{\cdot i}$ is also the ith column of $R^{-1}X'ZA$, we conclude

$$(w - Q\delta)'\Phi^{-1}(w - Q\delta) = \text{tr } (R^{-1}X'ZA\Sigma^{-1}A'Z'XR'^{-1}) \tag{8.5.33}$$

But

$$\text{tr } (R^{-1}X'ZA\Sigma^{-1}A'Z'XR'^{-1}) = \text{tr } (\Sigma^{-1}A'Z'X(X'X)^{-1}X'ZA) \tag{8.5.34}$$

---

[2] The reader should verify that 2SLS is obtained by minimizing tr $\{A'\tilde{Z}'\tilde{Z}A\}$.

Also, note that

$$X(X'X)^{-1}X'Z = [\tilde{Y}, X] = \tilde{Z} \tag{8.5.35}$$

and

$$Z = \tilde{Z} + [\tilde{V}, 0] \quad Z'\tilde{Z} = \tilde{Z}'\tilde{Z} \tag{8.5.36}$$

Thus

$$\text{tr}\, (\Sigma^{-1}A'Z'X(X'X)^{-1}X'ZA) = \text{tr}\, (\Sigma^{-1}A'\tilde{Z}'\tilde{Z}A) \tag{8.5.37}$$

which demonstrates the validity of (8.5.25).

Since

$$L_1(A, \Sigma; Y, X) = -\frac{mT}{2}(\ln\,(2\pi) + 1) - \frac{T}{2}\ln\left|\frac{\tilde{V}'\tilde{V}}{T}\right| - \frac{1}{2}\text{tr}\,(\Sigma^{-1}A'\tilde{Z}'\tilde{Z}A) \tag{8.5.38}$$

we see that 3SLS obtains an estimator for *A by maximizing L_1 conditionally on Σ and thereafter substituting for the latter a consistent estimator.*

As we saw earlier, FIML obtains an estimator by a procedure that, asymptotically, is equivalent to maximizing L_1 and substituting for Σ the specific (consistent) estimator

$$\hat{\Sigma} = \frac{A'Z'ZA}{T} \tag{8.5.39}$$

While 3SLS is a two-step procedure, FIML is a simultaneous procedure, for $\hat{\Sigma}$ is explicitly a function of A, the parameter matrix to be estimated. It is clear, of course, that to the extent that 3SLS uses a prior *consistent* estimator of Σ, the two procedures will be, in large samples, approximately equivalent and one would expect them to have the *same asymptotic distribution.* Indeed, it has been shown by direct, if cumbersome, methods [15, 19, 20] that the two estimators have the same asymptotic distribution, a result that is entirely transparent from the preceding discussion.

With this informal development, we have therefore established the following important points:

i. 3SLS and FIML estimators are asymptotically equivalent in the sense of having the same asymptotic distribution. More precisely, they differ only in the way they treat the estimation of the covariance matrix Σ; 3SLS is a two-step procedure, whereas FIML is a simultaneous one, obtaining in a single step estimators for A and Σ.
ii. *If we iterate 3SLS*—that is, if, after we estimate A, we use it to compute another estimate of Σ and then use the latter to obtain another estimate of A and so on until convergence is attained—*we do not converge to the FIML estimator, as is sometimes thought.*

Equation (8.5.23) makes our contention perfectly clear. It is apparent that if the relation in (8.5.23) were exact, then iterating 3SLS will indeed lead to the FIML estimator. *For finite samples, however, this cannot possibly hold since the relation in (8.5.23) is approximate, not exact.* This will be particularly so if the sample size were only moderate. If the sample size were quite large, then iteration will converge approximately to the FIML estimator.

Finally, we should remark that the small sample properties of the estimators studied in this and preceding sections still remain an open question and usually cannot be dealt with satisfactorily by analytical methods.

8.6 MONTE CARLO METHODS

THE GENERAL FRAMEWORK

Throughout this book, and particularly as we remarked in the previous section, it was found that while large sample properties of estimators could be established, small sample properties typically could not.

On the other hand, the samples with which we deal in practice are rather small, seldom exceeding 80 observations and frequently much smaller. Thus it would be of great interest to inquire into the properties of estimators for the typical sample sizes encountered in practice. While, for example, we have shown that 2SLS and LIML estimators are asymptotically equivalent—the same is true with respect to 3SLS and FIML estimators—it is conceivable that they may differ systematically in samples of small or moderate size. Furthermore, we have shown that 2SLS and LIML are less (not more) efficient than 3SLS and FIML estimators respectively. Still, the question of small sample properties remains open. Beyond that, we have the following additional complication. In any limited information technique (such as 2SLS and LIML), we rely solely on the explicit specification of the particular equation under consideration. With full information techniques (such as 3SLS and FIML), we must rely on the specification of *every equation* in the system. Thus we run a higher risk of misspecification error, and *this error though it may be present in only one equation propagates throughout the entire system.*

Finally, one might wonder whether OLS is, in small samples, sufficiently inferior to simultaneous equations techniques so as to warrant its complete exclusion from serious consideration as an estimation procedure for structural parameters.

These are questions of great practical importance to which, in the general case, no analytical answer can be given. Nonetheless, some tentative results can be obtained in terms of Monte Carlo methods. Perhaps the simplest way of explaining these methods is by analogy with numerical analysis.

Frequently we may be faced with an equation whose solution may not be obtainable explicitly in closed form; that is, it may not be possible to express the solution, explicitly, in terms of the parameters of the problem. In such cases, it may be possible to solve the equation by numerical methods *for given values of its parameters*. Then by varying the parameters we may observe the variation in the solution, and in this fashion we may, perhaps, infer the functional dependence of the solution on the parameters of the problem. Although we cannot, of course, possibly obtain the solution for every admissible value of the parameters, nonetheless, we can do so for a sufficiently dense subset of the parameter space so that we can form a reasonable impression of the nature of the dependence.

An entirely similar situation prevails with respect to the estimation problems we are considering here. In order to form a reasonable impression of the small sample distribution of a given estimator, we may obtain a number of estimates from various samples of a given size. By observing the behavior of the resulting estimates, we may infer some of the properties of the small sample distribution.

Can we use actual, real world data for this purpose? Obviously not. For several reasons. First, we cannot state with certitude that such data have been generated by the general structural model we have been considering. Hence we may be committing a misspecification error. This may be of various forms: some variables may have been omitted, or some variables may not have been entered in their proper mathematical form, for example, we may have used as a predetermined variable, say x, where in fact we should have used ln x. Or the error terms may not, in fact, have the properties required by our model. Second, even if we are entirely certain of the specification, we have no idea of what the "true" numerical magnitude of the parameters is, that is, we may not know the numerical magnitude of the elements of B and C. Thus no inference, for example, can be made regarding the *bias properties* of the particular estimator.

Finally, it is impossible to obtain real world samples in which the exogenous variables are held constant, for, in economics at least, we generally do not deal with replicated samples. Hence if we are to judge the small sample performance of alternative estimators of structural parameters, we must abstract from all influences not directly related to such estimators. Obviously, it is inappropriate to use real world data. What can we do then? Well, we use artificial models and generate, through them, artificial data. Specifically, we may proceed as follows: Suppose we wish to study the comparative performance of 2SLS and LIML estimators in the context, say, of a two-equation structural model. Thus

$$y_{t1} = \beta_{21}y_{t2} + \gamma_{11}x_{t1} + \gamma_{21}x_{t2} + u_{t1}$$
$$y_{t2} = \beta_{12}y_{t1} + \gamma_{12}x_{t1} + \gamma_{32}x_{t3} + u_{t2} \qquad (8.6.1)$$

What must we do in order to ensure that the data at our disposal actually correspond to the model in (8.6.1)?

Suppose that we generate the sequence of vectors

$$\{(x_{t1}, x_{t2}, x_{t3}): t = 1, 2, \ldots, T\}.$$

This may be done, for example, either by copying three random series out of some publication or, better still, by obtaining such data through a standard "random number generator" computer program. If we wish the error terms to be $N(0, \Sigma)$ and intertemporally independent, we may similarly obtain from a standard computer program two mutually independent $N(0, 1)$ sequences, say $\{(\varepsilon_{t1}, \varepsilon_{t2}): t = 1, 2, \ldots, T\}$. Thus if we put

$$\varepsilon_t = (\varepsilon_{t1}, \varepsilon_{t2})' \tag{8.6.2}$$

we know by construction that

$$E(\varepsilon_t) = 0 \qquad \mathrm{Cov}\,(\varepsilon_t, \varepsilon_{t'}) = \delta_{tt'} I \tag{8.6.3}$$

Since Σ is a positive definite matrix, we can decompose it by a nonsingular triangular matrix P such that

$$\Sigma = PP' \tag{8.6.4}$$

Consider now the random vectors

$$u_t = P\varepsilon_t \tag{8.6.5}$$

By construction, the vectors $\{u_t: t = 1, 2, \ldots, T\}$ have the properties

$$E(u_t) = 0 \qquad \mathrm{Cov}\,(u_t, u_{t'}) = \delta_{tt'}\, PIP' = \delta_{tt'} \Sigma \tag{8.6.6}$$

where $\delta_{tt'}$ is the Kronecker delta.

In this fashion, the desired error terms are obtained. We must also assign specific values to the structural parameters

$$\delta_{\cdot 1} = \begin{pmatrix} \beta_{21} \\ \gamma_{11} \\ \gamma_{21} \end{pmatrix} \qquad \delta_{\cdot 2} = \begin{pmatrix} \beta_{12} \\ \gamma_{12} \\ \gamma_{32} \end{pmatrix} \tag{8.6.7}$$

say

$$\delta^0 = \begin{pmatrix} \delta^0_{\cdot 1} \\ \delta^0_{\cdot 2} \end{pmatrix} \tag{8.6.8}$$

Put

$$B_0^* = \begin{bmatrix} 1 & -\beta^0_{12} \\ -\beta^0_{21} & 1 \end{bmatrix} \qquad C_0 = \begin{bmatrix} \gamma^0_{11} & \gamma^0_{12} \\ \gamma^0_{21} & 0 \\ 0 & \gamma_{32} \end{bmatrix} \tag{8.6.9}$$

and write the reduced form of the system as

$$(y_{t1}, y_{t2}) = (x_{t1}, x_{t2}, x_{t3}) C_0 B_0^{*-1} + (u_{t1}, u_{t2}) B_0^{*-1} \tag{8.6.10}$$

Since all quantities in the right-hand member of (8.6.10) are known, we can easily generate the vectors $\{(y_{t1}, y_{t2}): t = 1, 2, \ldots, T\}$. In this manner, we have indeed ensured that the data at our disposal

$$\{(y_{t1}, y_{t2}, x_{t1}, x_{t2}, x_{t3}): t = 1, 2, \ldots, T\}$$

have been generated by a model such as that in (8.6.1) with fixed parameter vector δ^0 and error terms that are "intertemporally independent" and distributed as $N(0, \Sigma)$, the matrix Σ being known.

Having done this, we forget that we know everything about the model and pretend that we are merely going to use the data in order to make inferences about its parameters. How can we use this scheme in order to shed some light on the small sample properties of estimators? We recall that ordinarily the distribution of estimators (of the parameters of a given model, the parameters being fixed but unknown constants) is obtained conditionally on the exogenous variables of the model. The estimator distribution is thus induced (solely) by the distribution of the error terms (and the manner in which the estimator uses the data).

Consequently, suppose that we generate a number, N, of samples—each of size T—on the random vector (u_1, u_2). Thus we have N samples of the form $\{(u_{t1}, u_{t2}): t = 1, 2, \ldots, T\}$. Suppose, further, that we choose *a* sample of size T on the exogenous variables; thus $\{x_{t1}, x_{t2}, x_{t3}): t = 1, 2, \ldots, T)\}$. These, in conjunction with the fixed parameter vector δ^0, will determine N samples of the form $\{(y_{t1}, y_{t2}): t = 1, 2, \ldots, T\}$, via the relation in (8.6.10). Notice *that both the parameter vector δ^0 as well as the set of exogenous variables*

$$\{(x_{t1}, x_{t2}, x_{t3}): t = 1, 2, \ldots, T\}$$

are common to all N samples.

We may now process the data thus obtained and derive N *estimates* of the parameter vector δ. Since each estimate corresponds to *a* random vector $\{(u_{t1}, u_{t2}): t = 1, 2, \ldots, T\}$, *we may treat this estimate as an "observation" from a population whose distribution is the distribution of the given estimator for samples of size T.*

If, for example, we are dealing with a single parameter, we could plot these N "observations," thus obtaining an "empirical distribution" (mass function) of the estimator.

Frequently, however, we are not interested in the distribution as such but in certain of its moments. In particular, we are interested in its mean and variance. This is so since we may wish to assess the bias or "efficiency" characteristics of the estimator.

Thus if we compute the mean (average) of all N estimates, and if N is sufficiently large, we may, with high degree of probability, assert that this is close, in a consistency sense, to the mean of the small sample distribution of the estimator. If we subtract the true value of the parameter from this average, we have a measure of the small sample bias of the estimator.

To be specific, let $\hat{\delta}_j$ be the estimate of the parameter vector obtained from the jth sample. We may take

$$\bar{\hat{\delta}}_T = \frac{1}{N} \sum_{j=1}^{N} \hat{\delta}_j \tag{8.6.11}$$

to be our estimate of the mean of the small (size T) sample distribution of the estimator. A measure of the bias is obtained as

$$b(\hat{\delta}_T) = \bar{\hat{\delta}}_T - \delta^0 \qquad (8.6.12)$$

δ^0 being the true value of the parameter vector; the subscript T is inserted to stress the fact that this is a result pertinent to samples of size T. The covariance matrix of the small sample distribution may be "estimated" by

$$\text{Cov}(\hat{\delta}_T) = \frac{1}{N} \sum_{j=1}^{N} (\hat{\delta}_j - \bar{\hat{\delta}}_T)(\hat{\delta}_j - \bar{\hat{\delta}}_T)' \qquad (8.6.13)$$

The covariance matrix about the true parameter value is given by

$$\overline{\text{Cov}}(\hat{\delta}_T) = \frac{1}{N} \sum_{j=1}^{N} (\hat{\delta}_j - \delta^0)(\hat{\delta}_j - \delta^0)' = \text{Cov}(\hat{\delta}_T) + (\bar{\hat{\delta}}_T - \delta^0)(\bar{\hat{\delta}}_T - \delta^0)' \qquad (8.6.14)$$

This last measure gives information simultaneously regarding the covariance and bias characteristics of the estimator. Now, suppose that we wish to compare the small sample properties of two estimators, say 2SLS and LIML. How do we proceed? First we determine what we wish to mean by "small sample." We may wish to consider samples of size $T = 20$, $T = 50$, etc.

We now generate N samples[3] of the chosen size, say $T = 20$, in the manner indicated above. We then obtain N 2SLS and N LIML estimates of δ. For each set we may compute the summary characteristics $\bar{\hat{\delta}}_T$, $b(\hat{\delta}_T)$, $\overline{\text{Cov}}(\hat{\delta}_T)$. We may rank the two estimators by comparing the quantities $b(\hat{\delta}_T)$ and $\overline{\text{Cov}}(\hat{\delta}_T)$ corresponding to each.

A particularly useful measure in this connection is

$$e = \frac{|\overline{\text{Cov}}(\hat{\delta}_T)_{\text{LIML}}|}{|\overline{\text{Cov}}(\hat{\delta}_T)_{\text{2SLS}}|} \qquad (8.6.15)$$

If $e \geq 1$, we may say that 2SLS is "efficient" relative to LIML. Of course, we can make similar comparisons with respect to individual elements of δ, but this is somewhat less satisfactory than the measure in (8.6.15), although we certainly gain in detail by such individual element comparisons.

The measure in (8.6.15) is a ratio of "generalized variances" (about the true parameter vector), which at the same time takes into account the bias characteristics of the two estimators. As we shall see in the example below, certain other measures are also in common use. Before we deal with examples, we might caution the reader on two points: First, before such studies are undertaken, one

---

[3] N would be chosen as large as possible if there were only negligible computational costs. The reader may ask himself why this is desirable.

must make certain that at least the first two moments of the small sample distribution exist, otherwise the quantities $\bar{\bar{\delta}}_T$ and $\overline{\text{Cov}}\,(\hat{\delta}_T)$ are meaningless.[4] Second, it must not be thought that Monte Carlo studies can entirely solve the small sample distribution problem. Notice that to give a satisfactory account of the small sample properties of various estimators, even in this small two equation model, we must explore the entire space of admissible parameters. What we have outlined above is a procedure for determining certain characteristics of the small sample distribution of, say, the 2SLS and LIML estimators *for a specific parameter vector* δ^0. It does not follow that whatever conclusions had been derived would continue to be valid if other parameter vectors had been considered instead, say $\delta^{(i)}$, $i = 1, 2, \ldots$.

In order to arrive at definitive conclusions, the admissible parameter space must be adequately explored. This will clearly involve immense computational problems. Furthermore, it may well be that increasing the number of predetermined and jointly dependent variables (equations) would substantially alter our conclusions. The same may be true if the exogenous variables are varied.

Thus it is almost impossible to reach a complete and satisfactory solution of the small sample distribution problem solely by Monte Carlo methods. On the other hand, when dealing with concrete problems in which a well-specified model is considered and where reliable a priori information confines its parameters within a relatively narrow region, Monte Carlo methods may be quite valuable in aiding us with the choice of the appropriate estimation procedure.

EXAMPLES AND RESULTS OF MONTE CARLO STUDIES

A number of well-designed Monte Carlo experiments are to be found in the literature [24, 5]. Here we shall consider a few of the results obtained in the comprehensive study by Summers [22], which deals with the comparative performance (primarily) of LIML, 2SLS, FIML, and OLS estimators. Of necessity, we shall cite only a small portion of these results.

The model under consideration is[5]

$$y_{t1} - \beta_{21}y_{t2} = \gamma_{01} + \gamma_{11}x_{t1} + \gamma_{21}x_{t2} \qquad\qquad + u_{t1}$$
$$y_{t1} - \beta_{22}y_{t2} = \gamma_{02} \qquad\qquad + \gamma_{32}x_{t3} + \gamma_{42}x_{t4} + u_{t2} \qquad (8.6.16)$$

The error vectors $\{(u_{t1}, u_{t2}): t = 1, 2, \ldots, T\}$ are chosen to be mutually independent and identically distributed as $N(0, \Sigma)$, where

$$\Sigma = 400 \begin{bmatrix} 1 & \frac{1}{2} \\ \frac{1}{2} & 1 \end{bmatrix} \qquad\qquad (8.6.17)$$

---

[4] The reader may ask himself: Are we justified in carrying out a Monte Carlo study with respect to the model as exhibited in (8.6.1)? If not, why not?

[5] Notice that the standard normalization is not imposed on the second equation; also, it is not clear that for this model limited information estimators possess finite second-order small sample moments; see Chapter 4.

The parameter vectors are (corresponding to his experiment 4)

$$\delta_{.1} = \begin{pmatrix} 1.3 \\ 149.5 \\ -0.8 \\ -0.7 \end{pmatrix} \qquad \delta_{.2} = \begin{pmatrix} -0.4 \\ 149.6 \\ -0.6 \\ 0.4 \end{pmatrix} \tag{8.6.18}$$

The sample size was $T = 20$ and the number of samples employed was $N = 50$. The predetermined variables were nearly uncorrelated, their correlation matrix being

$$\text{Corr }(x) = \begin{bmatrix} 1 & .078 & .16 & .38 \\ & 1 & .017 & -0.057 \\ & & 1 & .31 \\ & & & 1 \end{bmatrix} \tag{8.6.19}$$

The results (of his Experiment 4) are summarized in Table 8.1.

The results given in Table 8.1 are more or less in accord with what we would expect from asymptotic theory: 2SLS and LIML estimators behave quite

TABLE 8.1. Bias and root mean square errors[a] of estimators (model correctly specified)

	$b(\hat{\delta}_{.1})$	R.M.S.E. $(\hat{\delta}_{.1})$	$b(\hat{\delta}_{.2})$	R.M.S.E. $(\hat{\delta}_{.2})$
LIML	.0276	.132	.0118	.182
	.2019	22.3	-4.032	75.000
	-0.0279	.173	.0084	.669
	-0.0022	.105	.0118	.062
2SLS	.0326	.133	-0.0005	.175
	.3508	22.3	-3.190	75.1
	-0.0322	.173	.0079	.668
	-0.0040	.105	.0075	.061
FIML	.0280	.131	.0099	.181
	.3471	22.0	-8.484	71.8
	-0.0279	.164	.0488	.628
	-0.0038	.103	.0045	.062
OLS	.1051	.170	-0.1294	.218
	2.565	22.2	7.876	72.7
	-0.0958	.197	-0.0174	.640
	-0.0290	.110	-0.0410	.072

[a] Root mean square errors (R.M.S.E.) are simply the square roots of the diagonal elements of the matrix $\overline{\text{Cov}}\ (\hat{\delta}_T)$. The off-diagonal elements are are not given in the study.

similarly, while FIML estimators are slightly more efficient in the sense that their R.M.S.E. are slightly lower than those corresponding to 2SLS and LIML estimators. While OLS is invariantly inferior to the others, it is, nonetheless, interesting that the difference between R.M.S.E. of coefficients of predetermined variables is rather slight as between OLS and other estimators.

In an attempt to test the sensitivity of various estimators to misspecification errors, Summers also considers the case (Experiment 5A) in which the model in (8.6.16) is modified so that its second equation contains in its right member $-0.5x_{t1}$. For this group of samples ($T = 20$, $N = 50$), the following (other) parameter values are assumed—corresponding to the equations as exhibited in (8.6.16).

$$
\delta_{\cdot 1} = \begin{pmatrix} 0.7 \\ 149.5 \\ -0.8 \\ -0.7 \end{pmatrix} \qquad
\delta_{\cdot 2} = \begin{pmatrix} -0.4 \\ 149.6 \\ -0.6 \\ 0.4 \end{pmatrix} \tag{8.6.20}
$$

The model is now estimated ignoring the variable x_{t1} appearing, by construction, in the second equation. The results (Experiment 5A) are given in Table 8.2 below.

TABLE 8.2.   Bias and root mean square errors of estimators (model misspecified)

	$b(\hat{\delta}_{\cdot 1})$	R.M.S.E. $(\hat{\delta}_{\cdot 1})$	$b(\hat{\delta}_{\cdot 2})$	R.M.S.E. $(\hat{\delta}_{\cdot 2})$
LIML	.0081	.078	.2871	.364
	.5413	23.2	31.01	77.2
	−0.0164	.176	.1154	.659
	.0116	.082	−0.0632	.108
2SLS	.0126	.078	.1669	.241
	.7452	23.2	42.22	77.7
	−0.0204	.176	.0643	.609
	.0092	.082	−0.0188	.071
FIML	.0363	.101	.3396	.491
	13.09	31.10	30.11	92.7
	−0.1443	.284	.1027	.783
	.0186	.100	−0.0823	.164
OLS	.0704	.099	.0325	.144
	3.680	22.9	54.58	83.5
	−0.0742	.183	.0099	.582
	−0.0217	.083	.0307	.064

From Table 8.2 we see that 2SLS is a bit less sensitive to the type of specification error considered here than LIML is; on the other hand, as we would expect, FIML is considerably more sensitive.

Finally, OLS, particularly in the second equation, compares rather well with FIML, a result one would not necessarily expect from the nature of the estimation schemes. It causes no surprise, of course, that FIML—indeed, any full information procedure—is more sensitive to specification error than is LIML or 2SLS. This is so since the specification of equations other than the one under consideration is of little consequence in limited information schemes. We never use this information explicitly. A misspecification due to the omission of a relevant variable in another equation would be of consequence in such a scheme if that variable is a predetermined one and *appears nowhere else in the system.* If this is so, then the (unrestricted) reduced form estimator is affected and through this, the structural estimators *for all equations.*

On the other hand, in the case of full information schemes, the (specification of the) structure of every equation is explicitly utilized in the estimation of every other equation and thus misspecification, no matter where committed, will propagate and thus affect the estimator of every parameter in the system. We would, however, expect that the parameters of the misspecified equation will be more affected than those of other equations.

Finally, it might be remarked that we need not confine ourselves to the bias and R.M.S.E. characteristics in making a choice among alternative estimators. In any concrete problem, we are interested in "correctly" explaining certain jointly dependent variables rather than in the distribution characteristics of the estimators per se. Indeed, we may be more interested in some variables than in others. In such a situation, it may well be desirable to define a loss function (weighting scheme) over the jointly dependent variables and choose the estimator that, in the context of the specific model we are studying, minimizes that loss function.

REFERENCES

1. Basmann, R. L., "A Note on the Exact Finite Sample Frequency Functions of Generalized Classical Linear Estimators in Two Leading Overidentified Cases," *Journal of the American Statistical Association*, vol. 56, 1961, pp. 619–636.
2. Basmann, R. L., "A Note on the Exact Finite Sample Frequency Functions of Generalized Classical Linear Estimators in a Leading Three-Equation Case," *Journal of the American Statistical Association*, vol. 58, 1963, pp. 161–171.
3. Chow, G. C., "A Comparison of Alternative Estimators for Simultaneous Equations," *Econometrica*, vol. 32, 1964, pp. 532–553.
4. Christ, C. F., "Simultaneous Equation Estimation: Any Verdict Yet?" *Econometrica*, vol. 28, 1960, pp. 835–845.
5. Cragg, J. G., "On the Relative Small Sample Properties of Several Structural Equation Estimators," *Econometrica*, vol. 35, 1967, pp. 89–110.

6. Cragg, J. G., "Some Effects of Incorrect Specification on the Small Sample Properties of Several Simultaneous Equation Estimators," *International Economic Review*, vol. 9, 1968, pp. 63–86.
7. Goldberger, A. S., "An Instrumental Variable Interpretation of *k*-Class Estimation," *Indian Economic Journal* (Econometric Annual), vol. 13, No. 3, 1965, pp. 424–431.
8. Goldfeld, S. M., and R. E. Quandt, "Nonlinear Simultaneous Equations: Estimation and Prediction," *International Economic Review*, vol. 9, 1968, pp. 113–136.
9. Hildreth, C., "Simultaneous Equations: Any Verdict Yet?" *Econometrica*, vol. 28, 1960, pp. 846–854.
10. Kabe, D. G., "A Note on the Exact Distributions of the GCL Estimators in Two Leading Overidentified Cases," *Journal of the American Statistical Association*, vol. 58, 1963, pp. 535–537.
11. Kabe, D. G., "On the Exact Distributions of the GCL estimators in a Leading Three-Equation Case," *Journal of the American Statistical Association*, vol. 59, 1964, pp. 881–894.
12. Klein, L. R., "On the Interpretation of Theil's Method of Estimating Economic Relationships," *Metroeconomica*, vol. 7, 1955, pp. 147–153.
13. Klein, L. R., "The Efficiency of Estimation in Econometric Models," in *Essays in Economics and Econometrics in Honor of Harold Hotelling*, R. W. Pfouts (Ed.) Chapel Hill, University of North Carolina Press, 1960, pp. 216–233.
14. Klein, L. R., "Single Equation versus Equation System Methods of Estimation in Econometrics," *Econometrica*, vol. 28, 1960, pp. 866–871.
15. Madansky, A., "On the Efficiency of Three-Stage Least Squares Estimation," *Econometrica*, vol. 32, 1964, pp. 51–56.
16. Nagar, A. L., "A Monte Carlo Study of Alternative Simultaneous Equation Estimators," *Econometrica*, vol. 28, 1960, pp. 573–590.
17. Quandt, R. E., "On Certain Small Sample Properties of *k*-Class Estimators," *International Economic Review*, vol. 6, 1965, pp. 92–104.
18. Richardson, D. H., "The Exact Distribution of a Structural Coefficient Estimator," Paper No. 16, Dept. of Economics, University of Kansas. To be published in *Journal of the American Statistical Association*.
19. Rothenberg, T. J., and C. T. Leenders, "Efficient Estimation of Simultaneous Equation Systems," *Econometrica*, vol. 32, 1964, pp. 57–76.
20. Sargan, J. D., "Three-Stage Least Squares and Full Maximum Likelihood Estimates," *Econometrica*, Vol. 32, 1964, pp. 77–81.
21. Sawa, Takamitsu, "The Exact Sampling Distribution of Ordinary Least Squares and Two-Stage Least Squares Estimators," Research Institute for the Japanese Economy, Faculty of Economics, University of Tokyo, 1968.
22. Summers, R., "A Capital Intensive Approach to the Small Sample Properties of Various Simultaneous Equation Estimators," *Econometrica*, vol. 33, 1965, pp. 1–41.
23. Takeuchi, K., "Exact Sampling Moments of Ordinary Least Squares, Instrumental Variables, and Two-Stage Least Squares Estimators," to be published in the *International Economic Review*.
24. Wagner, H. M., "A Monte Carlo Study of Estimates of Simultaneous Linear Structural Equations," *Econometrica*, vol. 26, 1958, pp. 117–133.

SPECTRAL
ANALYSIS

9 ## 9.1 STOCHASTIC PROCESSES

MOTIVATION AND GENERALITIES

The entire discussion so far has been conducted within the following framework: A population was postulated and was asserted to be characterized by a density function whose parameters were unknown but fixed. We had at our disposal, a sample of size T (typically a random sample) from the population and on the basis of this sample we sought to make inferences regarding the unknown parameters. Generally we had used, at most, the second moment characteristics of the sample. Occasionally the analysis of (properties of) random variables in terms of moments of their distribution is said to be analysis "in the time domain."

Frequently, however, we may encounter a more difficult situation. For example, we may be dealing with a situation in which the sample at our disposal consists of *single* observations on *different* random variables, and the problem may be whether circumstances exist under which such samples may yield useful information. If, for instance, we are confronted with a series of prices (over time) of a given commodity, say $\{p_t : t = 1, 2, \ldots, T\}$, it might be more appropriate to consider p_t as a single observation on the population of all possible prices (for this commodity) that could have been generated at time t, this population being characterized by the density $f_t(\cdot)$. In such a case, we call the sequence of random variables a stochastic process, a term that will be defined more precisely below.

Under certain circumstances, a stochastic process can be decomposed into an "infinite sum" of sinusoids of *different* (nonstochastic) frequencies and *random* amplitudes. For instance, the price process above might be expressed in terms of the sinusoids $z(\lambda) \exp(it\lambda)$, where $z(\lambda)$ is a (complex) *random* variable, λ is *nonstochastic*, $\exp(it\lambda) = \cos \lambda t + i \sin \lambda t$, and i is the imaginary unit obeying $i^2 = -1$. This is said to be a representation of the random variable in the "frequency domain," and *spectral analysis* consists of examining various aspects of a stochastic process when its constituent elements (random variables) have been given a representation in the frequency domain.

Unfortunately, it is not possible at this stage to give a meaningful intuitive insight into the scope of the applications of spectral analytic techniques or of its merits relative to analysis in the time domain. A clear understanding of the more elementary aspects of the theory of stochastic processes is needed first.

Definition 1: If T is a set such that if $t_1, t_2 \in T$ then $t_1 + t_2 \in T$, T is said to be a linear set.

Definition 2: Let $\{X_t\}$ be a family of random variables indexed by the linear (index) set T. Then $\{X_t\}$ is said to be a stochastic process and is usually denoted by $\{X(t): t \in T\}$.

The notations X_t and $X(t)$ will be used interchangeably.

The term *time series* is often used synonymously with the term *stochastic process*, particularly in the statistical literature. The index t is often referred to as *time*.

Since the index set is typically infinite, the question of how to specify the probability characteristics of a stochastic process arises. The convention adopted is the following.

Convention: The probability characteristics of a stochastic process $\{X(t): t \in T\}$ are completely specified if we determine the joint density (or mass) function of a finite (but arbitrary) number of members of the family of random variables comprising the process.

Example 1: Let $t_i \in T$, $i = 1, 2, \ldots, n$, n arbitrary, T a linear set. If we are able to specify the joint density (or mass) function of $(X_{t_1}, X_{t_2}, \ldots, X_{t_n})$ for any n, then we say that we have specified the probability characteristics of the stochastic process $\{X(t): t \in T\}$.

The mean function of a stochastic process is defined by

$$E[X(t)] = m(t) \qquad\qquad (9.1.1)$$

The covariance function, or covariance kernel as it is occasionally called, is defined by

$$\text{Cov}\,[X(t), X(s)] = E\{[X(t) - m(t)][X(s) - m(s)]\} = K(t, s) \qquad s, t \in T. $$
$$(9.1.2)$$

Example 2: Consider the stochastic process

$$X(t) = X_1 + X_2 t \qquad T = \{t: t \in N\} \tag{9.1.3}$$

N being the set $(0, 1, 2, \ldots)$.

Let the X_i, $i = 1, 2$, be normal, independently distributed, random variables with mean μ_i and variance σ_i^2.

The mean function of the stochastic process in (9.1.3) is

$$E[X(t)] = m(t) = \mu_1 + \mu_2 t \tag{9.1.4}$$

The covariance kernel is given by

$$\text{Cov}\,[X(t), X(s)] = \sigma_1^2 + \sigma_2^2 ts \tag{9.1.5}$$

Example 3: Let the index set T be defined by $T = \{t: t \geq 0\}$ and define

$$X(t) = A \cos \lambda t + B \sin \lambda t \tag{9.1.6}$$

where λ is a fixed number and A, B are independently distributed normal variables with mean 0 and variance σ_1^2, σ_2^2 respectively.

The mean function of (9.1.6) is given by

$$E[X(t)] = m(t) = 0 \tag{9.1.7}$$

and its covariance function by

$$\text{Cov}\,[X(s), X(t)] = E[X(s)X(t)] = \sigma_1^2 \cos \lambda t \cos \lambda s + \sigma_2^2 \sin \lambda t \sin \lambda s \tag{9.1.8}$$

Note that if $\sigma_1^2 = \sigma_2^2 = \sigma^2$, then (9.1.8) reduces to

$$\text{Cov}\,[X(s), X(t)] = \sigma^2(\cos \lambda t \cos \lambda s + \sin \lambda t \sin \lambda s)$$
$$= \sigma^2 \cos \lambda (t - s) \tag{9.1.9}$$

which depends only on $|t - s|$ because $\cos \alpha = \cos(-\alpha)$.

The correlation function of a stochastic process is defined by

$$\text{Corr}\,[X(t), X(s)] = r(t, s) = \frac{K(t, s)}{[K(t, t)K(s, s)]^{\frac{1}{2}}} \tag{9.1.10}$$

The correlation function of the series in (9.1.3) is simply

$$r(t, s) = \frac{\sigma_1^2 + \sigma_2^2 ts}{[(\sigma_1^2 + \sigma_2^2 t^2)(\sigma_1^2 + \sigma_2^2 s^2)]^{\frac{1}{2}}} \tag{9.1.11}$$

while that of the process in (9.1.6) is given by (for $\sigma_1^2 = \sigma_2^2 = \sigma^2$)

$$r(t, s) = \frac{\sigma^2 \cos \lambda (t - s)}{\sigma^2} = \cos \lambda (t - s) \tag{9.1.12}$$

Stochastic processes are usually classified as either *stationary* or *evolutionary*.

Definition 3: The stochastic process $\{X(t): t \in T\}$, T being a linear index set, is said to be

i. strictly stationary of order k if for fixed k and $t_i \in T$, $i = 1, 2, \ldots, k$, $h \in T$, the joint density (or mass) function of $(X_{t_1}, X_{t_2}, \ldots, X_{t_k})$ is identical with the joint density (or mass) function of $(X_{t_1+h}, \ldots, X_{t_k+h})$.

ii. strictly stationary if for any k the stochastic process is strictly stationary of order k, that is, if i above holds for *arbitrary* k.

iii. covariance stationary (or weakly stationary, or stationary in the wide sense) if the covariance function exists, that is if $K(t, s)$ is finite, and it is a function only of $|t - s|$.

Although condition iii does not require it, an *additional* restriction is usually imposed for covariance stationary processes, namely, that the mean function be a constant over the index set of the process. Generally we shall assume this restriction to hold.

Example 4: The process defined in (9.1.3) has covariance kernel

$$\text{Cov}\,[X(t), X(s)] = \sigma_1^2 + \sigma_2^2 ts \tag{9.1.13}$$

It is clear that

$$\text{Cov}\,[X(t + h), X(s + h)] = \sigma_1^2 + \sigma_2^2(t + h)(s + h) \neq \sigma_1^2 + \sigma_2^2 ts \tag{9.1.14}$$

and hence that the process is not stationary either in the sense i, or ii, or iii.

Example 5: The stochastic process defined in (9.1.6) has mean function zero and covariance kernel

$$\text{Cov}\,[X(t), X(s)] = \sigma^2 \cos \lambda(t - s) \tag{9.1.15}$$

in the special case, $\sigma_1^2 = \sigma_2^2 = \sigma^2$.

Because the cosine is an even[1] function (9.1.6) is clearly a covariance stationary process.

Incidentally, consider again the process in (9.1.6) but assume A has mean μ_1 and variance σ_1^2, B has mean μ_2 and variance σ_2^2, and as before A and B are mutually independent.

Then

$$E[X(t)] = \mu_1 \cos \lambda t + \mu_2 \sin \lambda t \tag{9.1.16}$$

$$\text{Cov}\,[X(t), X(s)] = \sigma_1^2 \cos \lambda t \cos \lambda s + \sigma_2^2 \sin \lambda t \sin \lambda s \tag{9.1.17}$$

which reduces to (9.1.15) if $\sigma_1^2 = \sigma_2^2 = \sigma^2$.

This demonstrates that strictly speaking, according to the definition in iii, a covariance stationary process need not have a constant mean function.

---

[1] A function $f(\cdot)$ is *even* if $f(-x) = f(x)$; it is *odd* if $f(-x) = -f(x)$.

Assume, additionally, that $A \sim N(\mu_1, \sigma^2)$, $B \sim N(\mu_1, \sigma^2)$ and are mutually independent.

In this context, let us ask: Is the process in (9.1.6) covariance stationary of some order k? It is elementary to show that the parameters of the (normal) joint distribution of $X(t)$, $X(s)$ are given by

$$E\begin{pmatrix} X(t) \\ X(s) \end{pmatrix} = V\begin{pmatrix} \mu_1 \\ \mu_2 \end{pmatrix} \qquad \text{Cov}\begin{pmatrix} X(t) \\ X(s) \end{pmatrix} = \sigma^2 VV' \qquad (9.1.18)$$

where

$$V = \begin{bmatrix} \cos \lambda t & \sin \lambda t \\ \cos \lambda s & \sin \lambda s \end{bmatrix} \qquad (9.1.19)$$

The diagonal elements of VV' are unity, while the off-diagonals are simply $\cos \lambda(t - s)$. Since for strict stationarity of order k we require that the joint density of $\{X(t), X(s)\}$ be identical with that of $\{X(t + h), X(s + h)\}$ for t, s, and h in the index set of the process, we conclude that our process is strictly stationary of order $k = 2$ only in the special case $\mu_1 = \mu_2 = 0$.

If the assumption of normality is dropped, then the density of A and B, and hence of the process itself, is insufficiently described. Therefore we cannot really answer the question of strict stationarity.

Remark 1: It is clear from the definition, and evident from the preceding example, that if a process is *strictly* stationary of order $k \geq 1$, then its mean function must be a constant. This is so since if $\{X(t): t \in T\}$ is the process and $t_1, h \in T$, then $X(t_1)$ and $X(t_1 + h)$ must have the same mean. Hence

$$m(t_1) = m(t_1 + h) \qquad (9.1.20)$$

for any $t_1, h \in T$.

Clearly, if T is a dense set, the conclusion is obvious that $m(\cdot)$ is a constant function.

Remark 2: Although, as pointed out above, the definition of a covariance stationary process does not require the mean function to be a constant, nonetheless, in subsequent discussions we shall always assume this to be so.

INFERENCE IN TIME SERIES; ERGODICITY

We defined the process $\{X(t): t \in T\}$, where T is a linear index set. The definition, however, was somewhat elliptic in that a more precise representation would have been $\{X(t, s): t \in T, s \in S\}$, where S is the sample space over which the random variables comprising the stochastic process are defined.

In the context of our new notation, $X(t, \cdot)$ is simply a family of random variables indexed by t. However, $X(\cdot, s)$ has not been given meaning yet.

Definition 4: The function—of time—$X(\cdot, s)$ is called a *realization* or *sample function* of the process.

Example 6: Suppose it were true that the behavior of a certain stock price average p can reasonably be considered a stochastic process. If we were to record observations on this average at the close of each trading day, then the resulting sequence gives a realization of the process.

Thus one realization may conceivably be the graph of Figure 9.1. The situation that typically arises in econometrics is that we have a single realization and from this we seek some information concerning the probability characteristics of the series at hand. Notice, however, that this situation is conceptually very different from that ordinarily encountered in problems of statistical inference. Notice that if we have, say, n observations on the stochastic process, then we have one observation each on n random variables. If the times of observation are $t_1, t_2, \ldots, t_n$, then we have one observation on each of the n random variables $X(t_i, \cdot)$, $i = 1, 2, \ldots, n$. In the usual problems of statistical inference, we have a number of observations, say k, on the *same* random variable and on the basis of that we seek to make inferences concerning the parameters of its distribution.

The importance and usefulness of the class of stationary stochastic processes are that *ergodic theorems* can be proved for such a class. The meaning of the term will be made clear below.

Before continuing, however, some mathematical concepts are needed.

Definition 5: Let $\{a_n : n \in N\}$, $N = 0, 1, 2, \ldots$, be a sequence of real numbers. Let the nth partial sum of the corresponding series be given by

$$s_n = \sum_{i=0}^{n} a_i \tag{9.1.21}$$

Let

$$s = \lim_{n \to \infty} s_n = \sum_{i=0}^{\infty} a_i \tag{9.1.22}$$

Consider now

$$S_n = \frac{1}{n} \sum_{k=0}^{n-1} s_k \qquad S_1 \equiv s_0 \equiv a_0 \tag{9.1.23}$$

FIGURE 9.1 Realization of an artificially constructed time series

Then

$$S = \lim_{n \to \infty} S_n \qquad (9.1.24)$$

is said to be the Cèsaro sum of the series in (9.1.22). If S is finite, then the series is said to be *Cèsaro convergent, or convergent in Cèsaro sum.*

Remark 3: Notice that S may exist even though s does not. Thus consider the sequence $a_n = (-1)^n$, $n = 0, 1, 2, \ldots$. Clearly the series $\sum_{i=0}^{\infty} a_i$ is divergent. On the other hand, its nth partial sum is given by

$$\begin{aligned} s_n &= 1 \qquad \text{if } n = 2k, k \geq 0 \\ &= 0 \qquad \text{if } n = 2k + 1, k \geq 0 \end{aligned} \qquad (9.1.25)$$

It follows, therefore, that

$$S = \lim_{n \to \infty} \frac{1}{n} \sum_{k=0}^{n-1} s_k = \frac{1}{2} \qquad (9.1.26)$$

Remark 4: Notice, also, that

$$S_n = \frac{1}{n} \sum_{k=0}^{n-1} s_k = \frac{1}{n} \sum_{k=0}^{n-1} \sum_{i=0}^{k} a_i = \frac{1}{n} \sum_{k=0}^{n} (n - k) a_k$$

$$= \sum_{k=0}^{n} \left(1 - \frac{k}{n} \right) a_k \qquad (9.1.27)$$

It follows, therefore, that if a series is Cèsaro convergent, then

$$S = \lim_{n \to \infty} \sum_{k=0}^{n} \left(1 - \frac{k}{n} \right) a_k \qquad (9.1.28)$$

Remark 5: It should be clear that if a series is convergent in the ordinary sense, then it is also Cèsaro convergent and the two sums are identical. The proof of this is quite simple.

Let

$$s = \lim_{n \to \infty} s_n \qquad (9.1.29)$$

and consider

$$R_n = |S_n - s| \qquad (9.1.30)$$

It follows from (9.1.29) that for any $\varepsilon > 0$ there exists an index $N(\varepsilon)$ such that for all $n > N(\varepsilon)$,

$$|s_n - s| < \varepsilon \qquad (9.1.31)$$

Rewriting (9.1.30), we have

$$R_n = \left| \frac{1}{n} \sum_{k=0}^{n-1} s_k - s \right| = \frac{1}{n} \left| \sum_{k=0}^{n-1} (s_k - s) \right|$$

$$< \frac{1}{n} \sum_{k=0}^{N(\varepsilon)} |s_k - s| + \left[\frac{n - 1 - N(\varepsilon)}{n} \right] \varepsilon \qquad (9.1.32)$$

Since the first term of the right-hand member of the inequality is finite, it follows that, letting $n \to \infty$, we obtain

$$\lim_{n \to \infty} R_n = \lim_{n \to \infty} |S_n - s| < \varepsilon \qquad (9.1.33)$$

for any $\varepsilon > 0$. Thus we conclude that if s exists, then $\lim_{n \to \infty} S_n$ also exists, and furthermore

$$\lim_{n \to \infty} S_n = s \qquad (9.1.34)$$

Convergence in Cèsaro mean is related to the form of convergence given in Definition 5. Thus,

Definition 6: Let $\{a_n : n \in N\}$, $N = 0, 1, 2, \ldots$, be a sequence; the sequence is said to converge if

$$\lim_{n \to \infty} u_n = a \qquad (9.1.35)$$

and a is finite.

It is said to converge in *Cèsaro mean* if

$$\lim_{n \to \infty} \frac{1}{n} \sum_{i=0}^{n-1} a_i = \alpha \qquad (9.1.36)$$

and α is finite.

It is, of course, clear that if (9.1.35) holds, then (9.1.36) holds as well; moreover,

$$a = \alpha \qquad (9.1.37)$$

The proof of this could easily be constructed by the reader and is thus omitted.

Remark 6: A sequence may not be convergent in the ordinary sense but may, nonetheless, converge in Cèsaro mean. Consider again the sequence $a_n = (-1)^n$, which is divergent. Quite clearly,

$$\left| \frac{1}{n} \sum_{i=0}^{n-1} a_i \right| < \frac{2}{n} \qquad (9.1.38)$$

From (9.1.38) it is obvious that the sequence converges to zero in Cèsaro mean.

Remark 7: It should be apparent that convergence in Cèsaro mean is a notion related to the convergence properties of sequences, whereas convergence in Cèsaro sum is one related to the convergence properties of series. This distinction, however, is more apparent than real.

As we noted earlier, one attractive feature of covariance stationary processes is that we can prove *ergodic* theorems with respect to them under fairly mild conditions. Ergodicity, in this context, is very closely anologous to the property of *consistency* in econometrics. In the literature of spectral analysis, however, the term *consistency is defined as convergence in quadratic mean*, and will have this meaning in the discussions of Chapters 10, 11 and 12. We remind the reader that, as we saw in Chapter 3, convergence in quadratic mean implies convergence in probability and (for an estimator) it also implies asymptotic unbiasedness and the asymptotic vanishing of its variance.

Definition 7: Let $\{X(t): t \in N\}$, $N = 0, 1, 2, \ldots$, be a stochastic process with mean function

$$E[X(t)] = m \qquad \text{all} \quad t \in N \tag{9.1.39}$$

The sequence

$$\overline{X}_T = \frac{1}{T} \sum_{t=0}^{T-1} X(t) \qquad T = 1, 2, \ldots \tag{9.1.40}$$

is said to be ergodic if and only if

$$\text{l.i.m.} (\overline{X}_T - m) = \lim_{T \to \infty} E |\overline{X}_T - m|^2 = 0 \tag{9.1.41}$$

For covariance stationary processes, we have the following useful

Theorem 1: Let $\{X(t): t \in N\}$, $N = 0, 1, 2, \ldots$, be a covariance stationary process. Then a necessary and sufficient condition for

$$\overline{X}_T = \frac{1}{T} \sum_{t=0}^{T-1} X(t)$$

to be ergodic is that the sequence $\{K(j): j \in N\}$ converge to zero in Cèsaro mean, where $K(j)$ is the covariance of $X(t)$ and $X(t+j)$.

A sufficient condition is that

$$\lim_{j \to \infty} K(j) = 0$$

PROOF: It is clear that

$$E[\overline{X}_T] = \frac{1}{T} \sum_{t=0}^{T-1} E[X(t)] = m \tag{9.1.42}$$

so that $\overline{X}_T$ is an unbiased estimator of m; it then follows that ergodicity of $\overline{X}_T$ is implied by

$$\lim_{T \to \infty} \text{Var} [\overline{X}_T] = 0 \tag{9.1.43}$$

Now

$$\text{Var } [\bar{X}_T] = \frac{1}{T^2} E\left\{\sum_{t=0}^{T-1} [X(t) - m]\right\}^2$$

$$= \frac{1}{T^2} \sum_{t=0}^{T-1} \sum_{s=0}^{T-1} E[(X(t) - m)(X(s) - m)]$$

$$= \frac{1}{T^2} \sum_{t=0}^{T-1} \sum_{s=0}^{T-1} K(t, s)$$

$$= \frac{2}{T^2} \sum_{t=0}^{T} \sum_{j=0}^{t-1} K(j) - \frac{K(0)}{T} \qquad (9.1.44)$$

Define

$$S(t) = \frac{1}{t} \sum_{j=0}^{t-1} K(j) \qquad (9.1.45)$$

Obviously the limit of $\text{Var } (\bar{X}_T)$ can be studied in terms of (9.1.45), since $K(0)$ is finite by assumption.

Substituting (9.1.45) in (9.1.44) and rearranging terms, we have

$$\text{Var } (\bar{X}_T) \leq \left| \frac{2}{T^2} \sum_{t=1}^{n} tS(t) - \frac{K(0)}{T} \right| + \frac{2}{T} \sum_{t=n+1}^{T} \frac{t}{T} |S(t)| \qquad (9.1.46)$$

Now suppose (sufficiency) that

$$\lim_{t \to \infty} S(t) = 0 \qquad (9.1.47)$$

Then for any $\varepsilon > 0$ there exists an index n such that for all $t > n$,

$$|S(t)| < \tfrac{1}{2}\varepsilon \qquad (9.1.48)$$

Hence if n in (9.1.46) is so chosen ($T > n$ of course), the expression there may be rewritten as

$$\text{Var } (\bar{X}_T) < \left| \frac{2}{T^2} \sum_{t=1}^{n} tS(t) - \frac{K(0)}{T} \right| + \left(1 - \frac{n}{T}\right)\varepsilon \qquad (9.1.49)$$

Because n is now fixed, letting $T \to \infty$ yields

$$\lim_{T \to \infty} \text{Var } (\bar{X}_T) < \varepsilon \qquad (9.1.50)$$

for any $\varepsilon > 0$, which of course means

$$\lim_{T \to \infty} \text{Var } (\bar{X}_T) = 0 \qquad (9.1.51)$$

On the other hand (necessity), suppose that

$$\lim_{T \to \infty} \text{Var } (\bar{X}_T) = 0 \qquad (9.1.52)$$

and consider

$$\text{Cov}\,[X(T-1), \overline{X}_T] = \frac{1}{T}\sum_{t=0}^{T-1} K(T-1, t) = \frac{1}{T}\sum_{j=0}^{T-1} K(j) = S(T) \qquad (9.1.53)$$

By Schwarz's inequality,

$$|S(T)|^2 \le \text{Var}\,[X(T-1)] \cdot \text{Var}\,[\overline{X}_T] = K(0) \cdot \text{Var}\,[\overline{X}_T] \qquad (9.1.54)$$

so that (9.1.51) implies

$$\lim_{T \to \infty} S(T) = 0 \qquad (9.1.55)$$

Consider now the sufficient condition stated at the end of the theorem. Thus assume

$$\lim_{j \to \infty} K(j) = 0 \qquad (9.1.56)$$

In view of (9.1.45), the assumption in (9.1.56) clearly implies

$$\lim_{t \to \infty} S(t) = 0 \qquad (9.1.57)$$

which through the argument following (9.1.47) implies

$$\lim_{T \to \infty} \text{Var}\,[\overline{X}_T] = 0 \qquad \text{Q.E.D.}$$
$$(9.1.58)$$

Ergodic theorems can also be proven about the covariance kernel of a covariance stationary process, but in this case we would require some assumptions concerning the fourth moment of the variables involved.

THE CORRELOGRAM OF A STOCHASTIC PROCESS

The correlation function of a stochastic process $\{X(t): t \in N\}$, $N = 0, 1, 2, \ldots,$ has already been defined as

$$r(s, t) = \frac{K(s, t)}{\sqrt{K(s, s)\,K(t, t)}} \qquad (9.1.59)$$

Definition 8: The graph (or trace) of the correlation function is called the *correlogram* of the stochastic process.

Remark 8: Notice that in the case of a covariance stationary process the correlation function depends only on $|t - s|$, and if the index set N is discrete, then the correlogram is simply a sequence of points in a one-dimensional Euclidean space.

It is interesting to note that the correlogram of special types of stochastic processes display distinctive characteristics and thus knowledge of the correlogram provides some information about the nature of the process we are dealing with.

Example 7: Consider the series

$$x_t = \sum_{s=0}^{m-1} a_s u_{t-s} \qquad t = 1, 2, \ldots \tag{9.1.60}$$

where the u_τ, $\tau = 0, \pm 1, \pm 2, \ldots$, have the properties

$$E(u_\tau) = 0 \qquad \text{all } \tau$$
$$E(u_\tau u_{\tau'}) = \delta_{\tau\tau'} \sigma^2 \tag{9.1.61}$$

$\delta_{\tau\tau'}$ being the Kronecker delta.

If we further assume that $u_t \sim N(0, \sigma^2)$ for all t, then it is clear that (9.1.60) represents a (strictly) stationary process. The mean function of the process is, of course, identically zero and its covariance kernel is given by

$$K(s, t) = E(X_s, X_t) = E\left(\sum_{i=0}^{m-1} \sum_{j=0}^{m-1} a_i a_j u_{t-i} u_{s-j} \right)$$

$$= \sum_{i=0}^{m-1} \sum_{j=0}^{m-1} a_i a_j \delta_{t-i, s-j} \sigma^2$$

$$= \sigma^2 \sum_{i=0}^{m-v-1} a_i a_{i+v} \tag{9.1.62}$$

where $v = |s - t|$.

Clearly $K(s, t) = 0$ if $|s - t| > m - 1$.

The correlation function is given by

$$r(s, t) = r(v) = \frac{\sum_{i=0}^{m-v-1} a_i a_{i+v}}{\sum_{i=0}^{m-1} a_i^2} \tag{9.1.63}$$

In the special case $a_i = 1/m$, $i = 0, 1, \ldots, m$, then

$$r(v) = 1 - \frac{v}{m} \qquad 0 \le v \le m - 1$$

$$= 0 \qquad \text{otherwise} \tag{9.1.64}$$

so that the correlogram is a linearly diminishing set of points. The stochastic process of this example (without the assumption of normality) is called a finite moving average process of order m.

Suppose that we are dealing with a process of the form

$$y_t = m(t) + u_t \tag{9.1.65}$$

where $m(t)$ is a polynomial of degree p and the u_t have the properties described in (9.1.61).

If the estimated trend—obtained by the well-known procedure of moving averages—is subtracted from (9.1.65), the residual would roughly be like

$$x_t = \sum_{i=-n}^{n} a_i u_{t-i} \tag{9.1.66}$$

and thus by the preceding discussion would be a moving average process of order $2n + 1 > p$. The correlation function of such a process is easily computed, for the coefficients a_i are determined if p and n are given.

The shape of the correlogram of such processes is typically one of fluctuations about zero—with a rapid convergence to that value.

Example 8: A second process of interest is one arising from a stochastic difference equation. Such situations are not uncommon in economics. Thus consider the process derived from

$$x_t + a_1 x_{t-1} + a_2 x_{t-2} = u_t \qquad t = 1, 2, \ldots \tag{9.1.67}$$

where the u_t have the properties ascribed to them in the preceding example and (x_0, x_1) are the initial conditions of the system.

In general, a process like

$$\sum_{i=0}^{m} a_i x_{t-i} = u_t \tag{9.1.68}$$

where the u_t have the properties described in (9.1.61), is said to be an auto-regressive process of order m. It is of interest to note that autoregressive processes can, under certain very mild conditions, be reduced to moving average processes of infinite order; the coefficients of the latter, however, would depend on the $(m + 1)$ parameters of the parent process. We illustrate this in the case of the process in (9.1.67). The first step consists in solving it.[2] Its characteristic equation is given by

$$z^2 + a_1 z + a_2 = 0 \tag{9.1.69}$$

which yields the two roots

$$z = \frac{-a_1 \pm \sqrt{a_1^2 - 4a_2}}{2} \tag{9.1.70}$$

Now suppose that $4a_2 - a_1^2 > 0$, so that the roots are complex. It is well known, then, that the solution to the homogeneous part of (9.1.67) is given by

$$x_t^h = \rho^t(A \cos \theta t + B \sin \theta t) \tag{9.1.71}$$

where A, B are arbitrary constants, fixed by initial conditions

$$\rho = a_2^{\frac{1}{2}} \tag{9.1.72}$$

and θ is the solution of

$$\cos \theta = -\frac{a_1}{a^{\frac{1}{2}}} \qquad \sin \theta = \left(\frac{4a_2 - a_1^2}{a}\right)^{\frac{1}{2}} \qquad 0 \le \theta \le 2\pi \tag{9.1.73}$$

---

[2] A more convenient method of solution will be discussed in Chapter 12.

where $a = 4a_2$,

A particular solution to (9.1.67) is given by

$$x_t^p = \sum_{j=0}^{\infty} s_j u_{t-j+1} \tag{9.1.74}$$

where

$$s_j = \rho^j \frac{2}{(4a_2 - a_1^2)^{\frac{1}{2}}} \sin \theta j \tag{9.1.75}$$

Notice that $s_0 = 0$ and $s_1 = 1$.

That (9.1.74) is a particular solution is verified as follows: Substituting in (9.1.67), we have

$$x_t^p + a_1 x_{t-1}^p + a_2 x_{t-2}^p = \sum_{j=0}^{\infty} s_j u_{t-j+1} + \sum_{j=0}^{\infty} a_1 s_j u_{t-j}$$

$$+ \sum_{j=0}^{\infty} a_2 s_j u_{t-j-1} = u_t + \sum_{j=2}^{\infty} s_j u_{t-j+1}$$

$$+ \sum_{j=1}^{\infty} a_1 s_j u_{t-j} + \sum_{j=1}^{\infty} a_2 s_j u_{t-j-1} \tag{9.1.76}$$

Now, if in the second term after the last equality sign in (9.1.76) we put $j = i$, if in the third term we put $j = i - 1$, while in the fourth term we put $j = i - 2$, we obtain

$$x_t^p + a_1 x_{t-1}^p + a_2 x_{t-2}^p = u_t + \sum_{i=2}^{\infty} (s_i + a_1 s_{i-1} + a_2 s_{i-2}) u_{t-i+1} = u_t \tag{9.1.77}$$

The last equality holds because the s_i satisfy the homogeneous part of the difference equation in (9.1.67). Explicitly,

$$s_i + a_1 s_{i-1} + a_2 s_{i-2} = \frac{2\rho^{i-2}}{b} [\rho^2 \sin \theta i + a_1 \rho \sin \theta(i-1) + a_2 \sin \theta(i-2)] \tag{9.1.78}$$

where $b = (4a_2 - a_1^2)^{\frac{1}{2}}$.

Now

$$\sin \theta(i-1) = \sin \theta i \cos \theta + \cos \theta i \sin \theta$$

$$= -\frac{a_1}{2\rho} \sin \theta i + \frac{b}{2\rho} \cos \theta i$$

In addition,

$$\sin \theta(i-2) = \sin \theta i \cos 2\theta + \cos \theta i \sin 2\theta$$

$$= \frac{2a_1^2 - 4\rho^2}{4\rho^2} \sin \theta i - \frac{a_1 b}{2\rho^2} \cos \theta i$$

This is so, since

$$\cos 2\theta = \cos^2 \theta - \sin^2 \theta = 2 \cos^2 \theta - 1 = \frac{2a_1^2}{4\rho^2} - 1$$

$$\sin 2\theta = 2 \cos \theta \sin \theta = -\frac{a_1 b}{2\rho^2}$$

the last equalities in the two relations above holding because θ satisfies (9.1.73).
Hence the term in square brackets in (9.1.78) yields

$$\rho^2 \sin \theta i + a_1\rho \sin \theta(i-1) + a_2 \sin \theta(i-2)$$

$$= \rho^2 \sin \theta i - \frac{a_1^2}{2} \sin \theta i + \frac{a_1 b}{2} \cos \theta i$$

$$+ a_2 \left(\frac{2a_1^2 - 4\rho^2}{4\rho^2} \right) \sin \theta i - \frac{a_1 a_2 b}{2\rho^2} \cos \theta i$$

$$= \left[\rho^2 - \frac{a_1^2}{2} + \frac{2a_1^2 - 4\rho^2}{4\rho^2} a_2 \right] \sin \theta i + \left(\frac{a_1 b}{2} - \frac{a_1 a_2 b}{2\rho^2} \right) \cos \theta i = 0$$

(9.1.79)

in view of (9.1.72).

Thus the general solution of (9.1.67) is simply

$$x_t = \rho^t (A \cos \theta t + B \sin \theta t) + \sum_{j=0}^{\infty} s_j u_{t-j+1}$$

(9.1.80)

Clearly the first term in the right-hand side of (9.1.80) would tend to zero as $t \to \infty$ if $\rho < 1$, that is, if the system is stable. Hence for sufficiently large t, the process would behave essentially like a moving average process of infinite extent.

The correlation function of the process in (9.1.80) is given by

$$r(v) = \frac{\sum_{j=0}^{\infty} s_j s_{j+v}}{\sum_{j=0}^{\infty} s_j^2} = \rho^v \frac{\sum_{j=0}^{\infty} \rho^{2j} \sin \theta j \sin \theta(j+v)}{\sum_{j=0}^{\infty} \rho^{2j} \sin^2 \theta j}$$

$$= \rho^v \left(\cos \theta v - \sin \theta v \frac{\sum_{j=0}^{\infty} \rho^{2j} \sin \theta j \cos \theta j}{\sum_{j=0}^{\infty} \rho^{2j} \sin^2 \theta j} \right)$$

$$= \rho^v \left(\cos \theta v - \sin \theta v \frac{\sin 2\theta}{2 \sin^2 \theta} \frac{1 - \rho^2}{1 + \rho^2} \right)$$

(9.1.81)

The second equality here is obtained by employing (9.1.75), the third by using the expression for $\sin(x+y)$, and the fourth by using

$$\sin x = \frac{\exp(ix) - \exp(-ix)}{2i} \qquad \cos x = \frac{\exp(ix) + \exp(-ix)}{2}$$

(9.1.82)

The oscillatory but decaying character of the correlogram of the process is thus quite obvious from (9.1.82)—provided that $\rho < 1$.

It should be mentioned at this stage that the fact that we assumed the roots of (9.1.69) to be complex does not restrict the validity of our conclusion concerning the shape of the correlogram, for the conclusion depends essentially on the particular solution. If the roots are assumed to be real, provided the largest is less than unity in absolute value, the same result would hold. In such a case, ρ and θ are defined by

$$\rho = |a_2|^{\frac{1}{2}} \qquad \cos\theta = -\frac{a_1}{2|a_2|^{\frac{1}{2}}} \qquad \sin\theta = \left(\frac{a_1^2 - 4a_2}{4\rho}\right)^{\frac{1}{2}}$$

$$0 \le \theta \le 2\pi \qquad (9.1.83)$$

Remark 9: It is of interest to note that since for $\rho < 1$, $\lim_{v \to \infty} r(v) = 0$; by an application of Theorem 1, we thus conclude that $\bar{x}_T = (1/T)\sum_{t=1}^{T} x_t$ is ergodic.

9.2 SPECTRAL REPRESENTATION OF COVARIANCE STATIONARY SERIES

COMPLEX PROCESSES

In the previous section we examined stochastic processes from the point of view of their covariance and correlation functions. Both were viewed as functions of "time." However, the study of stochastic processes in the time domain is neither simple nor very illuminating and becomes mathematically rather cumbersome and inelegant.

In the following discussion we shall see that changing our point of view and considering time series in the "frequency" domain (a term defined in Section 9.1) will be both simpler and more rewarding.

Definition 9: A complex random variable is defined by

$$z = x + iy \qquad (9.2.1)$$

where x and y are real random variables and $i^2 = -1$. The expectation of a complex random variable is given by

$$E(z) = E(x) + iE(y) \qquad (9.2.2)$$

The variance of a complex variable is defined by

$$\text{Var}(z) = E[z - E(z)][\overline{z - E(z)}] \qquad (9.2.3)$$

where the overbar denotes the operation of conjugation, that is,

$$\bar{z} = x - iy \qquad (9.2.4)$$

In the following pages it will be more convenient to use the notation x_t for $x(t)$.

Definition 10: A complex stochastic process is defined by

$$z_t = x_t + iy_t \qquad t \in T \tag{9.2.5}$$

where $\{x_t: t \in T\}$, $\{y_t: t \in T\}$ are real stochastic processes.

The mean function and the covariance kernel of the complex process in (9.2.5) are defined, respectively, by

$$m(t) = E(z_t) = E(x_t) + iE(y_t) = m_1(t) + im_2(t)$$

$$K(s, t) = E[z_s - m(s)][\overline{z_t - m(t)}] \tag{9.2.6}$$

Remark 10: If the time series $\{x_t: t \in T\}$, $\{y_t: t \in T\}$ are orthogonal, that is, if

$$E[x_t - m_1(t)][\overline{y_s - m_2(s)}] = 0 \qquad \text{all } t, s \tag{9.2.7}$$

then it is clear that $K(s, t)$ of (9.2.6) is a real function.

Definition 11: The complex series $\{z_t: t \in N\}$, where $N = 0, \pm1, \pm2, \ldots$, is said to be covariance stationary if and only if its covariance function depends only on $t - s$.

Remark 11: It should be pointed out that for a complex covariance stationary time series we have

$$K(t - s) = \overline{K(s - t)} \tag{9.2.8}$$

This is so since

$$K(t - s) = E[z_t - m(t)][\overline{z_s - m(s)}] \tag{9.2.9}$$

On the other hand,

$$\overline{K(t - s)} = E\overline{[z_t - m(t)]}[z_s - m(s)]$$
$$= E[z_s - m(s)][\overline{z_t - m(t)}] = K(s - t) \tag{9.2.10}$$

which after conjugation is identical with (9.2.8).

Remark 12: A sufficient condition for the complex process in (9.2.5) to be covariance stationary is for both its component real processes $\{x_t: t \in T\}$ and $\{y_t: t \in T\}$ to be covariance stationary and that (9.2.7) be satisfied.

In what follows and until the contrary is indicated, we shall study only complex covariance stationary processes, and the terms "process" or "time series" are to be so understood.

REPRESENTATION OF COVARIANCE KERNELS

Definition 12: A sequence $\{s_{rk}\}$ is said to be positive definite if and only if

$$\Sigma_{r, k} a_r \bar{a}_k s_{rk} \geq 0 \tag{9.2.11}$$

for all a_r, where the a_r and s_{rk} are complex members.

Theorem 2: Let $K(t - s)$ be the covariance function of a covariance stationary process. Then $K(t - s)$ is a positive definite sequence.

PROOF: Let n be a fixed—but otherwise arbitrary—number and consider

$$V_n = \sum_{t=1}^{n} a_t z_t \tag{9.2.12}$$

where the $\{a_t\}$ form a complex sequence and $\{z_t\}$ is a stochastic process with covariance function $K(t - s)$ and, for simplicity, mean function identically zero. Then we have

$$0 \le E(V_n \bar{V}_n) = E\left(\sum_{t=1}^{n} \sum_{s=1}^{n} a_t \bar{a}_s z_t \bar{z}_s \right)$$

$$= \sum_t \sum_s a_t \bar{a}_s E(z_t \bar{z}_s) = \sum_t \sum_s a_t \bar{a}_s K(t - s) \tag{9.2.13}$$

Since n is arbitrary, the conclusion follows.

The converse can also be proved, namely,

Theorem 3: Let $K(\tau)$ be a positive definite sequence such that $\overline{K(\tau)} = K(-\tau)$. Then there exists a covariance stationary process $\{z_t : t \in N\}$, $N = 0, \pm 1, \pm 2, \ldots$, such that $K(\tau)$ is its covariance kernel.

The proof of this theorem is omitted.

The fundamental theorem in this aspect of the theory of stochastic processes is, however, the following

Theorem 4: A function $K(\cdot)$ defined on the set $\{N: 0, \pm 1, \pm 2, \ldots\}$ is positive definite if and only if it can be expressed in the following form:

$$K(\tau) = \int_{-\pi}^{\pi} \exp(i\tau\lambda)\, dF(\lambda) \tag{9.2.14}$$

where F (defined for $|\lambda| \le \pi$) is monotone nondecreasing. The function F is uniquely defined, if suitably normalized, by the equations[3]

$$\frac{F(\lambda_2 +) - F(\lambda_2 -)}{2} - \frac{F(\lambda_1 +) - F(\lambda_1 -)}{2}$$

$$= \frac{1}{2\pi} \left[K(0)(\lambda_2 - \lambda_1) + \lim_{n \to \infty} \sum_{\tau = -n}^{n}{}' K(\tau) \frac{\exp(-i\tau\lambda_2) - \exp(-i\tau\lambda_1)}{-i\tau} \right]$$

$$-\pi < \lambda_1 < \lambda_2 < \pi \tag{9.2.15}$$

and

$$F(\pi) - F(-\pi) = K(0) \tag{9.2.16}$$

---

[3] The notations $F(\lambda +)$, $F(\lambda -)$ indicate, respectively, the right- and left-hand limits of $F(\cdot)$ at the point λ; the notation $\sum_{\tau=-n}^{n}{}'$ indicates that the term corresponding to $\tau = 0$ is omitted from the sum.

If $K(\cdot)$ is a real function, then (9.2.14) can be replaced by

$$K(\tau) = \int_0^\pi \cos \tau\lambda \, dG(\lambda) \tag{9.2.17}$$

where G (defined for $0 < \lambda \le \pi$) is monotone nondecreasing and is uniquely defined, if suitably normalized, by the equations

$$\frac{G(\lambda+) + G(\lambda-)}{2} - G(0) = \frac{1}{\pi} K(0)\lambda + \frac{1}{\pi} \sum_{\tau=1}^\infty K(\tau) \frac{\sin \tau\lambda}{\tau} \quad \text{for} \quad 0 < \lambda < \pi \tag{9.2.18}$$

and

$$G(\pi) - G(0) = K(0) \tag{9.2.19}$$

The proof of the above may be found in Doob [7, pp. 473ff] and is best omitted in a book such as this.

Below, however, we give a procedure for constructing a function $F(\cdot)$ in the case of the covariance kernel of a covariance stationary (complex) stochastic process. Let $\{z_t : t \in N\}$, $N = 0, \pm 1, \pm 2, \ldots$, be a covariance stationary complex process and $K(\cdot)$ be its covariance kernel; note that this is also defined on the set N.

Define

$$F_n(\lambda) = \frac{1}{2\pi} \left[\sum_{t=-n}^{n}{}' K(t) \frac{\exp(it\pi) - \exp(-it\lambda)}{it} \left(1 - \frac{|t|}{n}\right) + K(0)(\pi + \lambda) \right] \tag{9.2.20}$$

Notice that $F_n(\cdot)$ is continuous in $(-\pi, \pi]$, and because of the periodicity of sinusoidal functions we need *only consider this interval*.

The second fact to note is that $F_n(\cdot)$ is monotone nondecreasing. Showing this is quite simple. Let $-\pi < \lambda_1 < \lambda_2 \le \pi$ and consider

$$F_n(\lambda_2) - F_n(\lambda_1) = \frac{1}{2\pi} \left\{ \sum_{t=-n}^{n}{}' \left[\frac{\exp(-it\lambda_1) - \exp(-it\lambda_2)}{it} K(t) \left(1 - \frac{|t|}{n}\right) \right] \right.$$
$$\left. + K(0)(\lambda_2 - \lambda_1) \right\} \tag{9.2.21}$$

Noting that

$$\lim_{x \to 0} \frac{\exp(-ix\lambda_1) - \exp(-ix\lambda_2)}{ix} = \lambda_2 - \lambda_1 \tag{9.2.22}$$

we may interpret $K(0)(\lambda_2 - \lambda_1)$ as the definition of

$$\frac{\exp(-it\lambda_1) - \exp(-it\lambda_2)}{it} K(t) \quad \text{for} \quad t = 0$$

With this in mind, let

$$S(t) = \frac{\exp(-it\lambda_1) - \exp(-it\lambda_2)}{it} K(t) \tag{9.2.23}$$

and note that we can write the right-hand side of (9.2.21) as

$$F_n(\lambda_2) - F_n(\lambda_1) = \frac{1}{2\pi} \sum_{t=-n}^{n} \left(1 - \frac{|t|}{n}\right) S(t) \tag{9.2.24}$$

Now the sum in (9.2.24) is simply

$$\sum_{t=-n}^{n} \left(1 - \frac{|t|}{n}\right) S(t) = \frac{1}{n} \sum_{t=1}^{n} \sum_{\tau=-n+t}^{-1+t} S(\tau) \tag{9.2.25}$$

and letting $s = t - \tau$, we have

$$F_n(\lambda_2) - F_n(\lambda_1) = \frac{1}{2\pi n} \sum_{t=1}^{n} \sum_{s=1}^{n} S(t - s) \tag{9.2.26}$$

But

$$S(t - s) = \frac{\exp(-i(t-s)\lambda_1) - \exp(-i(t-s)\lambda_2)}{i(t-s)} K(t - s)$$

$$= \left[\int_{\lambda_1}^{\lambda_2} \exp(-i(t-s)\lambda)\, d\lambda\right] K(t - s) \tag{9.2.27}$$

But since the process we are considering is covariance stationary, it follows from (9.2.27) that

$$F_n(\lambda_2) - F_n(\lambda_1) \geq 0 \tag{9.2.28}$$

and the function $F_n(\cdot)$ is monotone nondecreasing for all n.

Remark: 13 Notice that $F_n(-\pi) = 0$ and that the functions $F_n(\cdot)$ are uniformly bounded by $K(0)$. Thus the functions $\{F_n(\cdot): n = 1, 2, \ldots\}$ form a uniformly bounded sequence of (continuous) monotone nondecreasing functions and (by the Arzelà theorem on the convergence of uniformly bounded and equicontinuous sequences of functions) there exists a limit function that is also (continuous) bounded and monotone (nondecreasing). Moreover, this function is simply

$$F(\lambda) = \frac{1}{2\pi} \left[K(0)(\pi + \lambda) + \lim_{n \to \infty} \sum_{t=-n}^{n}{}' \frac{\exp(it\pi) - \exp(-it\lambda)}{it} \left(1 - \frac{|t|}{n}\right) K(t) \right] \tag{9.2.29}$$

which, as may be verified, is the function described in the previous theorem.

We amplify this now in the case of a real (covariance stationary) process. Clearly the covariance kernel now has the property

$$K(t) = K(-t) \tag{9.2.30}$$

Hence the function in (9.2.29) can be written as

$$G(\lambda) = \frac{1}{2\pi} \left[K(0)(\pi + \lambda) + \lim_{n \to \infty} \sum_{t=1}^{n} \frac{\exp(it\lambda) - \exp(-it\lambda)}{it} \left(1 - \frac{t}{n}\right) K(t) \right] \tag{9.2.31}$$

where we have used $G(\cdot)$ instead of $F(\cdot)$ to conform with the notation of (9.2.18). Noting that

$$\frac{\exp(it\lambda) - \exp(-it\lambda)}{it} = 2 \frac{\sin t\lambda}{t}$$

and that if

$$\sum_{t=1}^{\infty} \frac{\sin t\lambda}{t} K(t)$$

converges, then by (9.1.34) we have

$$\sum_{t=1}^{\infty} \frac{\exp(it\lambda) - \exp(-it\lambda)}{it} \left(1 - \frac{t}{n}\right) K(t) = 2 \sum_{t=1}^{\infty} K(t) \frac{\sin t\lambda}{t} \tag{9.2.32}$$

we may thus rewrite (9.2.31) as

$$G(\lambda) = \frac{1}{2\pi} \left[K(0)(\pi + \lambda) + 2 \sum_{t=1}^{\infty} K(t) \frac{\sin t\lambda}{t} \right] \tag{9.2.33}$$

Then

$$dG(\lambda) = \frac{1}{2\pi} \left[K(0) + 2 \sum_{t=1}^{\infty} K(t) \cos t\lambda \right] d\lambda = g(\lambda) \, d\lambda \tag{9.2.34}$$

But now notice

$$\int_{-\pi}^{\pi} \exp(i\tau\lambda) \, dG(\lambda) = K(0) \qquad \text{if} \quad \tau = 0 \tag{9.2.35}$$

since

$$\int_{-\pi}^{\pi} \cos t\lambda \, d\lambda = \frac{\sin t\lambda}{t} \bigg|_{-\pi}^{\pi} = 0 \tag{9.2.36}$$

On the other hand, for $\tau \neq 0$,

$$\int_{-\pi}^{\pi} \exp(i\tau\lambda) \, dG(\lambda) = \frac{1}{\pi} \sum_{t=1}^{\infty} K(t) \int_{-\pi}^{\pi} \exp(i\tau\lambda) \cos t\lambda \, d\lambda \tag{9.2.37}$$

Now

$$\int_{-\pi}^{\pi} \exp{(i\tau\lambda)} \cos t\lambda \, d\lambda = \int_{-\pi}^{\pi} \cos \tau\lambda \cos t\lambda + i \int_{-\pi}^{\pi} \sin \tau\lambda \cos t\lambda \, d\lambda \qquad (9.2.38)$$

Since

$$\sin \tau\lambda \cos t\lambda = \tfrac{1}{2}[\sin{(\tau + t)\lambda} + \sin{(\tau - t)\lambda}]$$

it follows that the second integral in the right member of (9.2.38) is zero.
Furthermore, since

$$\cos \tau\lambda \cos t\lambda = \tfrac{1}{2}[\cos{(\tau + t)\lambda} + \cos{(\tau - t)\lambda}]$$

it follows that

$$\int_{-\pi}^{\pi} \exp{(i\tau\lambda)} \cos t\lambda \, d\lambda = 0 \quad \text{if} \quad \tau \neq t$$
$$= \pi \quad \text{if} \quad \tau = t \qquad (9.2.39)$$

Thus we have found that for $\tau \neq 0$, we have

$$\int_{-\pi}^{\pi} \exp{(i\tau\lambda)} \, dG(\lambda) = K(\tau) \qquad (9.2.40)$$

which, of course, means that the covariance kernel of the process is simply the Fourier transform of the function $g(\lambda)$.
On the other hand, consider

$$\frac{1}{2\pi} \sum_{\tau=-\infty}^{\infty} K(\tau) \exp{(-i\tau\lambda)} = \frac{1}{2\pi}\left\{K(0) + \sum_{\tau=1}^{\infty} K(\tau)[\exp{(i\tau\lambda)} + \exp{(-i\tau\lambda)}]\right\}$$

$$= \frac{1}{2\pi} K(0) + \frac{1}{\pi} \sum_{\tau=1}^{\infty} K(\tau) \cos \tau\lambda = g(\lambda) \qquad (9.2.41)$$

which shows that $g(\lambda)$ is the Fourier transform of the covariance kernel.
This is an extremely important relationship and totally motivates the spectral point of view in studying time series.
Notice the great simplification achieved. The function $g(\cdot)$ is defined on the interval $(-\pi, \pi]$, while the covariance kernel was defined on $N = 0, \pm 1, \pm 2, \ldots$. Its parent function $G(\cdot)$ is a bounded monotone nondecreasing function; it is thus very much like the distribution functions of probability theory about which a great deal is known.
Furthermore, since there is a one-to-one correspondence in pairs of Fourier transforms, it follows that we can study the properties of the covariance kernel by studying the properties of the function $G(\cdot)$.
Since in dealing with covariance stationary processes the implication is that we wish to restrict our attention to questions involving moments of the random variables no higher than the second, it is obvious that such questions could be adequately studied by studying the function $G(\cdot)$.

In summary, if $\{Z_t: t \in N\}$, $N = 0, \pm 1, \pm 2, \ldots$, is a covariance stationary process, then its covariance function $K(\cdot, \cdot)$ is positive definite and, in fact, depends only on the difference of its two arguments. This being so, there exists a function $F(\cdot)$ that is bounded and monotone nondecreasing such that

$$K(\tau) = \int_{-\pi}^{\pi} \exp(i\tau\lambda)\, dF(\lambda) \tag{9.2.42}$$

where $\tau = t - s$ and $t, s \in N$.

Remark 14: The function $F(\cdot)$ need not be continuous but at any point left- and right-hand limits exist. In most discussions we will, however, take $F(\cdot)$ to be differentiable.

Definition 13: The function $F(\cdot)$ is called the spectral distribution function associated with the process $\{Z_t: t \in N\}$, and its derivative $f(\cdot) = F'(\cdot)$, if it exists, is called the spectral density function.

The covariance kernel of the process satisfies

$$dF(\lambda) = \frac{1}{2\pi} \sum_{\tau = -\infty}^{\infty} K(\tau) \exp(-i\tau\lambda)\, d\lambda \tag{9.2.43}$$

or, if the derivative of $F(\cdot)$ exists (as we shall typically assume),

$$f(\lambda) = \frac{1}{2\pi} \sum_{\tau = -\infty}^{\infty} K(\tau) \exp(-i\tau\lambda) \tag{9.2.44}$$

Thus the spectral density and the covariance functions of a covariance stationary stochastic process form a pair of Fourier transforms.

Remark 15: Sometimes the spectral density function is also referred to as the power spectrum of the process.

DECOMPOSITION OF COVARIANCE STATIONARY PROCESSES; SPECTRAL DISTRIBUTION AND DENSITY FUNCTIONS

Here we shall derive a representation of a (covariance stationary) stochastic process closely related to some of the quantities we discussed above. In this context, the intuitive interpretation of the spectral density function will become quite clear. Some additional results are needed first, however.

Definition 14: Let $\{X_t: t \in T\}$ be a stochastic process, T being some linear set. The process is said to have independent increments if for any $t_i \in T$, $i = 0, 1, 2, \ldots, n$, the random variables $X_{t_1} - X_{t_0}$, $X_{t_2} - X_{t_1}, \ldots, X_{t_n} - X_{t_{n-1}}$ are mutually independent, where $t_0 < t_1 < t_2 < \cdots < t_n$.

Definition 15: The process above is said to have stationary independent increments if in addition $X_{t_i + h} - X_{t_j + h}$, $i > j$ has the same distribution as $X_{t_i} - X_{t_j}$.

Finally, the process is said to have orthogonal increments if

$$E(X_{t_i} - X_{t_j})(\overline{X_{t_k} - X_{t_s}}) = 0 \qquad (9.2.45)$$

where $t_i, t_j, t_k, t_s \in N$ and $t_j < t_i < t_s < t_k$.

The processes of Definition 15 are extremely important in the spectral theory of stochastic processes. Thus let $\{X_t : t \in N\}$ be a covariance stationary process with constant mean function, which may, without loss of generality, be taken as the zero function. Now, it may be shown that we can find a set of orthogonal random variables (with mean zero), $\{\zeta_s : s = 1, 2, \ldots\}$, a linear combination of which can provide an arbitrarily close approximation to the X process over any interval of N.

Or, to be more precise, for any $t \in (-N_1, N_1] \subset N$ and $\varepsilon > 0$ there exists an m such that

$$E\left|X_t - \sum_{k=1}^{m} \exp{(it\lambda_k)}\zeta_k\right|^2 < \varepsilon \qquad (9.2.46)$$

where $\lambda_k \in (-\pi, \pi]$ and $t \in (-N_1, N_1]$.

As we saw earlier, this implies that for any $\varepsilon, \delta > 0$ there exists an m^* such that for all $m > m^*$ we may write

$$\Pr\left\{\left|X_t - \sum_{k=1}^{m} \exp{(it\lambda_k)}\zeta_k\right| < \varepsilon\right\} > 1 - \delta \qquad (9.2.47)$$

Thus what (9.2.47) implies is that a covariance stationary process can be arbitrarily closely approximated (in a probability sense) by a linear combination of sinusoids with random (and mutually uncorrelated) amplitude.

In general, m^* will depend on ε and δ and as we require the approximation to be closer, we must increase the number of sinusoids and reduce the length of the intervals

$$\Delta\lambda_k = \lambda_{k+1} - \lambda_k$$

In fact, it may be shown that as we let $\varepsilon, \delta \to 0$ and $N_1 \to \infty$, then $m^* \to \infty$ and the number of frequencies λ_k in an arbitrary (nondegenerate) interval becomes arbitrarily large. It is also the case that in these circumstances the sum of random variables ζ_k corresponding to a frequency interval $\Delta\lambda$ will converge to a well-defined random variable, say $Z(\Delta\lambda)$. We write this symbolically

$$\lim \Sigma_{\Delta\lambda} \zeta_k = Z(\Delta\lambda)$$

The function $Z(\Delta\lambda)$ is an interval random function, that is, one that assigns the random variable $Z(\Delta\lambda)$ to the interval $\Delta\lambda$.

It is this basic fact that allows us to represent the stochastic process by means of the so-called Fourier-Stiltjes integral, defined by

$$X_t = \int_{-\pi}^{\pi} \exp{(it\lambda)}Z(d\lambda) = \lim_{\max |\lambda_{k+1} - \lambda_k| \to 0} \sum_{k=1}^{m} \exp{(it\lambda_k)}Z(\Delta\lambda_k) \qquad (9.2.48)$$

where $-\pi < \lambda_1 < \lambda_2 < \cdots < \lambda_m \leq \pi$.

The notation $Z(d\lambda)$ is perhaps unfamiliar and one is probably better acquainted with the standard Stiltjes notation $dZ(\lambda)$. We may, however, effectively change the notation by altering the definition of the Z process. Thus instead of the interval function, consider the point function $Z(-\pi, \lambda]$, that is, now the Z process is effectively defined by the point $\lambda \in (-\pi, \pi]$, and is otherwise the sum of the orthogonal variables ζ_k (in the limit) lying in the interval $(-\pi, \lambda]$.

Now notice that if $\lambda_i, \lambda_j \in (-\pi, \pi]$, $\lambda_i < \lambda_j$, then

$$Z(\lambda_j) - Z(\lambda_i) = Z(\Delta\lambda) \qquad (9.2.49)$$

where $\Delta\lambda = \lambda_j - \lambda_i$. Hence we may think of the process $Z(\Delta\lambda)$ described above as the "increment process" associated with the process $Z(\lambda)$. The latter is then a process with uncorrelated (or orthogonal) increments.

Noting in (9.2.48) that $Z(\Delta\lambda_k) = Z(\lambda_{k+1}) - Z(\lambda_k) = \Delta Z(\lambda_k)$, the integral may be written in the more standard form

$$X_t = \int_{-\pi}^{\pi} \exp(it\lambda)\, dZ(\lambda) = \lim_{\max |\lambda_{k+1} - \lambda_k| \to 0} \sum_{k=1}^{m} \exp(it\lambda_k)\, \Delta Z(\lambda_k) \qquad (9.2.50)$$

From the definition of the point process $Z(\lambda)$, the following properties are obvious:

i. $E[Z(\lambda)] = 0$

ii. $E\{[Z(\lambda_1 + \Delta\lambda) - Z(\lambda_1)][\overline{Z(\lambda_2 + \Delta\lambda) - Z(\lambda_2)}]\} = 0$

provided the intervals $(\lambda_1 + \Delta\lambda) - \lambda_1$ and $(\lambda_2 + \Delta\lambda) - \lambda_2$ do not overlap.

It is apparent, of course, from (9.2.50) or (9.2.48) that if the X process is real, then

$$\overline{\Delta Z(\lambda)} = \Delta Z(-\lambda) \qquad (9.2.51)$$

The preceding discussion may be summarized in

Theorem 5: Let $\{X_t : t \in N\}$ be a covariance stationary process with zero mean function. Then there exists a process with orthogonal increments, say $\{Z(\lambda) : -\pi < \lambda \le \pi\}$, such that

$$X_t = \int_{-\pi}^{\pi} \exp(it\lambda)\, dZ(\lambda) \qquad (9.2.52)$$

In addition, the Z process has the properties

$$E[dZ(\lambda_1)\, \overline{dZ(\lambda_2)}] = 0 \qquad \lambda_1 \neq \lambda_2$$

$$E[dZ(\lambda)\, \overline{dZ(\lambda)}] = dF(\lambda) \qquad (9.2.53)$$

where $F(\cdot)$ is the spectral distribution of the X process. If $\{X_t : t \in N\}$ is a real process, then there exist real stochastic processes

$$\{u(\lambda): 0 < \lambda \le \pi\}, \{v(\lambda): 0 < \lambda \le \pi\}$$

with orthogonal increments such that

$$X_t = \int_0^\pi \cos t\lambda \, du(\lambda) + \int_0^\pi \sin t\lambda \, dv(\lambda) \tag{9.2.54}$$

Furthermore, the u and v processes have the properties

$$E|du(\lambda)|^2 = E|dv(\lambda)|^2 = dG(\lambda) \qquad 0 < \lambda \leq \pi$$
$$E[du(\lambda_1) \, du(\lambda_2)] = E[dv(\lambda_1) \, dv(\lambda_2)]$$
$$= E[du(\lambda) \, dv(\lambda)] = 0 \qquad \lambda_1 \neq \lambda_2 \tag{9.2.55}$$

where $G(\cdot)$ is the spectral distribution of the X process.

The proof of this theorem, as well as certain other useful results in this connection, may be found in standard references on the theory of stochastic processes; see, for example, Doob [7, pp. 481–488].

Remark 16: It should be noted for clarity that if $\{X_t : t \in N\}$ is a real process, then (9.2.54) can be derived from (9.2.52). Hence we do not have two distinct representations; rather, (9.2.54) is the simplification of (9.2.52) resulting from the fact that the process is real. To see this, extend $u(\lambda)$ and $v(\lambda)$ of (9.2.54) to the range $(-\pi, \pi]$ by the definitions

$$u(-\lambda) = u(\lambda) \qquad v(-\lambda) = -v(\lambda) \tag{9.2.56}$$

and put

$$Z(\lambda) = \frac{1}{2} [u(\lambda) - iv(\lambda)] \tag{9.2.57}$$

Then

$$X_t = \int_{-\pi}^\pi \exp(it\lambda) \, dZ(\lambda) = \frac{1}{2} \int_{-\pi}^\pi \cos t\lambda \, du(\lambda) + \frac{1}{2} i \left[\int_{-\pi}^\pi \sin t\lambda \, du(\lambda) \right.$$

$$\left. - \int_{-\pi}^\pi \cos t\lambda \, dv(\lambda) \right] + \frac{1}{2} \int_{-\pi}^\pi \sin t\lambda \, dv(\lambda) \tag{9.2.58}$$

Because the integral of $\sin t\lambda \, du(\lambda)$ [resp. $\cos t\lambda \, dv(\lambda)$] over $(-\pi, 0]$ is exactly the negative of its integral over $(0, \pi]$, it follows that the bracketed expression in (9.2.58) vanishes. Moreover, in view of (9.2.56), the integral of $\cos t\lambda \, du(\lambda)$ [resp. $\sin t\lambda \, dv(\lambda)$] over $(-\pi, \pi]$ is twice its integral over $(0, \pi]$, and thus it follows that (9.2.58) can be rewritten as

$$X_t = \int_0^\pi \cos t\lambda \, du(\lambda) + \int_0^\pi \sin t\lambda \, dv(\lambda) \tag{9.2.59}$$

Utilizing either (9.2.52) or (9.2.54), it is possible to give the promised intuitive interpretation of the spectral distribution or the power spectrum of a stochastic process. Notice that in both cases we are able to express the process as an infinite (nondenumerable) combination of sinusoids with different frequencies (λ) and random (uncorrelated) amplitudes—$dZ(\lambda)$ or $du(\lambda)$ and $dv(\lambda)$.

In this connection we must stress that it is $Z(\lambda)$ or $u(\lambda)$ and $v(\lambda)$ that are random, *not* λ. For convenience let us assume that the mean function of the process is zero, so that

$$\text{Var}(X_t) = E[X_t \, \bar{X}_t] = E\left[\int_{-\pi}^{\pi} \exp{(it\lambda)}\, dZ(\lambda) \int_{-\pi}^{\pi} \exp{(-it\theta)}\, \overline{dZ(\theta)}\right]$$

$$= E\left[\int_{-\pi}^{\pi}\int_{-\pi}^{\pi} \exp{[it(\lambda - \theta)]}\, dZ(\lambda)\, \overline{dZ(\theta)}\right]$$

$$= \int_{-\pi}^{\pi}\int_{-\pi}^{\pi} \exp{[it(\lambda - \theta)]} E[dZ(\lambda)\, \overline{dZ(\theta)}]$$

$$= \int_{-\pi}^{\pi} dF(\lambda) = \int_{-\pi}^{\pi} f(\lambda)\, d\lambda \tag{9.2.60}$$

The next to the last equality above is valid in view of (9.2.53), and the last reflects an implicit assumption that the spectral distribution function is differentiable.

But what (9.2.60) indicates is that we may express the variance (of the elements) of the process as the integral of the contributions of sinusoids of frequency λ. Conversely, we may look upon the spectral density function as a decomposition of the variance of the series into components attributable to various frequencies.

Quite often it is much more meaningful to consider a stochastic process in the frequency rather than in the time domain. Thus if we are dealing with an unemployment series, the (auto-)covariance function is rather hard to interpret in terms of the significance of the contribution of various sources, such as seasonal, cyclical and secular. Consideration of the time series in the frequency domain—that is, dealing with the spectrum—is much more natural and very easy to interpret. In this context, one may be able to infer what fraction of the variance is due to seasonal or cyclical sources and thus be able to frame policies appropriate to the nature of the problem

It is also interesting to observe that the spectral density conveys information as to the type of stochastic process we are dealing with. This is, of course, quite obvious because for a given spectral density there corresponds a unique co-variance function, its Fourier transform, and vice-versa. We illustrate this last remark by means of several examples.

Example 10: Suppose that $F(\cdot)$ is a differentiable spectral distribution function, and let the spectral density be given by

$$f(\lambda) = \frac{\sigma^2}{2\pi} \qquad -\pi < \lambda \leq \pi \tag{9.2.61}$$

The covariance function is therefore given by

$$K(\tau) = \frac{\sigma^2}{2\pi} \int_{-\pi}^{\pi} \exp(i\tau\lambda)\, d\lambda = \sigma^2 \quad \text{if} \quad \tau = 0$$
$$= 0 \quad \text{if} \quad \tau \neq 0 \qquad (9.2.62)$$

It is clear from (9.2.62) that the stochastic process in question consists of orthogonal elements with common variance σ^2.

Example 11: Consider the case where $F(\cdot)$ is a pure jump function and suppose that it has n jumps at λ_j, $j = 1, 2, \ldots, n$.
Thus

$$dF(\lambda) = f_j \quad \text{if} \quad \lambda = \lambda_j, j = 1, 2, \ldots, n$$
$$= 0 \quad \text{otherwise.} \qquad (9.2.63)$$

What information does this give us about the process? First, notice that

$$E[dZ(\lambda)\, \overline{dZ(\lambda)}] = dF(\lambda) = f_j \quad \text{if} \quad \lambda = \lambda_j, j = 1, 2, \ldots, n$$
$$= 0 \quad \text{otherwise} \qquad (9.2.64)$$

where the process $\{Z(\lambda): -\pi < \lambda \leq \pi\}$ has the properties given it in Theorem 4.
On the other hand,

$$E[dZ(\lambda)\, \overline{dZ(\lambda)}] = \int |dZ(\lambda)|^2\, dH(Z) \qquad (9.2.65)$$

where H is the probability distribution function of the elements of the Z process.
Since

$$|dZ(\lambda)|^2 \geq 0$$

then (9.2.65) implies

$$dZ(\lambda) = z_j \quad \text{if} \quad \lambda = \lambda_j, j = 1, 2, \ldots, n$$
$$= 0 \quad \text{otherwise} \qquad (9.2.66)$$

Thus the process can be represented by

$$X_t = \int_{-\pi}^{\pi} \exp(i t\lambda)\, dZ(\lambda) = \sum_{j=1}^{n} \exp(i t\lambda_j) z_j \qquad (9.2.67)$$

and in this way we see that the process $\{X_t : t \in N\}$ can be thought of as a sinusoidal combination of n orthogonal variables.
Notice, further, that from (9.2.67) we obtain

$$E(X_{t+s}\,\overline{X_t}) = E\left(\int_{-\pi}^{\pi} \exp[i(t+s)\lambda]\, dZ(\lambda) \int_{-\pi}^{\pi} \exp(-it\theta)\, \overline{dZ(\theta)} \right)$$
$$= \int_{-\pi}^{\pi} \int_{-\pi}^{\pi} \exp[i(t+s)\lambda] \exp(-it\theta) E[dZ(\lambda)\, \overline{dZ(\theta)}]$$
$$= \sum_{j=1}^{n} \exp(i s\lambda_j) f_j \qquad (9.2.68)$$

So that the covariance function is again a sinusoidal combination of the n jumps of the spectral distribution function.

Looking at (9.2.67) as well as (9.2.68), we see that the process bears sufficient resemblance to a moving average process so as to encourage further probing in that direction.

Example 12: Consider the case where not only is $F(\cdot)$ differentiable but its derivative, $f(\cdot)$, is continuous on $(-\pi, \pi]$. Since this is so, $f(\cdot)$ may be approximated to any desired degree of accuracy by a trigonometric polynomial. Thus

$$f(\lambda) = \frac{1}{2\pi} \sum_{s=-n}^{n} \exp(is\lambda) r_s \qquad (9.2.69)$$

such that $r_s = \bar{r}_{-s}$ and obviously $r_n \neq 0$.

Now let y be a complex variable and note that $\sum_{s=-n}^{n} r_s y^{n+s}$ is a complex polynomial of degree $2n$ and hence that it has $2n$ roots. It is also the case that if y_0 is a root of this polynomial, then so is $\bar{y}_0^{-1}$; of course, y_0 cannot be zero, for $r_{-n} \neq 0$.

To show that, observe

$$\sum_{s=-n}^{n} r_s \bar{y}_0^{-(n+s)} = \bar{y}_0^{-2n} \sum_{s=-n}^{n} r_s \bar{y}_0^{-s} = \bar{y}_0^{-2n} \sum_{s=-n}^{n} \bar{r}_{-s} \bar{y}_0^{-s}$$

$$= \bar{y}_0^{-2n} \overline{\left\{ \sum_{s=-n}^{n} r_{-s} y_0^{-s} \right\}} = 0 \qquad (9.2.70)$$

The last equality holds, for y_0 satisfies

$$\sum_{s=-n}^{n} r_s y^{n+s} = 0 \qquad (9.2.71)$$

Thus we can pair the $2n$ roots of the polynomial by $(y_1, \bar{y}_1^{-1})$, $(y_2, \bar{y}_2^{-2})$, ..., $(y_n, \bar{y}_n^{-1})$; and bearing in mind that a monic polynomial can be expressed as a product of simple factors involving its roots, we may in fact write

$$f(\lambda) = \frac{r_n}{2\pi} \exp(-in\lambda) \sum_{s=-n}^{n} \exp(i(n+s)\lambda) \frac{r_s}{r_n}$$

$$= \frac{r_n \exp(-in\lambda)}{2\pi} \prod_{j=1}^{n} [\exp(i\lambda) - y_j][\exp(i\lambda) - \bar{y}_j^{-1}] \qquad (9.2.72)$$

On the other hand,

$$\exp(i\lambda) - \bar{y}_j^{-1} = -\exp(i\lambda)\bar{y}_j^{-1}(\exp(-i\lambda) - \bar{y}_j) = -\exp(i\lambda)\bar{y}_j^{-1}\overline{(\exp(i\lambda) - y_j)} \qquad (9.2.73)$$

Hence (9.2.72) can be expressed as

$$f(\lambda) = \frac{r_n}{2\pi} \prod_{j=1}^{n} (\bar{y}_j^{-1}) \prod_{j=1}^{n} [(\exp(i\lambda) - y_j)\overline{(\exp(i\lambda) - y_j)}]$$

$$= \frac{1}{2\pi} \left| \sum_{j=0}^{n} a_j \exp(ij\lambda) \right|^2 \qquad (9.2.74)$$

since

$$\prod_{j=1}^{n} [\exp(i\lambda) - y_j]\overline{[\exp(i\lambda) - y_j]} = \left| \prod_{j=1}^{n} [\exp(i\lambda) - y_j] \right|^2$$

We should, of course, remember that the representation given to $f(\cdot)$ in (9.2.74) is not unique, for we could have chosen to pair off the roots in any one of 2^n ways.

But within this degree of arbitrariness we can represent the spectral density (9.2.69) as in (9.2.74). Define now

$$w(\theta) = \int_{-\pi}^{\theta} \left[\sum_{j=1}^{n} \bar{a}_j \exp(-ij\lambda) \right]^{-1} dZ(\lambda) \qquad -\pi < \theta \leq \pi$$

$$= 0 \qquad \qquad \text{otherwise} \qquad (9.2.75)$$

where $\{Z(\lambda): -\pi < \lambda \leq \pi\}$ is the process with orthogonal increments such that the stochastic process $\{X_t: t \in N\}$ with spectral density (9.2.69) can be represented by

$$X_t = \int_{-\pi}^{\pi} \exp(it\lambda) \, dZ(\lambda) \qquad (9.2.76)$$

Now

$$dw(\theta) = \left[\sum_{j=1}^{n} \bar{a}_j \exp(-ij\theta) \right]^{-1} dZ(\theta) \qquad (9.2.77)$$

and

$$E[dw(\theta) \, \overline{dw(\theta)}] = E\left\{ \left[\sum_{j=1}^{n} \bar{a}_j \exp(-ij\theta) \right]^{-1} \left[\sum_{j=1}^{n} a_j \exp(ij\theta) \right]^{-1} dZ(\theta) \, \overline{dZ(\theta)} \right\}$$

$$= \left| \sum_{j=1}^{n} a_j \exp(ij\theta) \right|^{-2} f(\theta) \, d\theta = \frac{d\theta}{2\pi} \qquad (9.2.78)$$

in virtue of (9.2.74).

Finally, defining

$$\varepsilon_t = \int_{-\pi}^{\pi} \exp(it\lambda) \, dw(\lambda) \qquad (9.2.79)$$

we conclude by (9.2.78) that the process $\{\varepsilon_t : t \in N\}$ consists of orthogonal variables. This is so since if $G(\cdot)$ is the spectral distribution of $\{\varepsilon_t\}$, then $E[dw(\theta)\ \overline{dw(\theta)}] = dG(\theta)$ and so the derivative of $G(\cdot)$ is given by the last member of (9.2.78). Then use the results of Example 10 to complete the reasoning.

Therefore any process whose spectral density is continuous, and thus can be sufficiently closely approximated by an expression such as (9.2.69), can be represented as a (finite) moving average of orthogonal variables. That this is the case follows from

$$X_t = \int_{-\pi}^{\pi} \exp{(it\lambda)}\, dZ(\lambda) = \int_{-\pi}^{\pi} \exp{(it\lambda)} \left[\sum_{j=1}^{n} \bar{a}_j \exp{(-ij\lambda)} \right] dw(\lambda)$$

$$= \sum_{j=1}^{n} \bar{a}_j \int_{-\pi}^{\pi} \exp{(i(t-j)\lambda)}\, dw(\lambda) = \sum_{j=1}^{n} \bar{a}_j \varepsilon_{t-j} \tag{9.2.80}$$

Example 13: Consider now a somewhat more complicated spectral distribution.

Let $F(\cdot)$ be a spectral distribution function and let its derivative be given by

$$f(\lambda) = \frac{1}{2\pi} \left| \sum_{j=0}^{p} \beta_j \exp{(ij\lambda)} \right|^{-2} \tag{9.2.81}$$

This representation, of course, requires the assumption that no root of

$$\sum_{j=0}^{p} \beta_j z^j = 0 \qquad z = \exp{(i\lambda)} \tag{9.2.82}$$

lies on the unit circle. That is, if z_0 is any root of (9.2.82), then $|z_0| \neq 1$; otherwise the function in (9.2.81) would not be defined everywhere in the interval $(-\pi, \pi]$.

Now let $\{X_t : t \in N\}$ be the process having the spectral density (9.2.81); we claim that the process obeys the relation

$$\sum_{j=0}^{p} \bar{\beta}_j X_{t-j} = \varepsilon_t \tag{9.2.83}$$

where $\{\varepsilon_t : \in N\}$ is a process consisting of orthogonal variables.

Definition 16: If $\{X_t : t \in N\}$ is a process satisfying (9.2.83), where $\{\bar{\beta}_j\}$ are some constants and $\{\varepsilon_t : t \in N\}$ is a process consisting of orthogonal variables, then $\{X_t : t \in N\}$ is said to be an *autoregressive process of order p*.

Recall, also, the definition of a moving average process: a process $\{X_t : t \in N\}$ is said to be a moving average process of order m if it can be expressed in the form

$$X_t = \sum_{j=0}^{m} a_j \varepsilon_{t-j} \tag{9.2.84}$$

where $\{\varepsilon_t : t \in N\}$ is a process consisting of orthogonal variables.

Return now to (9.2.83) and note that the representation there would be valid if an orthogonal process can be derived, taking into account the fact that (9.2.81) is the spectral density of $\{X_t: t \in N\}$.

To show that this is so, we proceed as follows: Let the spectral representation of the X process be

$$X_t = \int_{-\pi}^{\pi} \exp{(it\lambda)} \, dZ(\lambda) \tag{9.2.85}$$

Then from (9.2.83) we should have

$$\varepsilon_t = \int_{-\pi}^{\pi} \sum_{j=1}^{p} \bar{\beta}_j \exp{[i(t-j)\lambda]} \, dZ(\lambda) \tag{9.2.86}$$

Now define

$$w(\theta) = \int_{-\pi}^{\theta} \sum_{j=0}^{p} \bar{\beta}_j \exp{(-ij\lambda)} \, dZ(\lambda) \qquad -\pi < \theta \le \pi$$
$$= 0 \qquad\qquad\qquad\qquad\qquad \text{otherwise} \tag{9.2.87}$$

Hence, using (9.2.87), we can rewrite (9.2.86) as

$$\varepsilon_t = \int_{-\pi}^{\pi} \exp{(it\lambda)} \, dw(\lambda) \tag{9.2.88}$$

so that the ε process can be defined in terms of the function in (9.2.87). It remains to show that the w process has orthogonal increments and that the spectral density of the ε process is constant.

With respect to the first requirement, note

$$dw(\theta) = \sum_{j=1}^{p} \bar{\beta}_j \exp{(-ij\theta)} \, dZ(\theta) \tag{9.2.89}$$

and thus

$$E[dw(\theta_1) \overline{dw(\theta_2)}] = E\left[\sum_j \bar{\beta}_j \exp{(-ij\theta_1)} \, dZ(\theta_1) \sum_s \beta_s \exp{(-is\theta_2)} \overline{dZ(\theta_2)} \right]$$

$$= \sum_j \sum_s \exp{(-ij\theta_1)} \exp{(-is\theta_2)} \bar{\beta}_j \, \beta_s \, E[dZ(\theta_1) \overline{dZ(\theta_2)}] = 0$$

$$\theta_1 \ne \theta_2$$

$$\tag{9.2.90}$$

The last equality holds because the Z process is that used in the spectral representation of $\{X_t: t \in N\}$ and thus obeys

$$E[dZ(\theta_1) \overline{dZ(\theta_2)}] = 0 \qquad \text{if } \theta_1 \ne \theta_2$$
$$= dF(\theta) \qquad \text{if } \theta_1 = \theta_2 = \theta$$

Conversely, for $\theta_1 = \theta_2 = \theta$, (9.2.90) yields

$$E[dw(\theta)\,\overline{dw(\theta)}] = \left| \sum_{j=0}^{p} \bar{\beta}_j \exp{(ij\theta)} \right|^2 dF(\theta) = \frac{1}{2\pi}\,d\theta \qquad (9.2.91)$$

Here the last equality holds in virtue of (9.2.81). However, it follows from (9.2.91) that the ε process, which has spectral representation (9.2.88), is one consisting of orthogonal variables.

It is an interesting fact that an autoregressive process can, typically, be represented as a moving average process. To see how this is accomplished and what the precise form of the relationship is, we may proceed as follows: Notice from (9.2.89) that we can write

$$dZ(\theta) = \frac{dw(\theta)}{\sum_{j=0}^{p} \bar{\beta}_j \exp{(-ij\theta)}} \qquad (9.2.92)$$

The expression (9.2.92) will be defined on $(-\pi, \pi]$ if none of the roots of (9.2.82) lies on the unit circle.

Consider now the roots of the complex polynomial

$$\sum_{j=0}^{p} \bar{\beta}_j u^j = 0 \qquad u = \exp{(-i\theta)} \qquad (9.2.93)$$

If all the roots of (9.2.93) lie outside the unit circle, then it is obvious that we can write

$$\left(\sum_{j=0}^{p} \bar{\beta}_j u^j \right)^{-1} = \frac{1}{\bar{\beta}_p} \prod_{j=1}^{p} (u - u_j)^{-1}$$

$$= (-1)^p \frac{1}{\bar{\beta}_p} \prod_{j=1}^{p} u_j^{-1} \prod_{j=1}^{p} \left(1 - \frac{u}{u_j} \right)^{-1} \qquad (9.2.94)$$

where the u_j, $j = 1, 2, \ldots, p$, are the roots of the polynomial in (9.2.93).

It is clear that for $|u/u_j| < 1$, the following equation is valid:

$$\frac{1}{1 - (u/u_j)} = \sum_{k=0}^{\infty} \left(\frac{u}{u_j} \right)^k \qquad (9.2.95)$$

In particular, this is valid for $u = \exp{(i\lambda)}$ because $|u| = 1$, and since $|u_j| > 1$, we have

$$\left| \frac{\exp{(i\lambda)}}{u_j} \right| < 1 \qquad (9.2.96)$$

But then we can write

$$\left[\sum_{j=0}^{p} \bar{\beta}_j \exp{(-ij\theta)} \right]^{-1} = \frac{(-1)^p}{\bar{\beta}_p} \prod_{s=1}^{p} (u_s^{-1}) \prod_{s=1}^{p} \sum_{k=0}^{\infty} \left[\frac{\exp{(-i\theta)}}{u_s} \right]^k$$

$$= \sum_{k=0}^{\infty} a_k \exp{(-i\theta k)} \qquad (9.2.97)$$

Hence (9.2.92) can be written also as

$$dZ(\theta) = \left[\sum_{k=0}^{\infty} a_k \exp\left(-ik\theta\right) \right] dw(\theta) \qquad (9.2.98)$$

It should be clear that since the roots of (9.2.93) are well-defined functions of the coefficients $\bar{\beta}_j$, $j = 0, 1, 2, \ldots, p$, the $\{a_k : k = 0, 1, 2, \ldots\}$ depend solely on the $(p + 1)$ parameters of the autoregressive scheme exhibited in (9.2.83). Now, using (9.2.98), rewrite (9.2.85) to obtain

$$X_t = \int_{-\pi}^{\pi} \exp\left(it\lambda\right) dZ(\lambda) = \int_{-\pi}^{\pi} \exp\left(it\lambda\right) \left[\sum_{k=0}^{\infty} a_k \exp\left(-ik\lambda\right) \right] dw(\lambda)$$

$$= \sum_{k=0}^{\infty} a_k \int_{-\pi}^{\pi} \exp\left[i(t - k)\lambda\right] dw(\lambda) = \sum_{k=0}^{\infty} a_k \varepsilon_{t-k} \qquad (9.2.99)$$

The last equality of (9.2.99) holds in view of (9.2.88). Thus we see that if we start with an autoregressive process of order p, then, provided that certain conditions are satisfied concerning the roots of the associated polynomial, we can represent it by a moving average process of infinite order. The coefficients of the latter, however, depend on a *finite* number of parameters.

Finally, one should note that it can easily be verified that the spectral density of the X process as shown in (9.2.99) fully agrees with the assumed density as given in (9.2.81). We must do this at least to show that our derivation does not entail any contradictions.

Therefore consider

$$K(s) = E[X_{t+s} \bar{X}_t]$$

$$= \int_{-\pi}^{\pi} \int_{-\pi}^{\pi} \exp\left[i(t + s)\lambda\right] \exp\left(-it\theta\right) \left[\sum_{k=0}^{\infty} a_k \exp\left(-ik\lambda\right) \right] \left[\sum_{j=0}^{\infty} \bar{a}_j \exp\left(ij\theta\right) \right]$$

$$\times E[dw(\lambda) \, \overline{dw(\theta)}]$$

$$= \frac{1}{2\pi} \int_{-\pi}^{\pi} \exp\left(is\lambda\right) \left| \sum_{k=0}^{\infty} a_k \exp\left(-ik\lambda\right) \right|^2 d\lambda \qquad (9.2.100)$$

which shows that $K(s)$ is the sth Fourier coefficient of the function

$$\left| \sum_{k=0}^{\infty} a_k \exp\left(-ik\lambda\right) \right|^2$$

It follows, therefore, that if $g(\cdot)$ is the spectral density of the process represented in (9.2.99), then

$$g(\lambda) = \frac{1}{2\pi} \sum_{s=-\infty}^{\infty} K(s) \exp\left(-is\lambda\right) = \frac{1}{2\pi} \left| \sum_{k=0}^{\infty} a_k \exp\left(-ik\lambda\right) \right|^2$$

$$= \frac{1}{2\pi} \left| \sum_{j=0}^{p} \beta_j \exp\left(ij\lambda\right) \right|^{-2} \qquad (9.2.101)$$

which is, of course, identical with the spectral density exhibited in (9.2.81). The second equality of (9.2.101) is, of course, valid only when the Fourier series of

$$\frac{1}{2\pi}\left|\sum_{k=0}^{\infty} a_k \exp\left(-ik\lambda\right)\right|^2$$

converges to that function.

Two additional observations are of significance in this context.

First, it bears repeating that there is a certain degree of arbitrariness in that the ε process could have been chosen to have variance $\sigma^2/2\pi$, where $\sigma^2 > 0$. Second, if all the roots of (9.2.93) lie within the unit circle, (9.2.97) should have to be modified so that it becomes

$$\left[\sum_{j=0}^{p} \bar{\beta}_j \exp\left(-ij\theta\right)\right]^{-1} = \sum_{k=0}^{\infty} b_k \exp\left[i(k+p+1)\lambda\right] \tag{9.2.102}$$

Thus, employing the same construction as above we shall obtain an ε process and an X process representable by

$$X_t = \sum_{k=0}^{\infty} b_k \varepsilon_{t+k+p+1} \tag{9.2.103}$$

But this depends on "future" members of ε process, that is, it is a forward process. Such systems are highly implausible, indeed nonrealizable, and hence we shall not consider them at all. Notice, however, that this situation corresponds to the case where the homogeneous part of the stochastic difference equation in (9.2.83) is unstable.

Example 14: Consider the case where the spectral density function is given by

$$f(\lambda) = \frac{1}{2\pi} \frac{|\sum_{j=0}^{p} \alpha_j \exp\left(ij\lambda\right)|^2}{|\sum_{j=0}^{m} \beta_j \exp\left(ij\lambda\right)|^2} \tag{9.2.104}$$

It is possible to specify the form of the stochastic process whose spectral density is given by (9.2.104)?

Well, consider the process defined by

$$u_t = \sum_{j=0}^{m} \bar{\beta}_j X_{t-j} \tag{9.2.105}$$

and let the spectral representation of the X process be

$$X_t = \int_{-\pi}^{\pi} \exp\left(it\lambda\right) dZ(\lambda) \tag{9.2.106}$$

Substituting (9.2.106) into (9.2.105), we find

$$u_t = \int_{-\pi}^{\pi} \exp\left(it\lambda\right) \left[\sum_{j=0}^{m} \bar{\beta}_j \exp\left(-ij\lambda\right)\right] dZ(\lambda) \tag{9.2.107}$$

Defining

$$w(\theta) = \int_{-\pi}^{\theta} \left[\sum_{j=0}^{m} \bar{\beta}_j \exp\left(-ij\lambda\right) \right] dZ(\lambda) \qquad -\pi < \theta \leq \pi$$

$$= 0 \qquad\qquad\qquad\text{otherwise} \qquad\qquad (9.2.108)$$

we obtain the spectral representation of the u process as

$$u_t = \int_{-\pi}^{\pi} \exp\left(it\lambda\right) dw(\lambda) \qquad\qquad (9.2.109)$$

If we denote the spectral distribution of the u process by $F_u(\cdot)$, then

$$dF_u(\theta) = E[dw(\theta)\,\overline{dw(\theta)}] = \frac{1}{2\pi} \left| \sum_{j=0}^{p} \alpha_j \exp\left(ij\theta\right) \right|^2 d\theta \qquad\qquad (9.2.110)$$

It may, of course, be verified that

$$E[dw(\theta_1)\,\overline{dw(\theta_2)}] = 0 \qquad \text{for} \quad \theta_1 \neq \theta_2 \qquad\qquad (9.2.111)$$

It should also be clear that the u process is covariance stationary, since

$$E[u_{t+s}\bar{u}_t] = \int_{-\pi}^{\pi} \int_{-\pi}^{\pi} \exp[i(t+s)\lambda]\exp(-it\theta)E[dw(\lambda)\,\overline{dw(\theta)}]$$

$$= \frac{1}{2\pi} \int_{-\pi}^{\pi} \exp\left(is\lambda\right) \left| \sum_{j=0}^{p} \alpha_j \exp\left(ij\lambda\right) \right|^2 d\lambda = K_u(s) \qquad\qquad (9.2.112)$$

and also

$$\overline{K_u(s)} = \frac{1}{2\pi} \int_{-\pi}^{\pi} \exp\left(-is\lambda\right) \left| \sum_{j=0}^{p} \alpha_j \exp\left(ij\lambda\right) \right|^2 d\lambda = K_u(-s) \qquad\qquad (9.2.113)$$

But in Example 12 we have shown that a process with spectral density as in (9.2.110) is representable as the moving average process

$$u_t = \sum_{j=0}^{p} \bar{\alpha}_j \varepsilon_{t-j} \qquad\qquad (9.2.114)$$

where the ε process consists of orthogonal variables with common variance.

Hence the X process having spectral density (9.2.104) is representable as

$$\sum_{j=0}^{m} \bar{\beta}_j X_{t-j} = \sum_{j=0}^{p} \bar{\alpha}_j \varepsilon_{t-j} \qquad\qquad (9.2.115)$$

To verify that the X process as implicitly defined in (9.2.115) does indeed have the spectral density (9.2.104), we proceed as follows. Let $K_x(\cdot)$ be the covariance kernel of the X process and $K_u(\cdot)$ the covariance kernel of the u process. Then note

$$K_u(s) = E[u_{t+s}\bar{u}_t] = \sum_{j=0}^{m} \sum_{r=0}^{m} \beta_j \bar{\beta}_r E(X_{t+s-j}\bar{X}_{t-r})$$

$$= \sum_{j=0}^{m} \sum_{r=0}^{m} \beta_j \bar{\beta}_r K_x(s + r - j) \tag{9.2.116}$$

Now, taking the Fourier transform of (9.2.116), we have

$$f_u(\lambda) = \sum_{s=-\infty}^{\infty} K_u(s) \exp(-is\lambda)$$

$$= \sum_{s=-\infty}^{\infty} \sum_{j=0}^{m} \sum_{r=0}^{m} \beta_j \bar{\beta}_r \exp(-is\lambda) K_x(s + r - j) \tag{9.2.117}$$

But the last member of (9.2.117) can be written as

$$\sum_{j=0}^{\infty} \sum_{r=0}^{\infty} \sum_{s=-\infty}^{\infty} \beta_j \bar{\beta}_r \exp(-is\lambda) K_x(s + r - j)$$

$$= \sum_{j=0}^{m} \beta_j \exp(ir\lambda) \sum_{r=0}^{m} \bar{\beta}_r \exp(-ij\lambda) \sum_{s=-\infty}^{\infty} \exp[-i(s + r - j)] K_x(s + r - j)$$

$$= \sum_{j=0}^{m} \beta_j \exp(ir\lambda) \sum_{s=0}^{m} \bar{\beta}_r \exp(-ij\lambda) \sum_{v=-\infty}^{\infty} \exp(-iv\lambda) K_x(v)$$

$$= \left| \sum_{j=0}^{m} \beta_j \exp(ij\lambda) \right|^2 f_x(\lambda) \tag{9.2.118}$$

where $f_x(\cdot)$ is the spectral density of the X process as given in (9.2.115). We must now show that this is exactly the function initially given; that is, it is identically (9.2.104). But this is obvious, for the spectral density of the u process is given by (9.2.110).

Before concluding, it is well to point out the following useful result.

Lemma 1: Let $\{X_t : t \in N\}$ be a stochastic process with spectral density $f(\cdot)$. Let $\{Y_t : t \in N\}$ be the process defined by

$$Y_t = \sum_{j=0}^{m} \alpha_j X_{t-j} \tag{9.2.119}$$

Then the spectral density of the Y process is given by

$$g(\lambda) = \left| \sum_{j=0}^{m} \bar{\alpha}_j \exp(ij\lambda) \right|^2 f(\lambda) \tag{9.2.120}$$

PROOF: The covariance kernel of the Y process is given by

$$K_y(s) = E[Y_{t+s}\bar{Y}_t] = \sum_{j=0}^{m} \sum_{k=0}^{m} \alpha_j \bar{\alpha}_k E[X_{t+s-j}\bar{X}_{t-k}]$$

$$= \sum_{j=0}^{m} \sum_{k=0}^{m} \alpha_j \bar{\alpha}_k K_x(s + k - j) \tag{9.2.121}$$

where $K_x(\cdot)$ is the covariance kernel of the X process. Now the spectral density of the Y process, say $g(\cdot)$, is given by

$$g(\lambda) = \sum_{s=-\infty}^{\infty} K_y(s) \exp(-is\lambda)$$

$$= \sum_{s=-\infty}^{\infty} \sum_{j=0}^{m} \sum_{k=0}^{m} \alpha_j \bar{\alpha}_k K_x(s+k-j) \exp(-is\lambda)$$

$$= \sum_{j=0}^{m} \sum_{k=0}^{m} \alpha_j \exp(-ij\lambda) \bar{\alpha}_k \exp(ik\lambda) \sum_{s=-\infty}^{\infty} K_x(s+k-j) \exp[-i(s+k-j)\lambda]$$

$$= \left(\sum_{j=0}^{m} \alpha_j \exp(-ij\lambda) \right) \left(\sum_{k=0}^{m} \bar{\alpha}_k \exp(ik\lambda) \right) f(\lambda)$$

$$= \left| \sum_{k=0}^{m} \bar{\alpha}_k \exp(ik\lambda) \right|^2 f(\lambda) \tag{9.2.122}$$

Remark 17: Equation (9.2.120) shows that if the X process is a covariance stationary process, then the Y process would also be covariance stationary.

9.3. ESTIMATION OF THE SPECTRUM

THE PERIODOGRAM

In early work with time series, the major research problem was considered to be the "search for hidden periodicities." By this, one meant the following. Realizations of time series quite often exhibit perceptible cyclicity. Although the appearance of cyclicity could be explained as the summation of random processes [22, p. 105], still early investigators sought to attribute the cyclicity to some deterministic (nonrandom) component which if isolated and subtracted from the sample would yield a "realization" not exhibiting such cyclicity.

The model implied by such an approach is roughly

$$X_t = \sum_{j=1}^{k} a_j \cos(\lambda_j t + b_j) + \varepsilon_t \tag{9.3.1}$$

where $\{\varepsilon_t : t \in N\}$ is a process of orthogonal variables. It was typically assumed that for all $t \in N$, $\varepsilon_t \sim N(0, 1)$. In this context, if one wished to test for the existence of a component of frequency λ, then it would be natural to form

$$P_n(\lambda) = \frac{1}{n^2} \left| \sum_{t=1}^{n} X_t \exp(it\lambda) \right|^2 \tag{9.3.2}$$

Before proceeding, it will be helpful to recall that

$$\cos t\lambda = \frac{\exp(it\lambda) + \exp(-it\lambda)}{2} \qquad \sin t\lambda = \frac{\exp(it\lambda) - \exp(-it\lambda)}{2i} \tag{9.3.3}$$

Hence

$$X_t = \sum_{j=1}^{k} a_j \left[\frac{\exp\left[i(t\lambda_j + b_j)\right] + \exp\left[-i(t\lambda_j + b_j)\right]}{2} \right] + \varepsilon_t \tag{9.3.4}$$

and

$$X_t \exp(it\lambda) = \sum_{j=1}^{k} a_j \left[\frac{\exp\{i[t(\lambda_j + \lambda) + b_j]\} + \exp\{-i[t(\lambda_j - \lambda) + b_j]\}}{2} \right]$$

$$+ \varepsilon_t \exp(it\lambda) \tag{9.3.5}$$

Furthermore,

$$\sum_{t=1}^{n} X_t \exp(it\lambda)$$

$$= \frac{1}{2} \sum_{j=1}^{k} a_j \left\{ \sum_{t=1}^{n} \exp\{i[t(\lambda_j + \lambda) + b_j]\} + \sum_{t=1}^{n} \exp\left[-i[t(\lambda_j - \lambda) + b_j]\right] \right\}$$

$$+ \sum_{t=1}^{n} \varepsilon_t \exp(it\lambda) \tag{9.3.6}$$

But

$$\sum_{t=1}^{n} \exp\{i[t(\lambda_j + \lambda) + b_j]\} = \exp(ib_j) \sum_{t=1}^{n} \exp\left[it(\lambda_j + \lambda)\right]$$

$$= \exp(ib_j) \frac{1 - \exp\left[i(n+1)(\lambda_j + \lambda)\right]}{1 - \exp\left[i(\lambda_j + \lambda)\right]}$$

$$= \exp(ib_j) \exp\left[i(n/2)(\lambda_j + \lambda)\right]$$

$$\times \frac{\exp\{-i[(n+1)/2](\lambda_j + \lambda)\} - \exp\{i[(n+1)/2](\lambda_j + \lambda)\}}{\exp\left[-\frac{1}{2}i(\lambda_j + \lambda)\right] - \exp\left[\frac{1}{2}i(\lambda_j + \lambda)\right]}$$

$$= \exp(ib_j) \exp\left[i(n/2)(\lambda_j + \lambda)\right] \frac{\sin\left[(n+1)/2\right](\lambda_j + \lambda)}{\sin\frac{1}{2}(\lambda_j + \lambda)} \tag{9.3.7}$$

It follows, therefore, that (9.3.6) can be expressed as

$$\sum_{t=1}^{n} X_t \exp(it\lambda) = \frac{1}{2} \sum_{j=1}^{k} a_j \left[\exp(ib_j) \exp\left[i(n/2)(\lambda_j + \lambda)\right] + \frac{\sin\left[(n+1)/2\right](\lambda_j + \lambda)}{\sin\frac{1}{2}(\lambda_j + \lambda)} \right.$$

$$\left. + \exp(-ib_j) \exp\left[-i(n/2)(\lambda_j - \lambda)\right] \frac{\sin\left[(n+1)/2\right](\lambda_j - \lambda)}{\sin\frac{1}{2}(\lambda_j - \lambda)} \right]$$

$$+ \sum_{t=1}^{n} \varepsilon_t \exp(it\lambda) \tag{9.3.8}$$

Hence

$$P_n(\lambda) = \frac{1}{n^2}\left|\sum_{t=1}^{n} X_t \exp(it\lambda)\right|^2$$

$$= \left|\frac{1}{2}\sum_{j=1}^{k} a_j\left[\exp(ib_j)\exp[i(n/2)(\lambda_j + \lambda)]\frac{1}{n}\frac{\sin([n+1]/2)(\lambda_j + \lambda)}{\sin\frac{1}{2}(\lambda_j + \lambda)}\right.\right.$$

$$\left.+ \exp(-ib_j)\exp[-i(n/2)(\lambda_j - \lambda)]\frac{1}{n}\frac{\sin[(n+1)/2](\lambda_j - \lambda)}{\sin\frac{1}{2}(\lambda_j - \lambda)}\right]$$

$$+ \left.\sum_{t=1}^{n}\frac{\varepsilon_t \exp(it\lambda)}{n}\right|^2 \tag{9.3.9}$$

Now if we wish to test for the existence of a component with frequency, say λ_1, we proceed as follows. Letting $\lambda = \lambda_1$ and $n \to \infty$, we find

$$\lim_{n\to\infty} P_n(\lambda_1) = |\tfrac{1}{2}a_1 \exp(ib_1)|^2 \tag{9.3.10}$$

This is so since

$$\lim_{n\to\infty} \frac{\sum_{t=1}^{n} \varepsilon_t \exp(it\lambda)}{n} = 0$$

by the strong law of large numbers and

$$\lim_{n\to\infty} \frac{1}{n}\frac{\sin[(n+1)/2](\lambda_j \pm \lambda)}{\sin\frac{1}{2}(\lambda_j \pm \lambda)} = 0$$

except for the term

$$\frac{1}{n}\frac{\sin[(n+1)/2](\lambda_j - \lambda)}{\sin\frac{1}{2}(\lambda_j - \lambda)} \qquad \text{for} \quad j = 1$$

In this case the fraction is defined by its limit as $\lambda \to \lambda_1$, which is given by

$$\lim_{\lambda\to\lambda_1} \frac{1}{n}\frac{\sin[(n+1)/2](\lambda_1 - \lambda)}{\sin\frac{1}{2}(\lambda_1 - \lambda)} = \frac{n+1}{n} = 1 + \frac{1}{n} \tag{9.3.11}$$

Hence taking the limit of $P_n(\lambda)$ as $n \to \infty$, we obtain the result in (9.3.10).

From this we see that if the series contains a component of frequency λ_1, then

$$\lim_{n\to\infty} P_n(\lambda_1) = \tfrac{1}{4}a_1^2 \neq 0 \tag{9.3.12}$$

whereas if it contains no such component, then

$$\lim_{n\to\infty} P_n(\lambda_1) = 0 \tag{9.3.13}$$

Also notice that since we assume $\varepsilon_t \sim N(0, 1)$, it follows that X_t is also normally distributed and thus so is $\sum_{t=1}^{n} X_t \exp{(it\lambda)}$.

Finally, we note that in testing the null hypothesis

H_0: the series contains a component of frequency λ_1

as against the alternative

H_1: the series does not contain such a component

the usual chi-square tests apply, at least asymptotically. This is so since under the null hypothesis $1/n \sum_{t=1}^{n} X_t \exp{(it\lambda)}$ is, for large n, approximately normal, and thus $P_n(\lambda)$ would be approximately chi square with two degrees of freedom. It has two degrees of freedom, for

$$P_n(\lambda) = \frac{1}{n^2} \left| \sum_{t=1}^{n} X_t \exp{(it\lambda)} \right|^2$$

$$= \frac{1}{n^2} \left[\left(\sum_{t=1}^{n} X_t \cos t\lambda \right)^2 + \left(\sum_{t=1}^{n} X_t \sin t\lambda \right)^2 \right] \qquad (9.3.14)$$

and it can be verified that

$$\frac{1}{n} \sum_{t=1}^{n} X_t \cos t\lambda \qquad \frac{1}{n} \sum_{t=1}^{n} X_t \sin t\lambda$$

are asymptotically $N(0, 1)$ and their covariance vanishes. Thus it is seen that $P_n(\lambda)$ can serve as a test statistic in the search of "hidden periodicities." $P_n(\lambda)$ is referred to as the *periodogram* of the series or the Schuster periodogram, after Sir Arthur Schuster who popularized it in the last part of the nineteenth century.

The use of this method of analysis, often called *harmonic analysis*, was greatly discredited in later years when, applied indiscriminately, apparently discovered "cycles" even in series that were constructed explicitly for purposes of testing and thus contained no cycles.

THE INCONSISTENCY OF THE PERIODOGRAM AS AN ESTIMATOR OF THE SPECTRAL DENSITY

It is rather extraordinary that a simple modification of the periodogram leads to an estimator of the spectral density function of a (covariance stationary) stochastic process.

Define

$$P_n^*(\lambda) = \frac{1}{2\pi n} \left| \sum_{t=1}^{n} X_t \exp{(it\lambda)} \right|^2 \qquad (9.3.15)$$

This will be referred to as the *modified periodogram*. We may prove the following

Theorem 6: Let $\{X_t : t \in N\}$ be a covariance stationary stochastic process with spectral density $f(\cdot)$. Let $\{X_1, X_2, \ldots, X_n\}$ be a realization of the process.

Then the statistic in (9.3.15) is an asymptotically unbiased estimator of the spectral density of the process.

PROOF: Let the spectral representation of the process be

$$X_t = \int_{-\pi}^{\pi} \exp(it\lambda)\, dZ(\lambda) \tag{9.3.16}$$

Using (9.3.16), we can write (9.3.15) as

$$
\begin{aligned}
P_n^*(\lambda) &= \frac{1}{2\pi n}\left[\sum_{t=1}^{n} X_t \exp(it\lambda)\right]\left[\sum_{s=1}^{n} \overline{X}_s \exp(-is\lambda)\right] \\
&= \frac{1}{2\pi n}\left[\sum_{t=1}^{n} \exp(it\lambda)\int_{-\pi}^{\pi}\exp(it\theta)\,dZ(\theta)\right] \\
&\quad \times \left[\sum_{s=1}^{n} \exp(-is\lambda)\int_{-\pi}^{\pi}\exp(-isw)\,\overline{dZ(w)}\right] \\
&= \frac{1}{2\pi n}\sum_{t=1}^{n}\sum_{s=1}^{n}\exp[i(t-s)\lambda]\int_{-\pi}^{\pi}\int_{-\pi}^{\pi}\exp(it\theta)\exp(-isw)\,dZ(\theta)\,\overline{dZ(w)}
\end{aligned}
\tag{9.3.17}
$$

Taking the expectation of $P_n^*(\lambda)$, we find

$$
\begin{aligned}
E[P_n^*(\lambda)] &= \frac{1}{2\pi n}\sum_{t=1}^{n}\sum_{s=1}^{n}\exp[i(t-s)\lambda]\int_{-\pi}^{\pi}\exp[i(t-s)\theta]f(\theta)\,d\theta \\
&= \frac{1}{2\pi n}\sum_{t=1}^{n}\sum_{s=1}^{n}\exp[i(t-s)\lambda]K(t-s)
\end{aligned}
\tag{9.3.18}
$$

where K is the covariance kernel of $\{X_t : t \in N\}$.
But setting $t - s = v$, $t = t$ in (9.3.18), we have

$$
\begin{aligned}
E[P_n^*(\lambda)] &= \frac{1}{2\pi n}\sum_{t=1}^{n}\sum_{v=t-n}^{t-1}\exp(iv\lambda)K(v) \\
&= \frac{1}{2\pi}\sum_{v=-n}^{n}\left(1 - \frac{|v|}{n}\right)\exp(iv\lambda)K(v)
\end{aligned}
\tag{9.3.19}
$$

Thus letting $n \to \infty$,

$$\lim_{n\to\infty} E[P_n^*(\lambda)] = \frac{1}{2\pi}\sum_{v=-\infty}^{\infty}\exp(iv\lambda)K(v) = f(\lambda) \tag{9.3.20}$$

It follows, therefore, that $P_n^*(\lambda)$ is an asymptotically unbiased estimator of the spectral density.

Unfortunately, however, it turns out that it is not a very good estimator of the spectral density, for it is not consistent.[4] Here consistency will mean convergence in quadratic mean.

Our next task is to show its inconsistency. To do this, we shall show first inconsistency in a very special case and then demonstrate it for a wide class of spectral densities. We take this very roundabout method, for to tackle the problem directly would involve rather messy manipulations. We first prove the simple

Theorem 7: Let $\{\varepsilon_t : t \in N\}$ be a real process consisting of orthogonal, identically, distributed random variables. Let it also be assumed that Var $(\varepsilon_t) = \sigma^2$. Then the periodogram of the ε process is an inconsistent estimator of its spectral density.

PROOF: Denote the (modified) periodogram of the ε process by

$$P_n^*(\lambda, \varepsilon) = \frac{1}{2\pi n} \left| \sum_{t=1}^{n} \varepsilon_t \exp(it\lambda) \right| \tag{9.3.21}$$

where n is the length of the realization at hand.

The spectral density of the process is simply

$$f(\lambda, \varepsilon) = \frac{\sigma^2}{2\pi} \tag{9.3.22}$$

We may rewrite the periodogram as

$$P_n^*(\lambda, \varepsilon) = \frac{1}{2\pi n} \sum_{t=1}^{n} \sum_{s=1}^{n} \varepsilon_t \bar{\varepsilon}_s \exp[i(t-s)\lambda] \tag{9.3.23}$$

Taking expectations, we find

$$E[P_n^*(\lambda, \varepsilon)] = \frac{1}{2\pi n} \sum_{t=1}^{n} \sum_{s=1}^{n} \exp[i(t-s)\lambda] E(\varepsilon_t \bar{\varepsilon}_s) = \frac{\sigma^2}{2\pi} = f(\lambda, \varepsilon) \tag{9.3.24}$$

which shows that in this special case the periodogram is an unbiased estimator (and not merely an asymptotically unbiased one) of the spectrum. Hence to show inconsistency we only need show that its variance does not vanish as $n \to \infty$. Now

Cov $[P_n^*(\lambda_1, \varepsilon), P_n^*(\lambda_2, \varepsilon)]$

$$= \left(\frac{1}{2\pi n}\right)^2 \sum_{t=1}^{n} \sum_{s=1}^{n} \sum_{v=1}^{n} \sum_{r=1}^{n} \exp[i(t-s)\lambda_1] \exp[i(v-r)\lambda_2] \cdot E[\varepsilon_t \bar{\varepsilon}_s \varepsilon_v \bar{\varepsilon}_r] \tag{9.3.25}$$

---

[4] It is precisely this characteristic that led to difficulties in the application of harmonic analysis and thus discredited the Schuster periodogram as a tool of empirical research.

Because the ε process is orthogonal, the expectation in (9.3.25) vanishes except for the following cases:

   i. $t = s, v = r, s \neq r$
   ii. $t = v, s = r, v \neq r$
  iii. $t = r, s = v, v \neq r$
  iv. $t = r = s = v$

Quite clearly the expectation is simply σ^4 in cases i, ii, and iii. In case iv we have

$$E(\varepsilon^4) = \kappa_4 + 3\sigma^4 \tag{9.3.26}$$

where κ_4 is the fourth cumulant of the distribution of the random variables of the ε process.[5]

The contribution of terms from case i is simply

$$\sum_{\substack{s \\ s \neq r}} \sum_r \sigma^4 = n^2\sigma^4 - n\sigma^4 \tag{9.3.27}$$

The contribution of terms from case ii is

$$\sigma^4 \sum_{\substack{v \\ v \neq r}} \sum_r \exp\left[i(v - r)(\lambda_1 + \lambda_2)\right] = \sigma^4 \sum_{r=1}^{n} \sum_{v=1}^{n} \exp\left[i(v - r)(\lambda_1 + \lambda_2)\right] - n\sigma^4 \tag{9.3.28}$$

The contribution of terms from case iii is

$$\sigma^4 \sum_{\substack{r \\ r \neq v}} \sum_v \exp\left[i(v - r)(\lambda_2 - \lambda_1)\right] = \sigma^4 \sum_{r=1}^{n} \sum_{v=1}^{n} \exp\left[i(v - r)(\lambda_2 - \lambda_1)\right] - n\sigma^4 \tag{9.3.29}$$

Finally, the contribution of terms from case iv is

$$\sum_{r=1}^{n} (\kappa_4 + 3\sigma^4) = n\kappa_4 + 3n\sigma^4 \tag{9.3.30}$$

Thus we have

$$\mathrm{Cov}\left[P_n^*(\lambda_1, \varepsilon), P_n^*(\lambda_2, \varepsilon)\right] = \left(\frac{1}{2\pi n}\right)^2 \left\{ n\kappa_4 + \sigma^4 \sum_{s=1}^{n} \sum_{r=1}^{n} \left[\exp\left(i(s - r)(\lambda_1 + \lambda_2)\right)\right.\right.$$

$$+ \left.\exp\left(i(s - r)(\lambda_2 - \lambda_1)\right)\right]\bigg\}$$

$$= \frac{\kappa_4}{(2\pi)^2 n} = \frac{\sigma^4}{(2\pi n)^2} \sum_{s=1}^{n} \sum_{r=1}^{n} \left\{\exp\left[i(s - r)(\lambda_1 + \lambda_2)\right]\right.$$

$$+ \left.\exp\left[i(s - r)(\lambda_2 - \lambda_1)\right]\right\} \tag{9.3.31}$$

---

[5] See, for example, Cramer [5, p. 186].

It is clear that for $\lambda_1 \neq \pm\lambda_2$ the last term (the one in curly brackets) above is bounded for all n and hence that

$$\lim_{n \to \infty} \text{Cov}\ [P_n^*(\lambda_1, \varepsilon), P_n^*(\lambda_2, \varepsilon)] = 0 \tag{9.3.32}$$

This is so since

$$\sum_{r=1}^{n} \sum_{s=1}^{n} \exp\ [i(s-r)x] = \sum_{r=1}^{n} \sum_{t=1-r}^{n-r} \exp\ (itx) = \sum_{t=-n}^{n} (n - |t|) \exp\ (itx) \tag{9.3.33}$$

Thus

$$\frac{1}{n} \sum_{r=1}^{n} \sum_{s=1}^{n} \exp\ [i(s-r)x] = \sum_{t=-n}^{n} \left(1 - \frac{|t|}{n}\right) \exp\ (itx) \tag{9.3.34}$$

and hence

$$\lim_{n \to \infty} \frac{1}{n} \sum_{r=1}^{n} \sum_{s=1}^{n} \exp\ [i(s-r)x] = \sum_{t=-\infty}^{\infty} \exp\ (itx) = 0 \tag{9.3.35}$$

so that $P_n^*(\lambda_1, \varepsilon)$, $P_n^*(\lambda_2, \varepsilon)$ are asymptotically uncorrelated for $\lambda_1 \neq \pm\lambda_2$. Consider, however, the variance of $P_n^*(\lambda, \varepsilon)$, which is obtained from (9.3.32) by putting $\lambda_1 = \lambda_2 = \lambda$. Here we have

$$\begin{aligned} \text{Var}\ [P_n^*(\lambda, \varepsilon)] &= \frac{\kappa_4}{(2\pi)^2 n} + \frac{\sigma^4}{(2\pi n)^2} \sum_{s=1}^{n} \sum_{r=1}^{n} [\exp\ [2i(s-r)\lambda] + 1] \\ &= \frac{\kappa_4}{(2\pi)^2 n} + \frac{\sigma^4}{(2\pi)^2} + \frac{\sigma^4}{(2\pi n)^2} \sum_{s=1}^{n} \sum_{r=1}^{n} \exp\ [2i(s-r)\lambda] \end{aligned} \tag{9.3.36}$$

From (9.3.36) we see

$$\lim_{n \to \infty} \text{Var}\ [P_n^*(\lambda, \varepsilon)] = \frac{\sigma^4}{(2\pi)^2} \tag{9.3.37}$$

which shows inconsistency.

Next consider a stochastic process, which can be represented by

$$X_t = \sum_{j=0}^{\infty} \alpha_j \varepsilon_{t-j} \tag{9.3.38}$$

If $g(\cdot)$ is the spectral density of the X process and $f(\cdot)$ that of the ε process, we have shown in the previous section that

$$g(\lambda) = \left| \sum_{k=0}^{\infty} \bar{\alpha}_k \exp\ (ik\lambda) \right|^2 f(\lambda) \tag{9.3.39}$$

We shall show that the periodogram is an inconsistent estimator of the process in (9.3.38), where the ε process has the properties ascribed to it in the previous theorem, if we can show that the periodogram of the X process can be represented as the periodogram of the ε process, plus a term whose expectation vanishes asymptotically.

Therefore we prove

Theorem 8: Let $\{X_t : t \in N\}$ be the process exhibited in (9.3.39) and let the ε process be as in Theorem 7. Suppose, also, that

$$\sum_{j=0}^{\infty} |\alpha_j| j^{\frac{1}{2}} < \infty \qquad (9.3.40)$$

Then the modified periodogram of $\{X_t : t \in N\}$ is an inconsistent estimator of its spectral density.

PROOF: Let the modified periodogram of the X process, based on a realization of length n, be given by

$$P_n^*(\lambda, x) = \frac{1}{2\pi n} \left| \sum_{t=1}^{n} X_t \exp(it\lambda) \right|^2 \qquad (9.3.41)$$

Substituting in (9.3.41) the representation of X_t as given in (9.3.38), we find

$$P_n^*(\lambda, x) = \frac{1}{2\pi n} \left| \sum_{t=1}^{n} \sum_{j=0}^{\infty} \alpha_j \varepsilon_{t-j} \exp(it\lambda) \right|^2$$

$$= \frac{1}{2\pi n} \left| \sum_{j=0}^{\infty} \alpha_j \exp(ij\lambda) \sum_{t=1}^{n} \varepsilon_{t-j} \exp[i(t-j)\lambda] \right|^2 \qquad (9.3.42)$$

Now, let

$$S_n(\lambda, x) = \frac{1}{\sqrt{2\pi n}} \sum_{j=0}^{\infty} \alpha_j \exp(ij\lambda) \sum_{t=1}^{n} \varepsilon_{t-j} \exp[i(t-j)\lambda] \qquad (9.3.43)$$

and note that

$$P_n^*(\lambda, x) = S_n(\lambda, x)\overline{S_n(\lambda, x)} \qquad (9.3.44)$$

Making the change in the indices of summation $t - j = s$, $j = j$, we may rewrite (9.3.43) as

$$S_n(\lambda, x) = \frac{1}{\sqrt{2\pi n}} \sum_{j=0}^{\infty} \alpha_j \exp(ij\lambda) \sum_{s=1-j}^{n-j} \varepsilon_s \exp(is\lambda) \qquad (9.3.45)$$

Thus

$$S_n(\lambda, x) = \frac{1}{\sqrt{2\pi n}} \sum_{j=0}^{\infty} \alpha_j \exp(ij\lambda) \sum_{s=1}^{n} \varepsilon_s \exp(is\lambda) + \frac{1}{\sqrt{2\pi n}} \sum_{j=0}^{\infty} \alpha_j \exp(ij\lambda) g_{j,n}(\lambda, \varepsilon)$$

$$= S_n^1 + S_n^2 \qquad (9.3.46)$$

Moreover,

$$\sum_{s=1-j}^{n-j} \varepsilon_s \exp(is\lambda) = \sum_{s=1}^{n} \varepsilon_s \exp(is\lambda) + \sum_{s=1-j}^{0} \varepsilon_s \exp(ij\lambda) - \sum_{s=n-j+1}^{n} \varepsilon_s \exp(is\lambda)$$

$$= \sum_{s=1}^{n} \varepsilon_s \exp(is\lambda) + g_{j,n}(\lambda, \varepsilon) \qquad (9.3.47)$$

where

$$g_{j,n}(\lambda, \varepsilon) = \sum_{s=1-j}^{0} \varepsilon_s \exp(is\lambda) - \sum_{s=n-j+1}^{n} \exp(is\lambda) \qquad \text{if} \quad j \geq 1$$

$$= 0 \qquad \qquad \text{if} \quad j = 0 \qquad (9.3.48)$$

We shall first show that the covariance of S_n^1 and S_n^2 vanishes, and that the variance of S_n^2 vanishes asymptotically. Thus to show inconsistency we would then only require that the variance of S_n^1 does not vanish asymptotically.

Now

$$E[S_n^1 \bar{S}_n^2] = \frac{1}{\sqrt{2\pi n}} \sum_{j=0}^{\infty} \sum_{k=0}^{\infty} \alpha_j \bar{\alpha}_k \exp[i(j-k)\lambda] \sum_{s=1}^{n} E(\exp(is\lambda)\varepsilon_s \bar{g}_{k,n}) \qquad (9.3.49)$$

On the other hand,

$$\sum_{s=1}^{n} E[\exp(is\lambda)\varepsilon_s \bar{g}_{k,n}] = \sum_{s=1}^{n} \sum_{\tau=k-1}^{0} \exp[i(s-t)\lambda]E(\varepsilon_s \bar{\varepsilon}_\tau)$$

$$- \sum_{s=1}^{n} \sum_{\tau=n-k+1}^{n} \exp[i(s-\tau)\lambda]E(\varepsilon_s \bar{\varepsilon}_\tau)$$

$$= \sigma^2(k-1) - \sigma^2(k-1) = 0 \qquad \text{for} \quad k \geq 1 \qquad (9.3.50)$$

But from (9.3.48) of course, (9.3.50) holds for $k = 0$ as well. This shows

$$E[S_n^1 \bar{S}_n^2] = 0 \qquad (9.3.51)$$

Now let us put as a matter of notation

$$\text{Var}[g_{j,n}] = \sigma_j^2 = E(g_{j,n}\bar{g}_{j,n}) \qquad (9.3.52)$$

and note

$$|E(g_{j,n}\bar{g}_{j,n})| \leq \sigma_j \sigma_k \qquad (9.3.53)$$

Also,

$$E[S_n^2 \bar{S}_n^2] = \frac{1}{2\pi n} \sum_{j=0}^{\infty} \sum_{k=0}^{\infty} \alpha_j \bar{\alpha}_k \exp[i(j+k)\lambda]E[g_{j,n}\bar{g}_{nj,n}] \qquad (9.3.54)$$

Clearly

$$|E[S_n^2 \bar{S}_n^2]| \leq \frac{1}{2\pi n} \sum_{j=0}^{\infty} \sum_{k=0}^{\infty} |\alpha_j| \, |\bar{\alpha}_k| \, |E[g_{j,n} \bar{g}_{j,n}]|$$

$$\leq \frac{1}{2\pi n} \sum_{j=0}^{\infty} \sum_{k=0}^{\infty} |\alpha_j| \, |\bar{\alpha}_k| \, \sigma_j \sigma_k = \frac{1}{2\pi n} \left(\sum_{j=0}^{\infty} |\alpha_j| \, \sigma_j \right)^2 \tag{9.3.55}$$

Thus

$$[\text{Var}\,(S_n^2)]^{\frac{1}{2}} \leq \frac{1}{\sqrt{2\pi n}} \sum_{j=0}^{\infty} |\alpha_j| \, \sigma_j \tag{9.3.56}$$

Now

$$\sigma_j^2 = [E\,|g_{j,n}|^2] \leq E \left[\left| \sum_{s=j-1}^{0} \varepsilon_s \exp(is\lambda) \right|^2 + \left| \sum_{s=n-j+1}^{n} \varepsilon_s \exp(is\lambda) \right|^2 \right]$$

$$= 2\sigma^2(j-1) \leq 2\sigma^2 j \tag{9.3.57}$$

Hence

$$[\text{Var}\,(S_n^2)]^{\frac{1}{2}} \leq \sqrt{\frac{1}{\pi n}} \, \sigma^2 \sum_{j=0}^{\infty} |\alpha_j| \, j^{\frac{1}{2}} \tag{9.3.58}$$

It follows, therefore, that if (9.3.40) holds, then

$$\lim_{n \to \infty} \text{Var}\,(S_n^2) = 0 \tag{9.3.59}$$

It now remains to show that

$$\lim_{n \to \infty} \text{Var}\,(S_n^1) \neq 0 \tag{9.3.60}$$

But this is trivial, for

$$S_n^1(\lambda, x) = \frac{1}{\sqrt{2\pi n}} \sum_{j=0}^{\infty} \alpha_j \exp(ij\lambda) \sum_{s=1}^{n} \varepsilon_s \exp(is\lambda) = \phi(\lambda) S_n(\lambda, \varepsilon) \tag{9.3.61}$$

where obviously

$$\phi(\lambda) = \sum_{j=0}^{\infty} \alpha_j \exp(ij\lambda) \quad \text{and} \quad S_n(\lambda, \varepsilon) = \frac{1}{\sqrt{2\pi n}} \sum_{s=1}^{n} \varepsilon_s \exp(is\lambda)$$

But

$$P_n^*(\lambda, \varepsilon) = S_n(\lambda, \varepsilon) \overline{S_n(\lambda, \varepsilon)} \tag{9.3.62}$$

and by the proof of Theorem 7 this was shown not to vanish asymptotically.

We have shown that

$$P_n^*(\lambda, x) = (S_n^1 + S_n^2)(\overline{S_n^1 + S_n^2}) = S_n^1 \bar{S}_n^1 + S_n^1 \bar{S}_n^2 + S_n^2 \bar{S}_n^1 + S_n^2 \bar{S}_n^2 \tag{9.3.63}$$

and thus

$$\lim_{n \to \infty} \text{Var} \left[P_n^*(\lambda, x) \right] = \lim_{n \to \infty} E[S_n^1 \bar{S}_n^1] = \phi(\lambda)\overline{\phi(\lambda)} \frac{\sigma^4}{(2\pi)^2} > 0 \qquad \text{Q.E.D.}$$

(9.3.64)

Remark 18: Since any covariance stationary stochastic process with continuous spectral density can be approximated by a moving average process with orthogonal components, the inconsistency of the periodogram as an estimator of the spectrum has been demonstrated for most processes of interest.

CONSISTENT ESTIMATION OF THE SPECTRUM

In the previous discussion we saw that although we might obtain an asymptotically unbiased estimator of the spectrum (the modified periodogram) at frequency λ, this estimator turned out to be inconsistent. On the other hand, it is also the case (although we shall not prove this) that the integral of the (modified) periodogram over the interval $(\lambda_1, \lambda_2) \subset (-\pi, \pi]$ provides a consistent estimator of the integral of the spectral density over the interval (λ_1, λ_2).

This led to the quest of consistent estimators of quantities that are, in effect, weighted averages of the spectrum over some narrow band of frequencies. Indeed, what one can best hope to do in this context is to devise consistent estimators of spectral averages over some frequency band, the width of which tends to zero as the length of the record approaches infinity.

Just why this particular approach works could be "intuitively" explained in many ways, but such intuitive explanations do not seem very enlightening. It is perhaps best at this juncture to sketch the basic theorem, due to Parzen [16], which constructs the properties of the weighting functions involved in the relevant spectral averages.

Before giving Parzen's theorem, however, two auxiliary definitions are needed.

Definition 17: Let $\{X_i: i = 1, 2, \ldots, n\}$ be a realization of the stochastic process $\{X_t: t \in N\}$. Suppose that

$$E(X_t) = \mu \qquad \text{for all } t \qquad\qquad (9.3.65)$$

Let m_n be an estimator of μ based on a record (realization) of length n. Then m_n is said to be unbiased of order n^α if and only if

$$\lim_{n \to \infty} n^\alpha [E(m_n) - \mu] = b \qquad\qquad (9.3.66)$$

for some finite constant b.

Definition 18: An estimator m_n, as in Definition 17, is said to be consistent of the order $n^{2\alpha}$ (and unbiased of order n^{α}) if and only if (9.3.66) holds and, in addition,

$$\lim_{n \to \infty} n^{2\alpha} \operatorname{Var}[m_n] = \gamma \qquad (9.3.67)$$

for some finite positive γ.

With these preliminaries aside, we give (without proof)

Theorem 9: Let $\{X_t : t \in N\}$ be a stochastic process with spectral density $f(\lambda)$ such that the fourth absolute moment of X_t exists for all t and its fourth moment function depends only on the time differences[6] τ_1, τ_2, τ_3, or, more precisely,

i. $E\{|X_t|^4\} < \infty$

ii. $E[X_t X_{t+\tau_1} X_{t+\tau_2} X_{t+\tau_3}] = M(\tau_1, \tau_2, \tau_3)$

Let $a(\cdot)$ be a bounded square integrable function such that

iii. $a(0) = 1 \qquad a(\lambda) = a(-\lambda)$

Suppose that for any positive constants B, m there exist positive constants C_1, ε such that

iv. $B \sum_{|\tau| \leq m} |a(B\tau)| \leq C_1(Bm)^{\frac{1}{2} - \varepsilon}$

For any $r > 0$, define

v. $a^{(r)} = \lim_{\lambda \to 0} \dfrac{1 - a(\lambda)}{|\lambda|^r}$

and suppose there exists a largest number[7] r^* such that $a^{(r)}$, above, exists and is (nonzero and) finite. Suppose, also, that there exists a $q > 0$ such that

vi. $\sum_{\tau = -\infty}^{\infty} |\tau|^q |K(\tau)| < \infty$

Define

vii. $\alpha = \dfrac{q}{1 + 2q}$

---

[6] It should be noted that if $\{X_t : t \in N\}$ is a *normal* covariance stationary stochastic process with mean zero and covariance kernel $K(\cdot)$, then

$$E[X_t X_{t+\tau_1} X_{t+\tau_2} X_{t+\tau_3}] = K(\tau_1)K(\tau_2 - \tau_3) + K(\tau_2)K(\tau_3 - \tau_1) + K(\tau_3)K(\tau_1 - \tau_2)$$

Thus the assumption in ii does not involve any additional restriction if we are dealing with a normal (covariance stationary stochastic) process.

[7] A function $f(\cdot)$ is said to be square integrable over a set S if the integral $\int_S |f(x)|^2 \, dx$ exists. The number r in v is called the characteristic exponent of $a(\cdot)$ and r^* is called its largest characteristic exponent.

and choose a sequence of constants $\{B_n : n = 0, 1, 2, \ldots\}$ such that

viii. $\lim_{n \to \infty} n^{\alpha/q} B_n = B$

for some finite positive constant B.

Then for any function $a(\cdot)$ with the properties above and characteristic exponent $r \geq q$,

ix. $\hat{f}_n(\lambda) = \dfrac{1}{2\pi} \displaystyle\sum_{|\tau| \leq n} \exp(-i\tau\lambda) a(B_n \tau) K_n(\tau) = \displaystyle\int_{-\pi}^{\pi} A_n(\lambda - \theta) P_n^*(\theta) \, d\theta$

is a consistent estimator of $f(\lambda)$ of order $n^{2\alpha}$.

Since the proof of Theorem 9 is not given and since its statement is indeed highly elliptical, it is desirable at this stage to discuss certain of its features and their implications somewhat briefly.

First, the functions $a(\cdot)$, $A(\cdot)$, which in subsequent work Parzen calls *weight* or *lag window generators* and (spectral) *window generators* respectively, are connected by

$A(\tau) = \dfrac{1}{2\pi} \displaystyle\sum_{\tau = -\infty}^{\infty} a(\tau) \exp(i\tau\lambda)$

$a(\tau) = \displaystyle\int_{-\pi}^{\pi} A(\theta) \exp(-i\tau\theta) \, d\theta \qquad\qquad (9.3.68)$

that is, they are a pair of Fourier transforms. The fact that $a(\cdot)$ is assumed to be square integrable guarantees the unicity of its transform, and thus to each lag window generator $a(\cdot)$ there corresponds a unique (spectral) window $A(\cdot)$ and conversely.

The function $A_n(\cdot)$ in ix is defined so that

$a(B_n \tau) = \displaystyle\int_{-\pi}^{\pi} \exp(-i\tau\theta) A_n(\theta) \, d\theta \qquad\qquad (9.3.69)$

The notation $K_n(\tau)$ in ix is defined by

$K_n(\tau) = \dfrac{1}{n} \displaystyle\sum_{t=1}^{n-\tau} X_{t+\tau} X_t \qquad\qquad (9.3.70)$

that is, it is an estimator of $K(\tau)$ based on a record of length n.[8]

---

[8] The assumption implicit in this computation is that the process is real; if it were complex, we would define $K_n(\tau)$ by

$K_n(\tau) = \dfrac{1}{n} \displaystyle\sum_{t=1}^{n-\tau} [X_{t+\tau} \bar{X}_t] \qquad \text{if } \tau \geq 0$

$\qquad = \dfrac{1}{n} \displaystyle\sum_{t=-\tau+1}^{n} [X_t \bar{X}_{t+\tau}] \qquad \text{if } \tau < 0$

Moreover, although we give two alternative forms of the consistent estimator of the spectrum in ix, actually it is only the first that is computationally convenient and thus for purposes of empirical implementation, the estimator is given by

$$\hat{f}_n(\lambda) = \frac{1}{2\pi} \sum_{|\tau| \le n} \exp\left(-i\tau\lambda\right)a(B_n\tau)K_n(\tau) \tag{9.3.71}$$

Notice that this simply means that we compute the estimator in the following four steps.

  i. Select the desired weight or lag generator $a(\cdot)$ and the appropriate sequence $\{B_i: i = 1, 2, \ldots\}$ so that B_n is determined by the length of the record.
 ii. Compute the sample covariance kernel $K_n(\tau)$ for $\tau = 0, 1, 2, \ldots, n-1$.
iii. Obtain the "weighted" autocovariances $a(B_n\tau)K_n(\tau)$.
 iv. Take their Fourier transform.

Two corollaries of this theorem are important and we note them before proceeding with some examples.

Corollary 1: If q (of vii) is chosen as the largest number satisfying vi, then ix is an "optimal" consistent estimator of $f(\lambda)$ in the sense that it is consistent of the highest possible order.

PROOF: From vii and vi it is seen that $\alpha \subset (0, \frac{1}{2})$, for $q \in (0, \infty)$ and α is monotone increasing in q. Thus α as a function of q is maximized when q is chosen as large as possible.

Corollary 2: Let $a(\cdot)$ be a lag window generator with largest characteristic exponent r. Then the order of consistency of the corresponding estimator of the spectrum cannot be greater than $n^{2\alpha(r)}$, where

$$\alpha(r) = \frac{r}{1 + 2r} \tag{9.3.72}$$

and it will be $n^{2\alpha}$, $\alpha \le \alpha(r)$ if the constants B_n are so chosen that they satisfy

$$\lim_{n \to \infty} \frac{1}{B_n n^{1-2\alpha}} = \gamma \tag{9.3.73}$$

for some finite $\gamma > 0$ and if vi of Theorem 8 holds for $q = \alpha/(1 - 2\alpha)$.

PROOF: Immediate from Theorem 9.

Corollary 2 makes clear the connection between the rapidity with which $K(\tau) \to 0$ as $\tau \to \infty$ and the nature of the sequence $\{B_n: n = 1, 2, \ldots\}$. But since the lag window generator $a(\cdot)$ enters ix of Theorem 9 as $a(B_n\tau)$ and since it presumably peaks for $B_n\tau = 0$ and then tapers off to zero, it follows that the smaller in magnitude the elements of $\{ B_n : n = 1, 2, \ldots \}$ are, the larger will be the number of covariance terms we shall make use of in ix.

But the larger α is, as is evident from (9.3.73), the larger may be the elements of $\{ B_n \}$, and hence the smaller the number of covariance terms we need consider in obtaining the consistent estimator of the spectrum. Intuitively, what this means is that if the covariance between X_t and $X_{t+\tau}$ declines rapidly with respect to τ, so that q may be "large," then we need consider relatively few covariance terms in consistently estimating the spectrum.

Some examples will clarify this issue.

Example 15: Suppose that

$$
\begin{aligned}
a(\lambda) &= 1 - |\lambda|^r && \text{if } |\lambda| \le 1 \\
&= 0 && \text{if } |\lambda| > 1
\end{aligned}
\tag{9.3.74}
$$

Then

$$
a^{(r)} = \lim_{\lambda \to 0} \frac{1 - a(\lambda)}{|\lambda|^r} = 1
\tag{9.3.75}
$$

so that the largest characteristic exponent of $a(\cdot)$ is r. Now

$$
a(B_n \tau) = 1 - \frac{|\tau|^r}{(M_n)^r}
\tag{9.3.76}
$$

where

$$
M_n = \frac{1}{B_n}
\tag{9.3.77}
$$

Since $a(\cdot)$ vanishes outside $|\lambda| \le 1$, it follows that the spectral estimator thus generated utilizes only M_n covariance terms at most.

The spectral estimate to which it leads is

$$
\hat{f}_n(\lambda) = \frac{1}{2\pi} \sum_{|\tau| \le M_n} \left[1 - \left(\frac{|\tau|}{M_n} \right)^r \right] \exp\left(-i\tau\lambda \right) K_n(\tau)
\tag{9.3.78}
$$

The choice of M_n (or equivalently B_n) may of course be determined, perhaps nonuniquely, by the largest q satisfying vi of Theorem 8 and will, in general, be some root of n, the length of the record at hand.

Example 16: If in Example 15 we put

$$
r = 1 \qquad B_n = \frac{1}{M_n} = \frac{1}{M}
\tag{9.3.79}
$$

where M is a (positive) integer less than n, we get Bartlett's modified periodogram

$$
\hat{f}_n(\lambda) = \frac{1}{2\pi} \sum_{|\tau| \le M} \left(1 - \frac{|\tau|}{M} \right) \exp\left(-i\tau\lambda \right) K_n(\tau)
\tag{9.3.80}
$$

At this stage a question of interest might be: What is the difference in the order of consistency of the estimators in the two examples above? Well, by Corollary 2, the order of consistency of the estimator in Example 16 is not greater than $n^{2r/1+2r}$, and it will be $n^{2\alpha}$ if the number of covariance terms used is, say, $n^{1-2\alpha}$, $\alpha \le \frac{1}{3}$. This, of course, is determined by the choice

$$M = n^{1-2\alpha} \tag{9.3.81}$$

Note that if this choice is made, then

$$\frac{1}{B_n n^{1-2\alpha}} = \frac{n^{1-2\alpha}}{n^{1-2\alpha}} = 1 \tag{9.3.82}$$

and hence the limit in (9.3.73) will exist.

This may be as good a time as any to show that the requirement in (9.3.73) does not uniquely determine the sequence $\{B_n\}$ or $\{M_n\}$.

Continuing the development just above, choose

$$M^* = M + s \tag{9.3.83}$$

where M is given by (9.3.81) and s may be a positive or negative integer. Then

$$\frac{1}{B_n n^{1-2\alpha}} = \frac{n^{1-2\alpha} + s}{n^{1-2\alpha}} \tag{9.3.84}$$

and the limit as $n \to \infty$ will again exist.

Suppose that there exists a $q > 1$ satisfying vi of Theorem 9. Then we may choose a lag window generator with largest characteristic exponent $r > 1$, and the order of consistency will be $n^{1-2\alpha}$, where

$$\alpha = \frac{r}{1+2r} = \frac{1}{3} + \delta \qquad \delta = \frac{h}{9+6h} \qquad h = r - 1 > 0 \tag{9.3.85}$$

In Example 16, suppose that $r > 1$ and that a constant sequence $\{B_n\}$ is chosen which is a simple but not necessarily optimal procedure. To attain the highest possible order of consistency, we need to use $n^{1-2\alpha} = n^{1/1+2r} = n^{1/3-2h/9+6h}$ covariance terms. But this is less than the number of covariances $(n^{\frac{1}{3}})$ needed in order to attain the highest possible order of consistency in the case of the Bartlett estimator.

Thus it is seen that the Bartlett modified periodogram, by failing to take into account the relation vi of Theorem 9, which may hold for $q > 1$ in certain cases, leads to nonoptimal estimators and also entails greater computational burdens. But, of course, it is seldom, if ever, that we know the largest q for which vi of Theorem 9 holds.

The discussion above seems to settle the question of the existence of consistent estimators for the spectrum, or certain spectral averages. However, from the point of view of empirical implementation, the results of Theorem 9 are not fully adequate. Unresolved problems still remain. Such problems are (nonexhaustively)

i. How to choose M, the maximal number of lags (covariance terms) for which the sample covariance kernel, $K_n(\cdot)$ is to be computed. It is often suggested, somewhat vaguely, that one ought to compute, say, $K_n(\tau)$, $\tau = 0, 1, 2, \ldots$ and terminate at a point N, where $|K_n(N)|$ is "small." Of course, it is not entirely clear what "small" is in this context.

ii. For given lag window generator $a(\cdot)$, for what values of λ, $\lambda \in (-\pi, \pi]$ should we compute $f_n(\lambda)$? It may be shown that $f_n(\lambda)$ is uniquely determined by its value at the points $\lambda_j = \pi j/M$, $j = 0, \pm 1, \pm 2, \ldots, \pm M$.

iii. What lag window generator should we use?

In a later chapter we shall attempt, at least partially, to answer these questions. For the moment, we shall merely give without comment a number of commonly employed lag window generators $a(\cdot)$, together with their associated spectral windows and the relevant approximations (see Table 9.6, page 442).

POSSIBLE APPLICATIONS AND EXAMPLES

Although this chapter is best regarded as laying the foundation for cross-spectral analysis—that is, the study, in the frequency domain, of multivariate stochastic processes—nonetheless it is possible to indicate some areas of potential application. The limits that are set by our discussion thus far are analogous to those inherent to the study of univariate random variables. Thus if one is only aware of the distribution theory of univariate random variables, one can hardly deal with inference problems involving several random variables.

The most fruitful view of the spectral density by far, in terms of empirical applications, is as a decomposition of the variance of the (elements of the) stochastic process. Since this decomposition ascribes certain "portions" of the variance to components of various frequencies, spectral analysis is seen as particularly suited to the study of cyclical characteristics of economic time series. For instance, it might be of great importance to determine how the variation of an economic time series is affected by cyclical movements and what the period of these cycles is.

We shall illustrate this application in terms of a rather simple example relating to the study of vehicular traffic over bridges connecting the Pennsylvania and New Jersey components of the Philadelphia metropolitan area. As the reader is aware, the latter extends over both sides of the Delaware River and is spanned by two major bridges, the Benjamin Franklin and the Walt Whitman.

As an initial step one might wish to subject flow of traffic data to spectral analysis in an attempt to identify cyclical patterns. Once this aspect is understood, one is better able to devise policies which will expedite the handling of vehicular flow.

In the context of this problem the nature of the cyclicity is quite apparent; one has only to think of the daily flow of commuters to and from work. Consequently, the results of spectral analysis will be readily interpretable and the reader will gain a vivid insight into the information one may expect to obtain from such techniques.

In Tables 9.1 through 9.4 we set forth the estimated spectra of (passenger) automobile traffic over the two bridges (eastbound and westbound). These estimates are based on 2016 hourly observations on the number of passenger

TABLE 9.1. Spectral density BF eastbound

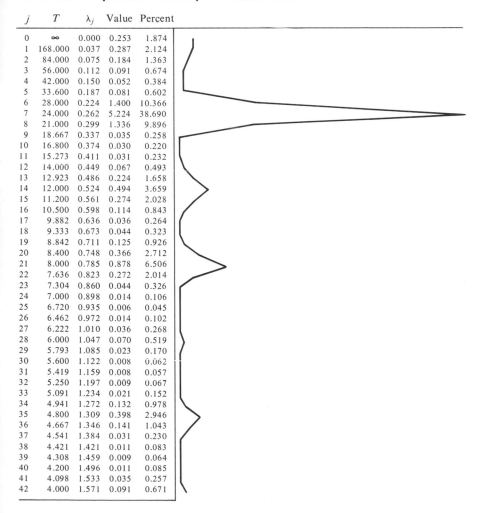

j	T	λ_j	Value	Percent
0	∞	0.000	0.253	1.874
1	168.000	0.037	0.287	2.124
2	84.000	0.075	0.184	1.363
3	56.000	0.112	0.091	0.674
4	42.000	0.150	0.052	0.384
5	33.600	0.187	0.081	0.602
6	28.000	0.224	1.400	10.366
7	24.000	0.262	5.224	38.690
8	21.000	0.299	1.336	9.896
9	18.667	0.337	0.035	0.258
10	16.800	0.374	0.030	0.220
11	15.273	0.411	0.031	0.232
12	14.000	0.449	0.067	0.493
13	12.923	0.486	0.224	1.658
14	12.000	0.524	0.494	3.659
15	11.200	0.561	0.274	2.028
16	10.500	0.598	0.114	0.843
17	9.882	0.636	0.036	0.264
18	9.333	0.673	0.044	0.323
19	8.842	0.711	0.125	0.926
20	8.400	0.748	0.366	2.712
21	8.000	0.785	0.878	6.506
22	7.636	0.823	0.272	2.014
23	7.304	0.860	0.044	0.326
24	7.000	0.898	0.014	0.106
25	6.720	0.935	0.006	0.045
26	6.462	0.972	0.014	0.102
27	6.222	1.010	0.036	0.268
28	6.000	1.047	0.070	0.519
29	5.793	1.085	0.023	0.170
30	5.600	1.122	0.008	0.062
31	5.419	1.159	0.008	0.057
32	5.250	1.197	0.009	0.067
33	5.091	1.234	0.021	0.152
34	4.941	1.272	0.132	0.978
35	4.800	1.309	0.398	2.946
36	4.667	1.346	0.141	1.043
37	4.541	1.384	0.031	0.230
38	4.421	1.421	0.011	0.083
39	4.308	1.459	0.009	0.064
40	4.200	1.496	0.011	0.085
41	4.098	1.533	0.035	0.257
42	4.000	1.571	0.091	0.671

TABLE 9.2. Spectral density BF westbound

j	T	λ_j	Value	Percent	
0	∞	0.000	0.249	1.843	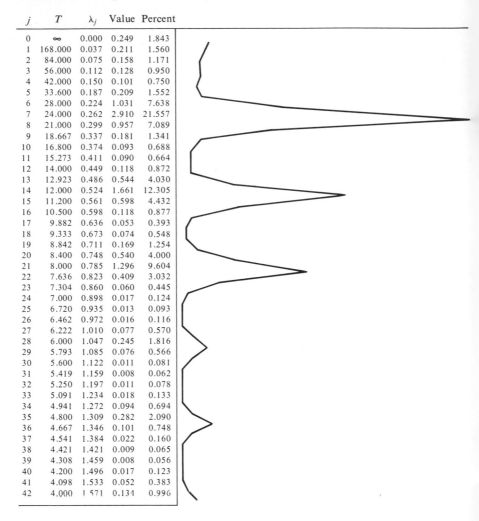
1	168.000	0.037	0.211	1.560	
2	84.000	0.075	0.158	1.171	
3	56.000	0.112	0.128	0.950	
4	42.000	0.150	0.101	0.750	
5	33.600	0.187	0.209	1.552	
6	28.000	0.224	1.031	7.638	
7	24.000	0.262	2.910	21.557	
8	21.000	0.299	0.957	7.089	
9	18.667	0.337	0.181	1.341	
10	16.800	0.374	0.093	0.688	
11	15.273	0.411	0.090	0.664	
12	14.000	0.449	0.118	0.872	
13	12.923	0.486	0.544	4.030	
14	12.000	0.524	1.661	12.305	
15	11.200	0.561	0.598	4.432	
16	10.500	0.598	0.118	0.877	
17	9.882	0.636	0.053	0.393	
18	9.333	0.673	0.074	0.548	
19	8.842	0.711	0.169	1.254	
20	8.400	0.748	0.540	4.000	
21	8.000	0.785	1.296	9.604	
22	7.636	0.823	0.409	3.032	
23	7.304	0.860	0.060	0.445	
24	7.000	0.898	0.017	0.124	
25	6.720	0.935	0.013	0.093	
26	6.462	0.972	0.016	0.116	
27	6.222	1.010	0.077	0.570	
28	6.000	1.047	0.245	1.816	
29	5.793	1.085	0.076	0.566	
30	5.600	1.122	0.011	0.081	
31	5.419	1.159	0.008	0.062	
32	5.250	1.197	0.011	0.078	
33	5.091	1.234	0.018	0.133	
34	4.941	1.272	0.094	0.694	
35	4.800	1.309	0.282	2.090	
36	4.667	1.346	0.101	0.748	
37	4.541	1.384	0.022	0.160	
38	4.421	1.421	0.009	0.065	
39	4.308	1.459	0.008	0.056	
40	4.200	1.496	0.017	0.123	
41	4.098	1.533	0.052	0.383	
42	4.000	1.571	0.134	0.996	

automobile crossings. The observations[9] were collected for the first week of each month in 1965. Hence, we are dealing with 12 sets of $(24 \times 7 =) 168$ observations. Unfortunately, the way in which the data was collected makes it impossible to ascertain the existence of cyclical components with period exceeding one week. Tables 9.1 through 9.4, and their associated figures give the spectral density of

---

[9] The data were collected in connection with a major study of transportation problems in the Northeastern region of the United States. They were kindly made available to me by Richard Quandt.

TABLE 9.3. Spectral density WW eastbound

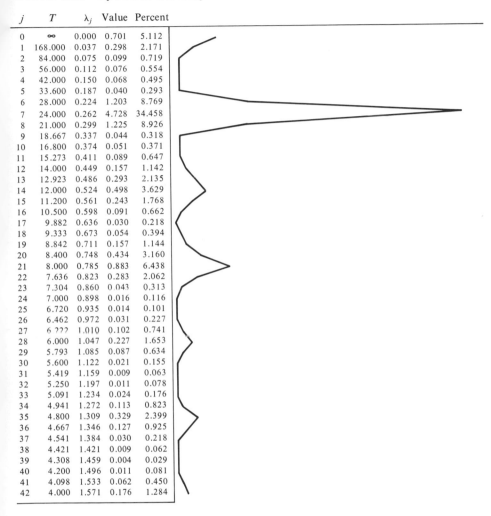

j	T	λ_j	Value	Percent
0	∞	0.000	0.701	5.112
1	168.000	0.037	0.298	2.171
2	84.000	0.075	0.099	0.719
3	56.000	0.112	0.076	0.554
4	42.000	0.150	0.068	0.495
5	33.600	0.187	0.040	0.293
6	28.000	0.224	1.203	8.769
7	24.000	0.262	4.728	34.458
8	21.000	0.299	1.225	8.926
9	18.667	0.337	0.044	0.318
10	16.800	0.374	0.051	0.371
11	15.273	0.411	0.089	0.647
12	14.000	0.449	0.157	1.142
13	12.923	0.486	0.293	2.135
14	12.000	0.524	0.498	3.629
15	11.200	0.561	0.243	1.768
16	10.500	0.598	0.091	0.662
17	9.882	0.636	0.030	0.218
18	9.333	0.673	0.054	0.394
19	8.842	0.711	0.157	1.144
20	8.400	0.748	0.434	3.160
21	8.000	0.785	0.883	6.438
22	7.636	0.823	0.283	2.062
23	7.304	0.860	0.043	0.313
24	7.000	0.898	0.016	0.116
25	6.720	0.935	0.014	0.101
26	6.462	0.972	0.031	0.227
27	6.222	1.010	0.102	0.741
28	6.000	1.047	0.227	1.653
29	5.793	1.085	0.087	0.634
30	5.600	1.122	0.021	0.155
31	5.419	1.159	0.009	0.063
32	5.250	1.197	0.011	0.078
33	5.091	1.234	0.024	0.176
34	4.941	1.272	0.113	0.823
35	4.800	1.309	0.329	2.399
36	4.667	1.346	0.127	0.925
37	4.541	1.384	0.030	0.218
38	4.421	1.421	0.009	0.062
39	4.308	1.459	0.004	0.029
40	4.200	1.496	0.011	0.081
41	4.098	1.533	0.062	0.450
42	4.000	1.571	0.176	1.284

east- and westbound traffic of passenger automobiles on the Benjamin Franklin
(BF) and Walt Whitman (WW) bridges. The spectral ordinates have been com-
puted for the points $\lambda_j = \pi j/84$, $j = 0, 1, 2, \ldots, 42$. The column labeled T gives
the *cyclical periods* corresponding to the (fundamental) frequencies of these
points.[10]

---

[10] Frequency λ is related to period P by $\lambda = 1/P$; this fact will be discussed further in the
next chapter. In the tables, the fundamental frequency corresponding to the point λ_j is simply
$\lambda_j/2\pi$.

TABLE 9.4. Spectral density WW westbound

j	T	λ_j	Value	Percent	
0	∞	0.000	0.559	4.090	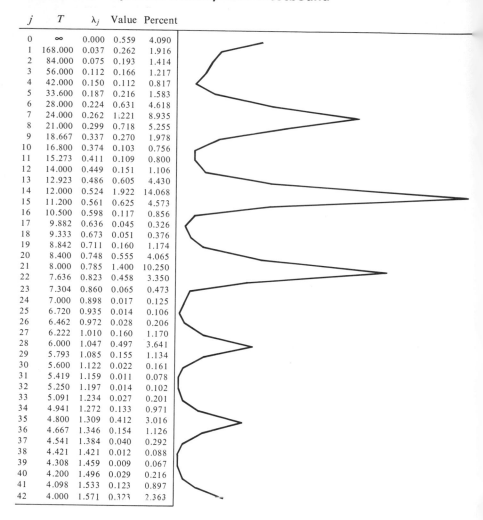
1	168.000	0.037	0.262	1.916	
2	84.000	0.075	0.193	1.414	
3	56.000	0.112	0.166	1.217	
4	42.000	0.150	0.112	0.817	
5	33.600	0.187	0.216	1.583	
6	28.000	0.224	0.631	4.618	
7	24.000	0.262	1.221	8.935	
8	21.000	0.299	0.718	5.255	
9	18.667	0.337	0.270	1.978	
10	16.800	0.374	0.103	0.756	
11	15.273	0.411	0.109	0.800	
12	14.000	0.449	0.151	1.106	
13	12.923	0.486	0.605	4.430	
14	12.000	0.524	1.922	14.068	
15	11.200	0.561	0.625	4.573	
16	10.500	0.598	0.117	0.856	
17	9.882	0.636	0.045	0.326	
18	9.333	0.673	0.051	0.376	
19	8.842	0.711	0.160	1.174	
20	8.400	0.748	0.555	4.065	
21	8.000	0.785	1.400	10.250	
22	7.636	0.823	0.458	3.350	
23	7.304	0.860	0.065	0.473	
24	7.000	0.898	0.017	0.125	
25	6.720	0.935	0.014	0.106	
26	6.462	0.972	0.028	0.206	
27	6.222	1.010	0.160	1.170	
28	6.000	1.047	0.497	3.641	
29	5.793	1.085	0.155	1.134	
30	5.600	1.122	0.022	0.161	
31	5.419	1.159	0.011	0.078	
32	5.250	1.197	0.014	0.102	
33	5.091	1.234	0.027	0.201	
34	4.941	1.272	0.133	0.971	
35	4.800	1.309	0.412	3.016	
36	4.667	1.346	0.154	1.126	
37	4.541	1.384	0.040	0.292	
38	4.421	1.421	0.012	0.088	
39	4.308	1.459	0.009	0.067	
40	4.200	1.496	0.029	0.216	
41	4.098	1.533	0.123	0.897	
42	4.000	1.571	0.323	2.363	

These spectra disclose quite clearly the existence of daily cycles in automobile traffic. Thus Table 9.1 indicates that the spectrum of eastbound traffic (from Philadelphia to New Jersey) is dominated by a peak associated with a 24-hour cycle. There are less important 12- and 8-hour cycles, corresponding to the harmonics of the dominant frequency.

The westbound spectrum indicates a similar pattern except that the 12- and 8-hour cycles are considerably more pronounced in their effects.

The eastbound spectrum for the WW bridge is quite similar to that of the BF bridge.

The westbound spectrum (for WW) is, however, quite dissimilar. In the first place, it is dominated by the peak at $T = 12$; this indicates a dominant cyclical component whose period is 12 hours. There are subsidiary peaks corresponding to cycles of 24 and 8 hours.

The similarities and contrasts of these spectra are best exhibited in Table 9.5.

The most obvious similarity in the eastbound spectra is that they show both series to be largely dominated by a 24-hour cycle. There are smaller, but still appreciable, contributions by components with periods of 8 and 12 hours. The westbound spectra are also rather similar; the contributions of components with periods 24, 12, and 8 hours are not as radically different, in order of magnitude, as with eastbound spectra. This is the striking difference between the east- and westbound spectra for both bridges.

In addition, there are contributions at other periods (say at $T = 6$, 4, and so on), but these are of negligible magnitude. They are probably not significantly different from zero (or very small numbers close to zero). For the WW spectra there is an appreciable contribution at zero frequency (infinite period), which may imply that there has been an upward trend in the use of the bridge over the sample period.

Now, what "explanation" is to be given to these results; or, alternatively, what is the traffic behavior implied by the results? The large east- and westbound cyclical component corresponding to a 24-hour period indicates, of course, heavy commuter use for work. Why are the westbound spectra not as "bunched" as the eastbound? This seems to indicate that shoppers enter Philadelphia (i.e., travel westbound) and recreation-connected traffic (from N.J. beaches, for example) returns to Philadelphia at well-defined times. This would account for the "non-bunched" appearance of the westbound spectra. Why is this phenomenon not reflected in the eastbound spectrum? Possibly because shopping and recreation-connected traffic leaves Philadelphia (travels eastbound) at irregular times, the former later in the day and the latter earlier, which merely generates a steady stream of traffic devoid of cyclical characteristics.

TABLE 9.5. **Contribution to variance by components of various periods**

Periods in vicinity of	BF(E)[a]	WW(E)	BF(W)[a]	WW(W)
24 hours	58.9%	52.2%	36.2%	18.8%
12 hours	7.3	8.0	20.7	23.0
8 hours	11.0	11.6	16.6	17.6

[a] E and W indicate, respectively, eastbound and westbound.

TABLE 9.6. Lag window and spectral window generators

Lag window generator $a(u)$	$a(\tau) = a(B_n \tau)$ $\left(B_n = \dfrac{1}{M}\right)$	Spectral window $A(\lambda) = \dfrac{1}{2\pi}\int \exp(-iu\lambda)\,a(u)\,du$	Approximation $A_M(\lambda) = M A(\lambda M)$
I. Dirichlet $a_D(u) = 1$ if $\lvert u \rvert \le 1$ $= 0$ otherwise	$a_n(\tau) = 1$ if $\tau = 0,\ \pm 1, \ldots, \pm M$ $= 0$ otherwise	$A_D(\lambda) = \dfrac{1}{\pi}\dfrac{\sin \lambda}{\lambda}$	$A_M(\lambda) = \dfrac{\sin M\lambda}{\lambda/2}$
II. Modified Dirichlet $a_D^*(u) = 1$ if $\lvert u \rvert < 1$ $= \tfrac{1}{2}$ if $\lvert u \rvert = 1$ $= 0$ if $\lvert u \rvert > 1$	$a_n(\tau) = 1$ if $\tau = 0,\ \pm 1, \ldots, \pm(M-1)$ $= \tfrac{1}{2}$ if $\tau = \pm M$ $= 0$ otherwise	$A_D^*(\lambda) = \dfrac{1}{\pi}\dfrac{\sin \lambda}{\lambda}$	$A_M(\lambda) = \dfrac{\sin M\lambda}{\lambda/2}$
III. Fejèr $a_F(u) = 1 - \lvert u \rvert$ if $\lvert u \rvert \le 1$ $= 0$ if $\lvert u \rvert > 1$	$a_n(\tau) = 1 - \dfrac{\lvert \tau \rvert}{M}$ if $\tau = 0,\ \pm 1, \ldots, \pm M$ $= 0$ otherwise	$A_F(\lambda) = \dfrac{1}{2\pi}\left(\dfrac{\sin(\lambda/2)}{\lambda/2}\right)^2$	$A_M(\lambda) = \dfrac{1}{M}\left(\dfrac{\sin(M\lambda/2)}{\lambda/2}\right)^2$
IV. Tukey-Hanning $a_{TH}(u) = \tfrac{1}{2}(1 + \cos \pi u)$ if $\lvert u \rvert \le 1$ $= 0$ if $\lvert u \rvert > 1$	$a_n(\tau) = \tfrac{1}{2}\left[1 + \cos\left(\dfrac{\pi\tau}{M}\right)\right]$ if $\tau = 0,\ \pm 1, \ldots, \pm M$ $= 0$ otherwise	$A_{TH}(\lambda) = \dfrac{1}{2\pi}\dfrac{\sin \lambda}{\lambda}\dfrac{\pi^2}{\pi^2 - \lambda^2}$	$A_M(\lambda) = \dfrac{\pi^2}{\pi^2 - (M\lambda)^2}\dfrac{\sin M\lambda}{\lambda}$
V. Parzen $a_P(u) = 1 - 6u^2 + 6\lvert u \rvert^3$ if $\lvert u \rvert < \tfrac{1}{2}$ $= 2(1 - \lvert u \rvert)^3$ if $\tfrac{1}{2} \le \lvert u \rvert \le 1$ $= 0$ if $\lvert u \rvert > 1$	$a_n(\tau) = 1 - 6\left(\dfrac{\tau}{M}\right)^2 + 6\left\lvert\dfrac{\tau}{M}\right\rvert^3$ if $\tau = 0,$ $\pm 1, \ldots, \pm[M/2]^a$ $= 2\left(1 - \left\lvert\dfrac{\tau}{M}\right\rvert\right)^3$ if $\tau = \pm[M/2],$ $\pm\{[M/2]+1\}, \ldots \pm M$	$A_P(\lambda) = \dfrac{3}{8\pi}\left(\dfrac{\sin(\lambda/4)}{\lambda/4}\right)^4$	$A_M(\lambda) = \dfrac{3}{4M^3}\left(\dfrac{\sin(M\lambda/4)}{\lambda/4}\right)^4$

[a] The notation $[x]$ here means the largest integer equal to or less than x.

REFERENCES

1. Bartlett, M. S., "Periodogram Analysis and Continuous Spectra," *Biometrika*, vol. 37 1950, pp. 1–16.
2. Bingham, C., M. Godfrey, and J. W. Tukey, "Modern Techniques of Power Spectrum Estimation," *IEEE Trans. on Audio and Electroacoustics*, June 1962, pp. 55–66.
3. Blackman, R., and J. W. Tukey, *The Measurement of Power Spectra*, New York, Dover Publications, 1959.
4. Brandes, O., J. Farley, M. Hinich, and V. Zackrisson, "The Time Domain and the Frequency Domain in Time Series Analysis," *The Swedish Journal of Economics*, vol. 70, 1968, pp. 25–49.
5. Cramer, H., *Mathematical Methods of Statistics*, Princeton, N.J., Princeton University Press, 1946.
6. Davis, H. T., *The Analysis of Economic Time Series*, Cowles Foundation Monograph No. 6, Bloomington, Indiana, Principia Press, 1941. A detailed but rather dated study on economic time series.
7. Doob, J. L., *Stochastic Processes*, New York, Wiley, 1952.
8. Goodman, N. R., "Some Comments on Spectral Analysis of Time Series," *Technometrics*, vol. 3, 1961, pp. 221–228.
9. Grenander, U., and M. Rosenblatt, *Statistical Analysis of Stationary Time Series*, New York, Wiley, 1957.
10. Hannan, E. J., "The Estimation of the Spectral Density After Trend Removal," *Journal of the Royal Statistical Society* (Series B), vol. 20, 1958, pp. 323–333.
11. Hannan E. J., *Times Series Analysis*, London, Methuen & Co., and New York, Wiley, 1960.
12. Hinich, M. J., and J. U. Farley, "Theory and Application of an Estimation Model for Nonstationary Time Series Means," *Management Science*, vol. 12, 1966, pp. 648–658.
13. Jenkins G. M., "General Considerations in the Estimation of Spectra," *Techometrics*, vol. 3, 1961, pp. 133–166.
14. Kendall, M. G., *Contributions to the Study of Oscillatory Time Series*, Cambridge, Cambridge University Press, 1946.
15. Kendall, M. G., and A. Stuart, *The Advanced Theory of Statistics*, New York, Hafner Publishing Co., 1966. Chapter 49 deals with spectral theory.
16. Parzen, E., "On Consistent Estimates of the Spectrum of a Stationary Time Series," *Annals of Mathematical Statistics*, vol. 28, 1957, pp. 329–348.
17. Parzen, E., "Mathematical Considerations in the Estimation of Spectra," *Technometrics*, vol. 3, 1961, pp. 167–190.
18. Parzen, E. *Stochastic Processes*, San Francisco, Holden-Day, 1962.
19. Parzen, E., "Notes on Fourier Analysis and Spectral Windows," unpublished Paper, U.S. Office of Naval Research, Dept. of the Navy, 1962.
20. Parzen, E., "The Role of Spectral Analysis in Time Series," Technical Report No. 2, Department of Statistics, Stanford University, 1965.
21. Schuster, A., "On the Investigation of Hidden Periodicities with Application to a Supposed 26-Day Period of Meteorological Phenomena," *Terrestrial Magnetism*, vol. 3, 1898, pp. 13–41.
22. Slutzsky, E., "The Summation of Random Causes as the Source of Cyclic Processes," *Econometrica*, vol. 5, 1937, pp. 105–147.
23. Tukey, J. W., "Discussion Emphasizing the Connection Between Analysis of Variance and Spectrum Analysis," *Technometrics*, vol. 3, pp. 191–219.
24. Wold, H., *A Study in the Analysis of Stationary Time Series*, Uppsala, Sweden, University of Uppsala, 1938.
25. Yaglom, A. N., *An Introduction to the Theory of Stationary Random Functions*, Englewood Cliffs, N.J., Prentice Hall, 1962. Part 1 gives a comprehensive discussion of spectral theory.

CROSS-SPECTRAL ANALYSIS

10 10.1 INTRODUCTION

MOTIVATION

In the previous chapter we have shown how one can characterize a single time series in the frequency domain and how one can estimate the spectral density of the series from a record of finite length.

Suppose, now, that we are dealing with two time series that are known to be related in some sense. Is there a way in which the techniques of the preceding chapter may be applicable? Of course, the techniques would have to be extended to take into account the fact that the two series are related, and thus it would be insufficient to treat them separately and in isolation.

Such a situation occurs quite forcefully in problems of long-run growth. Various authors [1, 2, 10, 24, 27] have claimed the existence of "long swings" in the growth patterns of certain economic aggregates. Such findings are based on data that represent various modifications of the relevant original series. Thus, in investigating the existence of long swings in the GNP series, one ordinarily does not employ the actual observations (on GNP) but, rather, one uses a 5- or 10-year moving average. Or, one might consider not the GNP series which can hardly be treated as a (covariance) stationary stochastic process, but rather its relative rate of growth for which we may perhaps claim stationarity with greater credence. Again, as a rule, one considers 5- or 10-year moving averages in relative rates of growth.

When data are thus manipulated (through the moving average procedure), the question would arise: To what extent, if any, do the characteristics of the modified series merely reflect the effects of the modifying procedure and thus tell us nothing about the characteristics of the original series? Evidently, the latter, is the only one in which we are really interested.

Thus we have a situation in which we wish to compare in a meaningful way two series that are related to each other by a strictly specified procedure.

Another, conceptually similar, situation occurs with regard to the process of deseasonalizing a given series. Now, the seasonal adjustment procedure is designed to remove the seasonal component of a process where traditionally one thinks of the series at hand as consisting of trend, cyclical, and seasonal components. If the trend is eliminated so that we may with some justification assert that the residual series can be treated as a (covariance) stationary stochastic process, a question of considerable importance (studied, e.g., by Nerlove [30]) is this: Has the seasonal adjustment procedure merely removed the seasonal component or has it also distorted some aspects of the (original) series unrelated to seasonality? Here again we are faced with the problem of comparing two series that are known to be related by some well-specified procedure. Of course, this need not always be the case. Thus the relation of the two series of interest may not be well structured, as, for example, in some unsuccessful attempts to treat in a spectral context the relationship between " the " short- and long-term interest rates.

FILTERS

We shall now develop techniques that would permit us to examine, in the frequency domain, the relationships between two series that may or may not be related by a well-specified procedure.

First, however, let us note that in the foregoing examples the two series were related roughly by

$$Y_t = \sum_{k=-m}^{m} w_k X_{t-k} \qquad (10.1.1)$$

In the case of the GNP moving average, the weights w_k are of the form

$$w_k = \frac{1}{2m+1} \qquad k = 0, \pm 1, \ldots, \pm m$$

$$= 0 \qquad \text{otherwise} \qquad (10.1.2)$$

while in the seasonal adjustment case the weights will, in general, be relatively complex. We also note, that in both cases the weights *do not* depend on t. Such weighting schemes are special cases of what is known in communication (and spectral analysis) literature as "linear time invariant" filters. Perhaps the intuitive meaning of "filters" is best illustrated by a reference to the engineer's proverbial "black box." If we have, say, a (continuous) input function $x(t)$ and we pass it through the black box, we shall generally expect to obtain a (continuous) output function. We may conceive of the process of passing through the "black box" as one in which various (mathematical) operations are performed on the input function to yield the observed output function $y(t)$. As a rule, we would not know the nature of these operations precisely. We would, however, be able to observe the output function, which in conjunction with our knowledge of the input function will enable us to say something about the properties of the "filter." The latter is simply the name we apply to the operations performed in the "black box." This interpretation will help to explain and render more meaningful some of the terminology employed below.

A filter is said to be *linear* and *time invariant* if it satisfies the following two conditions:

i. If inputs $x_1(t)$, $x_2(t)$ correspond to the outputs $y_1(t)$, $y_2(t)$ respectively, then the input $ax_1(t) + bx_2(t)$ corresponds to the output $ay_1(t) + by_2(t)$, where a and b are two arbitrary constants.
ii. If the input $\{x(t) : t \in (-\infty, \infty)\}$ corresponds to the output $\{y(t) : t \in (-\infty, \infty)\}$, then the input $\{x(t + \tau) : t \in (-\infty, \infty)\}$ corresponds to the output $\{y(t + \tau) : t \in (-\infty, \infty)\}$.

The first condition gives linearity, the second gives time invariance.

In more precise terms, we have

Definition 1: A filter is said to be linear time invariant if and only if the relation between the input and output functions [$x(t)$ and $y(t)$ respectively] can be expressed as

$$y(t) = \int_{-\infty}^{\infty} \phi(\tau)x(t - \tau) \, d\tau \tag{10.1.3}$$

The function $\phi(\cdot)$ is called the *kernel* of the filter.

Remark 1: It will be more convenient to work with continuous inputs (and outputs). If the latter are discrete, however, (10.1.3) may be modified to read

$$y(t) = \sum_{\tau = -\infty}^{\infty} \phi_\tau x(t - \tau) \tag{10.1.4}$$

where $\{\phi_\tau : \tau = 0 \pm 1, \pm 2 \ldots\}$ is a sequence of constants. Notice that in both (10.1.3) and (10.1.4) time invariance holds because of the fact that $\phi(\cdot)$ (or ϕ_τ) does not depend on t, while linearity holds because integration (and summation) are linear operations.

The following terminology will be useful in our subsequent discussion and thus is developed here with some care.

Definition 2: A function of the form

$$b(\omega) = B \exp(i\omega t) \qquad \omega \in (-\pi, \pi) \tag{10.1.5}$$

is said to be a *complex harmonic* of amplitude $|B|$ and (angular) *frequency* ω. Functions like

$$b_1(\omega) = B \cos \omega t \qquad b_2(\omega) = B \sin \omega t \tag{10.1.6}$$

are said to be *real harmonics* of amplitude $|B|$ and (angular) frequency ω. Such harmonics are also referred to as sinusoids (of amplitude $|B|$ and angular frequency ω). Since

$$\exp(i\omega t) = \cos \omega t + i \sin \omega t \tag{10.1.7}$$

the connection between real and complex harmonics is obvious.

Definition 3: The *period* of a harmonic with (angular) frequency ω is given by $2\pi/\omega$.

Intuitively the period of a (real) harmonic is simply the "time" required for it to describe a complete cycle as θ varies between, say, 0 and 2π. If

$$\theta = \omega t \tag{10.1.8}$$

and t is the only variable, ω being a fixed constant, then $\cos \omega t$ describes a complete cycle as t varies between 0 and $2\pi/\omega$. Conversely, if it is given that a harmonic has period P, then its angular frequency can be derived as

$$\omega = \frac{2\pi}{P} \tag{10.1.9}$$

Notice that if a sinusoid has a relatively "high" frequency, then it describes a full cycle in a relatively short period of "time"; conversely, if it has a relatively "low" frequency, then it describes a full cycle in a relatively long period of "time." Obviously, if it has a relatively long "period," then it must have, by (10.1.9), a relatively "low" frequency, and so on.

Occasionally it might be desirable to deal not in angular frequency, which tells us how "long" the sinusoid takes to describe a full cycle, but to employ another concept, which is related to the number of full cycles the sinusoid describes per unit of "time."

Definition 4: The true or fundamental λ of a sinusoid of angular frequency ω is given by

$$\lambda = \frac{\omega}{2\pi} \tag{10.1.10}$$

Comparing (10.1.10) with (10.1.9), we see that the true frequency is related to the period of the sinusoid by

$$\lambda = \frac{1}{P} \tag{10.1.11}$$

Definition 5: The phase (or phase angle) α of a sinusoid $s(t)$ is defined by

$$s(t) = \cos{(\omega t + \alpha)} \tag{10.1.12}$$

Notice that the role of α is to indicate where the function $s(\cdot)$ "is at the origin," for $s(0) = \cos{\alpha}$.

Example 1: An example will clarify the nature of the quantities defined above. Consider the sinusoid

$$\sigma(t) = A \cos{(\omega t + \alpha)} \tag{10.1.13}$$

This has amplitude $|A|$, angular frequency ω, and phase α. It may also be written in the equivalent forms

$$\sigma(t) = A \cos{[2\pi\lambda t + \alpha]} = A \cos{\left(\frac{2\pi t}{P} + \alpha\right)} \tag{10.1.14}$$

where the two representations indicate clearly the true frequency and period of the sinusoid.

We should remark that the same holds for a complex harmonic as well. Thus

$$s(t) = A \exp{[i(\omega t + \alpha)]} \tag{10.1.15}$$

is a complex harmonic of angular frequency ω and amplitude $|A|$. The representation in (10.1.15) can be alternatively expressed as

$$s(t) = A \exp{[i(2\pi\lambda t + \alpha)]} = A \exp{\{i[(2\pi t/P) + \alpha]\}} \tag{10.1.16}$$

This is so in view of (10.1.7).

Let us return to our discussion of filters and consider the impact of a filter of the type (10.1.3) on an input function that is given by the complex harmonic of unit amplitude ($A = 1$) and frequency ω.

We find

$$y(t) = \int_{-\infty}^{\infty} \phi(\tau) \exp{[i\omega(t - \tau)]}\, d\tau - \exp{(i\omega t)} \int_{-\infty}^{\infty} \phi(\tau) \exp{(-i\omega \tau)}\, d\tau$$

$$= \Phi(\omega) \exp{(i\omega t)} \tag{10.1.17}$$

Notice that

$$\Phi(\omega) = \int_{-\infty}^{\infty} \phi(\tau) \exp{(-i\omega\tau)}\, d\tau \tag{10.1.18}$$

is the Fourier transform of the kernel of the filter.

Hence the effect of the filter in producing the output function is simply to multiply the amplitude of the input function by the Fourier transform of the kernel of the filter, which is a function of the frequency ω, but leave the frequency unchanged.[1] The function in (10.1.18) is important and thus deserves a name.

Definition 6: Let a linear time invariant filter be characterized by the kernel $\phi(\cdot)$. Then the Fourier transform of the kernel

$$\Phi(\omega) = \int_{-\infty}^{\infty} \phi(\tau) \exp\left(-i\omega\tau\right) d\tau \tag{10.1.19}$$

is said to be the *frequency response* function of the filter.

The usefulness of this characterization is immediate if one considers the fact that every continuous function can be approximated arbitrarily closely by a linear combination of complex harmonics (trigonometric polynomials).

Thus if $x(t)$ is such a function, we may write

$$x(t) \approx \sum_{j=-r}^{r} \alpha_j \exp\left(i\omega_j t\right) \tag{10.1.20}$$

Hence if we pass $x(t)$ through the filter $\phi(\cdot)$, then the output function may be written immediately as

$$y(t) \approx \sum_{j=-r}^{r} \alpha_j \Phi(\omega_j) \exp\left(i\omega_j t\right) \tag{10.1.21}$$

Another useful quantity in this connection is the "transfer function" associated with the filter. More precisely,

Definition 7: Let $\phi(\cdot)$ be the kernel of a linear time invariant filter and $\Phi(\cdot)$ its associated frequency response function. Then

$$\Psi(\omega) = |\Phi(\omega)|^2 \tag{10.1.22}$$

is said to be the *transfer function* associated with the filter.

Remark 2: Notice that, in general, the frequency response function is complex and thus may be written in terms of a pair of real-valued functions as

$$\Phi(\omega) = \Phi_1(\omega) + i\Phi_2(\omega) \tag{10.1.23}$$

where the $\Phi_j(\cdot)$ are real functions, $j = 1, 2$.

---

[1] For clarity in subsequent discussion, let us state here that all characteristics of interest determined with respect to a filter remain valid whether we are dealing with a continuous or a discrete situation. Thus suppose that the input process is discrete. Then

(*) $y(t) = \sum_{\tau=-\infty}^{\infty} \phi_\tau \exp\left[i\omega(t-\tau)\right] = \exp\left(i\omega t\right) \sum_{\tau=-\infty}^{\infty} \phi_\tau \exp\left(-i\omega\tau\right) = \Phi(\omega) \exp\left(i\omega t\right)$

where now

(**) $\Phi(\omega) = \sum_{\tau=-\infty}^{\infty} \phi_\tau \exp\left(-i\omega\tau\right)$

that is, it is the Fourier transform of the *sequence* $\{\phi_\tau : \tau \in N\}$. Clearly any characterization of the filter based on manipulations of (10.1.17) and (10.1.18) would hold equally well in the discrete case if we replace the equation in (10.1.18) by the equation in (**) above.

On the other hand, the transfer function is real. The connection between the two will become obvious if we write the frequency response function not as in (10.1.23) but in polar form.

$$\Phi(\omega) = \psi(\omega) \exp\left[i\alpha(\omega)\right] \tag{10.1.24}$$

where $\alpha(\omega)$ is the argument of Φ—arg Φ—defined by

$$\cos\alpha(\omega) = \frac{\Phi_1(\omega)}{\psi(\omega)} \qquad \sin\alpha(\omega) = \frac{\Phi_2(\omega)}{\psi(\omega)} \tag{10.1.25}$$

and

$$\psi(\omega) = [\Psi(\omega)]^{\frac{1}{2}} \tag{10.1.26}$$

Remark 3: In view of Remark 2, we are now in a position to express (10.1.17) in a more meaningful way. Notice that the result as it stands in (10.1.17) takes a real coefficient—unity—of $\exp(i\omega t)$ in the input function and transforms it into a complex coefficient—$\Phi(\omega)$—in the output function. This may be a somewhat inconvenient representation, but we now have the means of rectifying this asymmetry. We may, as a result of (10.1.24), express the output function in a form similar to that of the input function and write, using (10.1.17) and (10.1.24),

$$y(t) = \psi(\omega) \exp\left\{i[\omega t + \alpha(\omega)]\right\} \tag{10.1.27}$$

The output function here clearly shows the effect of the filter on the amplitude, frequency, and phase of the harmonic. In particular, the filter induces an amplification (or attenuation depending on whether $\psi \gtrless 1$) by a factor $\psi(\omega)$ and a phase shift through an angle $\alpha(\omega)$ but otherwise leaves the angular frequency of the harmonic unaltered.

It is precisely these two features of a filter's impact that will be of primary interest in cross-spectral analysis. A final word on terminology.

Definition 8: Let $\phi(\cdot)$ be the kernel of a linear time invariant filter and let $\psi(\cdot)$ and $\alpha(\cdot)$ be defined by (10.1.26) and (10.1.25) respectively. Then $\psi(\cdot)$ is called the *gain* and $\alpha(\cdot)$ the *phase angle* associated with the filter.

EFFECT OF FILTERING ON THE SPECTRUM

Here we shall characterize the effect of filtering by showing the relation between the spectra of the input and output series and some characteristics of the filter. We shall then give an example that will clarify the relationships we are about to derive as well as the discussion of the preceding paragraphs.

Lemma 1: Let $\{x(t) : t \in R\}^2$ be a continuous (covariance stationary)

---

[2] Here R denotes the real numbers.

process defined on the real line and let it be passed through a linear time invariant filter with kernel $\phi(\cdot)$. Then

$$f_y(\lambda) = \Psi(\lambda) f_x(\lambda) \tag{10.1.28}$$

where $f_y(\cdot)$ and $f_x(\cdot)$ are the spectral densities of the output and input series, respectively, and $\Psi(\cdot)$ is the transfer function associated with the filter.

PROOF: The output series $\{y(t) : t \in R\}$ is related to the input series by

$$y(t) = \int_{-\infty}^{\infty} \phi(\tau) x(t - \tau) \, d\tau \tag{10.1.29}$$

Since the x process is covariance stationary, it has the spectral representation

$$x(t) = \int_{-\infty}^{\infty} \exp{(it\lambda)} \, dZ_x(\lambda) \tag{10.1.30}$$

where the Z process is one having orthogonal increments and such that

$$E[dZ_x(\lambda) \, \overline{dZ_x(\lambda)}] = f_x(\lambda) \, d\lambda \tag{10.1.31}$$

Thus (10.1.29) can also be represented as

$$\begin{aligned}
y(t) &= \int_{-\infty}^{\infty} \phi(\tau) \int_{-\infty}^{\infty} \exp{[i(t - \tau)\lambda]} \, dZ_x(\lambda) \, d\tau \\
&= \int_{-\infty}^{\infty} \exp{(it\lambda)} \left[\int_{-\infty}^{\infty} \exp{(-i\tau\lambda)} \phi(\tau) \, d\tau \right] dZ_x(\lambda) \\
&= \int_{-\infty}^{\infty} \exp{(it\lambda)} \Phi(\lambda) \, dZ_x(\lambda)
\end{aligned} \tag{10.1.32}$$

This immediately suggests that $y(t)$ has the spectral representation

$$y(t) = \int_{-\infty}^{\infty} \exp{(it\lambda)} \, dZ_y(\lambda) \tag{10.1.33}$$

where

$$dZ_y(\lambda) = \Phi(\lambda) \, dZ_x(\lambda) \tag{10.1.34}$$

Moreover,

$$\begin{aligned}
E[dZ_y(\lambda) \overline{dZ_y(\lambda')}] &= \Psi(\lambda) f_x(\lambda) \, d\lambda & \text{if} \quad \lambda = \lambda' \\
&= 0 & \text{if} \quad \lambda \neq \lambda'
\end{aligned} \tag{10.1.35}$$

From (10.1.35) we conclude

$$f_y(\lambda) = \Psi(\lambda) f_x(\lambda) \qquad\qquad\qquad\qquad \text{Q.E.D.} \tag{10.1.36}$$

Remark 4: Lemma 1 shows that the quotient of the spectral density of the output to that of the input series is simply the transfer function corresponding to the filter by which the two series are related. Thus if we know the kernel of the filter and one of the spectral densities, the other is easily obtained from (10.1.36).

Remark 5: Although the lemma is stated for continuous processes and filters with continuous kernel, it remains equally valid when we deal with discrete processes and filters whose kernel is a sequence. In this particular case, we should have

$$y(t) = \sum_{\tau = -\infty}^{\infty} \phi_\tau x(t - \tau) \qquad t = 0, \pm 1, \pm 2, \ldots \tag{10.1.37}$$

Since

$$x(t) = \int_{-\pi}^{\pi} \exp(it\lambda) \, dZ_x(\lambda) \tag{10.1.38}$$

we have, by properly modifying (10.1.32) through (10.1.34),

$$y(t) = \int_{-\pi}^{\pi} \exp(it\lambda) \, dZ_y(\lambda) \tag{10.1.39}$$

where now

$$dZ_y(\lambda) = \Phi(\lambda) \, dZ_x(\lambda) \qquad \Phi(\lambda) = \sum_{\tau = -\infty}^{\infty} \phi_\tau \exp(-i\lambda\tau) \tag{10.1.40}$$

The role played by the gain (or transfer function) and phase angle of the filter becomes quite clear from the preceding discussion. Thus suppose $\Psi(\lambda_0) \approx 0$. Then from (10.1.36) we would have $f_y(\lambda_0) \approx 0$, which means that components of frequency λ_0 are weeded out of the series as it passes through the filter. Conversely, if $\Psi(\lambda_0)$ is large (greater than unity), then the contribution of components of frequency λ_0 to the variability of the series is "magnified." Hence the term "filter" is quite appropriate in that by proper choice of the kernel $\phi(\cdot)$ we can suppress or accentuate components of given frequency, say λ_0.

Thus, to use an example, a good seasonal filter is one that filters out components corresponding to seasonal fluctuations while at the same time it does not perceptibly distort the contribution of components of frequencies not corresponding to seasonal fluctuations.

The import of the phase shift of a filter is best seen by examining (10.1.32), which, in view of (10.1.24), may be written as

$$y(t) = \int_{-\infty}^{\infty} \exp\{i[\lambda t + \alpha(\lambda)]\}\psi(\lambda) \, dZ_x(\lambda) \tag{10.1.41}$$

We see that the phase angle of components of amplitude $|dZ_x(\lambda)|$ in the input series is shifted by $\alpha(\lambda)$ in obtaining the output series. This is important if the series $x(t)$ is to be compared with another, $w(t)$, and the lead-lag characteristics of the comparison are crucial. In general, the lead lag characteristics of $y(t)$ and $w(t)$ will not be similar to those of $x(t)$ and $w(t)$, and care should be exercised to design a filter with "small" phase shift in such cases. The following example will help clarify matters.

Example 2: Consider the well-known first-order Markov process with parameter $\beta, 0 < |\beta| < 1, \beta \in R$. As is well known, this process may be represented as

$$x(t) = \sum_{\tau=0}^{\infty} \beta^\tau \varepsilon_{t-\tau} \qquad t \in N \tag{10.1.42}$$

where N is the set of integers $(0, \pm 1, \pm 2, \ldots)$ and

$$E(\varepsilon_t) = 0 \qquad E(\varepsilon_t \varepsilon_{t'}) = \delta_{tt'} \sigma^2 \tag{10.1.43}$$

By our previous discussion, the x process can be regarded as the output process of a linear time invariant filter with kernel $\{\beta_\tau : \beta_\tau = \beta^\tau, \tau = 0, 1, 2, \ldots\}$ and input process $\{\varepsilon_t : t \in N\}$, the latter consisting of identically distributed, orthogonal random variables. The ε process is thus a covariance stationary process.

The frequency response function of the filter above is simply

$$\Phi(\lambda) = \sum_{\tau=0}^{\infty} \beta^\tau \exp(-i\tau\lambda) = \frac{1}{1 - \beta \exp(-i\lambda)} \tag{10.1.44}$$

Multiplying numerator and denominator by the complex conjugate of the denominator, namely, $1 - \beta \exp(i\lambda)$, we can rewrite (10.1.44) as

$$\Phi(\lambda) = \frac{1 - \beta \exp(i\lambda)}{(1 - \beta \cos \lambda)^2 + \beta^2 \sin^2 \lambda} \tag{10.1.45}$$

In view of the conditions imposed on β, the denominator above does not vanish in the relevant range and thus (10.1.45) is a valid representation.

The transfer function of the filter is given by

$$\Psi(\lambda) = \frac{1}{(1 - \beta \cos \lambda)^2 + \beta^2 \sin^2 \lambda} \tag{10.1.46}$$

The gain of the filter is given by

$$\psi(\lambda) = \frac{1}{[(1 - \beta \cos \lambda)^2 + \beta^2 \sin^2 \lambda]^{\frac{1}{2}}} \tag{10.1.47}$$

The phase angle $\alpha(\lambda)$ is given (implicitly) by

$$\cos \alpha(\lambda) = \frac{1 - \beta \cos \lambda}{\psi(\lambda)} \qquad \sin \alpha(\lambda) = \frac{-\beta \sin \lambda}{\psi(\lambda)} \tag{10.1.48}$$

or, more compactly,

$$\tan \alpha(\lambda) = -\frac{\beta \sin \lambda}{1 - \beta \cos \lambda} \tag{10.1.49}$$

Thus the frequency response function can be written as

$$\Phi(\lambda) = \frac{\exp\{i[\tan^{-1}(-\beta \sin \lambda/1 - \beta \cos \lambda)]\}}{[(1 - \beta \cos \lambda)^2 + \beta^2 \sin^2 \lambda]^{\frac{1}{2}}} \tag{10.1.50}$$

Actually, the denominator of this equation can be further simplified to $1 - 2\beta \cos \lambda + \beta^2$.

Since the spectral density of the ε process is simply $\sigma^2/2\pi$, it follows immediately that the spectral density of the x process is given by

$$f_x(\lambda) = \frac{\sigma^2}{2\pi} \frac{1}{1 - 2\beta \cos \lambda + \beta^2} \tag{10.1.51}$$

The role played by the phase angle of the filter is best seen through the spectral representation of the x process. Since the ε process is assumed real, we can define

$$Z_\varepsilon(\lambda) = \tfrac{1}{2}[u_\varepsilon(\lambda) - iv_\varepsilon(\lambda)] \qquad -\pi < \lambda \le \pi \tag{10.1.52}$$

such that $u_\varepsilon(-\lambda) = u_\varepsilon(\lambda)$ and $v_\varepsilon(-\lambda) = -v_\varepsilon(\lambda)$.
Now the spectral representation of the ε process is

$$\varepsilon_t = \int_{-\pi}^{\pi} \exp(i\lambda t)\, dZ_\varepsilon(\lambda) = \int_0^{\pi} \cos \lambda t\, du_\varepsilon(\lambda) + \int_0^{\pi} \sin \lambda t\, dv_\varepsilon(\lambda) \tag{10.1.53}$$

It follows, from (10.1.42), (10.1.49), and (10.1.50), that

$$x_t = \int_{-\pi}^{\pi} \exp\{i[\lambda t + \alpha(\lambda)]\}\psi(\lambda)\, dZ_\varepsilon(\lambda) \tag{10.1.54}$$

We shall now express (10.1.54) in a form similar to that appearing after the second equality sign in (10.1.53). The role of the phase angle will then become obvious.
Now

$$\exp\{i[\lambda t + \alpha(\lambda)]\} = \cos[\lambda t + \alpha(\lambda)] + i\sin[\lambda t + \alpha(\lambda)]$$
$$= \cos \lambda t \cos \alpha(\lambda) - \sin \lambda t \sin \alpha(\lambda) + i[\sin \lambda t \cos \alpha(\lambda)$$
$$+ \cos \lambda t \sin \alpha(\lambda)] \tag{10.1.55}$$

Using (10.1.52), the integrand of (10.1.54) becomes

$$\tfrac{1}{2}\psi(\lambda)\{[\cos \lambda t \cos \alpha(\lambda) - \sin t\lambda \sin \alpha(\lambda)]\, du_\varepsilon(\lambda)$$
$$+ [\sin \lambda t \cos \alpha(\lambda) + \cos t\lambda \sin \alpha(\lambda)]\, dv_\varepsilon(\lambda)\}$$
$$+ \tfrac{1}{2}i\psi(\lambda)\{[\sin \lambda t \cos \alpha(\lambda) + \cos \lambda t \sin \alpha(\lambda)]\, du_\varepsilon(\lambda)$$
$$- [\cos \lambda t \cos \alpha(\lambda) - \sin \lambda t \sin \alpha(\lambda)]\, dv_\varepsilon(\lambda)\, dv_\varepsilon(\lambda)\}$$

From (10.1.47) note that

$$\psi(\lambda) = \psi(-\lambda) \tag{10.1.56}$$

and from (10.1.49) we have

$$\alpha(-\lambda) = \tan^{-1}\left[\frac{\beta \sin \lambda}{1 - \beta \cos \lambda}\right] = -\tan^{-1}\left[\frac{-\beta \sin \lambda}{1 - \beta \cos \lambda}\right] = -\alpha(\lambda) \tag{10.1.57}$$

since the inverse tangent function is odd.

Consider now the imaginary part of the integrand. The "coefficient" of $dv_\varepsilon(\lambda)$ is

$$-\psi(\lambda)[\cos \lambda t \cos \alpha(\lambda) - \sin \lambda t \sin \alpha(\lambda)]$$

and hence is an even function (i.e., its value at λ is the same as its value at $-\lambda$). Since $v_\varepsilon(\lambda)$ is an odd function—that is, $v_\varepsilon(-\lambda) = -v_\varepsilon(\lambda)$—it follows that when we integrate over the range $(-\pi, \pi)$ the integrand vanishes.

The "coefficient" of $du_\varepsilon(\lambda)$ is an odd function. Since $u_\varepsilon(\lambda)$ is an even function, it follows that

$$\int_{-\pi}^{\pi} \psi(\lambda)[\sin \lambda t \cos \alpha(\lambda) + \cos \lambda t \sin \alpha(\lambda)] \, du_\varepsilon(\lambda) = 0 \tag{10.1.58}$$

On the other hand, the "coefficient" of $du_\varepsilon(\lambda)$ in the real part of the integrand is even and thus the integral over $(-\pi, \pi)$ is simply twice the integral over $(0, \pi)$. Similarly,

$$\int_{-\pi}^{\pi} \psi(\lambda)[\sin \lambda t \cos \alpha(\lambda) + \cos \lambda t \sin \alpha(\lambda)] \, dv_\varepsilon(\lambda)$$

$$= 2 \int_{0}^{\pi} \psi(\lambda)[\sin \lambda t \cos \alpha(\lambda) + \cos \lambda t \sin \alpha(\lambda)] \, dv_\varepsilon(\lambda) \tag{10.1.59}$$

since the "coefficient" of dv_ε is odd and so is $v_\varepsilon(\lambda)$.

Thus we conclude

$$x_t = \int_{0}^{\pi} \frac{\cos[\lambda t + \alpha(\lambda)]}{(1 - 2\beta \cos \lambda + \beta^2)^{\frac{1}{2}}} \, du_\varepsilon(\lambda) + \int_{0}^{\pi} \frac{\sin[\lambda t + \alpha(\lambda)]}{(1 - 2\beta \cos \lambda + \beta^2)^{\frac{1}{2}}} \, dv_\varepsilon(\lambda)$$

$$\tag{10.1.60}$$

Comparing (10.1.60) with (10.1.53), we see that the effect of the filter has been to shift the phase angle of the sinusoid components of the ε process by $\alpha(\lambda)$ and to amplify or attenuate their (random) amplitude by $(1 - 2\beta \cos \lambda + \beta^2)^{-\frac{1}{2}}$. Finally, the spectrum of the x process can be shown to be as illustrated in

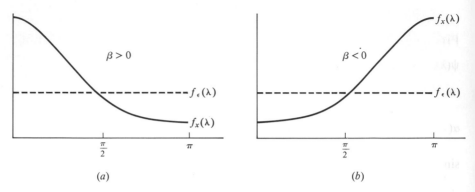

FIGURE 10.1 a and b   Spectral density of a first order Markov process with parameter β.

Figures 10.1a and 10.1b. It is clear from the figures that for some λ the spectral ordinates of $f_x(\cdot)$ and $f_\varepsilon(\lambda)$ are the same. This occurs for

$$\lambda = \cos^{-1}\left(\frac{\beta}{2}\right) \qquad \lambda \in \left(0, \frac{\pi}{2}\right) \quad \text{if } \beta > 0$$

$$\lambda = \cos^{-1}\left(\frac{\beta}{2}\right) \qquad \lambda \in \left(\frac{\pi}{2}, \pi\right) \quad \text{if } \beta < 0 \qquad (10.1.61)$$

10.2 CROSS SPECTRUM: COSPECTRUM, QUADRATURE SPECTRUM, AND COHERENCY

COMPLEX PROCESSES

In the previous section we had briefly examined, in the frequency domain, the relationship between two series when it was known that they were related as input and output through a specified linear time invariant filter. But, of course, it is not always the case that any two series in whose relation we are interested are so related.

In this section we shall develop systematically the relevant spectral relations under relatively mild restrictions as to the kind of connection that is specified a priori.

When dealing with *random variables*, we define their covariance by

$$E[(x_i - \mu_i)(x_j - \mu_j)] = \text{Cov}(x_i, x_j),$$

where the μ_i, μ_j are, respectively, the means of x_i and x_j. It is apparent from the operations involved that

$$\text{Cov}(x_i, x_j) = \text{Cov}(x_j, x_i).$$

In addition, if ρ_{ij} is the correlation coefficient between x_i and x_j and ρ_{ji} is the correlation coefficient between x_j and x_i, then $\rho_{ij} = \rho_{ji}$.

In dealing with stochastic processes, however, the simplicity just noted disappears. Although relationships analogous to those above may be obtained, care must be taken in operating with them as will immediately become apparent below.

Definition 9: Let $\{X(t): t \in N\}$, $Y(t): t \in N\}$ be two stochastic processes with mean functions $m_x(\cdot)$, $m_y(\cdot)$ respectively. Their cross-covariance function (or kernel) is defined by

$$K_{xy}(t, s) = E\{[X(t) - m_x(t)][\overline{Y(s) - m_y(s)}]\} \tag{10.2.1}$$

Remark 6: Notice the convention involved in (10.2.1), namely, that the first argument of $K_{xy}(\cdot, \cdot)$ refers to the index of the unconjugated process $X(t)$, while the second refers to the index of the conjugated process $\overline{Y}(s)$. The same convention applies to the order in which the subscripts appear in $K_{xy}(\cdot, \cdot)$. Thus, for example,

$$K_{yx}(t, s) = E\{[Y(t) - m_y(t)][\overline{X(s) - m_x(s)}]\} \tag{10.2.2}$$

In general, $K_{yx}(t, s) \neq K_{xy}(t, s)$ and hence it would appear that we have two covariance kernels.

Hoever, for the type of processes considered in this book, we shall establish a well-defined relation between $K_{xy}(\cdot, \cdot)$ and $K_{yx}(\cdot, \cdot)$ so that knowledge of one implies knowledge of the other. Thus we have essentially only one covariance kernel and (10.2.1) serves to establish our notational convention.

Definition 10: Two stochastic processes $\{X(t): t \in N\}$, $\{(Y(t): t \in N\}$ are said to be *jointly covariance stationary* if each is covariance stationary and, in addition,

$$K_{xy}(s + \tau, s) = K_{xy}(\tau) \tag{10.2.3}$$

that is, if their cross-covariance kernel depends, in the notation of (10.2.1) only on the time difference $t - s = \tau$.

In connection with Definition 10, observe that since each process is covariance stationary, we shall make the customary assumption that their respective mean functions are constant. Hence without loss of generality we shall assume in what follows that

$$m_x(t) = m_y(t) \equiv 0 \tag{10.2.4}$$

Notice further that the restriction in (10.2.3) is not a vacuous one. Therefore, for any two arbitrary covariance stationary processes, (10.2.3) need not hold, as the following example will make clear.

Example 3: Consider the two processes

$$X(t) = A_1 \cos \lambda t + B_1 \sin \lambda t$$
$$Y(t) = A_2 \cos \lambda t + B_2 \sin \lambda t \tag{10.2.5}$$

We specify

$$E(A_i) = E(B_i) = 0$$
$$\text{Var } (A_i) = \text{Var } (B_i) = \sigma_{ii} \qquad i = 1, 2$$
$$E(A_i B_i) = 0 \tag{10.2.6}$$

Under (10.2.6), the two processes in (10.2.5) are each covariance stationary. The cross covariance between $X(t + \tau)$ and $Y(t)$ is given by

$$
\begin{aligned}
E[X(t + \tau)Y(t)] = {} & [E(A_1 A_2)](\cos^2 \lambda t \cos \lambda\tau - \cos \lambda t \sin \lambda t \sin \lambda\tau) \\
& + [E(A_1 B_2)](\cos \lambda t \sin \lambda t \cos \lambda\tau - \sin^2 \lambda t \sin \lambda\tau) \\
& + [E(A_1 B_2)](\sin \lambda t \cos \lambda t \cos \lambda\tau + \cos^2 \lambda t \sin \lambda\tau) \\
& + [E(B_1 B_2)](\sin^2 \lambda t \cos \lambda t + \cos \lambda t \sin \lambda t \sin \lambda\tau)
\end{aligned}
\tag{10.2.7}
$$

where use has been made of the trigonometric identities

$$\cos (A + B) = \cos A \cos B - \sin A \sin B$$
$$\sin (A + B) = \sin A \cos B + \cos A \sin B \tag{10.2.8}$$

Even if we impose the requirement

$$E(A_1 B_2) = E(A_2 B_1) = 0 \tag{10.2.9}$$

which is analogous to the last condition in (10.2.6), the right-hand side of (10.2.7) will not be a function of τ alone and thus the two processes *will not be jointly covariance stationary*. This is so since we cannot, in general, expect that the covariance between A_1 and A_2 is equal to that between B_1 and B_2.

When the latter is true, however, that is, when

$$E(A_1 A_2) = E(B_1 B_2) = \sigma_{12} \tag{10.2.10}$$

then

$$E[X(t + \tau)Y(t)] = \sigma_{12} \cos \lambda\tau = K_{xy}(\tau) \tag{10.2.11}$$

In Chapter 9 we saw that there is a well-defined relation between the (auto) covariance kernel of a (covariance stationary) stochastic process and its associated spectral density. In particular, the two were shown to form a pair of Fourier transforms.

Thus we are tempted to inquire: Is there a similar relation between the cross-covariance kernel of two (jointly covariance stationary) stochastic processes and something analogous to a spectral density?

It turns out that this is indeed the case, and we shall develop this relation below. Actually, it will be just as simple to talk of a set of m stochastic processes as it is to talk of just two. The degree of complexity involved in making the transition between two stochastic processes and an arbitrary but finite number, say m, of stochastic processes is comparable to that entailed in the transition from a bivariate to an m-variate distribution.

Since in most of this book we are typically interested only in second-order moments, we only need the additional notion of a covariance matrix when dealing with a bivariate distribution. But once we make use of this, we might as well treat the general m-variate distribution. Similarly, with just two processes we still need the notions of a spectral matrix and a Hermitian matrix. Once these are introduced, however, we may just as well deal with a set of m stochastic processes.

We first extend Definition 10 to an arbitrary but finite set of stochastic processes.

Definition 11: A set of stochastic processes $\{X_\mu(t): t \in N, \mu = 1, 2, \ldots, m\}$, where m is a finite positive integer, are said to be *jointly covariance stationary* if

$$E[X_\mu(t)] = c_\mu \qquad \mu = 1, 2, \ldots, m \tag{10.2.12}$$

$$E[X_\mu(t + \tau) - c_\mu)\overline{(X_\nu(t) - c_\nu)}] = K_{\mu\nu}(\tau) \qquad \mu, \nu = 1, 2, \ldots, m \tag{10.2.13}$$

where the c_μ are constants independent of t and the $K_{\mu\nu}(\tau)$ are finite for any $\tau = 0, \pm 1, \pm 2, \ldots$.

Remark 7: Without loss of generality, we may take

$$c_\mu = 0 \qquad \mu = 1, 2, \ldots, m \tag{10.2.14}$$

a convention to which we shall adhere below.

Definition 12: Let

$$A = (a_{ij}) \tag{10.2.15}$$

be a square matrix of order n, with complex elements. Then A is said to be a *Hermitian matrix* if

$$A = \bar{A}' \tag{10.2.16}$$

where

$$\bar{A} = (\bar{a}_{ij}) \tag{10.2.17}$$

and $\bar{a}_{ij}$ is the complex conjugate of a_{ij}.

Remark 8: If A is a Hermitian matrix with real elements, then it is symmetric. Indeed, a Hermitian matrix is the natural extension of a symmetric matrix when the field over which the elements of the matrix are defined is that of the complex numbers.

Definition 13: Let A be Hermitian; then A is said to be positive semi-definite if for any complex vector ζ

$$Q = \bar{\zeta}' A \zeta \geq 0 \tag{10.2.18}$$

where $\bar{\zeta}$ denotes the complex conjugate of ζ.

We may now state without proof the basic theorem in this area, which was discovered independently by Cramer [7] and Kolmogorov [23].

Theorem 1: Let $\{X_\mu(t): t \in N, \mu = 1, 2, \ldots, m\}$ be a set of jointly covariance stationary stochastic processes in the sense of Definition 11. Then the covariance kernels (both auto- and cross-) have the representation

$$K_{\mu\nu}(\tau) = \int_{-\pi}^{\pi} \exp(i\tau\lambda)\, dF_{\mu\nu}(\lambda) \qquad \begin{matrix} \tau = 0, \pm 1, \pm 2, \ldots \\ \mu, \nu = 1, 2, \ldots, m \end{matrix} \tag{10.2.19}$$

where the $F_{\mu\nu}(\cdot)$ are functions of bounded variation on $(-\pi, \pi]$ and everywhere possess right-hand limits. Moreover, if $(\alpha, \beta) \subset (-\pi, \pi]$ and we define

$$\Delta F = (\Delta F_{\mu\nu}) \qquad \mu, \nu = 1, 2, \ldots, m \tag{10.2.20}$$

where

$$\Delta F_{\mu\nu} = F_{\mu\nu}(\beta) - F_{\mu\nu}(\alpha) \tag{10.2.21}$$

then the matrix ΔF is positive semidefinite and Hermitian. Conversely, if $K_{\mu\nu}(\cdot)$ is a set of m^2 functions given by (10.2.19) and the $F_{\mu\nu}(\cdot)$ possess the properties above—that is, they are of bounded variation on $(-\pi, \pi]$, possess everywhere right-hand limits, and the matrix ΔF as was defined in (10.2.20) is positive semidefinite and Hermitian—then there exists a set of jointly covariance stationary processes $\{X_\mu(t): t \in N, \mu = 1, 2, \ldots, m\}$ having covariance kernels $K_{\mu\nu}(\cdot)$.

Remark 9: A sufficient condition for the functions $F_{\mu\nu}(\cdot)$ to be differentiable and thus have the representation

$$F_{\mu\nu}(\lambda) = \int_{-\pi}^{\lambda} f_{\mu\nu}(\theta)\, d\theta \tag{10.2.22}$$

where

$$f_{\mu\nu}(\lambda) = \frac{d}{d\lambda} F_{\mu\nu}(\lambda) \tag{10.2.23}$$

is that

$$\sum_{\tau = -\infty}^{\infty} |K_{\mu\nu}(\tau)| < \infty \tag{10.2.24}$$

Definition 14: The functions $F_{\mu\nu}(\cdot)$ are called the *cross-spectral distribution functions* (for $\mu \neq \nu$) associated with the processes $\{X_\mu(t): t \in N\}\{X_\nu(t): t \in N\}$. If the $F_{\mu\nu}(\cdot)$ are differentiable, their derivatives $f_{\mu\nu}(\cdot)$, $\mu \neq \nu$, are called the *cross-spectral density functions*.

Remark 10: Clearly, for $\mu = \nu$, the results of the theorem coincide with the results obtained in Chapter 9 where we dealt with single stochastic processes. Thus $F_{\mu\mu}(\cdot)$ is the spectral distribution function of the μth process and, if differentiable, $f_{\mu\mu}(\cdot)$ is its spectral density function.

Several other simple relations are worth mentioning at this point.

Consider the matrix

$$K(\tau) = [K_{\mu\nu}(\tau)] \qquad \mu, \nu = 1, 2, \ldots, m \qquad (10.2.25)$$

This is simply the matrix of covariance kernels evaluated at τ. Clearly we have one such matrix for each $\tau = 0, \pm 1, \pm 2, \ldots$. From the definition of the $K_{\mu\nu}(\cdot)$ in (10.2.13), we easily see that

$$\overline{K_{\mu\nu}(\tau)} = E[X_\nu(t)\overline{X_\mu(t + \tau)}] = K_{\nu\mu}(-\tau) \qquad (10.2.26)$$

Since, in general,[3]

$$K_{\mu\nu}(\tau) \neq K_{\mu\nu}(-\tau) \qquad \mu \neq \nu \qquad (10.2.27)$$

we see that the matrix $K(\tau)$ of (10.2.25) is not Hermitian except for $\tau = 0$.

We shall now give a rigorous proof that the covariance kernels and the cross-spectral densities form pairs of Fourier transforms, something we had not done explicitly in the previous chapter.

It will facilitate the discussion and detract little from the empirical relevance of this result if in addition to the assumption that the (cross-) spectral distributions are differentiable, that is, that the (cross) spectral densities exist and are given by

$$\frac{d}{d\lambda} F_{\mu\nu}(\lambda) = f_{\mu\nu}(\lambda) \qquad \mu, \nu = 1, 2, \ldots, m \qquad (10.2.28)$$

we also require that the $f_{\mu\nu}(\cdot)$, by appropriate modification at the endpoints if necessary, are continuous and have a finite number of maxima and minima on $[-\pi, \pi]$.

This implies that the $f_{\mu\nu}(\cdot)$ are continuous functions of bounded variation[4] on $[-\pi, \pi]$.

Notice that continuity of the $f_{\mu\nu}(\cdot)$ on $[-\pi, \pi]$ implies their boundedness on that set. Moreover, since we may now write

$$K_{\mu\nu}(\tau) = \int_{-\pi}^{\pi} \exp(i\tau\lambda) f_{\mu\nu}(\lambda) \, d\lambda \qquad \mu, \nu = 1, 2, \ldots, m \qquad (10.2.29)$$

---

[3] The reader may consider, for example, $X_1(t) = A_1 \exp(it)$, $X_2(t) = A_2 \exp(it)$, where say, $(A_1, A_2)' \sim N(0, \Sigma)$. This is easily shown to be a bivariate covariance stationary process. Now $K_{12}(\tau) = \sigma_{12} \exp(i\tau)$, $K_{12}(-\tau) = \sigma_{12} \exp(-i\tau)$, and thus $K_{12}(\tau) \neq K_{12}(-\tau)$.

[4] For a discussion of this class of functions, the reader is referred to the Mathematical Appendix.

we see that the boundedness of the $f_{\mu\nu}(\cdot)$ on $(-\pi, \pi)$ is implied by the assumption that the covariance kernels $K_{\mu\nu}(\cdot)$ are bounded. So what we have done by the additional restrictions imposed above is to add continuity to the properties of the (cross) spectral densities and remove from consideration the pathological case where the $f_{\mu\nu}(\cdot)$ have infinitely many maxima and minima on $[-\pi, \pi]$. Obviously these are not very restrictive requirements.

We may now prove

Lemma 2: Let $\{X_\mu(t): t \in N, \ \mu = 1, 2, \ldots, m\}$, $K_{\mu\nu}(\cdot)$, $F_{\mu\nu}(\cdot)$ be as in Theorem 1. Suppose, in addition, that the derivatives of the (cross) spectral distributions $F_{\mu\nu}(\cdot)$ exist and can be defined as continuous functions possessing a finite number of maxima and minima on $[-\pi, \pi]$. Then the cross-spectral densities

$$f_{\mu\nu}(\lambda) = \frac{d}{d\lambda} F_{\mu\nu}(\ ) \qquad \mu, \nu = 1, 2, \ldots, m \tag{10.2.30}$$

and the covariance kernels $K_{\mu\nu}(\cdot)$ form pairs of Fourier transforms, that is,

$$K_{\mu\nu}(\tau) = \int_{-\pi}^{\pi} \exp(i\tau\lambda) f_{\mu\nu}(\lambda) \, d\lambda \tag{10.2.31}$$

$$f_{\mu\nu}(\lambda) = \frac{1}{2\pi} \sum_{\tau=-\infty}^{\infty} K_{\mu\nu}(\tau) \exp(-i\tau\lambda) \tag{10.2.32}$$

PROOF: Since the (cross) spectral distributions are assumed to be differentiable, the validity of (10.2.31) follows immediately from (10.2.19) of Theorem 1. Thus we need only demonstrate the validity of (10.2.32).

Now the nth (complex) Fourier coefficient of $f_{\mu\nu}(\lambda)$ is given by

$$c_{\mu\nu}^{(n)} = \frac{1}{2\pi} \int_{-\pi}^{\pi} \exp(in\lambda) f_{\mu\nu}(\lambda) \, d\lambda \qquad \begin{array}{l} \mu, \nu = 1, 2, \ldots, m \\ n = 0, \pm 1, \pm 2, \ldots \end{array} \tag{10.2.33}$$

Comparing (10.2.33) with (10.2.31), we conclude

$$K_{\mu\nu}(\tau) = 2\pi c_{\mu\nu}^{(\tau)} \qquad \begin{array}{l} \mu, \nu = 1, 2, \ldots, m \\ \tau = 0, \pm 1, \pm 2, \ldots \end{array} \tag{10.2.34}$$

Since the $f_{\mu\nu}(\cdot)$ are continuous functions of bounded variation on $[-\pi, \pi]$, we know that their associated Fourier series converge uniformly to $f_{\mu\nu}(\cdot)$ on any open subinterval of $[-\pi, \pi]$.

Hence we have

$$\lim_{n \to \infty} \sum_{\tau=-n}^{n} c_{\mu\nu}^{(\tau)} \exp(-i\tau\lambda) = f_{\mu\nu}(\lambda) \qquad \text{for } \lambda \in (a, b) \qquad (a, b) \subset [-\pi, \pi] \tag{10.2.35}$$

Inserting (10.2.34) in (10.2.35), we conclude

$$\frac{1}{2\pi} \sum_{\tau=-\infty}^{\infty} K_{\mu\nu}(\tau) \exp\left(-i\tau\lambda\right) = f_{\mu\nu}(\lambda)$$

Q.E.D

(10.2.36)

Another useful result may be derived from Lemma 2. Before we do so, however, we need the following

Definition 15: Let $\{X_\mu(t): t \in N, \mu = 1, 2, \ldots, m\}$ be a set of jointly covariance stationary stochastic processes. Let $f_{\mu\nu}(\lambda)$, $\mu, \nu = 1, 2, \ldots, m$, be their associated (cross) spectral densities. The matrix

$$f(\lambda) = [f_{\mu\nu}(\lambda)] \qquad \mu, \nu = 1, 2, \ldots, m \tag{10.2.37}$$

is said to be the spectral matrix associated with the set.

We may now prove

Lemma 3: Let

$$f(\lambda) = [f_{\mu\nu}(\lambda)] \tag{10.2.38}$$

be a spectral matrix as in Definition 15 and suppose that, in addition, the $f_{\mu\nu}(\cdot)$ satisfy the conditions of Lemma 2. Then $f(\lambda)$ is a positive semidefinite Hermitian matrix for every $\lambda \in (-\pi, \pi)$.

PROOF: We first show that $f(\lambda)$ is a Hermitian matrix. Now, from (10.2.32) and (10.2.26) we obtain for any (μ, ν)

$$\overline{f_{\mu\nu}(\lambda)} = \frac{1}{2\pi} \sum_{\tau=-\infty}^{\infty} \overline{K_{\mu\nu}(\tau)} \exp\left(i\tau\lambda\right)$$

$$= \frac{1}{2\pi} \sum_{\tau=-\infty}^{\infty} K_{\nu\mu}(-\tau) \exp\left(i\tau\lambda\right) = \frac{1}{2\pi} \sum_{\tau=-\infty}^{\infty} K_{\nu\mu}(\tau) \exp\left(-i\tau\lambda\right)$$

$$= f_{\nu\mu}(\lambda) \tag{10.2.39}$$

This shows that

$$\overline{f(\lambda)}' = f(\lambda) \tag{10.2.40}$$

and thus that $f(\lambda)$ is Hermitian.

To show that it is positive semidefinite, we show that for any (complex) vector ζ,

$$\bar{\zeta}' f(\lambda)\zeta \geq 0 \tag{10.2.41}$$

Now if we put

$$f_{\mu\nu}(\lambda) = c_{\mu\nu}^*(\lambda) + i q_{\mu\nu}^*(\lambda) \qquad \mu, \nu = 1, 2, \ldots, m \tag{10.2.42}$$

where the $c_{\mu\nu}^*(\cdot)$ and $q_{\mu\nu}^*(\cdot)$ are real functions, we have

$$f(\lambda) = C^*(\lambda) + iQ^*(\lambda) \tag{10.2.43}$$

where

$$C^*(\lambda) = [c_{\mu\nu}^*(\lambda)] \qquad Q^*(\lambda) = [q_{\mu\nu}^*(\lambda)] \qquad \mu, \nu = 1, 2, \ldots, m \tag{10.2.44}$$

Since f is a Hermitian matrix, it follows that C^* and Q^* are, respectively, symmetric and skew-symmetric matrices for every $\lambda \in (-\pi, \pi)$.

Thus if ζ is any complex vector

$$\bar{\zeta}' f(\lambda)\zeta = \zeta_1' C^* \zeta_1 + \zeta_2' C^* \zeta_2 + 2\zeta_2' Q^* \zeta_1 + i(\zeta_1' Q^* \zeta_1 + \zeta_2' Q^* \zeta_2) \tag{10.2.45}$$

where

$$\bar{\zeta} = \zeta_1 + i\zeta_2 \tag{10.2.46}$$

the ζ_j, $j = 1, 2$, being real vectors.

Since Q^* is skew symmetric, it follows that

$$(\zeta_j' Q^* \zeta_j)' = \zeta_j' Q^{*\prime} \zeta_j = -(\zeta_j' Q^* \zeta_j) \qquad j = 1, 2 \tag{10.2.47}$$

Since $\zeta_j' Q^* \zeta_j$ is a scalar, we conclude that

$$\zeta_j' Q^* \zeta_j = 0 \qquad j = 1, 2 \tag{10.2.48}$$

and, also, from (10.2.48) and (10.2.45), that

$$s(\lambda) = \bar{\zeta}' f(\lambda)\zeta \tag{10.2.49}$$

is a real-valued function of λ.

Now the matrix ΔF of (10.2.20) is positive semidefinite from Theorem 1. Thus for any (complex) vector ζ,

$$\bar{\zeta}' \Delta F \zeta \geq 0 \tag{10.2.50}$$

Moreover, from the conditions of the lemma, the elements of ΔF have the representation

$$\Delta F_{\mu\nu} = \int_\alpha^\beta f_{\mu\nu}(\lambda)\, d\lambda \tag{10.2.51}$$

where (α, β) is any nondegenerate subinterval of $[-\pi, \pi]$ and the $f_{\mu\nu}(\cdot)$ are continuous functions of bounded variation. In view of (10.2.49), (10.2.50), and (10.2.51), we obtain

$$\int_\alpha^\beta s(\lambda)\, d\lambda \geq 0 \tag{10.2.52}$$

where $s(\cdot)$ is defined in (10.2.49) and (α, β) is any nondegenerate subinterval of $[-\pi, \pi]$.

To complete the proof, we must show that (10.2.52) implies

$$s(\lambda) \geq 0 \qquad \text{for any} \qquad \lambda \in (-\pi, \pi) \qquad\qquad (10.2.53)$$

Thus suppose not; that is, suppose that there exists a $\lambda_0 \in (-\pi, \pi)$ for which

$$s(\lambda_0) < 0 \qquad\qquad (10.2.54)$$

Since $s(\cdot)$ is continuous—in virtue of the continuity of the $f_{\mu\nu}(\cdot)$—there exists an interval about λ_0, say (α_0, β_0) where $\alpha_0 = -\delta + \lambda_0$, $\beta_0 = \lambda_0 + \delta$ and $\delta > 0$, such that

$$s(\lambda) < 0 \qquad \text{for} \qquad \lambda \in (\alpha_0, \beta_0) \qquad\qquad (10.2.55)$$

Then

$$\int_{\alpha_0}^{\beta_0} s(\lambda) \, d\lambda < 0 \qquad\qquad (10.2.56)$$

which contradicts (10.2.52)   Q.E.D.

Corollary: The spectral densities and cross-spectral densities of any two jointly covariance stationary processes $\{X_\mu(t): t \in N\}$, $\{X_\nu(t): t \in N\}$ satisfy the *coherency conditions*

$$f_{\mu\mu}(\lambda) f_{\nu\nu}(\lambda) \geq |f_{\mu\nu}(\lambda)|^2 \qquad\qquad (10.2.57)$$

PROOF: Since $f(\lambda)$ is a positive semidefinite Hermitian matrix, it follows that every submatrix of the form

$$f^{(\mu\nu)} = \begin{bmatrix} f_{\mu\mu}(\lambda) & f_{\mu\nu}(\lambda) \\ f_{\nu\mu}(\lambda) & f_{\nu\nu}(\lambda) \end{bmatrix} \qquad\qquad (10.2.58)$$

is also a positive semidefinite Hermitian matrix. To see this, one need only take in the proof of the Lemma 3 a vector ζ, all of whose elements are zero except for its μth and νth elements. But a positive semidefinite Hermitian matrix has a real and nonnegative determinant. Thus

$$f_{\mu\mu}(\lambda) f_{\nu\nu}(\lambda) - f_{\mu\nu}(\lambda) f_{\nu\mu}(\lambda) \geq 0 \qquad\qquad (10.2.59)$$

In view of (10.2.39), (10.2.59) may be written as

$$f_{\mu\mu}(\lambda) f_{\nu\nu}(\lambda) \geq |f_{\mu\nu}(\lambda)|^2 \qquad \lambda \in (-\pi, \pi) \qquad\qquad \text{Q.E.D.}$$

$$(10.2.60)$$

Definition 16: The *coherency* (function) between two jointly covariance stationary stochastic processes $\{X_\mu(t): t \in N\}$, $\{X_\nu(t): t \in N\}$ admitting of spectral and cross-spectral densities is given by

$$\gamma(\lambda) = \frac{|f_{\mu\nu}(\lambda)|^2}{f_{\mu\mu}(\lambda) f_{\nu\nu}(\lambda)} \qquad\qquad (10.2.61)$$

Remark 11: The coherency function as defined by (10.2.61) is very much like the square of the correlation coefficient between two random variables. Note that from (10.2.60) and (10.2.61)

$$0 \le \gamma(\lambda) \le 1 \tag{10.2.62}$$

Notice, also, that if $\gamma_{\mu\nu}(\lambda)$ is the coherency function between the μth and νth processes, the coherency function between $\{X_\nu(t): t \in N\}$ and $\{X_\mu(t): t \in N\}$ would be defined as

$$\gamma_{\nu\mu}(\lambda) = \frac{|f_{\nu\mu}(\lambda)|^2}{f_{\nu\nu}(\lambda)f_{\mu\mu}(\lambda)} \tag{10.2.63}$$

In virtue of (10.2.39), we see that $\gamma_{\nu\mu}(\lambda) = \gamma_{\mu\nu}(\lambda)$, which justifies our leaving out the subscripts in (10.2.61). Thus the result from probability distribution theory that the correlation ρ_{xy} between the random variables x and y is equal to ρ_{yx}, the correlation between y and x, is preserved here when dealing with the coherency function.

Before concluding, an additional bit of terminology is needed.

Definition 17: The real-valued functions $c_{\mu\nu}^*(\cdot)$ and $q_{\mu\nu}^*(\cdot)$ are called, respectively, the *cospectral* and *quadrature spectral densities* of the jointly covariance stationary stochastic processes $\{X_\mu(t): t \in N\}$ and $\{X_\nu(t): t \in N\}$.

Remark 12: In view of the fact that the matrices $C^*(\lambda)$ and $Q^*(\lambda)$ of (10.2.44) are symmetric and skew symmetric respectively, we conclude that

$$c_{\mu\nu}^*(\lambda) = c_{\nu\mu}^*(\lambda) \tag{10.2.64}$$

$$q_{\mu\nu}^*(\lambda) = -q_{\nu\mu}^*(\lambda) \tag{10.2.65}$$

Note, further, that in virtue of (10.2.65)

$$q_{\mu\mu}^*(\lambda) = 0 \tag{10.2.66}$$

and thus that the spectral density of any covariance stationary process is always real. We had actually shown this in the previous chapter as well.

In order to gain an intuitive insight into the informational content of such quantities as the coherency function cospectral or quadrature spectral densities of jointly covariance stationary stochastic processes, it would be best to examine the case of real stochastic processes. Before we do so, however, let us briefly summarize the development of this section.

We have seen that

i. if we deal with two arbitrary covariance stationary stochastic processes, this does not automatically imply that the two processes are jointly covariance stationary in the sense that their cross-covariance function depends only on the difference in the "time indices" of the two processes.

ii. if we are dealing with an arbitrary but finite set of m stochastic processes such that they are jointly covariance stationary and they possess spectral and cross-spectral densities that are continuous functions of bounded variation on $[-\pi, \pi]$, then the covariance kernels $K_{\mu\nu}(\cdot)$ and the spectral and cross-spectral densities $f_{\mu\nu}(\cdot)$ form pairs of Fourier transforms.

iii. the spectral matrix of the set of jointly covariance stationary processes $\{X_{\mu}(t): t \in N, \mu = 1, 2, \ldots, m\}$ is a positive semidefinite Hermitian matrix. The matrix of covariance kernels, however, is generally neither positive semidefinite nor Hermitian.

iv. finally, using the properties of the spectral matrix given in iii we have defined the coherency function, the cospectral and quadrature spectral densities and their relation to the real and imaginary parts of the cross spectrum of any two jointly covariance stationary stochastic processes.

REAL PROCESSES

In what follows we shall deal specifically with real stochastic processes and essentially specialize the results of the discussion above. No new results will be derived, our objective being to obtain an intuitive insight into the informational content of such quantities as the cross spectrum, cospectrum, quadrature spectrum, and coherency function of jointly covariance stationary stochastic processes.

In the following material, we shall assume that all processes considered are jointly covariance stationary and that they possess spectral and cross-spectral densities that are continuous functions of bounded variation.

Thus suppose that $\{X_{\mu}(t): t \in N, \mu = 1, 2, \ldots, m\}$ is such a set. Then each is covariance stationary, and we have seen in the preceding chapter that each has the spectral representation

$$X_{\mu}(t) = \int_{-\pi}^{\pi} \exp(i\lambda t) \, dZ_{\mu}(\lambda) \qquad \mu = 1, 2, \ldots, m \qquad (10.2.67)$$

which can be reduced to

$$X_{\mu}(t) = \int_{0}^{\pi} \cos \lambda t \, du_{\mu}(\lambda) + \int_{0}^{\pi} \sin \lambda t \, dv_{\mu}(\lambda) \qquad \mu = 1, 2, \ldots, m \qquad (10.2.68)$$

where the $u_{\mu}(\cdot)$, $v_{\mu}(\cdot)$ are stochastic processes defined on $(0, \pi)$ with mean function zero and uncorrelated increments. It may also be shown that when the representations in (10.2.68) refer to jointly covariance stationary processes, then the $u_{\mu}(\cdot)$, $v_{\mu}(\cdot)$ satisfy the conditions

$$E[du_{\mu}(\lambda) \, du_{\nu}(\theta)] = E[dv_{\mu}(\lambda) \, dv_{\nu}(\theta)] = E[du_{\mu}(\lambda) \, dv_{\nu}(\theta)] = 0$$
$$\text{for} \quad \lambda \neq \theta \quad \text{and} \quad \mu, \nu = 1, 2, \ldots, m \qquad (10.2.69)$$

The u and v processes can be extended to the domain $(-\pi, \pi)$ by the definition

$$u_{\mu}(-\lambda) = u_{\mu}(\lambda), \quad v_{\mu}(-\lambda) = -v_{\mu}(\lambda) \qquad \mu = 1, 2, \ldots, m \qquad (10.2.70)$$

The connection to the Z processes of (10.2.67) is given by

$$Z_\mu(\lambda) = \tfrac{1}{2}[u_\mu(\lambda) - iv_\mu(\lambda)] \qquad \mu = 1, 2, \ldots, m \tag{10.2.71}$$

Notice that

$$dZ_\mu(-\lambda) = \overline{dZ_\mu(\lambda)} \qquad \mu = 1, 2, \ldots, m \tag{10.2.72}$$

and that the restrictions (10.2.69) imply

$$E[dZ_\mu(\lambda)\,\overline{dZ_\nu(\theta)}] = 0 \qquad \lambda \neq \theta$$
$$\mu, \nu = 1, 2, \ldots, m \tag{10.2.73}$$

as required by joint stationarity. Hence the cross spectrum of any two series, say the μth and the νth, obeys

$$f_{\mu\nu}(-\lambda) = E[dZ_\mu(-\lambda)\,\overline{dZ_\nu(-\lambda)}] = E[\overline{dZ_\nu(\lambda)}\,dZ_\mu(\lambda)] = f_{\nu\mu}(\lambda) \tag{10.2.74}$$

From Lemma 2 we conclude therefore that

$$\overline{f_{\mu\nu}(\lambda)} = f_{\mu\nu}(-\lambda) = f_{\nu\mu}(\lambda) \tag{10.2.75}$$

Since, in general,

$$f_{\mu\nu}(\lambda) = c_{\mu\nu}^*(\lambda) + iq_{\mu\nu}^*(\lambda) \tag{10.2.76}$$

such that

$$c_{\mu\nu}^*(\lambda) = c_{\nu\mu}^*(\lambda) \qquad q_{\mu\nu}^*(\lambda) = -q_{\nu\mu}^*(\lambda) \tag{10.2.77}$$

we further conclude that (for real processes)

$$c_{\mu\nu}^*(-\lambda) = c_{\mu\nu}^*(\lambda) \qquad q_{\mu\nu}^*(-\lambda) = -q_{\mu\nu}^*(\lambda) \tag{10.2.78}$$

Since the relations (10.2.77) and (10.2.78) are valid for any (μ, ν), it follows that in dealing with real stochastic processes we need only define the relevant spectral and cross-spectral densities on $(0, \pi)$ instead of $(-\pi, \pi)$.

This is, of course, apparent from the representation given in (10.2.68). In terms of the processes $u_\mu(\cdot)$, $v_\mu(\cdot)$ appearing there, we may obtain the spectral density of the μth process as

$$E[du_\mu(\lambda)du_\mu(\lambda)] = E[dv_\mu(\lambda)\,dv_\mu(\lambda)] = g_{\mu\mu}(\lambda)\,d\lambda \tag{10.2.79}$$

where now $g_{\mu\mu}(\cdot)$ is defined on $(0, \pi)$. Since

$$f_{\mu\mu}(\lambda)\,d\lambda = E[Z_\mu(\lambda)\,\overline{dZ_\mu(\lambda)}]$$
$$= \tfrac{1}{4}E[du_\mu(\lambda)\,du_\mu(\lambda) + dv_\mu(\lambda)\,dv_\mu(\lambda)] = \tfrac{1}{2}g_{\mu\mu}(\lambda)\,d\lambda \tag{10.2.80}$$

we conclude that

$$g_{\mu\mu}(\lambda) = 2f_{\mu\mu}(\lambda) \tag{10.2.81}$$

This is also consistent with (10.2.76) and (10.2.78), for $q_{\mu\mu}^*(\lambda) \equiv 0$. This being so, the relation between $g_{\mu\mu}(\cdot)$ and $f_{\mu\mu}(\cdot)$ is best expressed not by (10.2.81) but by

$$g_{\mu\mu}(\lambda) = f_{\mu\mu}(\lambda) + f_{\mu\mu}(-\lambda) \qquad \lambda \in (0, \pi) \tag{10.2.82}$$

Because, as we observed earlier, the cross spectrum of two jointly covariance stationary stochastic processes need only be defined on $(0, \pi)$, let us use $g_{\mu\nu}(\cdot)$ to denote the cross spectrum of the two series so defined. Since, in general, $g_{\mu\nu}(\cdot)$ is a complex-valued function, we may represent it by

$$g_{\mu\nu}(\lambda) = c_{\mu\nu}(\lambda) + iq_{\mu\nu}(\lambda) \qquad \lambda \in (0, \pi)$$
$$\mu, \nu = 1, 2, \ldots, m \tag{10.2.83}$$

where $c_{\mu\nu}(\cdot)$, $q_{\mu\nu}(\cdot)$ are real valued.

It may also be shown that, in terms of the representation in (10.2.68), the processes $du_\mu(\cdot)$, $dv_\mu(\cdot)$ satisfy

$$E[du_\mu(\lambda)\, du_\nu(\lambda)] = E[dv_\mu(\lambda)\, dv_\nu(\lambda)] = c_{\mu\nu}(\lambda)\, d\lambda \tag{10.2.84}$$

$$E[du_\mu(\lambda)\, dv_\nu(\lambda)] = -E[du_\nu(\lambda)\, dv_\mu(\lambda)] = q_{\mu\nu}(\lambda)\, d\lambda \tag{10.2.85}$$

We may now ask: What is the connection between $g_{\mu\nu}(\cdot)$ as defined in (10.2.83), (10.2.84), and (10.2.85) and

$$f_{\mu\nu}(\lambda)\, d\lambda = E[dZ_\mu(\lambda)\, \overline{dZ_\nu(\lambda)}] \tag{10.2.86}$$

which is defined on $(-\pi, \pi)$?

Carrying out the operation in the right-hand member of (10.2.86), we find

$$\begin{aligned} E[dZ_\mu(\lambda)\, \overline{dZ_\nu(\lambda)}] &= \tfrac{1}{4}E[du_\mu(\lambda)\, du_\nu(\lambda) + dv_\mu(\lambda)\, dv_\nu(\lambda) \\ &\quad + i[du_\mu(\lambda)\, dv_\nu(\lambda) - du_\nu(\lambda)\, dv_\mu(\lambda)]\} \\ &= \tfrac{1}{4}[2c_{\mu\nu}(\lambda) + 2iq_{\mu\nu}(\lambda)] = \tfrac{1}{2}g_{\mu\nu}(\lambda) \end{aligned} \tag{10.2.87}$$

Hence we conclude that

$$g_{\mu\nu}(\lambda) = 2f_{\mu\nu}(\lambda) \qquad \lambda \in (0, \pi) \tag{10.2.88}$$

Equating real and imaginary parts, we find

$$c_{\mu\nu}(\lambda) = 2c_{\mu\nu}^*(\lambda) \qquad q_{\mu\nu}(\lambda) = 2q_{\mu\nu}^*(\lambda) \tag{10.2.89}$$

In view of (10.2.77) and (10.2.78), however, a more meaningful way of representing the relations in (10.2.89) is

$$c_{\mu\nu}(\lambda) = c_{\mu\nu}^*(\lambda) + c_{\mu\nu}^*(-\lambda) \qquad q_{\mu\nu}(\lambda) = q_{\mu\nu}^*(\lambda) - q_{\mu\nu}^*(-\lambda) \tag{10.2.90}$$

Thus the relation between $g_{\mu\nu}(\cdot)$ and $f_{\mu\nu}(\cdot)$, for all μ, ν, is best represented as

$$g_{\mu\nu}(\lambda) = f_{\mu\nu}(\lambda) + \overline{f_{\mu\nu}(-\lambda)} \qquad \lambda \in (0, \pi) \tag{10.2.91}$$

In terms of the development above, note that the coherency function of two real processes is defined on $(0, \pi)$ and is given by

$$\gamma_{\mu\nu}(\lambda) = \frac{|g_{\mu\nu}(\lambda)|^2}{g_{\mu\mu}(\lambda)g_{\nu\nu}(\lambda)} = \frac{|c_{\mu\nu}(\lambda)|^2 + |q_{\mu\nu}(\lambda)|^2}{c_{\mu\mu}(\lambda)c_{\nu\nu}(\lambda)} \tag{10.2.92}$$

Now we are ready to answer the question: What is the informational content of the cospectrum $c_{\mu\nu}(\cdot)$ and the quadrature spectrum $q_{\mu\nu}(\cdot)$?

Quite clearly, in view of (10.2.68), (10.2.84), and (10.2.85), we see that $c_{\mu\nu}(\lambda)$ represents the covariance of the "in phase" components of frequency λ in the two processes $\{X_\mu(t), X_\nu(t): t \in N\}$, while $q_{\mu\nu}(\cdot)$ represents the covariance of components of frequency λ that are out of phase by an angle of $\pi/2 = 90°$—or components that are "in quadrature." In this connection, note that

$$\cos\left(\theta - \frac{\pi}{2}\right) = \sin\theta \qquad \sin\left(\theta + \frac{\pi}{2}\right) = \cos\theta \tag{10.2.93}$$

so that the cosine "leads" the sine function by 90°. To be precise, $c_{\mu\nu}(\lambda)$ is the covariance of the (random) amplitude of components of the form $\cos\lambda(t + \tau)\cos\lambda t$ or $\sin\lambda(t + \tau)\sin\lambda t$, and $q_{\mu\nu}(\lambda)$ is the covariance of the (random) amplitudes of components of the form $\cos\lambda(t + \tau)\sin\lambda t$—hence the terms "in phase" and "in quadrature" employed above.

Moreover, since

$$K_{\mu\nu}(\tau) = \int_{-\pi}^{\pi} \exp(i\lambda\tau)f_{\mu\nu}(\lambda)\,d\lambda \tag{10.2.94}$$

we have

$$K_{\mu\nu}(0) = \int_{-\pi}^{\pi} f_{\mu\nu}(\lambda)\,d\lambda \tag{10.2.95}$$

so that the cross spectrum of the two series may be thought of as apportioning the covariance of the two random *variables* $X_\mu(t)$, $X_\nu(t)$ among the harmonic components of their spectral representation having frequency λ.

Also, since

$$f_{\mu\nu}(\lambda) = c_{\mu\nu}^*(\lambda) + iq_{\mu\nu}^*(\lambda) \tag{10.2.96}$$

if the two processes are real, then from (10.2.78) we have

$$\int_{-\pi}^{\pi} q_{\mu\nu}^*(\lambda)\,d\lambda = 0 \tag{10.2.97}$$

Thus, for real processes (10.2.95) reduces to

$$K_{\mu\nu}(0) = \int_{0}^{\pi} c_{\mu\nu}(\lambda)\,d\lambda \tag{10.2.98}$$

so that the cospectrum simply gives a covariance decomposition as indicated just after (10.2.95).

Noting that

$$K_{\mu v}(\tau) = \int_0^\pi \cos \lambda\tau c_{\mu v}(\lambda)\, d\lambda + \int_0^\pi \sin \lambda\tau q_{\mu v}(\lambda)\, d\lambda^5 \qquad (10.2.99)$$

we see that the quadrature spectrum does make a contribution in the decomposition of *lag* covariances ($\tau > 0$).

Finally, it is evident from (10.2.92) that the coherency function gives information regarding the correlation of in phase and in quadrature components of the two series (at given frequency).

CROSS SPECTRA AND FILTERS

Let us return to our discussion of filters and review the problem in the context of our new concepts and terminology. Suppose that we have a (complex) covariance stationary process $\{X(t): t \in N\}$ with mean function identically zero. Let this serve as an input process in a linear time invariant filter to produce the output process $\{Y(t): t \in N\}$. The first problem that arises is: Are the two series jointly covariance stationary? This is answered by

Lemma 4: Let $\{X(t): t \in N\}$ be a covariance stationary process serving as an input function in the linear time invariant filter with kernel

$$\phi = \{\phi_\tau: \tau - 0, \pm 1, \pm 2, \ldots\} \qquad (10.2.100)$$

Let $\{Y(t): t \in N\}$ be the resulting output process. Then the latter is also covariance stationary and, moreover, the two processes are jointly covariance stationary.

PROOF: Let

$$\Phi(\lambda) = \sum_{\tau=-\infty}^{\infty} \phi_\tau \exp(-i\lambda\tau) \qquad (10.2.101)$$

be the frequency response function of the filter. Then the Y process has the spectral representation

$$Y(t) = \int_{-\pi}^{\pi} \exp(i\lambda\tau)\Phi(\lambda)\, dZ_x(\lambda) \qquad (10.2.102)$$

where $Z_x(\cdot)$ is the process associated with the spectral representation of the X process. Since the latter is covariance stationary, we have

$$K_{yy}(t + \tau, t) = \int_{-\pi}^{\pi}\int_{-\pi}^{\pi} \exp(i\lambda\tau) \exp[it(\lambda - \theta)]\Phi(\lambda)\overline{\Phi(\theta)}E[dZ_x(\lambda)\, \overline{dZ_x(\theta)}]$$

$$= \int_{-\pi}^{\pi} \exp(i\lambda\tau)|\Phi(\lambda)|^2 f_{xx}(\lambda)\, d\lambda = K_{yy}(\tau) \qquad (10.2.103)$$

---

[5] If we are dealing with real processes, is the autocovariance matrix $[K_{\mu v}(\tau)]$ symmetric? Compare your answer with the discussion of equations (10.2.25) through (10.2.27) and footnote 3.

where $f_{xx}(\cdot)$ is the spectral density of the X process. The covariance stationarity of the Y process is immediate from (10.2.103). To show joint covariance stationarity, we proceed as follows.

$$K_{xy}(t + \tau, t) = \int_{-\pi}^{\pi} \int_{-\pi}^{\pi} \exp(i\lambda\tau) \exp[it(\lambda - \theta)]\overline{\Phi}(\theta)E[dZ_x(\lambda)\,\overline{dZ_x(\theta)}]$$

$$= \int_{-\pi}^{\pi} \exp(i\lambda\tau)\overline{\Phi}(\lambda)f_{xx}(\lambda)\,d\lambda = K_{xy}(\tau) \qquad \text{Q.E.D.}$$

$$(10.2.104)$$

Earlier we saw that the relation between $f_{xx}(\cdot)$ and $f_{yy}(\cdot)$, the spectral densities of the input and output processes, is given by

$$f_{yy}(\lambda) = \Psi(\lambda)f_{xx}(\lambda) \qquad (10.2.105)$$

where $\Psi(\cdot)$ is the transfer function of the filter. But we still have the problem of determining the cross spectrum of the two series. This is solved by

Lemma 5: Let $\{X(t), Y(t): t \in N\}$ be two processes as in Lemma 4. Then their cross-spectral density is given by

$$f_{xy}(\lambda) = \overline{\Phi}(\lambda)f_{xx}(\lambda) \qquad (10.2.106)$$

PROOF: From (10.2.102) we see that the Y process has the spectral representation

$$Y(t) = \int_{-\pi}^{\pi} \exp(i\lambda t)\,dZ_y(\lambda) \qquad (10.2.107)$$

where

$$dZ_y(\lambda) = \Phi(\lambda)\,dZ_x(\lambda) \qquad (10.2.108)$$

It follows that

$$f_{xy}(\lambda)\,d\lambda = E[dZ_x(\lambda)\,\overline{dZ_y(\lambda)}] = \overline{\Phi}(\lambda)f_{xx}(\lambda)\,d\lambda \qquad \text{Q.E.D.}$$

$$(10.2.109)$$

If we represent the complex-valued function $\Phi(\lambda)$ by a pair of real-valued functions $\Phi_1(\lambda)$, $\Phi_2(\lambda)$, we have

$$\Phi(\lambda) = \Phi_1(\lambda) + i\Phi_2(\lambda) \qquad (10.2.110)$$

Then the cross spectrum has the representation

$$f_{xy}(\lambda) = \Phi_1(\lambda)f_{xx}(\lambda) - i\Phi_2(\lambda)f_{xx}(\lambda) \qquad (10.2.111)$$

Thus the cospectral and quadrature spectral densities of the output series are given by

$$c_{xy}^*(\lambda) = \Phi_1(\lambda)f_{xx}(\lambda) \qquad (10.2.112)$$

$$q_{xy}^*(\lambda) = -\Phi_2(\lambda)f_{xx}(\lambda) \qquad (10.2.113)$$

Incidentally, note that the input and output series satisfy the coherency relation of Lemma 2. In particular, we find

$$\gamma(\lambda) = \frac{|f_{xy}(\lambda)|^2}{f_{xx}(\lambda)f_{yy}(\lambda)} = \frac{\Psi(\lambda)|f_{xx}(\lambda)|^2}{\Psi(\lambda)|f_{xx}(\lambda)|^2} = 1 \qquad (10.2.114)$$

This is, of course, not surprising, for the elements of the output process are simply (infinite) linear combinations of the elements of the inputs. From elementary probability theory we know that if y is a linear function of the random variable x, then their correlation coefficient ρ_{xy} is unity.

In dealing with filters earlier in this chapter, several concepts were introduced to characterize the filter, such as its frequency response and transfer functions and the gain and phase angle.

The transfer function and gain of the filter can easily be obtained from the spectral densities of the input and output processes. The same cannot be said about the frequency response function. However, this is not a particularly vexing problem, for it is unlikely that we would want to estimate it in an econometric context.

We would, however, invariably be interested in the phase angle of the filter, and thus it is useful to establish its relation, if any, to the (cross) spectral densities of the two series.

We recall from equation (10.1.25) that the phase angle is defined by

$$\alpha(\lambda) = \tan^{-1}\left[\frac{\Phi_2(\lambda)}{\Phi_1(\lambda)}\right] \qquad (10.2.115)$$

Thus it is an immediate consequence of (10.2.112) and (10.2.113) that

$$\alpha(\lambda) = \tan^{-1}\left[\frac{q_{yx}^*(\lambda)}{c_{yx}^*(\lambda)}\right] = \tan^{-1}\left[-\frac{q_{xy}^*(\lambda)}{c_{xy}^*(\lambda)}\right] \qquad (10.2.116)$$

where $\tan^{-1}(\cdot)$ is the inverse tangent function.

All the relationships obtained above are defined over the set $\{\lambda : \lambda \in (-\pi, \pi)\}$. However, if the input process $\{X(t) : t \in N\}$ is real and the kernel of the filter is real, then the output process $\{Y(t) : t \in N\}$ is also real. Therefore the various quantities of interest reduce to

$$g_{yy}(\lambda) = f_{xx}(\lambda)\Psi(\lambda) + f_{xx}(-\lambda)\Psi(-\lambda) \qquad \lambda \in (0, \pi) \qquad (10.2.117)$$

$$g_{xy}(\lambda) = f_{xx}(\lambda)\overline{\Phi}(\lambda) + f_{xx}(-\lambda)\Phi(-\lambda) \qquad \lambda \in (0, \pi) \qquad (10.2.118)$$

$$c_{xy}(\lambda) = f_{xx}(\lambda)\Phi_1(\lambda) + f_{xx}(-\lambda)\Phi_1(-\lambda) \qquad \lambda \in (0, \pi) \qquad (10.2.119)$$

$$q_{xy}(\lambda) = f_{xx}(-\lambda)\Phi_2(-\lambda) - f_{xx}(\lambda)\Phi_2(\lambda) \qquad \lambda \in (0, \pi) \qquad (10.2.120)$$

$$\alpha(\lambda) = \tan^{-1}\left[\frac{q_{yx}(\lambda)}{c_{yx}(\lambda)}\right] = \tan^{-1}\left[-\frac{q_{xy}(\lambda)}{c_{xy}(\lambda)}\right] \qquad \lambda \in (0, \pi) \qquad (10.2.121)$$

In conclusion, let us note that in any estimation problem, whether or not it involves a filter, we need only estimate the relevant spectral and cross-spectral densities provided the series we are dealing with are covariance stationary. When we have done so, we have extracted from our sample (or record) as much information as it can give us about the second moment properties of the series.

Our next task is to show how one can estimate, at least consistently, the elements of the spectral matrix, that is, the relevant cross-spectral densities.

10.3 ESTIMATION OF THE CROSS SPECTRUM

Suppose that we have a record of length n on the jointly covariance stationary processes $\{X_\mu(t): \mu = 1, 2, \ldots, m\}$. Thus our record consists of the observations $\{X_\mu(t): \mu = 1, 2, \ldots, m, t = 1, 2, \ldots, n\}$.

A natural extension of the considerations that led to the modified periodogram as an estimator of the spectrum leads to the following estimator for the cross spectrum between the μth and νth processes:

$$P_{\mu\nu}^{(n)}(\lambda) = \frac{1}{2\pi n}\left[\sum_{t=1}^{n} X_\mu(t)\exp(-it\lambda)\right]\overline{\left[\sum_{s=1}^{n} X_\nu(s)\exp(-is\lambda)\right]}$$

$$\mu, \nu = 1, 2, \ldots, m \qquad (10.3.1)$$

Notice that the superscript in (10.3.1) denotes the length of the record. Notice, also, that putting $\mu = \nu$ yields the modified periodogram considered in the previous chapter. Unfortunately, however, just as in the case of the spectral estimation problem, the estimator here is asymptotically unbiased but inconsistent.

Asymptotic unbiasedness is easy to show. Thus we have

Lemma 6: Let $\{X_\mu(t): t = 1, 2, \ldots, n, \mu = 1, 2, \ldots, m\}$ be a record (sample) of length n from a set of m jointly covariance stationary stochastic processes such that their covariance kernels have the property

$$\sum_{\tau=-\infty}^{\infty} |K_{\mu\nu}(\tau)| < \infty \qquad \mu, \nu = 1, 2, \ldots, m \qquad (10.3.2)$$

Then

$$P_{\mu\nu}^{(n)}(\lambda) = \frac{1}{2\pi n}\left[\sum_{t=1}^{n} X_\mu(t)\exp(-i\lambda t)\right]\overline{\left[\sum_{s=1}^{n} X_\nu(s)\exp(-i\lambda s)\right]}$$

$$\mu, \nu = 1, 2, \ldots, m \qquad (10.3.3)$$

are asymptotically unbiased estimators respectively of the cross-spectral densities $f_{\mu\nu}(\cdot)$, $\mu, \nu = 1, 2, \ldots, m$.

PROOF: Taking expectations and rearranging terms in (10.3.3), we find

$$E[P_{\mu\nu}^{(n)}(\lambda)] = \frac{1}{2\pi n} \sum_{t=1}^{n} \sum_{s=1}^{n} E[X_\mu(t)\overline{X_\nu(s)}] \exp[-i\lambda(t-s)]$$

$$= \frac{1}{2\pi n} \sum_{t=1}^{n} \sum_{s=1}^{n} K_{\mu\nu}(t-s) \exp[-i\lambda(t-s)]$$

$$= \frac{1}{2\pi} \sum_{\tau=-n}^{n} K_{\mu\nu}(\tau) \exp(-i\lambda\tau)\left(1 - \frac{|\tau|}{n}\right) \qquad (10.3.4)$$

where, after the last equality sign, we have put $\tau = t - s$. By the condition in (10.3.2), the covariance kernels form absolutely convergent series and thus the right-hand side of (10.3.4)—being essentially a partial Cèsaro sum of a convergent series—converges as well. Hence we obtain

$$\lim_{n \to \infty} E[P_{\mu\nu}^{(n)}(\lambda)] = \frac{1}{2\pi} \sum_{\tau=-\infty}^{\infty} K_{\mu\nu}(\tau) \exp(-i\lambda\tau) = f_{\mu\nu}(\lambda) \qquad \text{Q.E.D.} \\ (10.3.5)$$

Inconsistency is a little more difficult to prove, but the following lemma and its somewhat elliptic proof will serve our purposes.

Lemma 7: The modified cross periodogram—given in (10.3.3)—is an inconsistent estimator of the cross-spectral density $f_{\mu\nu}(\cdot)$; moreover, its asymptotic variance is given by

$$\text{Var}\,[P_{\mu\nu}^{(n)}(\lambda)] = \frac{A}{\pi} + \text{terms of order } \frac{1}{n^\alpha} \qquad \alpha > 0 \qquad (10.3.6)$$

where

$$A = \int_{-\pi}^{\pi} f_{\mu\mu}(z) f_{\nu\nu}(z)\, dz \qquad (10.3.7)$$

PROOF: Rearranging terms in (10.3.3), we obtain

$$P_{\mu\nu}^{(n)}(\lambda) = \frac{1}{2\pi n} \sum_{t=1}^{n} \sum_{s=1}^{n} X_\mu(t)\overline{X_\nu(s)} \exp[-i\lambda(t-s)]$$

$$= \frac{1}{2\pi} \sum_{\tau=-n+1}^{n-1} \hat{K}_{\mu\nu}(\tau) \exp(-i\lambda\tau) \qquad (10.3.8)$$

where we have put $\tau = t - s$, and

$$\hat{K}_{\mu\nu}(\tau) = \frac{1}{n} \sum_{s=1}^{n-\tau} X_\mu(s+\tau)\overline{X_\nu(s)} \qquad \text{if } \tau \geq 0$$

$$= \frac{1}{n} \sum_{s=-\tau+1}^{n} X_\mu(s)\overline{X_\nu(s+\tau)} \qquad \text{if } \tau < 0 \qquad (10.3.9)$$

Now, in Jenkins [21, Ch. 18] it is shown that, for $\tau_2 \geq \tau_1$,

$$\lim_{n \to \infty} n \, \text{Cov} \, [\hat{K}_{\mu\nu}(\tau_1), \hat{K}_{\mu\nu}(\tau_2)]$$

$$= 2\pi \int_{-\pi}^{\pi} \{f_{\mu\mu}(z)f_{\nu\nu}(z) \exp \left[-iz(\tau_2 - \tau_1)\right] + f_{\mu\nu}^2(z) \exp \left[-iz(\tau_1 + \tau_2)\right]\} \, dz$$

$$= 2\pi B(\tau_1, \tau_2) \tag{10.3.10}$$

It follows, therefore, that for large n we have approximately

$$\text{Cov} \, [P_{\mu\nu}^{(n)}(\lambda), P_{\mu\nu}^{(n)}(\omega)] = \frac{1}{2\pi n} \sum_{\tau_1 = -n+1}^{n-1} \sum_{\tau_2 = -n+1}^{n-1} B(\tau_1, \tau_2) \exp \left(-i\lambda\tau_1\right) \exp \left(i\omega\tau_2\right) \tag{10.3.11}$$

Now, for $\lambda = \omega$, we obtain

$$\text{Var} \, [P_{\mu\nu}^{(n)}(\lambda)] = \frac{1}{2\pi n} \sum_{\tau_1 = -n+1}^{n-1} \sum_{\tau_2 = -n+1}^{n-1} B(\tau_1, \tau_2) \exp \left[-i\lambda(\tau_1 - \tau_2)\right] \tag{10.3.12}$$

The double sum in the right-hand side above contains the term (for $\tau_1 = \tau_2$)

$$\sum_{\tau = -n+1}^{n-1} \left[\int_{-\pi}^{\pi} f_{\mu\mu}(z)f_{\nu\nu}(z) \, dz\right] = 2(n-1)A \tag{10.3.13}$$

The other terms are bounded with respect to n. Hence we may write

$$\text{Var} \, [P_{\mu\nu}^{(n)}(\lambda)] = \frac{A}{\pi} + \text{terms involving} \, \frac{1}{n^\alpha} \qquad \alpha > 0 \tag{10.3.14}$$

from which the inconsistency of the cross periodogram as an estimator of the cross-spectral density follows.   Q.E.D.

Consistency is obtained in the present case, as in the case of the modified periodogram, by the use of lag windows that yield, in effect, estimators of certain (cross) spectral averages. In general, the same considerations that govern the choice of windows for spectral estimators prevail here as well, although with somewhat diminished force. Thus if we are dealing with real processes, then their autocovariance kernel is symmetric and this argues for the use of a symmetric window. On the other hand, the cross-covariance kernel of two real processes is not generally symmetric. Consequently, an asymmetrical window might perhaps be better suited in this instance. Also, in this connection, it might be more appropriate to employ two truncation points, one upper and one lower. Beyond that, the cross-covariance kernel of any two arbitrary (jointly covariance stationary) stochastic processes is complex. Thus there may be valid arguments for employing complex windows.

Nonetheless, the windows discussed in the previous chapter appear quite satisfactory for most empirical situations likely to be encountered in econometrics.

In all our subsequent discussion, whenever we employ a window it will be assumed to be one of those listed in Table 9.6 of Chapter 9.

To make the estimation procedure absolutely transparent, we give below a careful account of the steps involved. Defining the sample (cross) covariance kernel as in (10.3.9), the cross-spectral density estimators are given by

$$\hat{f}_{\mu\nu}(\lambda) = \frac{1}{2\pi} \sum_{\tau=-n+1}^{n-1} a(\tau)\hat{K}_{\mu\nu}(\tau) \exp(-i\lambda\tau) \qquad \mu, \nu = 1, 2, \ldots, m \qquad (10.3.15)$$

where $a(\cdot)$ is one of the lag window generators referred to above.

Even if we deal with real processes which we agreed to do when dealing with estimation problems, the cross spectrum is generally a complex-valued function. Thus it will be convenient to deal with its real and imaginary parts separately rather than with (10.3.15) directly.

Note that from (10.3.8) we obtain

$$P_{\mu\nu}^{(n)}(\lambda) = \frac{1}{2\pi} \left[\sum_{\tau=-n+1}^{n-1} \hat{K}_{\mu\nu}(\tau) \cos \lambda\tau - i \sum_{\tau=-n+1}^{n-1} \hat{K}_{\mu\nu}(\tau) \sin \lambda\tau \right] \qquad (10.3.16)$$

It will be notationally simpler if we define

$$\hat{K}_{\mu\nu}(n) = \hat{K}_{\mu\nu}(-n) \equiv 0 \qquad (10.3.17)$$

Thus (10.3.16) can be written most conveniently as

$$P_{\mu\nu}^{(n)}(\lambda) = \frac{1}{2\pi} \sum_{\tau=-n}^{n} \hat{K}_{\mu\nu}(\tau) \cos \lambda\tau - \frac{i}{2\pi} \sum_{\tau=-n}^{n} \hat{K}_{\mu\nu}(\tau) \sin \lambda\tau \qquad (10.3.18)$$

It follows, therefore, that the estimator in (10.3.15) can be written as

$$\hat{f}_{\mu\nu}(\lambda) = \frac{1}{2\pi} \sum_{\tau=-n}^{n} \hat{K}_{\mu\nu}(\tau)a(\tau) \cos \lambda\tau$$

$$- \frac{i}{2\pi} \sum_{\tau=-n}^{n} \hat{K}_{\mu\nu}(\tau)a(\tau) \sin \lambda\tau \qquad -\pi < \lambda \leq \pi \qquad (10.3.19)$$

Recall that for $\tau \geq 0$ we have defined

$$\hat{K}_{\mu\nu}(\tau) = \frac{1}{n} \sum_{s=1}^{n-\tau} X_\mu(s + \tau)X_\nu(s) \qquad (10.3.20)$$

while for $\tau < 0$ we have defined

$$\hat{K}_{\mu\nu}(\tau) = \frac{1}{n} \sum_{s=-\tau+1}^{n} X_\mu(s)X_\nu(s + \tau) \qquad (10.3.21)$$

In addition, note that, to be consistent with the development in Section 10.2, the quantity in (10.3.21) should have been defined as $\hat{K}_{\nu\mu}(\tau)$.

From (10.3.19) it is apparent that the proposed estimators of the cospectrum and quadrature spectrum are given by

$$\hat{c}_{\mu\nu}^{*}(\lambda) = \frac{1}{2\pi} \sum_{\tau=-n}^{n} a(\tau)\hat{K}_{\mu\nu}(\tau) \cos \lambda\tau \qquad -\pi < \lambda \le \pi \qquad (10.3.22)$$

$$\hat{q}_{\mu\nu}^{*}(\lambda) = -\frac{1}{2\pi} \sum_{\tau=-n}^{n} a(\tau)\hat{K}_{\mu\nu}(\tau) \sin \lambda\tau \qquad -\pi < \lambda \le \pi \qquad (10.3.23)$$

It is seen that these estimators obey

$$\hat{c}_{\mu\nu}^{*}(-\lambda) = \hat{c}_{\mu\nu}^{*}(\lambda) \qquad \hat{q}_{\mu\nu}^{*}(-\lambda) = -\hat{q}_{\mu\nu}^{*}(\lambda) \qquad (10.3.24)$$

which correspond to similar properties characterizing their parent quantities.

We shall not give the proof of the consistency of the estimators in (10.3.22) and (10.3.23), for it is very cumbersome and not particularly informative. In general, it follows the lines of the proof sketched in Chapter 9 in connection with the windowed estimator of the spectral density. The interested reader may find such a proof, however, in Goodman [14].

As we saw in Section 10.2, we need only define the quantities in (10.3.22) and (10.3.23) on $(0, \pi)$] because the processes we deal with are real.

Thus, the relevant estimators reduce to

$$\hat{c}_{\mu\nu}(\lambda) = \hat{c}_{\mu\nu}^{*}(\lambda) + \hat{c}_{\mu\nu}^{*}(-\lambda) \quad 0 < \lambda \le \pi \qquad (10.3.25)$$

$$\hat{q}_{\mu\nu}(\lambda) = \hat{q}_{\mu\nu}^{*}(\lambda) - \hat{q}_{\mu\nu}^{*}(-\lambda) \quad 0 < \lambda \le \pi \qquad (10.3.26)$$

In terms of the sample covariance kernels, the estimators are

$$\hat{c}_{\mu\nu}(\lambda) = \frac{1}{\pi} \sum_{\tau=-n}^{n} a(\tau)\hat{K}_{\mu\nu}(\tau) \cos \lambda\tau \qquad 0 < \lambda \le \pi \qquad (10.3.27)$$

$$\hat{q}_{\mu\nu}(\lambda) = -\frac{1}{\pi} \sum_{\tau=-n}^{n} a(\tau)\hat{K}_{\mu\nu}(\tau) \sin \lambda\tau \qquad 0 < \lambda \le \pi \qquad (10.3.28)$$

The gain and the phase angle—of great empirical relevance when we are dealing with filtered processes—are estimated respectively by

$$\hat{\psi}_{\mu\nu}(\lambda) = \left[\frac{\hat{f}_{\mu\mu}(\lambda)}{\hat{f}_{\nu\nu}(\lambda)}\right]^{\frac{1}{2}} \qquad (10.3.29)$$

$$\hat{\alpha}_{\mu\nu}(\lambda) = \tan^{-1}\left[\frac{\hat{q}_{\mu\nu}(\lambda)}{\hat{c}_{\mu\nu}(\lambda)}\right] \qquad (10.3.30)$$

where the μth process is to be interpreted as the output and the νth process as the input of the filter. It is clear that $\hat{\psi}(\lambda)$ is a consistent estimator of the gain in virtue of the consistency of $\hat{f}_{\mu\mu}(\cdot)$ and $\hat{f}_{\nu\nu}(\cdot)$ as estimators of $f_{\mu\mu}(\cdot)$ and $f_{\nu\nu}(\cdot)$

respectively. Similar arguments may be made with respect to the phase angle except that $\hat{\alpha}(\lambda)$ is not unique. In fact, if $\hat{\alpha}^*(\lambda)$ is one angle obeying (10.3.30), then $\hat{\alpha}^*(\lambda) + 2k\pi$ for $k = 0, \pm1, \pm2, \ldots$ will also obey it.

Finally, the coherency of any two processes is consistently estimated by

$$\hat{\gamma}_{\mu v}(\lambda) = \frac{\hat{c}_{\mu v}^2(\lambda) + \hat{q}_{\mu v}^2(\lambda)}{\hat{g}_{\mu\mu}(\lambda)\hat{g}_{vv}(\lambda)} \qquad \lambda \in (0, \pi] \tag{10.3.31}$$

where, in accordance with the notation of Section 10.2, we have put

$$\hat{g}_{\mu\mu}(\lambda) = \hat{f}_{\mu\mu}(\lambda) + \hat{f}_{\mu\mu}(-\lambda) \tag{10.3.32}$$

and similarly for $\hat{g}_{vv}(\lambda)$.

In summary, we have shown that the modified cross periodogram is an asymptotically unbiased but inconsistent estimator of the cross-spectral density. A consistent estimator for it is given by a "windowed" cross periodogram.

The procedure for obtaining the latter is as follows:

i. Compute the sample cross-covariance kernels for $\tau = 0, \pm1, \pm2, \ldots, \pm M$, where M is the maximal lag to be employed.
ii. Choose an appropriate lag window generator and modify the cross covariance by the window $a(\tau)$.
iii. Take the finite Fourier (cosine) transform of the modified cross covariances (with a factor $1/\pi$) to obtain an estimator of the cospectrum.
iv. Take the finite Fourier (sine) transform of the cross covariances (with a factor of $1/\pi$) to obtain an estimator of the quadrature spectrum.

From the basic estimators of the spectral densities, cospectra, and quadrature spectra of any two series, we may derive consistent estimators of other quantities of interest, their coherency, for example.

In the case where the two series are related as input and output process of a linear time invariant filter, we may derive estimators of the gain and phase angle of the filter estimators above.

10.4 AN EMPIRICAL APPLICATION OF CROSS-SPECTRAL ANALYSIS

Farley and Hinich [11] investigate the relationship between factory sales of automobiles (by Volvo) and national (new) automobile registrations in Sweden. The authors call these firm sales and industry registrations respectively. Their data consist of 120 monthly observations over the period 1956 through 1965. A plot of the raw data appears in Figures 10.2 and 10.3. Even from the unprocessed data a cyclical pattern is evident. In addition, one detects a trend.

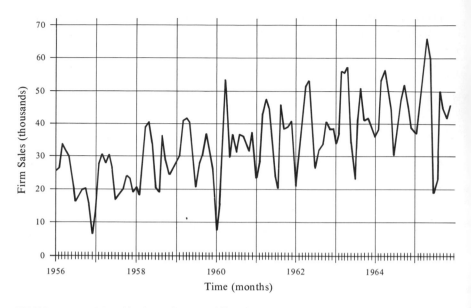

FIGURE 10.2. Monthly data of automobile sales (Volvo), Sweden, 1956-1965

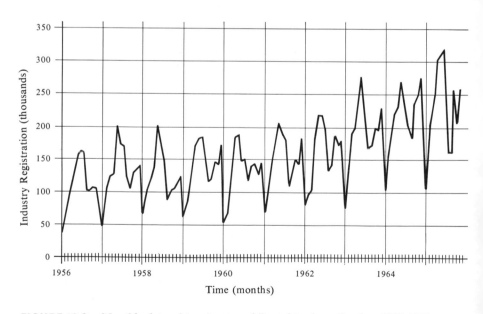

FIGURE 10.3. Monthly data of (new) automobile registrations, Sweden, 1956–1965

If one denotes factory (firm) sales by $X_1^*(t)$ and national (industry) registrations by $X_2^*(t)$, the authors assume that the series are generated by

$$X_1^*(t) = a_1 + b_1 t + X_1(t)$$
$$X_2^*(t) = a_2 + b_2 t + X_2(t) \tag{10.4.1}$$

where $X_1(t)$, $X_2(t)$ are assumed to be jointly covariance stationary processes with zero means. This, of course, means that the corresponding starred processes are also covariance stationary, but with mean functions

$$m_1(t) = a_1 + b_1 t$$
$$m_2(t) = a_2 + b_2 t \tag{10.4.2}$$

Thus the authors first *detrend* their series; this is done by simple regression on time to obtain the estimated mean functions

$$\hat{m}_1(t) = 21.1 + .2104t \qquad R^2 = .392$$
$$(.0241)^6$$

$$\hat{m}_2(t) = 93.25 + 1.088t \qquad R^2 = .412 \tag{10.4.3}$$
$$(.1197)$$

Then they obtain the residuals of these regressions [by subtracting the quantities in (10.4.3) from their data] and treat these residuals as observations on the processes $X_1(t)$, $X_2(t)$. Hence it is *these residuals that are then subjected to cross-spectral analysis*. What can one hope to accomplish by this? Well, one may be interested in the following questions:

i. Are there any cyclical components in these series and, if so what are their associated periods?
ii. Are the cycles similar in the two series?
iii. Are there any important lead-lag relations? Are the cycles synchronized?

To answer these questions, and perhaps others, we need the spectra of the two series and their associated coherencies, phase angles, and gains. These are given in Table 10.1 on page 482.

In both spectra we observe that the ordinate corresponding to the first entry is appreciable, which means that the trend may not have been entirely eliminated. Notice that the constant term may be represented, for example, by $a \exp(i2\pi\lambda)$, where λ is the fundamental frequency of the sinusoid. We recall that the period of the sinusoid is $1/\lambda$. Thus if $\lambda = 0$ then the term above reduces to the constant a (since $\exp(i2\pi 0) = 1$), which is seen to correspond to a component of "infinite period." But beyond this minor point, the spectra of the two series indicate unmistakably the existence of a cyclical component with a 12-month period. This is, of course, the *seasonal component*. Another important feature of the spectra is the disclosure that a significant cyclical component with a

---

[6] The quantity in parenthesis is the standard error of the coefficient.

TABLE 10.1. **Spectral and cross-spectral characteristics of detrended series**

Period (in months)	Spectrum (X_1)	Spectrum (X_2)	Coherency	Phase angle (in radians)	Gain
∞	6.84	1078.34	.635	−.294	.064
48.00	13.42	661.40	.366	−.519	.086
24.00	16.99	201.93	.338	−1.244	.169
16.00	33.84	1101.83	.787	1.047	.155
12.00	55.74	2448.14	.915	1.007	.144
9.60	30.83	1190.22	.799	.987	.144
8.00	20.33	222.31	.403	.807	.192
6.85	78.12	1464.78	.888	.930	.218
6.00	142.62	2889.35	.963	.934	.218
5.33	64.73	1153.88	.883	.933	.223
4.80	19.42	53.28	.535	1.250	.442
4.36	25.73	199.84	.198	−.588	.160
4.00	25.46	408.26	.244	−.253	.123
3.69	16.50	273.84	.195	−1.293	.108
3.42	10.29	131.78	.719	1.389	.237
3.20	9.46	233.68	.483	.500	.139
3.00	15.80	372.70	.619	.114	.162
2.82	12.80	187.67	.199	.376	.117
2.66	8.71	78.66	.311	−.797	.186
2.52	6.70	340.52	.189	−.229	.061
2.40	3.54	638.04	.325	.221	.042
2.28	2.07	276.97	.151	.391	.034
2.18	6.67	30.09	.203	.684	.212
2.08	5.85	144.73	.082	.824	.058
2.00	2.71	301.48	.023	1.464	.014

6-month period also exists. Evidence of cyclicality of shorter (or longer) periods is rather tenuous.

It is interesting that the coherency measures indicate that the two series, at these two frequencies (of $\frac{1}{12}$ and $\frac{1}{6}$ respectively), are very significantly correlated (.915, .963 respectively). This indicates that these two cyclical components are governed by the same factors, as one might well expect. The coherencies of the table are not uniformly high, indicating that appreciable forces impinge on one series but not on the other at various frequencies. Notice, for instance, that coherency is rather low for components having period 4 months.

Now, what is the meaning of the phase angle in this context? As we pointed out in Section 10.2, this gives information regarding the lead-lag relationship of the series. For example, the entry 1.007 associated with the component having period 12 months indicates that the seasonal in the firm *leads* the seasonal component of the industry. What is the "translation" of one radian in terms of months or weeks? Heuristically we are dealing with harmonics of the form $\exp \{i[2\pi\lambda t + \alpha(\lambda)]\}$, where λ is the fundamental frequency, α is the phase angle, and time is stated in months. One month is "equivalent" to $2\pi\lambda$ degrees at frequency λ. Here $\lambda = 1/P = 1/12$ so that, at the frequency of the seasonal, one month is "equivalent" to $2\pi/12 = 360/12 = 30°$ (degrees). One radian equals approximately $60°$ (degrees). Thus the lead indicated is approximately 2 months. A lead is also indicated for the component with period of 6 months. At the corresponding frequency $(\frac{1}{6})$, a month is equivalent to $60°$; thus the phase angle of .934 radians indicates a lead of $.934 \times 60°/60° = .934$ months, or a little over 3 weeks. A *lag* is indicated at other frequencies, but the value of the spectra there does not argue convincingly for the presence of appreciable cycles.

The gain column of the table indicates that at the seasonal component firm sales are about .14 of industry sales, whereas at the component with period 6 months the corresponding fraction is .22. This is suggested by the fact that if

$$X_1^*(t) = gX_2^*(t) \tag{10.4.4}$$

then the gain corresponding to the simple filter in (10.4.4) is g. However, the gain results of Table 10.1 do not support the simple scheme in (10.4.4), although perhaps a regression of that form might have led one to accept a constant share of industry sales hypothesis.

REFERENCES

1. Abramovitz, M., *Evidences of Long Swings in Aggregate Construction Since the Civil War*," New York, National Bureau of Economic Research, 1964.
2. Abramovitz, M., "The Nature and Significance of Kuznets Cycles," in the American Economic Association *Readings in Business Cycles*, R. A. Gordon and L. R. Klein (Eds.), Homewood, Illinois, Richard D. Irwin, Inc., 1965, pp. 519–545.
3. Abramovitz, M., "The Passing of the Kuznets Cycle," *Economica*, New Series, vol. 35, 1968, pp. 349–367.
4. Adelman, I., "Long Cycles—Fact or Artifact?" *American Economic Review*, vol. 55, 1965, pp. 444–463.
5. Bird, R. C., M. J. Desai, J. J. Engler, and P. J. Taubman, "Kuznets Cycles in Growth Rates; The Meaning," *International Economic Review*, vol. 6, 1965, pp. 229–239.
6. Brandes, O., J. Farley, M. Hinich, and U. Zackrisson, "The Time Domain and the Frequency Domain in Time Series Analysis," *The Swedish Journal of Economics*, vol. 70, 1968, pp. 25–49.
7. Cramer, H., "Stationary Random Processes," *Annals of Mathematical Statistics*, vol. 41, 1940, pp. 215–230.
8. Easterlin, R. A., "The American Baby Boom in Historical Perspective," *American Economic Review*, vol. 51, 1961, pp. 869–911.
9. Easterlin, R. A., "Economic-Demographic Interactions and Long Swings in Economic Growth," *American Economic Review*, vol. 56, 1966, pp. 1063–1104.
10. Easterlin, R. A., *Population, Labor Force, and Long Swings in Economic Growth*, New York National Bureau of Economic Research. In press.
11. Farley, J. U., and M. J. Hinich, "On Methods; Spectra," *Technical Report, Pittsburgh*, Carnegie-Mellon University, 1968.

12. Garvy, G., "Kondratieff's Theory of Long Cycles," *Review of Economics and Statistics*, vol. 25, 1943, pp. 203–220.
13. Goodman, N. R., "On the Joint Estimation of the Spectra, Cospectra, and Quadrature Spectrum of a Two-Dimensional Stationary Gaussian Process," Scientific Paper No. 10, Engineering Statistics Laboratory of New York University, 1957.
14. Goodman, N. R., "Spectral Analysis of Multiple Stationary Time Series," in *Proceedings of the Symposium on Time Series Analysis*, M. Rosenblatt, (Ed.), New York, Wiley, 1963, pp. 260–266.
15. Granger, C. W. J., and M. Hatanaka, *Spectral Analysis of Economic Time Series*, Princeton, N.J., Princeton University Press, 1964.
16. Granger, C. W. J., and O. Morgenstern, "Spectral Analysis of New York Stock Market Prices," *Kyklos*, vol. 16, 1963, pp. 1–27.
17. Granger, C. W. J., and H. J. B. Rees, "Spectral Analysis of the Term Structure of interest Rates," *The Review of Economic Studies*, vol. 35(1), 1968, pp. 67–76.
18. Harkness, J. P., "A Spectral-Analytic Test of the Long-Swing Hypothesis in Canada," *The Review of Economics and Statistics*, vol. 50, 1968, pp. 429–436.
19. Hickman, B. G., "The Postwar Retardation: Another Long Swing in the Rate of Growth?" *American Economic Review Papers and Proceedings*, vol. 53, 1963, pp. 490–507.
20. Howrey, P. E., "A Spectrum Analysis of the Long-Swing Hypothesis," *International Economic Review*, vol. 9, 1968, pp. 228–252.
21. Jenkins, G. M., "Cross-Spectral Analysis and the Estimation of Linear Open Loop Transfer Functions," In *Proceedings of the Symposium on Time Series Analysis*, M. Rosenblatt (Ed.), New York, Wiley, 1963, pp. 267–276.
22. Klein, L. R., "*Economic Fluctuations in the United States, 1921–1941*," Cowles Commission Monograph 11, New York, Wiley, 1950.
23. Kolmogorov, A. N., "Stationary Sequences in Hilbert Space," *Bulletin: Mathematical Moscow University*, vol. 2(6), 1941.
24. Kuznets, S. *Secular Movements in Production and Prices*, Boston, Houghton-Miffin, 1930.
25. Kuznets, S., *National Income, 1919–1938*. Occasional Paper No. 2, New York, National Bureau of Economic Research, 1941.
26. Kuznets, S., *National Income: A Summary of Findings*, New York, National Bureau of Economic Research, 1946.
27. Kuznets, S. "Long Swings in the Growth of Population and in Related Economic Variables," *Proceedings of the American Philosophical Society*, vol. 102, 1958, pp. 25–52.
28. Lewis, W. A., and P. J. O'Leary, "Secular Swings in Production and Trade, 1870–1913," in the American Economic Association *Readings in Business Cycles*, R. A. Gordon and L. R. Klein (Eds.), Homewood, Illinois, Richard D. Irwin, 1965, pp. 546–572.
29. Murthy, V. K., "Estimation of the Cross Spectrum," *Technical Report No. 11*, Applied Math. and Stat. Laboratories, Stanford University, 1962.
30. Nerlove, M., "Spectral Analysis of Seasonal Adjustment Procedures," *Econometrica*, vol. 32, 1964, pp. 241–286.
31. Nettheim, N., "The Estimation of Coherence," *Technical Report No. 5*, Dept. of Statistics, Stanford University, 1966.
32. Parzen, E., "On Empirical Multiple Time Series Analysis," *Technical Report No. 3*, Dept. of Statistics, Stanford University, 1965.
33. Parzen, E., "Analysis and Synthesis of Linear Models for Time Series," *Technical Report No. 4*, Dept. of Statistics, Stanford University, 1966.
34. Quennouille, M. H., *The Analysis of Multiple Time Series*, London, Griffin; and New York, Hafner Publishing Co., 1957.
35. Thomas, B., *Migration and Economic Growth*, Cambridge, Cambridge University Press, 1954.
36. Tinbergen, J., *Business Cycles in the United Kingdom, 1870–1914*, Amsterdam, North Holland Publishing Co., 1951.
37. Wiener, N., *Extrapolation, Interpolation, and Smoothing of Stationary Time Series*, New York, Wiley, 1949.
38. Wilkinson, M., "Evidences of Long Swings in the Growth of Swedish Population and Related Economic Variables, 1860–1965," *Journal of Economic History*, vol. 27, 1967, pp. 17–38.

APPROXIMATE SAMPLING
DISTRIBUTIONS
AND OTHER STATISTICAL ASPECTS
OF SPECTRAL ANALYSIS

11

This chapter deals with two essential problems. First, if we are free to choose our sample, how many "observations" should we collect and how are the "observations" to be obtained? Second, once we have a sample, how can we make a reasoned determination as to how to process the data? Earlier we gave some rough criteria by which one could discriminate among the several lag window generators proposed. In this chapter, the development of some sampling distribution theory will enhance our discriminating ability.

11.1   ALIASING

A problem that inevitably arises in practice is the following: We typically have a record that consists of observations on a given series at equidistant points in time. Now the series at hand is intrinsically continuous, and even if discrete it is unlikely that we would have sampled at the precisely appropriate time interval.

As an example, consider the problem of analyzing price behavior for some commodity over time. The price process is intrinsically continuous in time, especially so if we agree to ignore the time during which markets are not operating. Or suppose that we wish to analyse the behavior of a patient's blood pressure; the process in question is inherently a continuous one. Nonetheless, it is unlikely that we can have a continuous record in either case. And even if we

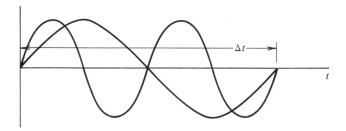

FIGURE 11.1. Illustration of aliasing

did, we might not wish to use analog methods in processing the data. Rather we would "digitalize" them, that is, would select "observations" by sampling from the continuous record at equidistant intervals Δt and then perform various algebraic operations on them. This is so since digital methods are considerably more precise and sensitive. However, if all our observations occur at points on the time axis given by $t = k \, \Delta t$, $k = 0, \pm 1, \pm 2, \ldots, \pm n$, can we assert that our sample process captures all the characteristics of the original process?

The simple diagram shown in Figure 11.1 will show precisely the nature of the problem. In it we have plotted a periodic function that describes a complete cycle in Δt time units. On it we have superimposed another periodic function that describes a complete cycle in $\frac{1}{2} \Delta t$ units of time.

If we only sample at time points $k \, \Delta t$, k integer, then obviously we cannot differentiate between the two series from the sample alone. Thus no analysis of such a sample can discover any characteristic that may enable us to discriminate between the two series simply because their ordinates coincide at these points. From Section 10.2 we note that a function having period Δt has angular frequency $\omega_1 = 2\pi/\Delta t$, and generally a function having period $(1/m) \, \Delta t$, m integer, has angular frequency $\omega = 2m\pi/\Delta t$. If we sample at equidistant intervals of length Δt, then one-half of the angular frequency

$$\omega = \frac{2\pi}{\Delta t} \tag{11.1.1}$$

is called the *Nyquist* frequency.

Since in the case of such samples, functions of period Δt cannot be distinguished from functions of period $(1/m) \, \Delta t$ for $m > 1$, it follows that if the sampled process is a linear combination of sinusoids then nothing can be inferred from the sample about components whose angular frequencies exceed the Nyquist frequency by an integral factor. This is so because if a component sinusoid has period $(1/m) \, \Delta t$, $m > 1$, then it has angular frequency $m(2\pi/\Delta t)$, which is greater than the Nyquist frequency by the factor $2m$. Yet it is clear from Figure 11.1

that we cannot tell this component apart from another of lower frequency (longer period).

The point is that if we only sample at intervals Δt, then the data cannot possibly convey any meaningful information about components of the sample series whose angular frequencies exceed the Nyquist frequency.

What is the consequence for spectral analysis? It is precisely this: If $\{X(t): t \in R\}$ is a continuous covariance stationary stochastic process and if we sample it only at the points $t = k \Delta t$, $k = 0, 1, 2, \ldots, n$, then the resulting spectral density estimator—applying the techniques herein developed—does not really estimate the spectral density $f(\cdot)$ of the process, but rather it estimates

$$\tilde{f}(\lambda) = \sum_{s=0}^{\infty} \left[f\left(\frac{2\pi s}{\Delta t} + \lambda\right) + f\left(\frac{2\pi s}{\Delta t} - \lambda\right) \right] \tag{11.1.2}$$

This phenomenon is called *aliasing* and $\tilde{f}(\cdot)$ is called the *alias* of $f(\cdot)$.

Notice that this problem generally does not arise, at least in principle, when we deal with the discrete processes studied in earlier chapters. There we sample the process at unit intervals, and these are exactly the points at which the process is defined.

Although being aware of the problem of aliasing is conceptually important, it is difficult to see what we can do about it in an econometric context. Typically, in econometric work, we are not at liberty to design our experiments, and we have only slight control over the type and size of the sample we deal with. If we did, however, there are certain conclusions we might derive from the preceding discussion.

Suppose that we have information leading to the belief that[1]

$$\int_{\lambda_0}^{\infty} f(\theta) \, d\theta = \alpha \int_{-\infty}^{\infty} f(\theta) \, d\theta \tag{11.1.3}$$

where α is very small, say $\alpha = .01$ or $\alpha = .03$ or $\alpha = .05$, and so on. This would mean that the fraction of the variance of the process contributed by components of frequency higher than λ_0 is rather small. Now if (11.1.3) holds, one reasonable way of choosing the sample interval is to set

$$\Delta t = \frac{\pi}{\lambda_0} \tag{11.1.4}$$

Thus although aliasing is still present, the problem is now well controlled due to the relative unimportance of the contribution of components of frequencies above λ_0.

Another accommodation to the problem may be as follows. Suppose that because of the nature of the empirical investigation, we are not interested in

---

[1] The limits of integration are $(-\infty, \infty)$, because the process is continuous.

components whose frequency is greater than λ_1. Under these circumstances, it would seem appropriate to set the sampling interval by

$$\Delta t = \frac{\pi}{\lambda_1} \tag{11.1.5}$$

Of course, if $\lambda_1 < \lambda_0$ for a suitably chosen α, then aliasing will again arise significantly. In such cases, perhaps a wiser choice might be to define the sampling interval by a frequency λ_2 defined by

$$\lambda_2 = \max(\lambda_1, \lambda_0) \tag{11.1.6}$$

The only cost to the procedure is that if λ_0 is substantially greater than λ_1, then some unnecessary expense will be incurred in obtaining a larger sample than is really warranted by the nature of the empirical investigation. In cases where data are obtained from instrument records, for instance in the analysis of pulse, or heart beat, or blood pressure data, another relevant consideration would be the frequency response function of the recording instrument employed. Thus suppose that for some frequency λ_3,

$$|\Phi(\lambda)| \leq \alpha|\Phi(\lambda^*)| \qquad \lambda \geq \lambda_3 \tag{11.1.7}$$

where $\Phi(\lambda)$ is the frequency response function above,

$$|\Phi(\lambda^*)| = \max_{\lambda} |\Phi(\lambda)| \tag{11.1.8}$$

and α is suitably small.

Then it is clearly a waste of effort to obtain data at intervals $\Delta t = \pi/\lambda$ for $\lambda > \lambda_3$ because the instrument effectively suppresses components of frequency higher than λ_3.

11.2 "PREWHITENING," "RECOLORING," AND RELATED ISSUES

Consider again the spectral estimator with window $a(\cdot)$. Thus

$$\hat{f}_n(\lambda) = \frac{1}{2\pi} \sum_{|\tau| \leq M_n} a(\tau B_n) K_n(\tau) \exp(-i\lambda\tau)$$

$$= \int_{-\pi}^{\pi} A_n(\lambda - \theta) P_n^*(\theta) \, d\theta \tag{11.2.1}$$

where $P_n^*(\cdot)$ is the modified periodogram of the series based on a record of length n.

The integral in (11.2.1) may be approximated by its Riemann sum

$$\hat{f}_n(\lambda) \approx \sum_{j=0}^{s} A_n(\lambda - \theta_j^*) P_n^*(\theta_j^*) \, \Delta\theta_j \tag{11.2.2}$$

where

$$\Delta\theta_j = \theta_{j+1} - \theta_j \qquad \theta_j^* \in (\theta_{j+1}, \theta_j) \qquad \theta_0 = -\pi \qquad \theta_{s+1} = \pi \tag{11.2.3}$$

Notice that

$$P_n^*(0) = \frac{1}{n}\left|\sum_{t=1}^{n} X_t\right|^2 = n|\bar{x}|^2 \tag{11.2.4}$$

where

$$\bar{x} = \frac{1}{n}\sum_{t=1}^{n} X_t \tag{11.2.5}$$

Since

$$\hat{f}_n(0) \approx \sum_{j=0}^{s} A_n(-\theta_j^*)P_n^*(\theta_j^*)\,\Delta\theta_j \tag{11.2.6}$$

and since $A_n(\cdot)$ assumes its maximum at zero and on either side of zero tapers off rapidly, it follows that $\hat{f}_n(0)$ is dominated by $P_n^*(0)$. In addition, it should be noted that since $A_n(\theta)$ does not vanish for values of θ adjacent to zero, $P_n^*(0)$ makes contributions to $\hat{f}_n(\lambda)$ for values of λ adjacent to zero as well. Thus if $|\varepsilon|$ is small, then

$$\hat{f}_n(\varepsilon) \approx \sum_{j=0}^{s} A_n(\varepsilon - \theta_j^*)P_n^*(\theta_j^*)\,\Delta\theta_j \tag{11.2.7}$$

and hence the terms $A_n(\varepsilon - \theta_j^*)P_n^*(\theta_j^*)$ for $|\theta_j^*|$ also small—and in particular for $\theta_j^* = 0$—are a significant component of $\hat{f}_n(\varepsilon)$.

This shows that if the process we deal with does not have zero mean but we process the data as if it did, then the estimator of the spectrum will be distorted at low frequencies, perhaps significantly.

Of course, a nonzero but constant mean is not the only instance in which distortion of the spectrum may occur. Suppose that due to the presence of a deterministic sinusoidal component, or otherwise, the spectrum of the series has a sharp peak at, say, λ_p. Suppose, further, that we use a spectral window with a truncation point[2] M, which is constant with respect to sample size, as one is prone to do in empirical applications.

Then it can be shown that

$$\lim_{n\to\infty} E[\hat{f}_n(\lambda)] = \int_{-\pi}^{\pi} A_M(\lambda - \theta)f(\theta)\,d\theta \tag{11.2.8}$$

where $A_M(\cdot)$ is the approximating spectral window associated with the constant

---

[2] This means that the lag autocovariances used in computing the spectral density estimator are at most of order M, irrespective of the length of the record.

truncation point M. Then, employing the same considerations as above, we conclude that for large n we can write the approximation as

$$E[\hat{f}_n(\lambda)] \approx \sum_{j=0}^{s} A_M(\lambda - \theta_j^*) f(\theta_j^*) \, \Delta\theta_j \qquad (11.2.9)$$

It is clear from (11.2.9) that, for λ near λ_p and θ_j^* near λ_p, the contribution of $f(\lambda_p)$ to $E[\hat{f}_n(\lambda)]$ could be so overwhelming as to distort the spectral estimator seriously. This is particularly so if $f(\cdot)$ changes rapidly in a neighborhood of λ_p. Clearly, if $f(\cdot)$ changes only slowly there, at least relative to the way in which $A_M(\cdot)$ changes, the distortion would be relatively negligible and hence of no particular concern to us. Similar phenomena would arise if the spectral window itself has secondary peaks that are "large" relative to $A_M(0)$.

Such phenomena are called "leakages" or "side lobe effects" and have contributed the main motivation for "prewhitening." The last term means that certain operations are performed on the data prior to their spectral analysis processing in order to render their spectrum as nearly constant as possible. Recalling that the constant spectrum corresponds to a stochastic process $\{\varepsilon_t : t \in N\}$ such that the ε's form a sequence of mutually uncorrelated random variables, and noting that in engineering parlance this is called "white noise," the term "prewhitening" becomes intuitively very meaningful. Prewhitening can be carried out by centering observations about the sample mean if the mean function of the process is constant, or by subtracting a suitable regression from the observation if the mean function is a well-specified time function.

If the process can be approximated reasonably well by an autoregressive scheme, then prewhitening can be carried out by subjecting to spectral analysis not the actual observations but rather the residuals from the appropriate autoregressive regression. Such a procedure is occasionally called "autoregressive prewhitening." In this connection, the interested reader may consult Schaerf [15].

If we do succeed in obtaining a series whose spectrum is constant, then all distortion phenomena will disappear. Afterward, to recover the information conveyed by the original series, we need somehow to transform this flat spectrum to the one corresponding to the original series. This involves allowing, in the final result, for the effects of the prewhitening process.

In many cases, the prewhitening process involves filtering the data through the use of a linear time invariant filter. If the transfer function of the filter is given by $\Psi(\lambda)$ and if $f_x(\cdot)$, $f_y(\cdot)$ are, respectively, the spectral densities of the original and filtered processes, then

$$f_y(\lambda) = \Psi(\lambda) f_x(\lambda) \qquad (11.2.10)$$

Since $\Psi(\lambda)$ can be easily calculated if the filter is known, the original spectrum can be readily estimated. This operation is often referred to as "recoloring" and the resulting spectrum as "recolored." The asymptotic expectation of the spectrum of the prewhitened series is given by

$$\lim_{n \to \infty} E[\hat{f}_y(\lambda)] = \int_{-\pi}^{\pi} \Psi(\theta)f_x(\theta)A_M(\lambda - \theta) \, d\theta \qquad (11.2.11)$$

The asymptotic expectation of the recolored spectrum is

$$\frac{\int_{-\pi}^{\pi} \Psi(\theta)f_x(\theta)A_M(\lambda - \theta) \, d\theta}{\Psi(\lambda)}$$

The impact of the prewhitening operation is that it suppresses the contribution of $f_x(\theta)$ at those frequencies at which $\Psi(\theta)$ is significantly smaller than $\Psi(\lambda)$. In particular, if there is a peak at λ_p and we wish to suppress the distortion it induces on the spectral estimator, then the prewhitening operation should be such that the filter associated with it yields a transfer function $\Psi(\cdot)$ such that $\Psi(\lambda_p)$ is rather small compared to $\Psi(\lambda)$, where λ ranges over a specified frequency range of interest to us.

A second consideration in prewhitening is that it ought to result in a series whose spectrum is indeed flat, for, if not, then none of the benefits outlined above will materialize.

Unfortunately, however, we cannot be certain, a priori, whether a given prewhitening procedure will have this effect. If we did, then this is tantamount to our knowing the spectrum of the original series and then clearly there is no estimation problem!

A lengthy discussion of such considerations lies outside the scope of this book. One may find a good discussion of prewhitening and recoloring and some alternative suggestions on the procedures discussed here in Hext [4]. An excellent discussion of the relative merits and consequences of various means of removing trends may be found in Durbin [2]. Finally, before we conclude this section we ought to mention a problem entailed by the use of certain windows. Suppose, again, that we employ a spectral window with a truncation point independent of sample size. Then the appropriate form of the spectral window is the approximation given in the last column of Table 9.6 in Chapter 9. In addition to the considerations that led to prewhitening, we ought to be concerned with the following question: Is the lag window generator employed such that it necessarily leads to nonnegative spectral estimators? If not, then the resulting estimator will be hard to interpret at frequencies for which $\hat{f}_n(\lambda)$ is negative. Recall that the spectrum is by definition a nonnegative quantity.

This is another manifestation of the phenomenon of "leakage" and may result when the spectral window employed has substantial secondary side lobes that are negative. This is perhaps best illustrated pictorially (see Figure 11.2). Since the spectral window has a "large" secondary lobe—actually a minimum —it is clear that in obtaining the estimator of the spectrum at the frequency λ_0

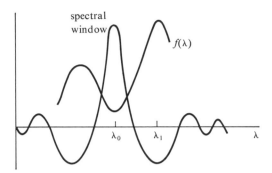

FIGURE 11.2. Illustration of leakage

we have a component consisting of the product of the ordinates of the spectrum and spectral window at λ_1. Since, as drawn in the figure, both happen to be "large" in absolute value but of opposite sign, it is quite conceivable that the spectral estimator at λ_0 may turn out to be negative.

Quite clearly, if one suspects a spectral shape such as the one given in Figure 11.2, one ought to avoid the use of lag window generators whose associated spectral windows have appreciably negative side lobes. In this connection, we should remark that the Tukey-Hanning spectral window whose approximation is given by

$$A_M(\lambda) = \frac{\pi^2}{\pi - (M\lambda)^2} \frac{\sin M\lambda}{\lambda} \tag{11.2.12}$$

could conceivably lead to negative spectral estimates. Consequently, one must be quite careful in employing it. The Parzen window, however, yields necessarily nonnegative estimators and at least on this account is to be preferred to the Tukey-Hanning window.

11.3 APPROXIMATE ASYMPTOTIC DISTRIBUTIONS; CONSIDERATIONS OF DESIGN AND ANALYSIS

In the following material, unless otherwise stated, all processes will be assumed to be real.

We noted earlier that the asymptotic variance of the spectral estimator

$$\hat{f}_n(\lambda) = \frac{1}{2\pi} \sum_{|\tau| \le M_n} a(B_n \tau) \hat{K}_n(\tau) \exp(-i\tau\lambda) \tag{11.3.1}$$

is given by

$$\text{Var}\,[\hat{f}_n(\lambda)] = \frac{M_n}{n} f^2(\lambda) G(a) \tag{11.3.2}$$

where

$$G(a) = \int_{-\infty}^{\infty} a^2(u) \, du \qquad (11.3.3)$$

More precisely, as Lomnicki and Zaremba [9] have pointed out, the variance is

$$\text{Var}\,[\hat{f}_n(\lambda)] = \frac{M_n}{n} f^2(\lambda) G(a)[1 + \delta(0, \lambda)][1 + \delta(\pi, \lambda)] \qquad (11.3.4)$$

where

$$\begin{aligned}
\delta(c, b) &= 1 && \text{if } b = c \\
&= 0 && \text{if } b \neq c
\end{aligned} \qquad (11.3.5)$$

The expression in (11.3.4) thus coincides with that in (11.3.2) for $\lambda \in (0, \pi)$; however, at the endpoints—0 and π—it is simply twice that quantity.

We also saw in the previous chapter that we may approximate $\hat{f}_n(\lambda)$ by

$$\hat{f}_n(\lambda) \approx \sum_{j=0}^{s} A_n(\lambda - \theta_j^*) P_n^*(\theta_j^*) \, \Delta\theta_j \qquad (11.3.6)$$

Now

$$\begin{aligned}
P_n^*(\theta_j^*) &= \frac{1}{2\pi} \left| \sum_{t=1}^{n} X_t \exp\,(it\theta_j^*) \right|^2 \\
&= \frac{1}{2\pi} \left[\left(\sum_{t=1}^{n} X_t \cos t\theta_j^* \right)^2 + \left(\sum_{t=1}^{n} X_t \sin t\theta_j^* \right)^2 \right]
\end{aligned} \qquad (11.3.7)$$

and, as we pointed out in Section 9.3, if the process $\{X(t): t \in N\}$ is normal, $P_n^*(\cdot)$ is asymptotically distributed as a chi-square variable with two degrees of freedom.

Since it was also shown earlier that distinct periodogram ordinates are asymptotically uncorrelated, it follows therefore that we may think of the spectral estimator (11.3.1) as a weighted sum of (uncorrelated) chi-square variables. Under these circumstances, it is eminently reasonable to approximate its asymptotic distribution by a chi-square distribution whose degrees of freedom are determined by the asymptotic mean and variance of the spectral estimator.

Recall that if u is a chi-square variable with r degrees of freedom, then its density is given by

$$d(u) = \frac{1}{2\Gamma(r/2)} \left(\frac{u}{2} \right)^{r/2} \exp\,(-\tfrac{1}{2}u) \qquad (11.3.8)$$

where $\Gamma(\cdot)$ is the gamma function defined by

$$\Gamma(a) = \int_{0}^{\infty} w^{a-1} \exp\,(-w) \, dw \qquad (11.3.9)$$

Now

$$E(u) = \frac{1}{\Gamma(r/2)} \int_0^\infty \left(\frac{u}{2}\right)^{(r/2)+1} \exp\left(-\tfrac{1}{2}u\right) du$$

$$= \frac{2\Gamma[(r/2)+1]}{\Gamma(r/2)} = \frac{2(r/2)\Gamma(r/2)}{\Gamma(r/2)} = r \tag{11.3.10}$$

$$E(u^2) = \frac{2}{\Gamma(r/2)} \int_0^\infty \left(\frac{u}{2}\right)^{(r/2)+2} \exp\left(-\tfrac{1}{2}u\right) du$$

$$= \frac{4\Gamma[(r/2)+2]}{\Gamma(r/2)} = r(r+2) \tag{11.3.11}$$

Thus

$$\text{Var}\,(u) = E(u^2) - [E(u)]^2 = 2r \tag{11.3.12}$$

It follows, therefore, that

$$\frac{2[E(u)]^2}{\text{Var}\,[u]} = r \tag{11.3.13}$$

which expresses the degrees of freedom as a function of the mean and variance of the distribution.

In the case of the spectral estimator, we have, asymptotically,

$$E[\hat{f}_n(\lambda)] = f(\lambda) \tag{11.3.14}$$

$$\text{Var}\,[\hat{f}_n(\lambda)] = \frac{M_n}{n} f^2(\lambda)G(a) \qquad \lambda \in (0, \pi) \tag{11.3.15}$$

We thus have

Definition 1: Let the estimator of the spectrum of a covariance stationary stochastic process $\{X(t): t \in N\}$ be given by

$$\hat{f}_n(\lambda) = \frac{1}{2\pi} \sum_{|\tau| \leq M_n}' a(B_n \tau)K_n(\tau) \exp\left(-i\lambda\tau\right) \tag{11.3.16}$$

Then the distribution of the spectral estimator at frequency λ is asymptotically approximately chi square with equivalent degrees of freedom (EDF)

$$r = \frac{n}{M_n} \frac{2}{G(a)} \tag{11.3.17}$$

The preceding definition makes clear what we mean by equivalent degrees of freedom (EDF). It also serves to point out the *inverse relationship* that exists between the number of lags employed in the spectral estimator and its "stability" —at least as the latter is measured by the size of the EDF parameter. Now, since

EDF and the number of lags employed, M_n, are, for given length of record, inversely related, it would follow that if this were the only relevant consideration, the smaller the number of lags the better. We would finally arrive at the *reductio ad absurdum* that no lags at all is best because then $M_n = 0$ and thus EDF is infinite! Fortunately, things are not quite so simpleminded.

To see this, we need another concept, namely, that of the *bandwidth* of a spectral estimator. This is related to problems of distortion or "smudging" of the spectrum due to the fact that windowed spectral estimators (with a maximum number of lags independent of sample size) in fact estimate spectral averages over some (small) interval of frequencies. We had already commented on this, in another context, in Section 11.2.

The general feature of a window we want to characterize by its bandwidth is the window's concentration about the frequency at which the spectrum is estimated.

Recall again from (11.2.1) that the (windowed) spectral estimator can be expressed as

$$\hat{f}_n(\lambda) = \int_{-\pi}^{\pi} A_n(\lambda - \theta) P_n^*(\theta) \, d\theta \tag{11.3.18}$$

Thus we can think of the spectral window $A_n(\cdot)$ as a screen that allows $P_n^*(\cdot)$ to determine $\hat{f}_n(\lambda)$ at frequencies other than λ; that is, $\hat{f}_n(\lambda)$ is made to depend on $P_n^*(\theta)$ for $\theta \neq \lambda$. The extent to which $A_n(\cdot)$ screens out values of $P_n^*(\theta)$ for $\theta \neq \lambda$, or the extent to which it allows $E[\hat{f}_n(\lambda)]$ to be "smudged" by values of $f(0)$ for $\theta \neq \lambda$, depends on the values assumed by $A_n(\cdot)$ on either side of the origin.

Of course, if

$$A_n(\theta) = 1 \quad \text{if } \theta = 0$$
$$= 0 \quad \text{if } \theta \neq 0 \tag{11.3.19}$$

then no such smudging will occur but we end up with the modified periodogram, which is an *inconsistent* estimator of the spectral density.

One convenient way in which we can express the extent of "smudging" permitted by a given spectral window is by constructing an equivalent (in some sense) *rectangular* window. In this case, the extent to which adjacent frequencies are allowed to determine the spectral estimator $\hat{f}_n(\cdot)$ at λ is most clearly apparent, for $P_n^*(\cdot)$ is allowed to determine (with equal weight) $\hat{f}_n(\lambda)$ by its values at $\theta \in (\lambda - \alpha, \lambda + \alpha)$, where 2α is the base of the (equivalent) rectangular window.

As in most instances of this type of representation, there is no unique manner in which it can be carried out. Thus, as we shall see, there are several useful definitions of the bandwidth. Before giving them, however, we need to recall certain significant relations. Note that if $a(\cdot)$ is a lag window generator (certainly if it is one of those exhibited in Table 9.6), then it is symmetric about the origin, that is,

$$a(-\theta) = a(\theta) \tag{11.3.20}$$

Furthermore,

$$a_n(\tau) = a(B_n \tau) \qquad (11.3.21)$$

where B_n is a sequence of positive numbers and τ an integer.

In addition, it is generally the case that

$$a(0) = \max a(\theta) \qquad a(\theta) \geq 0 \quad \text{all } \theta \qquad (11.3.22)$$

If $a(\cdot)$ is the lag window generator employed in obtaining a (windowed) spectral estimator with truncation point—maximal lag—M_n, then the corresponding spectral window is given by

$$A_n(\theta) = \frac{1}{2\pi} \sum_{\tau=-n}^{n} a_n(\tau) \exp(i\tau\theta) \qquad (11.3.23)$$

Due to the symmetry of $a(\cdot)$, we note that

$$A_n(-\theta) = A_n(\theta) \qquad (11.3.24)$$

Due to the nonnegativity of $a(\cdot)$, we have

$$|A_n(\theta)| \leq \frac{1}{2\pi} \sum_{\tau=-n}^{n} |a_n(\tau)| = \frac{1}{2\pi} \sum_{\tau=-n}^{n} a_n(\tau) = A_n(0) \qquad (11.3.25)$$

It would also be convenient occasionally to normalize the spectral window so that its integral is unity. This is absolutely innocuous and involves only a division by a constant. Thus

$$\int_{-\infty}^{\infty} A_n^*(\theta) \, d\theta = 1 \qquad (11.3.26)$$

where $A_n^*(\cdot)$ is the normalized window.

In line with these considerations, one possibility is to define the bandwidth of a spectral window as the base of the rectangle having unit area and height equal to the *maximal* ordinate of the spectral window. Thus we have

Definition 2: (Parzen): Let $H(\cdot)$ be a spectral window having the properties (11.3.24), (11.3.25), and (11.3.26). Then its *bandwidth* is defined by

$$\beta_1(H) = \frac{1}{H(0)} \qquad (11.3.27)$$

Although this is an extremely simple notion and the quantity (11.3.27) is easy to calculate, nonetheless it is not entirely satisfactory, for it does not take into account any feature of the window except the height of its maximal ordinate. Perhaps one would be interested in knowing how much the ordinates of the window fluctuate, for this fact, in a way, gives some indication of the weight the window attaches to $P_n^*(\cdot)$ for frequencies adjacent to λ in producing an estimate for $\hat{f}_n(\lambda)$.

Let us define the *variance* of the window, assuming it exists, by

$$V(H) = \int_{-\infty}^{\infty} \theta^2 H(\theta) \, d\theta \tag{11.3.28}$$

Notice that from (11.3.24) the "mean" of the window vanishes; that is,

$$m(H) = \int_{-\infty}^{\infty} \theta H(\theta) \, d\theta = 0 \tag{11.3.29}$$

Thus we have the alternative

Definition 3 (Parzen): Let $H(\cdot)$ be a spectral window having the properties (11.3.24), (11.3.25), (11.3.26), and, in addition, assume that its variance is finite. Then the *bandwidth* of the window is defined as the base of the rectangle having unit area and the *same variance* as the spectral window. More precisely, the bandwidth is defined by

$$\beta_2(H) = \sqrt{12V(H)} \tag{11.3.30}$$

To see how one obtains (11.3.30), let a rectangular distribution be defined on $(0, s)$. Then its density is

$$d(x) = \frac{1}{s} \quad \text{if } x \in (0, s)$$

$$= 0 \quad \text{otherwise} \tag{11.3.31}$$

This clearly has unit area. The rth moment of the distribution is

$$E(x^r) = \frac{1}{s} \int_0^s x^r \, dx = \frac{s^r}{r+1} \tag{11.3.32}$$

The variance of the distribution is

$$\text{Var}\,(x) = E(x^2) - [E(x)]^2 = \frac{s^2}{3} - \frac{s^2}{4} = \frac{s^2}{12} \tag{11.3.33}$$

Hence the base s of the "rectangle" defined by the density is

$$s = \sqrt{12 \, \text{Var}\,(x)} \tag{11.3.34}$$

Since we require that the variance here equal the "variance" of the spectral window, (11.3.30) follows immediately from (11.3.34). For reasons that will seem a little clearer below, an alternative definition of bandwidth proposed by Jenkins is a more convenient one for certain purposes.

Definition 4 (Jenkins): Let $H(\cdot)$ be a spectral window having the properties (11.3.24), (11.3.25), and (11.3.26). Then its bandwidth is defined as half the base of a rectangle having unit area and which if employed as a spectral window yields a spectral estimator with the same *asymptotic variance* as the estimator obtained by the use of the spectral window $H(\cdot)$.

Remark 1: Jenkins actually termed this *equivalent equivariability bandwidth*, EEVB. Because the derivation of the formal expression of EEVB in terms of some characteristics of $H(\cdot)$ is rather involved, we shall omit it for the moment.

Finally, let us note

Definition 5: Let $\{X_i: i = 1, 2, \ldots, n\}$ be a set of observations on the covariance stationary stochastic process $\{X(t): t \in N\}$ admitting of the spectral density $f(\cdot)$. Let

$$\hat{f}_n^{(H)}(\lambda) = \int_{-\pi}^{\pi} P_n^*(\theta) H(\lambda - \theta) \, d\theta \qquad (11.3.35)$$

be the estimator of $f(\lambda)$ corresponding to the spectral window $H(\cdot)$. Then the *bandwidth of the spectral estimator* (11.3.35) is defined by

$$\beta[\hat{f}_n^{(H)}] = \beta(H) \qquad (11.3.36)$$

where $\beta(\cdot)$ may be obtained according to Definition 2, 3, or 4.

Let us remind ourselves that we have embarked on this short digression because we wished to see the connection between "smudging" and the number of lagged covariances actually employed in computing the spectral estimator. We have already seen that a small number of lags implies a "large" EDF parameter, which is clearly desirable. Does a small number of lags imply a "narrow" bandwidth as well, which is also a desirable feature? Unfortunately, precisely the reverse is true, as we shall presently see. Thus let us now establish the relation that exists between the number of lags (M_n) actually employed by the spectral estimator and its bandwidth.

Notice that we can write

$$\hat{f}_n^{(A_n)}(\lambda) = \int_{-\pi}^{\pi} A_n(\lambda - \theta) P_n^*(\theta) \, d\theta$$

$$= \frac{1}{2\pi} \sum_{|\tau| \leq M_n} a_n(\tau) K_n(\tau) \exp(-i\tau\lambda) \qquad (11.3.37)$$

Here we employed the somewhat novel notation $\hat{f}_n^{A_n}(\cdot)$ to emphasize the spectral window employed. From Definitions 2 and 5, we easily conclude that

$$\beta_1[\hat{f}_n^{(A_n)}(\lambda)] = \frac{1}{A_n(0)} \qquad (11.3.38)$$

But from Table 9.6,

$$A_n(\theta) = M_n A(M_n \theta) \qquad (11.3.39)$$

at least for large n. Thus we may rewrite (11.3.38) as

$$\beta_1[\hat{f}_n^{(A_n)}(\lambda)] = \frac{1}{M_n A(0)} \tag{11.3.40}$$

To compute the bandwidth of (11.3.37), according to Definition 3, we need the "variance" of $A_n(\cdot)$. Thus

$$V(A_n) = \int_{-\infty}^{\infty} \theta^2 A_n(\theta) \, d\theta = \frac{1}{M_n^2} \int_{-\infty}^{\infty} z^2 A(z) \, dz = \frac{V(A)}{M_n^2} \tag{11.3.41}$$

where we have made the change in variable

$$z = M_n \theta \tag{11.3.42}$$

and we have made use of (11.3.39).

It follows, therefore, that

$$\beta_2[\hat{f}_n^{(A_n)}(\lambda)] = \sqrt{12 V(A_n)} = \frac{\sqrt{12 V(A)}}{M_n} \tag{11.3.43}$$

Finally, to compute the bandwidth according to Definition 4, we need to recall that the asymptotic variance of (11.3.37) is given by

$$\text{Var}\left[\hat{f}_n^{(A_n)}(\lambda)\right] = \frac{M_n}{n} f^2(\lambda) G(a) \qquad \lambda \in (0, \pi) \tag{11.3.44}$$

where

$$G(a) = \int_{-\infty}^{\infty} a^2(u) \, du \tag{11.3.45}$$

and $a(\cdot)$ is the lag window generator associated with the ("truncated") spectral window $A_n(\cdot)$ employed in (11.3.37).

Now observe that

$$G(a) = \int_{-\infty}^{\infty} a^2(u) \, du = B_n \int_{-\infty}^{\infty} a^2(B_n z) \, dz = B_n \int_{-\infty}^{\infty} a_n^2(z) \, dz$$

$$= B_n G(a_n) \tag{11.3.46}$$

where in (11.3.46) we have made the change of variable

$$u = B_n z \tag{11.3.47}$$

and made use of the relation

$$a_n(\theta) = a(B_n \theta) \tag{11.3.48}$$

Hence in view of the fact that

$$M_n = \frac{1}{B_n} \tag{11.3.49}$$

we can write (11.3.44) in the form

$$\text{Var}\left[f_n^{(A_n)}(\lambda)\right] = \frac{f^2(\lambda)}{n} G(a_n) \tag{11.3.50}$$

which is more suitable for our current discussion. To compute the bandwidth of (11.3.37) according to Jenkins, we need to determine s, which is half the base of a rectangle of unit area that when *employed as a spectral window yields the same asymptotic variance of the spectral estimator* as the given window $A_n(\cdot)$.

Let this rectangular window be given by

$$R(\theta) = \frac{1}{2s} \quad \text{if } -s \le \theta \le s$$

$$= 0 \quad \text{otherwise} \tag{11.3.51}$$

The asymptotic variance of the spectral estimator it yields is given, according to (11.3.50), by

$$\text{Var}\left[f_n^{(R)}(\lambda)\right] = \frac{f^2(\lambda)}{n} G(r_n) \tag{11.3.52}$$

where $r_n(\cdot)$ is simply the Fourier transform of $R(\cdot)$, and $G(\cdot)$ is the function defined by (11.3.45). Now, the Fourier transform of $R(\cdot)$ is given by

$$r_n(\theta) = \int_{-\infty}^{\infty} R(u) \exp(iu\theta)\, du = \frac{1}{2s}\int_{-s}^{s} \exp(iu\theta)\, du$$

$$= \frac{\exp(is\theta) - \exp(-is\theta)}{2is\theta} = \frac{\sin s\theta}{s\theta} \tag{11.3.53}$$

Thus

$$G(r_n) = \int_{-\infty}^{\infty} \frac{\sin^2 s\theta}{s^2\theta^2}\, d\theta = 2\int_{0}^{\infty} \frac{\sin^2 s\theta}{s^2\theta^2}\, d\theta = \frac{2}{s}\int_{0}^{\infty} \frac{\sin^2 x}{x^2}\, dx \tag{11.3.54}$$

where we used the symmetry of the integrand about the origin and have made the change in variable

$$x = s\theta \tag{11.3.55}$$

From standard integral tables, the last integral in (11.3.54) may be found to equal $\pi/2$, and hence we conclude

$$G(r_n) = \frac{\pi}{s} \tag{11.3.56}$$

Equating (11.3.52) with (11.3.50), we conclude in view of (11.3.56) and (11.3.46) that

$$s = \frac{\pi}{M_n G(a)} \tag{11.3.57}$$

Hence

$$\beta_3[\hat{f}_n^{(A_n)}(\lambda)] = \text{EEVB}[f_n^{(A_n)}] = \frac{\pi}{M_n G(a)} \qquad (11.3.58)$$

Thus no matter what definition of bandwidth is employed, the conclusion is, in view of (11.3.40), (11.3.43), and (11.3.58), that for given lag window generator $a(\cdot)$ the bandwidth of the resulting spectral estimator is *inversely* proportional to the number of lag covariances, M_n, it employs.

Although we can reduce the variance of the spectral estimator by reducing M_n, or alternatively increase the EDF parameter associated with it, we are also at the same time increasing its bandwidth, thereby increasing "smudging."

Indeed we are led to certain remarkably striking relations, occasionally called "uncertainty principles" (UP) after the famous uncertainty principle of Heisenberg in physics. Using the three definitions of bandwidth and the asymptotic mean and variance of the spectral estimator in (11.2.1), we have the following three "uncertainty principles" (UP):

$$\text{UP 1:} \; \frac{\text{Var}\,[\hat{f}_n(\lambda)]}{E[\hat{f}_n(\lambda)]} \beta_1[\hat{f}_n(\lambda)] = \frac{G(a)}{nA(0)} \qquad (11.3.59)$$

$$\text{UP 2:} \; \frac{\text{Var}\,[\hat{f}_n(\lambda)]}{E[\hat{f}_n(\lambda)]} \beta_2[\hat{f}_n(\lambda)] = \frac{G(a)\sqrt{12V(A)}}{n} \qquad (11.3.60)$$

$$\text{UP 3:} \; \frac{\text{Var}\,[\hat{f}_n(\lambda)]}{E[\hat{f}_n(\lambda)]} \beta_3[\hat{f}_n(\lambda)] = \frac{\pi}{n} \qquad (11.3.61)$$

What these relations disclose unmistakably is that for given record length, n, and given lag window generator, $a(\cdot)$, *it is not possible to simultaneously reduce smudging and increase the* EDF *parameter associated with a spectral estimator by operating on the number of lag covariances employed in obtaining it.* The attractiveness of Jenkins' definition of bandwidth is enhanced by the particularly simple form of the "uncertainty principle" to which it leads—UP 3.

The operational importance of the preceding considerations is that in a given empirical situation we shall also be called upon to make a judgment as to how many lags we are to employ in computing the spectral estimator. We recall that Blackman and Tukey [1, p. 11 and p. 112] recommend that only a relatively small number of lag covariances be employed. This presupposes a preoccupation with EDF and a relative neglect of the problem of "smudging." The price we pay for this preoccupation is that it makes it more difficult to separate effectively the ordinates of the spectral density. Thus our resolution of the variance of the series to the contribution of components of different frequency will suffer.

More recently, it has been proposed [12] that alternative spectral estimators be computed with truncation points M_i lying in the intervals

$$.05 \le \frac{M_1}{n} \le .10 \quad .10 \le \frac{M_2}{n} \le .25 \quad .25 < \frac{M_3}{n} \le .75$$

This will allow us to see whether peaks in the spectral density are obscured due to the size of the bandwidth of the estimator. An alternative approach would be to compute the sample covariance kernel $K_n(\tau)$ and use a truncation point M such that $|K_n(\tau)| < \varepsilon$ for $\tau \geq M$, where ε is a preassigned (small) number. Needless to say, a definitive solution to this has not yet been established.

A notion, somewhat related to the previous considerations, that the reader is likely to encounter in the literature is that of the *equivalent number of independent estimates* (ENIE) of a spectral estimator associated with a given lag window generator $a(\cdot)$. This is particularly useful in comparing two different spectra.

The idea behind this concept involves the following considerations. Recall that distinct ordinates of the modified periodogram are asymptotically independent if the underlying stochastic process is normal. Now if in obtaining a (consistent) spectral estimator we employ a rectangular spectral window with base $2s$, then there will be $[\pi/s]$ independent spectral ordinates corresponding to the fact that on the interval $(-\pi, \pi)$ there are $[\pi/s]$ *nonoverlapping* subintervals of length $2s$. Since the spectral estimator corresponding to such a rectangular window is simply proportional to the sum of periodogram ordinates over a subinterval of length $2s$, it follows that spectral ordinates corresponding to nonoverlapping intervals will also be (asymptotically) independent.

Now, if the spectral window actually employed is not a rectangular one, then the foregoing considerations will hold but only as a reasonable approximation.

However, we have already established a relation between s and the number of lag covariances employed by a spectral estimator with spectral window $A_n(\cdot)$ in (11.3.57). Thus we conclude

$$\text{ENIE} \left[f_n^{(A_n)}(\lambda) \right] = M_n \, G(a) \tag{11.3.62}$$

From (11.3.62) we see that ENIE varies directly with the number of lags employed. Since, intuitively, the information conveyed by the spectral estimates varies directly with ENIE, it is apparent that a large ENIE parameter is a desirable feature for a spectral estimator.

It is remarkable, however, that the product of ENIE and EDF is a constant depending only on the length of the record. Thus we cannot increase the stability *and* the independent information content of a spectral estimator by operating on the number of lags it employs, for we have the alternative form of the "uncertainty principle"

$$\text{ENIE} \times \text{EDF} = 2n \tag{11.3.63}$$

Since we have agreed to use the same lag window generator in estimating spectral as well as cross-spectral estimators, the same considerations about EDF, bandwidth, and ENIE will govern empirical work in cross-spectral analysis as those discussed above.

Before concluding, we shall give, in very brief form, some aspects of the approximate asymptotic distribution of spectral and cross-spectral estimators on the assumption that the underlying stochastic processes, in addition to being jointly covariance stationary, are also normal.

A detailed discussion of these aspects is clearly beyond the scope of this book. Such discussion may be readily found in Jenkins and Priestley [8], Lomnicki and Zaremba [10], Jenkins [7], and Goodman [3].

We saw earlier that, for long records, the distribution of the spectral estimator can be taken to be approximately chi square with degrees of freedom given by the EDF parameter as obtained in (11.3.17). On the other hand, as pointed out by Jenkins and Priestley [8],

$$\text{Var}\,[\ln \hat{f}_n(\lambda)] \approx \frac{M_n}{n}\,G(a) \tag{11.3.64}$$

which is independent of frequency.

Moreover, the log transformation permits us to take the distribution of the (log of the) spectral estimator as approximately normal—for large EDF parameter—so that we have the following rather simple derivation of confidence intervals for estimates of spectral ordinates.

Thus if $x \sim N(0, 1)$ and s_α is such that

$$\Pr\,\{|x| \leq s_\alpha\} = \alpha \tag{11.3.65}$$

then

$$\ln \hat{f}_n(\lambda) \pm s_\alpha \frac{\sqrt{M_n\,G(a)}}{n}$$

forms an approximate confidence interval with confidence coefficient α for the spectral estimator.

Of course, in all the preceding discussion the implicit assumption is that the errors in $\hat{f}_n(\lambda)$ are due mainly to its variance and not to its "smudging" or, alternatively, that $f(\cdot)$ does not vary very much over the bandwidth of the spectral window employed.

An application of the preceding considerations and the notion of ENIE is as follows. Suppose that we have two records on a given series of length, n_1 and n_2. We may want to ask: Has the spectrum changed over the two periods?

Well, if we compute the spectral ordinates $\hat{f}_{n_1}(\lambda), \hat{f}_{n_2}(\lambda)$ for

$$\lambda_j = \frac{\pi j}{k} \qquad j = 1, 2, \ldots, k$$

where k is the ENIE parameter, then under the null hypothesis of no change

$$\ln \hat{f}_{n_1}(\lambda_j) - \ln \hat{f}_{n_2}(\lambda_j) \qquad j = 1, 2, \ldots, k$$

is

$$N\left[0,\,\left(\frac{M_{n_1}}{n_1} + \frac{M_{n_2}}{n_2}\right)G(a)\right]$$

TABLE 11.1. Some standardized characteristics of spectral windows and their associated spectral estimators

Lag window generator $a(\cdot)$	$G(a) = \int_{-\infty}^{\infty} a^2(u)\,du$	$EDF = \dfrac{2n}{M_n G(a)}$	$\beta_1[f_n] = \dfrac{1}{M_n A(0)}$	$\beta_3[f_n]^a = \dfrac{\pi}{M_n G(a)}$	$ENIE[f_n] = M_n G(a)$
I. Dirichlet $a_D(u) = 1$ if $|u| \leq 1$ $= 0$ otherwise	2.00	$\dfrac{n}{M_n}$	$\dfrac{\pi}{M_n}$	$.5\,\dfrac{\pi}{M_n}$	$2M_n$
II. Modified Dirichlet $a_D^*(u) = 1$ if $|u| < 1$ $= \tfrac{1}{2}$ if $|u| = 1$ $= 0$ otherwise	2.00	$\dfrac{n}{M_n}$	$\dfrac{\pi}{M_n}$	$.5\,\dfrac{\pi}{M_n}$	$2M_n$
III. Fejèr $a_F(u) = 1 - |u|$ if $|u| \leq 1$ $= 0$ otherwise	.67	$2.99\,\dfrac{n}{M_n}$	$2\,\dfrac{\pi}{M_n}$	$1.49\,\dfrac{\pi}{M_n}$	$.67\,M_n$
IV. Tukey-Hamming $a_{TH}(u) = \tfrac{1}{2}[1 + \cos \pi u]$ if $|u| \leq 1$ $= 0$ otherwise	.75	$2.67\,\dfrac{n}{M_n}$	$2\,\dfrac{\pi}{M_n}$	$1.33\,\dfrac{\pi}{M_n}$	$.75 M_n$
V. Parzen $a_P(u) = 1 - 6u^2 + 6|u|^3$ if $|u| < \tfrac{1}{2}$ $= 2(1 - |u|)^3$ if $\tfrac{1}{2} \leq |u| \leq 1$ $= 0$ if $|u| > 1$	.54	$3.70\,\dfrac{n}{M_n}$	$2.67\,\dfrac{\pi}{M_n}$	$1.85\,\dfrac{\pi}{M_n}$	$.54\,M_n$

[a] The spectral windows associated with the bandwidth given in this Table have been standardized so that their integral is unity; $\beta_2[f_n]$ has not been presented because the variance, $V(A)$, of some spectral windows is not defined.

It follows, therefore, that the statistic

$$J = \frac{1}{k}\left[\sum_{j=1}^{k} \ln \frac{\hat{f}_{n_1}(\lambda_j)}{\hat{f}_{n_2}(\lambda_j)}\right] \bigg/ \sqrt{G(a)\left(\frac{M_{n_1}}{n_1} + \frac{M_{n_2}}{n_2}\right)} \qquad (11.3.66)$$

is distributed as $N(0, 1)$. Thus the test may be carried out using the readily available tables of the standardized normal distribution.

Some formulas of the asymptotic variances and covariances of various quantities occurring in cross-spectral analysis are given in Jenkins [7, Ch. 18]. Little, however, will be gained by reproducing them here. We note in passing that since $\hat{c}_{\mu\nu}(\cdot)$, $\hat{q}_{\mu\nu}(\cdot)$ are quadratic forms in normal variables, it follows that their distribution would be approximately chi square with degrees of freedom determined by fitting their first two asymptotic moments according to the relation given in (11.3.13).

In summary, we have established the following:

Aliasing is a problem arising when we sample at equidistant time points from a continuous stochastic process. Its consequence is that the resulting spectral estimator no longer estimates the spectrum but rather a sum of spectral ordinates at frequencies related to the Nyquist frequency according to the relation (11.1.2). Hence aliasing amounts to a distortion of the spectrum we are interested in estimating. Problems of distortion (or smudging) also occur when we operate with a lag window truncation point which is fixed independently of sample size. Such problems are particularly acute when the spectrum we are interested in estimating varies appreciably over the bandwidth of the spectral window, and/ or when the spectral window has large secondary peaks (or "side lobes"). Prewhitening (and recoloring) are procedures designed to cope with or at least ameliorate these problems.

The bandwidth of a spectral estimator is designed to give some standardized measure of the extent of smudging permitted by the spectral window.

Several other standardized characteristics associated with commonly discussed spectral windows are also derived. A summary of these characteristics is given in Table 11.1.

Finally, approximations to the asymptotic distributions of spectral, cospectral and quadrature spectral estimators are proposed. All are chi-square distributions with degrees of freedom determined from the asymptotic means and variances of the relevant estimator.

REFERENCES

1. Blackman, R., and J. W. Tukey, *The Measurement of Power Spectra*, New York, Dover 1959.
2. Durbin, J., "Trend Elimination by Moving Average and Variate Difference Filters," *Bulletin International Statistical Institute*, vol. 39, 1962, pp. 131–141.

3. Goodman, N. R., *On the Joint Estimation of the Spectra, Cospectra, and Quadrature Spectrum of a Two-Dimensional Stationary Gaussian Process*, Ph.D. Dissertation, Princeton University, 1957.
4. Hext, G. R., "A Note on Prewhitening and Recoloring," *Technical Report No. 5*, Institute for Mathematical Studies in the Social Sciences, Stanford University, September 1964.
5. Jenkins, G. M., "General Considerations in the Analysis of Spectra," *Technometrics*, vol. 3, 1961, pp. 133–166.
6. Jenkins, G. M., "An Example of the Estimation of a Linear Open Loop Transfer Function," *Technometrics*, vol. 5, 1963, pp. 227–245.
7. Jenkins, G. M., "Cross-Spectral Analysis and the Estimation of Linear Open Loop Transfer Functions," in *Proceedings of the Symposium on Time Series Analysis*, M. Rosenblatt, (Ed.), New York, Wiley, 1963, pp. 267–276.
8. Jenkins, G. M., and M. B. Priestley, "The Spectral Analysis of Time Series," *Journal of the Royal Statistical Society*, Series B, vol. 19, 1957, pp. 1–12.
9. Lomnicki, Z., and S. K. Zaremba, "On Estimating the Spectral Density Function of a Stochastic Process," *Journal of the Royal Statistical Society*, Series B, vol. 19, 1957, pp. 13–37.
10. Lomnicki, Z., and S. K. Zaremba, "Bandwidth and Resolvability in Statistical Spectral Analysis," *Journal of the Royal Statistical Society*, Series B, vol. 21, 1959, pp. 169–171.
11. Parzen, E., "Mathematical Considerations in the Estimation of Spectra," *Technometrics*, Vol. 3, 1961, pp. 167–190.
12. Parzen, E., "The Role of Spectral Analysis in Time Series," *Technical Report No. 2*, Department of Statistics, Stanford University, 1965.
13. Priestley, M. B., "The Analysis of Stationary Processes with Mixed Spectra" *Journal of the Royal Statistical Society*, Series B, vol. 24, 1962, pp. 215–229.
14. Priestley, M. B., "Estimation of the Spectral Density Function in the Presence of Harmonic Components," *Journal of the Royal Statistical Society*, vol. 26, 1964, pp. 124–132.
15. Schaerf, M., *Estimation of the Covariance and Autoregressive Structure of a Stationary Time Series*. Ph.D. dissertation, Department of Statistics, Stanford University, 1964.

APPLICATIONS OF SPECTRAL ANALYSIS TO SIMULTANEOUS EQUATIONS SYSTEMS

12

12.1 GENERALITIES

Spectral and cross spectral analysis, developed in some detail over the previous chapters, has potentially fruitful applications to econometrics as an adjunct to estimation. We shall not touch on this aspect here, but we shall develop its application to the analysis of the dynamic behavior of (linear) econometric models.

Recall the structural model as presented, say, in Chapter 7,

$$y_{t\cdot} = y_{t\cdot}.B + x_{t\cdot}.C + u_{t\cdot}. \tag{12.1.1}$$

where $y_{t\cdot}$, $x_{t\cdot}$ are, respectively, the (row) vectors of jointly dependent and predetermined variables and $u_{t\cdot}$ is the (row) vector of disturbances in the entire system "at time t." B and C are the matrices of structural parameters to be estimated. Typically we assume, in addition, that the predetermined variables are uncorrelated (or independent) of the error terms of the system and that

$$u'_{t\cdot} \sim N(0, \Sigma) \qquad \text{Cov}(u'_{t\cdot}, u'_{t'\cdot}) = \delta_{tt'}\Sigma \tag{12.1.2}$$

$\delta_{tt'}$ being the Kronecker delta.

In studying the estimation problems presented by this model (Chapter 7), we were not particularly interested in differentiating between *lagged endogenous* and *exogenous* variables. Rather, we subsumed both under the classification "predetermined" variables. As we shall see below, this distinction is of fundamental importance here. If no lagged endogenous variables appear among the predetermined variables of the system, then the reduced form gives a complete description of the evolution of the system over time. Indeed, the position of the system at "time t" may be completely determined solely from a knowledge of exogenous variables (and, of course, the structural parameters) within the additive stochastic disturbances.

On the other hand, if lagged endogenous variables appear among the predetermined variables of the system, then we are actually dealing with a system of difference equations and the behavior of the system at "time t" depends on its position at "time $t - 1$" and cannot be solely inferred from a knowledge of exogenous variables.

In such dynamic systems, there is an important distinction between short- and long-run behavior, and the reduced form does not constitute an adequate representation of the long-run characteristics of the model.

To recapitulate: Although the distinction between lagged endogenous and exogenous variables is superfluous from an estimation point of view,[1] this distinction is quite important if we are interested in the dynamic behavior of the system. Suppose, for example, that we effect a change in one of the system's exogenous variables. What is the impact of this on the dependent variables?

One possible answer is to obtain the reduced form

$$y_t. = x_t. \, BD + u_t. \, D \qquad D = (I - B)^{-1} \tag{12.1.3}$$

By convention, the matrix BD is denoted by Π and is termed the matrix of *reduced-form coefficients* in the estimation context of previous chapters. The partial derivative of (the expected value of), say, y_{ti} with respect to a specified *exogenous* variable, say x_{tj}, is seen to be the appropriate element of Π. Thus we see that these elements convey information about the impact of exogenous on current endogenous variables after all contemporaneous feedbacks—due to the simultaneity of the system—have been allowed for. The corresponding submatrix of Π is thus termed the matrix of *impact multipliers*.

If the system contains no lagged endogenous variables, this is the end of the story, so to speak. If it does, however, then the repercussions of changes in the exogenous variables will carry into the future. Intuitively, this period's current *endogenous* become next period's *lagged endogenous variables*, and as such will affect next period's current endogenous variables, and so on.

Obviously, we are dealing with a system of (stochastic) difference equations, and in this context the answer to the original question is considerably more complex than was intimated above. We might also want to know: Suppose that all exogenous variables are kept constant save one, which is incremented by some

---

[1] As pointed out in Chapter 4, if our sole concern is with estimation, then what is important in classifying variables in a structural model is their correlation (or absence thereof) with the error terms of the system.

amount and is maintained at the new level forever; what is the ultimate effect of this on the jointly dependent variables?

While we were asking about a short-run (indeed, instantaneous) effect earlier, we are now asking about a long-run effect. To answer this last query, we need to obtain the solution of the system of difference equations. A set of equations expressing the jointly dependent variables solely in terms of the exogenous variables of the system is termed the *final form* of the model. Typically one also incorporates initial conditions into the final form; we shall not, however, follow this practice.

In order to answer the dynamical questions posed earlier and to develop the implications of the final form fully, we shall require a slightly different type of analysis and notational scheme than that employed in an estimation context.

12.2 LAG OPERATORS

POLYNOMIAL AND POWER SERIES OPERATORS

Recall (Chapter 10) the discussion of linear time invariant filters. In particular, we had shown that if the output function $y(t)$ and the input function $x(t)$ are connected by a linear time invariant filter, then we have the relation

$$y(t) = \sum_{\tau=0}^{\infty} \phi_\tau x(t - \tau) \tag{12.2.1}$$

where

$$\phi = \{\phi_\tau : \tau = 0, 1, 2, \ldots\} \tag{12.2.2}$$

was termed the *kernel* (of the linear time invariant filter).

Suppose that we introduce the *lag operator* L, defined by

$$L^k x(t) = x(t - k) \qquad k = 0, 1, 2, \ldots \tag{12.2.3}$$

Here the operator corresponding to $k = 0$ is said to be the *identity operator* and is denoted by I.[2] With the aid of the operator, we can rewrite the relation in (12.2.1) as

$$y(t) = \left(\sum_{\tau=0}^{\infty} \phi_\tau L^\tau \right) x(t) = \Phi(L) x(t) \tag{12.2.4}$$

provided that some meaning may be ascribed to the notation

$$\Phi(L) = \sum_{\tau=0}^{\infty} \phi_\tau L^\tau \tag{12.2.5}$$

---

[2] Occasionally this may be confused with the identity matrix; when the meaning of the symbol is not clear from the context, we shall use the notation I_0 to distinguish the operator from the identity matrix.

Even in the simple context of (12.2.3)—and *a fortiori* in the context of a simultaneous equations system—the convenience of the operator notation is obvious, and that reason alone would warrant its use. Actually, more is true, as we shall presently see.

Multiplication of lag operators is defined by

$$L^k L^s = L^{k+s} \tag{12.2.6}$$

This follows immediately from (12.2.3); thus let

$$x^*(t) = L^s x(t) = x(t - s) \tag{12.2.7}$$

Then

$$L^k x^*(t) = x^*(t - k) \tag{12.2.8}$$

But (12.2.7) and (12.2.8) imply

$$L^k L^s x(t) = x(t - k - s) \tag{12.2.9}$$

Since $x(t)$ is any arbitrary function, the relation in (12.2.6) is valid.

Scalar multiplication is defined by

$$c L^k x(t) = c x(t - k) \tag{12.2.10}$$

and generally linear operations are defined by

$$(c_1 L^k + c_2 L^s) x(t) = c_1 x(t - k) + c_2 x(t - s) \tag{12.2.11}$$

where c, c_1, c_2 are scalars and k, s are positive integers. In fact, it may be shown that the vector space generated by $\{I, L, L^2, \ldots\}$ over the field of real (complex) numbers, together with the operation of (operator) multiplication, as defined in (12.2.6), forms an *algebra*. This is an *algebra with identity*, the identity element being the identity operator defined above. To complete the algebraic structure, one ought to define the zero element, which may, of course, be defined by the zero operator $\mathbf{0}$, having the property that for any function $x(t)$,

$$\mathbf{0} x(t) = 0 \tag{12.2.12}$$

We shall not establish the *algebraic structure* of *lag operators* now. The interested reader may consult Dhrymes [5]. Here we shall only assert it and make use of the fact that in view of this structure we can perform with polynomials (or power series) of lag operators the same operations as we do with polynomials (or power series) in real or complex variables. Indeed, we can treat L as if it were a real (or complex) variable. The role of unity is played by the identity operator and the role of zero by the zero operator. The following examples will make these considerations clear.

Example 1: Consider the (polynomial) operator

$$a(L) = \sum_{i=0}^{m} a_i L^i \tag{12.2.13}$$

What meaning are we to ascribe to

$$y(t) = a(L)x(t) \tag{12.2.14}$$

From (12.2.10) and (12.2.11) we see immediately that the meaning of (12.2.14) is simply

$$y(t) = \sum_{i=0}^{m} a_i x_{t-i} \tag{12.2.15}$$

Example 2: If $a(L)$ is as in the previous example and

$$b(L) = \sum_{j=0}^{n} b_j L^j \qquad m \geq n \tag{12.2.16}$$

what meaning is to be ascribed to

$$c(L) = a(L) + b(L) \tag{12.2.17}$$

Bearing in mind the algebraic structure of lag operators, simply replace L by the real (or complex) variable s and note that

$$c(s) = a(s) + b(s) = \sum_{i=0}^{n} (a_i + b_i)s^i + \sum_{i=n+1}^{m} a_i s^i \tag{12.2.18}$$

Thus

$$c(L) = \sum_{i=0}^{m} c_i L^i \tag{12.2.19}$$

where

$$\begin{aligned} c_i &= a_i + b_i & i &= 1, 2, \ldots, n \\ &= a_i & i &= n+1, \ldots, m \end{aligned} \tag{12.2.20}$$

Example 3: If $a(L)$, $b(L)$ are as in the previous example, what meaning are we to ascribe to

$$c(L) = a(L)b(L) \tag{12.2.21}$$

By the usual rules for multiplying real (or complex) polynomials, we conclude

$$c(L) = \sum_{i=0}^{m} \sum_{j=0}^{n} a_i b_j L^{i+j} \tag{12.2.22}$$

We notice that

$$a(L)b(L) = b(L)a(L) \tag{12.2.23}$$

The reader may verify this as follows. Put

$$y_1(t) = b(L)x(t) \tag{12.2.24}$$

and

$$y(t) = a(L)y_1(t) \tag{12.2.25}$$

thus obtaining

$$y(t) = \sum_{i=0}^{m} a_i \, y_1(t-i) = \sum_{i=0}^{m} a_i \sum_{j=0}^{n} b_j x(t-i-j) = \left(\sum_{i=0}^{m} \sum_{j=0}^{n} a_i \, b_j \, L^{i+j} \right) x(t) \tag{12.2.26}$$

We may then compute

$$y^*(t) = b(L)a(L)x(t) \tag{12.2.27}$$

and verify the relation in (12.2.23).

Example 4: If $a(L)$ is as in previous examples, what meaning is to be ascribed to

$$y(t) = a(L)[x_1(t) + x_2(t)] \tag{12.2.28}$$

Putting

$$x_1(t) + x_2(t) = x(t) \tag{12.2.29}$$

and applying $a(L)$ to $x(t)$, we find

$$a(L)[x_1(t) + x_2(t)] = a(L)x_1(t) + a(L)x_2(t) \tag{12.2.30}$$

Example 5: What meaning may be ascribed to the power series operator

$$\lambda(L) = \sum_{i=0}^{\infty} \lambda^i L^i \tag{12.2.31}$$

Remembering the algebraic structure of operators, the question is equivalent to: What meaning is to be ascribed to the real (or complex) power series

$$\lambda(s) = \sum_{i=0}^{\infty} \lambda^i s^i = \sum_{i=0}^{\infty} (\lambda s)^i \tag{12.2.32}$$

But we know that this power series is divergent unless

$$|\lambda s| < 1 \tag{12.2.33}$$

If we wish this power series to converge for all s in the unit disk, that is, for all $|s| \leq 1$, then we must have the condition

$$|\lambda| < 1 \tag{12.2.34}$$

If (12.2.34) holds, then for all $|s| \leq 1$, the series is convergent and may be summed to

$$\lambda(s) = \frac{1}{1 - \lambda s} \tag{12.2.35}$$

Thus if (12.2.34) holds, the operator in (12.2.31) can be represented as

$$\lambda(L) = \frac{I}{I - \lambda L} \qquad (12.2.36)$$

Example 6: In previous examples, we had made clear what meaning is to be attached to

$$b(L) = \sum_{j=0}^{n} b_j L^j \qquad (12.2.37)$$

and in Example 5 we have, in fact, shown what meaning is to be attached to $I/(I - \lambda L)$, where, of course, $I - \lambda L$ is a rather special form of the polynomial $b(L)$ in (12.2.37). Let us now establish what meaning is to be attached to $I/b(L)$. Consider

$$y(t) = \frac{I}{b(L)} x(t) \qquad (12.2.38)$$

Suppose that the quantity in (12.2.38) is well defined so that we can apply $b(L)$ to both sides to obtain

$$b(L)y(t) = x(t) \qquad (12.2.39)$$

Let us make the convention

$$b_0 = 1 \qquad (12.2.40)$$

and notice that (12.2.39) is a standard nth-order difference equation with constant coefficients and "forcing function" $x(t)$. For the quantity in (12.2.38) to be well defined, the equation in (12.2.39) must be stable; that is, the roots of its associated characteristic equation must be less than unity in absolute value.[3]
    The characteristic equation of the homogeneous part is given by

$$\sum_{j=0}^{n} b_j \phi^{n-j} = 0 \qquad (12.2.41)$$

Let the roots of (12.2.41) be $\{\phi_i : i = 1, 2, \ldots, n\}$; then the stability conditions require

$$|\phi_i| < 1 \qquad i = 1, 2, \ldots, n \qquad (12.2.42)$$

Now, why is this relevant to the problem of giving meaning to the operator $I/b(L)$? Well, consider the polynomial equation

$$b(s) = \sum_{j=0}^{n} b_j s^j = 0 \qquad (12.2.43)$$

---

[3] The reader may ask himself, why is this so? *Hint:* The "solution" in (12.2.38) does not contain initial conditions.

If $\{s_i: i = 1, 2, \ldots, n\}$ are the roots of (12.2.43), it is easily verified that they are also the roots of

$$b^*(s) = \sum_{j=0}^{n} b_j^* s^j = 0 \qquad b_j^* = \frac{b_j}{b_n} \qquad j = 0, 1, 2, \ldots, n \tag{12.2.44}$$

But $b^*(s)$ is a monic polynomial, and as such has the representation

$$b^*(s) = \prod_{i=1}^{n} (s - s_i) \tag{12.2.45}$$

Therefore we can write

$$b(s) = b_n b^*(s) = b_n \prod_{i=1}^{n} (s - s_i) = b_n \prod_{i=1}^{n} (-s_i)\left(1 - \frac{s}{s_i}\right)$$

$$= b_n(-1)^n \left(\prod_{i=1}^{n} s_i\right) \prod_{i=1}^{n} \left(1 - \frac{s}{s_i}\right) \tag{12.2.46}$$

But, as is well known,

$$(-1)^n \prod_{i=1}^{n} s_i = \frac{1}{b_n} \tag{12.2.47}$$

Hence

$$b(L) = \prod_{i=1}^{n} (I - \lambda_i L) \tag{12.2.48}$$

where $\lambda_i = 1/s_i$, $i = 1, 2, \ldots, n$. If we can show that

$$|\lambda_i| < 1 \qquad i = 1, 2, \ldots, n \tag{12.2.49}$$

we see that $I/b(L)$ can be given a power series interpretation, for $b(L)$ can be expressed as a *product* of operators of the type considered in the previous example. Thus let us see whether (12.2.49) holds.

It is clear from (12.2.44) that zero is not a root of that equation. Consider

$$b^*(s) = s^n \sum_{j=0}^{n} b_j^* s^{-n+j} \tag{12.2.50}$$

If s_i is a root of

$$b^*(s) = 0 \tag{12.2.51}$$

then $s_i \neq 0$ and thus it is also a root of

$$\sum_{j=0}^{n} b_j^* s^{-n+j} = \sum_{j=0}^{n} b_j^* \left(\frac{1}{s}\right)^{n-j} = 0 \tag{12.2.52}$$

But if s_i is a root of (12.2.52), then it is also a root of

$$b_n \sum_{j=0}^{n} b_j^* s^{-n+j} = \sum_{j=0}^{n} b_j \left(\frac{1}{s}\right)^{n-j} = 0 \qquad (12.2.53)$$

that is,

$$\sum_{j=0}^{n} b_j \left(\frac{1}{s_i}\right)^{n-j} = 0 \qquad (12.2.54)$$

Comparing (12.2.41) and (12.2.53), we see that we have the relation

$$\phi_i = \frac{1}{s_i} \qquad i = 1, 2, \ldots, n \qquad (12.2.55)$$

Since the difference equation is assumed to be stable, it is clear that (12.2.49) holds.

Hence we can write

$$\frac{I}{b(L)} = \left(\frac{I}{\prod_{i=1}^{n} (I - \lambda_i L)}\right) = \prod_{i=1}^{n} \left(\sum_{k=0}^{\infty} \lambda_i^k L^k\right) \qquad (12.2.56)$$

Remark 1: Notice that the roots of

$$b(s) = 0 \qquad (12.2.57)$$

must lie *outside* the unit circle for (12.2.56) to be valid; otherwise the representation is meaningless. *The roots of (12.2.57) are the inverse of the roots of the associated characteristic equation of the homogeneous difference equation.*

Example 7: Consider now the operator

$$c(L) = \frac{a(L)}{b(L)} \qquad (12.2.58)$$

$a(L)$, $b(L)$ being as defined in Examples 1 and 2. An operator like this will be referred to as a *rational operator*. Now the meaning to be attached to it is quite evident from the preceding discussion. In Example 6 we have explained the meaning of $I/b(L)$, while in Example 3 we have explained how to "multiply" two polynomial operators. The extension to the multiplication of a polynomial and a power series operator (or two power series operators) is quite obvious and will not be elaborated here.

MATRICES WITH OPERATOR ELEMENTS

In subsequent discussions we shall find it useful to deal with matrices whose elements are polynomial operators. Thus let

$$A(L) = [a_{ij}(L)] \qquad (12.2.59)$$

where

$$a_{ij}(L) = \sum_{k=0}^{d_{ij}} a_{ijk} L^k \qquad i = 1, 2, \ldots, m, j = 1, 2, \ldots, n \tag{12.2.60}$$

If $x(t)$ is an n-dimensional vector, then the meaning of

$$y(t) = A(L)x(t) \tag{12.2.61}$$

is that $y(t)$ is an m-dimensional vector whose ith element is given by

$$y_i(t) = \sum_{j=1}^{n} a_{ij}(L)x_j(t) = \sum_{j=1}^{n} \sum_{k=0}^{d_{ij}} a_{ijk} x_j(t-k) \tag{12.2.62}$$

If

$$B(L) = [b_{ij}(L)] \qquad i = 1, 2, \ldots, q, j = 1, 2, \ldots, r \tag{12.2.63}$$

each $b_{ij}(L)$ being a polynomial operator, then

$$C(L) = [c_{ij}(L)] = A(L) + B(L) \tag{12.2.64}$$

is defined by

$$c_{ij}(L) = a_{ij}(L) + b_{ij}(L) \qquad \text{all } i \text{ and } j \tag{12.2.65}$$

provided, of course,

$$m = q \qquad n = r \tag{12.2.66}$$

If $n = q$, the product

$$C(L) = A(L)B(L) \tag{12.2.67}$$

is defined by

$$c_{ij}(L) = \sum_{k=1}^{n} a_{ik}(L)b_{kj}(L) \qquad i = 1, 2, \ldots, m, j = 1, 2, \ldots, r \tag{12.2.68}$$

What are we to mean by the inverse of a matrix whose elements are lag operators? Well we would want such a matrix, to be denoted by $A^{-1}(L)$, to have the property that if applied to $A(L)$ it will yield an identity operator. Thus we wish to have

$$A(L)A^{-1}(L) = A^{-1}(L)A(L) = D(I_0) \tag{12.2.69}$$

where

$$D(I_0) = \text{diag}\,(I_0, I_0, \ldots, I_0) \tag{12.2.70}$$

that is, it is a diagonal matrix whose nonzero elements consist of the identity (lag) operator.

Thus if

$$y(t) = A(L)x(t) \tag{12.2.71}$$

then the inverse of (the square matrix) $A(L)$ is defined by the property

$$A^{-1}(L)y(t) = A^{-1}(L)A(L)x(t) = x(t)$$
$$A(L)x(t) = A(L)A^{-1}(L)y(t) = y(t) \tag{12.2.72}$$

How can we define the elements of $A^{-1}(L)$, explicitly in terms of the elements of $A(L)$? Again, remembering the equivalence between the algebras of real (or complex) polynomials and operators, we consider the problem of defining the inverse of $A(s)$, whose elements are polynomials in a real (or complex) variable.

Let $|A(s)|$ be the determinant of $A(s)$; then $|A(s)|$ is a polynomial of degree $n \times (\max_{i,j} d_{ij})$ at most, n being the dimension of the matrix and d_{ij} being the degree of the polynomial $a_{ij}(s)$.

Denote by $A_{ij}(s)$ the cofactor of the element $a_{ij}(s)$; then the (i, j) element of $A^{-1}(s)$, say $a^{ij}(s)$, may be defined by

$$a^{ij}(s) = \frac{A_{ji}(s)}{|A(s)|} \qquad i, j = 1, 2, \ldots, n \tag{12.2.73}$$

The reader may verify that this definition of an inverse obeys the requirement given in (12.2.69).

Just as in the case of matrices with scalar elements, the inverse will not always exist. Under what conditions will the inverse, $A^{-1}(L)$, exist? It is clear from the formalism in (12.2.73) that the inverse will exist if and only if the *rational operator* in (12.2.73) is well defined.

This problem, however, was dealt with in Examples 6 and 7. Thus the inverse will exist when the roots of the polynomial

$$|A(s)| = 0 \tag{12.2.74}$$

lie *outside the unit circle*.

12.3   AN OPERATOR REPRESENTATION OF THE FINAL FORM

As pointed out earlier, the study of the final form and dynamic characteristics of the general structural model requires a somewhat different notation and emphasis than was necessary in the estimation context of previous chapters.

Here we shall carefully develop a representation of the final form in the context of which the dynamic characteristics of the model will be more conveniently identified. Consider again the general structural model

$$Y = YB + XC + U \tag{12.3.1}$$

As we have seen, the reduced form

$$Y = X\Pi + V \qquad \Pi = CD \qquad V = UD \qquad D = (I - B)^{-1} \tag{12.3.2}$$

gives information concerning the "impact" or instantaneous response of the dependent variables of the system to changes in its *exogenous* variables after feedbacks due to simultaneity have been allowed for. Indeed, this information is conveyed by a certain subset of the elements of the matrix Π, which for that reason was termed the *matrix of instantaneous (or impact) multipliers*.

If we are interested in the long-run response of the system's jointly dependent variables to changes in its *exogenous* variables, the representation in (12.3.2) is inappropriate to the purpose. Hence let us develop a more convenient representation.

The tth observation on the entire system is

$$y_{t.} = y_{t.} \, B + x_{t.} \, C + u_{t.}. \tag{12.3.3}$$

Let us settle on a particular numbering convention for the jointly dependent variables; having done so, it will be very convenient to number the *predetermined variables*—that is, the elements of $x_{t.}$—as follows:

$$x_{t.} = (y_{t-1.}, y_{t-2.}, \ldots, y_{t-r.}, w_{t.}, w_{t-1.}, \ldots, w_{t-k.}) \tag{12.3.4}$$

where $w_{t.}$ is a vector of s elements representing the *exogenous* variables of the system. The assumption in (12.3.4) is that the system contains lagged endogenous variables, their maximal lag being of order r, and *lagged exogenous* variables whose maximal lag is of order k.

In terms of the convention employed in Chapters 4 through 8, the number of jointly dependent variables is still m, so that $y_{t.}$ is an m-element row vector, and the number of predetermined variables, G, obeys[4]

$$G = mr + s(k + 1) \tag{12.3.5}$$

The number of basic exogenous variables is of course s, while the total number of *current* and *lagged exogenous* variables is $s(k + 1)$; the number of lagged endogenous variables is mr. In this context, we do not require any numbering convention that refers to variables appearing in any given equation and none will be made, contrary to our practice in earlier chapters.

Let us now write (12.3.3) in the more customary form

$$y'_{t.} = B'y'_t + C'x'_t + u'_t. \tag{12.3.6}$$

and partition C' conformally with $x_{t.}$ of (12.3.4) so that

$$C' = (C_1, C_2, \ldots, C_r, C_0^*, C_1^*, \ldots, C_k^*) \tag{12.3.7}$$

Here each C_i, $i = 1, 2, \ldots, r$, is an $m \times m$ matrix—not necessarily nonsingular—and each C_j^*, $j = 0, 1, 2, \ldots, k$, is an $m \times s$ matrix.

---

[4] For this count to be accurate, the equations must not contain a constant term because the corresponding fictitious variable unity has no meaningful lags. Alternatively, we can think of all variables as deviations from sample means.

Thus the system in (12.3.6) can be written more conveniently as

$$\left(C_0 I_0 - \sum_{i=1}^{r} C_i L^i\right) y'_t. = \left(\sum_{j=0}^{k} C_j^* L^j\right) w'_t. + u'_t. \tag{12.3.8}$$

Let

$$C(L) = \left(C_0 I_0 - \sum_{i=1}^{r} C_i L^i\right) \quad C^*(L) = \sum_{j=0}^{k} C_j^* L^j \quad C_0 = I - B \tag{12.3.9}$$

and notice that the general structural model may be written as

$$C(L) y'_t. = C^*(L) w'_t. + u'_t. \tag{12.3.10}$$

If the operator matrix $C(L)$ is invertible, then the final[5] form may be obtained explicitly as

$$y'_t. = [C(L)]^{-1} C^*(L) w'_t. + [C(L)]^{-1} u'_t. \tag{12.3.11}$$

As we saw in the previous section, $C(L)$ will be invertible if the roots of

$$|C(\rho)| = 0 \tag{12.3.12}$$

lie outside the unit circle, $|C(\rho)|$ being a polynomial in the real (or complex) variable ρ, which is obtained by substituting ρ for the operator L in $C(L)$. Hence we see that *the general structural econometric model is basically a system of rational distributed lags in the exogenous variables.*

From the expression in (12.3.10) it is evident that we are dealing with a system of stochastic difference equations with constant coefficients and "forcing functions" $C^*(L) w'_t.$.

Presumably we would want this to be a stable system, so that if the values of the exogenous variables are specified to be finite, then the conditional expectation of the jointly dependent variables is also finite. If this does not hold, then the economic system we purport to describe by (12.3.10) is unstable and will diverge to $+\infty$ or $-\infty$, depending on initial conditions, or it will experience oscillations of increasing amplitude.

Stability for a system of difference equations as in (12.3.8) is ensured if the roots of the polynomial

$$|C_0 \phi^r - C_1 \phi^{r-1} - C_2 \phi^{r-2}, \ldots, -C_r| = 0 \tag{12.3.13}$$

are less than unity in absolute value.

---

[5] The term *final form* is also used to denote the following system $|C(L)| y'_t. = |C(L)| [C(L)]^{-1} \times C^*(L) w'_t. + |C(L)| [C(L)]^{-1} u'_t.$ Notice that in this version every current endogenous variable is expressed solely in terms of its *own lags* and the exogenous variables of the system. The expression in (12.3.11) is, however, preferable and a more appropriate term for the representation above would be *autoregressive final form.*

It is easily verified that if ϕ_i, ρ_i are, respectively, the ith roots of (12.3.13) and (12.3.12), then they are related by

$$\phi_i = \frac{1}{\rho_i} \qquad (12.3.14)$$

Thus no further assumption is needed beyond the stability of the economic system under consideration in order that the representation in (12.3.11) be valid. Such an assumption is customary in the estimation of dynamic systems; see, for example, Mann and Wald [12].

Remark 2: Intuitively, the representation in (12.3.11) is, in fact, the solution to the system of difference equations when the initial conditions "are pushed back to minus infinity," so that they no longer affect the system at "time t."
We illustrate this by means of a simple example. Consider the equation

$$x(t) = \lambda x(t-1) + f(t) \qquad (12.3.15)$$

$f(t)$ being the "forcing function." Consider the system as beginning at "time" α so that the initial condition is $x(\alpha)$. We have, solving the equation iteratively,

$$x(\alpha + 1) = \lambda x(\alpha) + f(\alpha + 1)$$
$$x(\alpha + 2) = \lambda^2 x(\alpha) + \lambda f(\alpha + 1) + f(\alpha + 2) \qquad (12.3.16)$$

or, generally,

$$x(\alpha + \tau) = \lambda^\tau x(\alpha) + \sum_{i=0}^{\tau-1} \lambda^i f(\alpha + \tau - i) \qquad (12.3.17)$$

Make the change in notation

$$t = \tau + \alpha \qquad (12.3.18)$$

and substitute in (12.3.17) to obtain

$$x(t) = \lambda^{t-\alpha} x(\alpha) + \sum_{i=0}^{t-\alpha-1} \lambda^i f(t - i) \qquad (12.3.19)$$

If

$$\lim_{\alpha \to -\infty} \lambda^{t-\alpha} x(\alpha) = 0 \qquad (12.3.20)$$

then the limiting form of (12.3.19) becomes

$$x(t) = \sum_{i=0}^{\infty} \lambda^i f(t - i) = \frac{I}{I - \lambda L}\, f(t) \qquad (12.3.21)$$

which is of the same form as the representation in (12.3.11).
Let us illustrate the derivations above by

Example 8: Consider the general structural model

$$y_{t1} = \beta_{21}y_{t2} + \gamma_{11}y_{t-1,1} + \gamma_{011}^* x_{t1} + \gamma_{121}^* x_{t-1,2} + u_{t1}$$
$$y_{t2} = \beta_{12}y_{t1} + \gamma_{12}y_{t-1,1} + \gamma_{22}y_{t-1,2} + \gamma_{022}^* x_{t2} + \gamma_{112}^* x_{t-1,1} + u_{t2}$$

$$(12.3.22)$$

In operator form, the system may be written as

$$\begin{bmatrix} I - \gamma_{11}L & -\beta_{21}I \\ -\beta_{12}I - \gamma_{12}L & I - \gamma_{22}L \end{bmatrix}\begin{pmatrix} y_{t1} \\ y_{t2} \end{pmatrix} = \begin{bmatrix} \gamma_{011}^* I & \gamma_{121}^* L \\ \gamma_{112}^* L & \gamma_{022}^* I \end{bmatrix}\begin{pmatrix} x_{t1} \\ x_{t2} \end{pmatrix} + \begin{pmatrix} u_{t1} \\ u_{t2} \end{pmatrix}$$

$$(12.3.23)$$

Here the exogenous variables are x_1, x_2 and

$$C(L) = \begin{bmatrix} I - \gamma_{11}L & -\beta_{21}I \\ -\beta_{12}I - \gamma_{12}L & I - \gamma_{22}L \end{bmatrix} \qquad C^*(L) = \begin{bmatrix} \gamma_{011}^* I & \gamma_{121}^* L \\ \gamma_{112}^* L & \gamma_{022}^* I \end{bmatrix}$$

$$(12.3.24)$$

Moreover,

$$|C(L)| = (1 - \beta_{12}\beta_{21})I - (\beta_{21}\gamma_{12} + \gamma_{11} + \gamma_{22})L + \gamma_{11}\gamma_{22}L^2 \qquad (12.3.25)$$

and

$$[C(L)]^{-1} = \frac{1}{|C(L)|}\begin{bmatrix} I - \gamma_{22}L & \beta_{21}I \\ \beta_{12}I + \gamma_{12}L & I - \gamma_{11}L \end{bmatrix} \qquad (12.3.26)$$

Thus the final form is

$$\begin{pmatrix} y_{t1} \\ y_{t2} \end{pmatrix} = [C(L)]^{-1}C^*(L)\begin{pmatrix} x_{t1} \\ x_{t2} \end{pmatrix} + [C(L)]^{-1}\begin{pmatrix} u_{t1} \\ u_{t2} \end{pmatrix} \qquad (12.3.27)$$

where

$$[C(L)]^{-1}C^*(L) = \frac{1}{|C(L)|} \times$$

$$\begin{bmatrix} \gamma_{011}^* I + (\beta_{21}\gamma_{112}^* - \gamma_{22}\gamma_{011}^*)L & \beta_{21}\gamma_{022}^* I + \gamma_{121}^* L - \gamma_{22}\gamma_{121}^* L^2 \\ \beta_{12}\gamma_{011}^* I + (\gamma_{112}^* + \gamma_{12}\gamma_{011}^*)L - \gamma_{11}\gamma_{112}^* L^2 & \gamma_{022}^* I + (\beta_{12}\gamma_{121}^* - \gamma_{11}\gamma_{022}^*)L + \gamma_{12}\gamma_{121}^* L^2 \end{bmatrix}$$

$$(12.3.28)$$

12.4 DYNAMIC MULTIPLIERS AND THE FINAL FORM

From the operator representation of the final form, equation (12.3.11), we easily conclude that the conditional expectation of the jointly dependent variables, *given* the exogenous variables of the system, is

$$E(y_{t\cdot}' \mid w_{t\cdot}') = [C(L)]^{-1}C^*(L)w_{t\cdot}'. \qquad (12.4.1)$$

Thus if the structural parameters are estimated by any standard simultaneous equations procedure, we can easily obtain the parameters of the conditional expectation of the final form.

Now, suppose that we evaluate (12.4.1) for constant exogenous vector

$$w_{t\cdot} = \bar{w} \tag{12.4.2}$$

The final form in (12.4.1) then yields

$$E(y_t' \mid \bar{w}) = [C(1)]^{-1} C^*(1)\bar{w}' \tag{12.4.3}$$

which results when we substitute, for the operator L, the *scalar* unity in the matrices $C(L)$, $C^*(L)$. The Jacobian matrix of the expected value of the final form with respect to the exogenous variables is thus

$$\frac{dE(y_t' \mid \bar{w})}{d\bar{w}} = [C(1)]^{-1} C^*(1) \tag{12.4.4}$$

and has the following interpretation. If we change the value of the jth exogenous variable from $\bar{w}_j$ to, say, $\bar{w}_j + 1$ and maintain the new level forever, all other exogenous variables remaining fixed, then the ultimate impact of this on, say, the expectation of the ith jointly dependent variable is given by the (i, j) element of $[C(1)]^{-1} C^*(1)$. Thus we may call the (i, j) element of the latter the *dynamic multiplier of the jth exogenous variable relative to the ith endogenous variable*. Hence $[C(1)]^{-1} C^*(1)$ is said to be *the matrix of dynamic multipliers*.

Example 9: In terms of the simple model of the previous example, the matrix of dynamic multipliers is given by

$$[C(1)]^{-1} C^*(1) = \frac{1}{|C(1)|} \times$$

$$\begin{bmatrix} \gamma_{011}^* + \beta_{21}\gamma_{112}^* - \gamma_{22}\gamma_{011}^* & \beta_{21}\gamma_{022}^* + \gamma_{121}^* - \gamma_{22}\gamma_{121}^* \\ \beta_{12}\gamma_{011}^* + \gamma_{112}^* + \gamma_{12}\gamma_{011}^* - \gamma_{11}\gamma_{112}^* & \gamma_{022}^* + \beta_{12}\gamma_{121}^* - \gamma_{11}\gamma_{022}^* + \gamma_{12}\gamma_{121}^* \end{bmatrix} \tag{12.4.5}$$

where, of course,

$$|C(1)| = 1 - \beta_{12}\beta_{21} - \beta_{21}\gamma_{12} - \gamma_{11} - \gamma_{22} + \gamma_{11}\gamma_{22} \tag{12.4.6}$$

Clearly, for the matrix of dynamic multipliers to exist, we must have

$$|C(1)| \neq 0 \tag{12.4.7}$$

As an exercise, the reader may determine whether our assumptions ensure that (12.4.7) indeed holds.

Other interesting inferences may be made with respect to the final form.

First, we observe that each element of $[C(L)]^{-1}C^*(L)$ is a *rational lag operator* with denominator polynomial $|C(L)|$. Denote by $A(L)$ the matrix

$$A(L) = |C(L)|[C(L)]^{-1}C^*(L) \qquad (12.4.8)$$

and let its (i, j) element be denoted by $a_{ij}(L)$. Observe that $a_{ij}(L)$ is a polynomial operator of degree $(m - 1)r + s(k + 1)$ at most. Let

$$|C(L)| = b(L) = \sum_{i=0}^{mr} b_i L^i \qquad (12.4.9)$$

and notice that $|C(L)|$ is of degree mr at most. Now, the (i, j) element of $[C(L)]^{-1}C^*(L)$ is simply $a_{ij}(L)/b(L)$. Let ρ_i, $i = 1, 2, \ldots, mr$, be the roots of (12.3.12) and define

$$\lambda_i = \frac{1}{\rho_i} \qquad (12.4.10)$$

From Example 6 we know that we can represent $b(L)$ by[6]

$$b(L) = \prod_{i=0}^{mr} (I - \lambda_i L) \qquad (12.4.11)$$

By the stability assumption, we know

$$|\lambda_i| < 1 \qquad i = 1, 2, \ldots, mr \qquad (12.4.12)$$

so that we may write formally

$$\frac{a_{ij}(L)}{b(L)} = \sum_{k=0}^{\infty} a_{ijk} L^k \qquad (12.4.13)$$

Therefore we have the representation

$$[C(L)]^{-1}C^*(L) = \left[\sum_{k=0}^{\infty} a_{ijk} L^k \right] \qquad i = 1, 2, \ldots, m, j = 1, 2, \ldots, s \qquad (12.4.14)$$

We are now in a position to answer the following question: Suppose that we change the jth exogenous variable from $\bar{w}_j$ to, say, $\bar{w}_j + 1$, all other exogenous variables remaining fixed. If we maintain the new level indefinitely, what is the effect on the conditional expectation of the ith current endogenous variable after τ periods?

Formally, we have

$$E(y_{ti} \mid w_{t.}) = \sum_{\alpha=1}^{s} \sum_{k=0}^{\infty} a_{i\alpha k} w_{t-k, \alpha} \qquad (12.4.15)$$

---

[6] The reader may ask himself as an exercise: Under what circumstances will $b(L)$ be exactly of degree mr?

Because of our assumptions, we may write

$$\sum_{\alpha=1}^{s} \sum_{k=0}^{\infty} a_{i\alpha k} w_{t-k,\alpha} = \sum_{\alpha=1}^{s} \sum_{k=0}^{\infty} a_{i\alpha k} \bar{w}_\alpha + \sum_{k=0}^{\infty} a_{ijk} \qquad (12.4.16)$$

But

$$E(y_{ti} \mid \bar{w}) = \sum_{\alpha=1}^{s} \sum_{k=0}^{\infty} a_{i\alpha k} \bar{w}_\alpha \qquad \bar{w} = (\bar{w}_1, \bar{w}_2, \ldots, \bar{w}_s) \qquad (12.4.17)$$

Hence

$$E[y_{ti} \mid \bar{w} + (0, \ldots, 1, 0, \ldots, 0)] - E[y_{ti} \mid \bar{w}] = \sum_{k=0}^{\infty} a_{ijk} \qquad (12.4.18)$$

The effect registered after τ periods is $\sum_{k=0}^{\tau} a_{ijk}$ and is thus seen to be nothing more than *the τth-order partial sum of the infinite series representation of the corresponding element in the matrix of dynamic multipliers,* $[C(1)]^{-1} C^*(1)$.

The quantity $\sum_{k=0}^{\tau} a_{ijk}$ is occasionally referred to as the *τ-period dynamic multiplier of the jth exogenous with respect to the ith current endogenous variable.*

To recapitulate our discussion of multipliers: *The matrix of instantaneous (or impact) multipliers is a submatrix of the coefficient matrix of the reduced form.* (As an exercise, the reader may determine what is the submatrix in question. *Hint:* What meaning can be attached to $C_0^{-1} C_0^*$?) *The matrix of dynamic multipliers is the matrix* $[C(1)]^{-1} C^*(1)$.

The matrix of τ-period dynamic multipliers is the matrix of τth-order partial sums of the corresponding elements of $[C(1)]^{-1} C^*(1)$, *when the latter have been expressed as infinite series.*

Perhaps in this terminologic scheme the matrix $[C(1)]^{-1} C^*(1)$ should be called the matrix of infinite period dynamic multipliers; we shall not, however, employ this cumbersome terminology in what follows.

The following example illustrates the considerations discussed above.

Example 10: Consider again the model in Example 8 and let the matrix $A(L)$ be defined as in (12.4.8). Let the quantity $|C(L)|$, as given in (12.3.25), be denoted by

$$|C(L)| = b(L) = b_0 I + b_1 L + b_2 L^2 \qquad (12.4.19)$$

where the symbols b_i, $i = 1, 2$, have the obvious meaning—by comparison with (12.3.25). Let ρ_1, ρ_2 be the roots of the equation

$$b_0 + b_1 \rho + b_2 \rho^2 = 0 \qquad (12.4.20)$$

and let

$$\lambda_i = \frac{1}{\rho_i} \qquad i = 1, 2 \qquad (12.4.21)$$

Then $b(L)$ has the representation

$$b(L) = \frac{I}{(I - \lambda_1 L)(I - \lambda_2 L)} = \sum_{\alpha=0}^{\infty} \sum_{\alpha'=0}^{\infty} \lambda_1^{\alpha} \lambda_2^{\alpha'} L^{\alpha+\alpha'} \tag{12.4.22}$$

Consider now the $(1, 1)$ element of $[C(L)]^{-1} C^*(L)$. It is obviously given by

$$\left(\sum_{\alpha=0}^{\infty} \sum_{\alpha'=0}^{\infty} \lambda_1^{\alpha} \lambda_2^{\alpha'} L^{\alpha+\alpha'} \right)(c_{011} I + c_{111} L)$$

$$= c_{011} I + \sum_{\tau=1}^{\infty} \left[c_{011} \sum_{\alpha=0}^{\tau} \lambda_1^{\alpha} \lambda_2^{\tau-\alpha} + c_{111} \sum_{\alpha=0}^{\tau-1} \lambda_1^{\alpha} \lambda_2^{\tau-\alpha-1} \right] L^{\tau}$$

$$\tag{12.4.23}$$

where, of course,

$$c_{011} = \gamma_{011}^* \qquad c_{111} = \beta_{21} \gamma_{112}^* - \gamma_{22} \gamma_{011}^* \tag{12.4.24}$$

In this representation, the $(1, 1)$ element of the matrix of dynamic multipliers is obviously

$$\frac{c_{011} + c_{111}}{(1 - \lambda_1)(1 - \lambda_2)}$$

and the τ-period dynamic multiplier corresponding to it is

$$c_{011} + \sum_{\tau'=1}^{\tau} \left(c_{011} \sum_{\alpha=0}^{\tau'} \lambda_1^{\alpha} \lambda_2^{\tau'-\alpha} + c_{111} \sum_{\alpha=0}^{\tau'-1} \lambda_1^{\alpha} \lambda_2^{\tau'-\alpha-1} \right)$$

12.5 SPECTRAL PROPERTIES OF THE FINAL FORM

In the preceding section, we had established that the final form of a (linear) dynamic structural econometric model can be expressed as a rational lag function of the *exogenous* variables of the system and its error terms.

We shall now make use of our knowledge of linear time invariant filters in order to determine the *spectral* matrix of the final form. If we succeed in this, then we can quite easily infer, *inter alia*, the nature of the cyclical behavior of the system.

Recall that the final form can be expressed as

$$y'_{t\cdot} = \frac{A(L)}{b(L)} w'_{t\cdot} + \frac{G(L)}{b(L)} u'_{t\cdot} \tag{12.5.1}$$

where, we remind the reader,

$$A(L) = G(L) C^*(L) \qquad b(L) = |C(L)| \tag{12.5.2}$$

and $G(L)$ is the adjoint of $C(L)$—that is, it is the transpose of the matrix of cofactors associated with the latter.

It was further established that the elements of $A(L)/b(L)$, $G(L)/b(L)$ are *rational lag operators*. From the stability assumption, the (i, j) element $A(L)/b(L)$ ·will have a power series representation, say $\sum_{k=0}^{\infty} a_{ijk} L^k$, $i = 1, 2, \ldots, m$, $j = 1, 2, \ldots, s$. Similarly, the (i, α) element of $G(L)/b(L)$ will also have a power series representation, say $\sum_{k=0}^{\infty} g_{i\alpha k} L^k$, $i = 1, 2, \ldots, m$, $\alpha = 1, 2, \ldots, m$. Under the standard conditions, we ordinarily assume

$$u'_t. \sim N(0, \Sigma) \qquad \text{Cov}(u'_t., u'_{t'}.) = \delta_{tt'} \Sigma \tag{12.5.3}$$

although the normality assumption is suppressed occasionally. Of course, we always maintain that the *exogenous* variables $w'_t.$ are independent of the error terms.

Suppose that the exogenous variables may be decomposed as

$$w_t. = \omega(t) + \varepsilon_t. \tag{12.5.4}$$

where $\omega(t)$ is a deterministic function—say a time trend—and $\varepsilon_t.$ is a (multivariate) covariance stationary process. The latter, of course, implies that the two vectors $\varepsilon_t.$ and $u_t.$ are mutually independent. If (12.5.4) actually holds, then the spectral matrix of $w_t.$ is exactly the spectral matrix of $\varepsilon_t..$ In particular, if we can assert that the vectors $\varepsilon_t.$ form a set of mutually independent, identically distributed random variables with mean 0 and covariance matrix Ω then the spectral matrix of the ε-process is easily shown to be[7]

$$F_\varepsilon(\theta) = \frac{1}{2\pi} \Omega \tag{12.5.5}$$

The spectral matrix of the exogenous variables is thus given by

$$F_w(\theta) = \frac{1}{2\pi} \Omega \tag{12.5.6}$$

Returning now to the final form in (12.5.1), we see that, if (12.5.4) holds, then we can write

$$y'_t. = \frac{A(L)}{b(L)} \omega'(t) + \frac{A(L)}{b(L)} \varepsilon'_t. + \frac{G(L)}{b(L)} u'_t. \tag{12.5.7}$$

The final form thus consists of a solely deterministic component, $A(L)/b(L)\omega'(t)$, and two stochastic components. Of the latter, one is contributed by the *random process associated with the exogenous variables and the other is contributed by the structural error process.* These two processes may be assumed mutually independent and covariance stationary.

---

[7] As an exercise, the reader should verify this assertion. (*Hint*: From Chapter 10, recall that the spectral matrix is the Fourier transform of the autocovariance matrix of the process $\varepsilon_t..$)

It is clear, therefore, that except for a deterministic mean, the jointly dependent variables form a covariance stationary stochastic process whose spectral matrix is the *sum of the two spectral matrices associated, respectively, with the (two) stochastic components in the representation of* (12.5.7). Thus to determine the spectral matrix of the jointly dependent variables of the system, we need only establish the spectral matrices, respectively, of the processes

$$\varepsilon_t^{*\prime} = \frac{A(L)}{b(L)} \varepsilon_t^{\prime}. \qquad u_t^{*\prime} = \frac{G(L)}{b(L)} u_t^{\prime}. \tag{12.5.8}$$

Now, by definition, the ith component of ε_t^{*}. is given by

$$\varepsilon_{ti}^{*} = \sum_{j=1}^{s} \sum_{k=0}^{\infty} a_{ijk} \varepsilon_{t-k,j} \tag{12.5.9}$$

Similarly, the ith component of u_t^{*}. is given by

$$u_{ti}^{*} = \sum_{j=1}^{m} \sum_{k=0}^{\infty} g_{ijk} u_{t-k,j} \tag{12.5.10}$$

Since the ε and u processes are (real) covariance stationary, their elements have the spectral representation

$$\varepsilon_{tj} = \int_{-\pi}^{\pi} \exp(it\theta) \, dZ_j(\theta) \qquad u_{t\alpha} = \int_{-\pi}^{\pi} \exp(it0) \, dW_\alpha(\theta) \tag{12.5.11}$$

where $Z_j(\theta)$, $W_\alpha(\theta)$ are the (continuous) processes with orthogonal increments associated, respectively, with ε_{tj} and $u_{t\alpha}$.

These processes have the properties

$$E[dZ_j(\theta) \, \overline{dW_\alpha(\theta')}] = 0 \qquad \text{all } \alpha, j, \theta, \text{ and } \theta' \tag{12.5.12}$$

$$E[dZ_j(\theta) \, \overline{dZ_{j'}(\theta')}] = f_{\varepsilon; \, jj'}(\theta) \, d\theta \qquad \text{if } \theta = \theta'$$
$$= 0 \qquad \text{if } \theta \ne \theta' \tag{12.5.13}$$

$$E[dW_\alpha(\theta) \, \overline{dW_{\alpha'}(\theta')}] = f_{u; \, \alpha\alpha'}(\theta) \, d\theta \qquad \text{if } \theta = \theta'$$
$$= 0 \qquad \text{if } \theta \ne \theta' \tag{12.5.14}$$

where, of course, $f_{\varepsilon; \, jj'}(\theta)$ is the cross spectrum of the j and j' elements o the ε process, while $f_{u; \, \alpha\alpha'}(\theta)$ is the cross spectrum of the α and α' elements of u process.

Thus we have

$$\varepsilon_{tj}^{*} = \sum_{\beta=1}^{s} \sum_{k=0}^{\infty} a_{j\beta k} \int_{-\pi}^{\pi} \exp[i(t-k)\theta] \, dZ_\beta(\theta) = \sum_{\beta=1}^{s} \int_{-\pi}^{\pi} \exp(it\theta) \frac{a_{j\beta}(\theta)}{b(\theta)} \, dZ_\beta(\theta)$$
$$\tag{12.5.15}$$

where, of course,

$$\frac{a_{j\beta}(\theta)}{b(\theta)} = \sum_{k=0}^{\infty} a_{j\beta k} \exp(-ik\theta) \tag{12.5.16}$$

'Lest the significance of the notation go unnoticed, we remind the reader that $a_{j\beta}(\theta)$ is the (j, β) element of $A(L)$ resulting when we substitute $\exp(-ik\theta)$ for the operator L^k.

Similarly,

$$u_{tj}^* = \sum_{\alpha=1}^{m} \int_{-\pi}^{\pi} \exp(it\theta) \frac{g_{j\alpha}(\theta)}{b(\theta)} dW_\alpha(\theta) \tag{12.5.17}$$

It easily follows from the above that the cross spectrum between the j and j' elements of the ε^* process is

$$f_{\varepsilon^*; jj'}(\theta) = \sum_{\beta=1}^{s} \sum_{\beta'=1}^{s} \left[\frac{a_{j\beta}(\theta)}{b(\theta)} f_{\varepsilon; \beta\beta'}(\theta) \frac{\bar{a}_{j\beta'}(\theta)}{\bar{b}(\theta)} \right] = \frac{a_{j.}(\theta) F_\varepsilon(\theta) \bar{a}_{j.}'(\theta)}{|b(\theta)|^2} \tag{12.5.18}$$

where $a_{j.}(\theta)$ indicates the jth row of $A(\theta)$ and $\bar{a}_{j.}$ its complex conjugate.

Thus the spectral matrix of the first stochastic component in the right-hand side of (12.5.7) is

$$F_{\varepsilon^*}(\theta) = \frac{A(\theta) F_\varepsilon(\theta) \bar{A}'(\theta)}{|b(\theta)|^2} \tag{12.5.19}$$

If, as above, the ε process is assumed to consist of mutually independent, identically distributed random vectors with mean zero and covariance matrix Ω, then (12.5.5) is valid and (12.5.19) simplifies to

$$F_{\varepsilon^*}(\theta) = \frac{1}{2\pi} \frac{A(\theta)\Omega\bar{A}'(\theta)}{|b(\theta)|^2} \tag{12.5.20}$$

In (12.5.19) and (12.5.20) $\bar{A}'(\theta)$ indicates the transpose of the matrix whose elements are the complex conjugates of corresponding elements in $A(\theta)$.

By an entirely similar argument, we establish that

$$F_{u^*}(\theta) = \frac{G(\theta) F_u(\theta) \bar{G}'(\theta)}{|b(\theta)|^2} \tag{12.5.21}$$

and, in particular, if (12.5.3) holds, then we have the simplification

$$F_{u^*}(\theta) = \frac{1}{2\pi} \frac{G(\theta)\Sigma\bar{G}'(\theta)}{|b(\theta)|^2} \tag{12.5.22}$$

We conclude, therefore, that the spectral matrix of the jointly dependent variables is given by

$$F_y(\theta) = \frac{A(\theta) F_\varepsilon(\theta) \bar{A}'(\theta)}{|b(\theta)|^2} + \frac{G(\theta) F_u(\theta) \bar{G}'(\theta)}{|b(\theta)|^2} \tag{12.5.23}$$

and in the special cases (12.5.20), (12.5.22) it reduces to

$$F_y(\theta) = \frac{1}{2\pi}\left(\frac{A(\theta)\Omega\bar{A}'(\theta)}{|b(\theta)|^2} + \frac{G(\theta)\Sigma\bar{G}'(\theta)}{|b(\theta)|^2}\right) \tag{12.5.24}$$

The perceptive reader would have noticed two aspects of the development above that require clarification.

i. If the system contains identities, then clearly the matrix Σ would be singular. One might then wonder whether this circumstance invalidates the derivation in (12.5.24).

ii. While many exogenous variables would no doubt be amenable to the representation in (12.5.4), still, if the equations contain constant terms, then one of our exogenous variables is the fictitious variable unity, and thus at least one of the elements of ε_t. would be identically zero. This, of course, means that one of the rows (and the corresponding column) of $F_\varepsilon(\theta)$ will be identically zero. Does this create problems?

Fortunately, neither of these two circumstances is troublesome. First, notice that $A(\theta)$ is $m \times s$ and thus if $m > s$ the determinant $|A(\theta)\Omega\bar{A}'(\theta)|$ will be identically zero. Thus, since no condition on the number of exogenous variables has been imposed, the fact that the rank of Ω will be $s - 1$ if the equations of the system contain a constant term is of no consequence.

Turning now to the problem of identities, we observe that in the context of the general (linear) structural model their presence means that strict linear dependencies exist among the current endogenous variables. If that is the case, then, of course, we would expect that the spectral matrix of a subset would be entirely expressible in terms of the spectral matrix of the remaining variables. We shall now show that the representation in (12.5.24) reflects this relation. Thus the "bookkeeping" of the notation in (12.5.23) and (12.5.24) will be shown adequate to the occasion.

If the system contains m^* identities, let us number the variables "defined" by the identities as $m, m - 1, \ldots, m - m^* + 1$—that is, they are to be the last m^* jointly dependent variables. Denote these variables by the vector $y_t^2.$; let $y_t^1.$ denote the remaining $m - m^*$ current endogenous variables.

The econometric model in (12.3.10) may thus be rewritten conveniently as

$$\begin{bmatrix} C_{11}(L) & C_{12}(L) \\ C_{21}(L) & C_{22}(L) \end{bmatrix}\begin{pmatrix} y_t^{1'} \\ y_t^{2'} \end{pmatrix} = \begin{bmatrix} C_1^*(L) \\ C_2^*(L) \end{bmatrix}w_t' + \begin{pmatrix} u_t^{1'} \\ 0 \end{pmatrix} \tag{12.5.25}$$

In the last vector above $u_t^1.$ is the vector of disturbances corresponding to the $m - m^*$ behavioral equations; the zero vector is of dimension m^* and corresponds to the identities of the system. Now, because the last m^* equations are identities, we must have

$$C_{22}(L) = I \qquad I = \text{diag}(I_0, I_0, \ldots, I_0) \tag{12.5.26}$$

$$C_{21}(L) = H \tag{12.5.27}$$

H being a matrix of known constants; in fact, typically, its elements will be either 0, 1, or -1.

In addition, we must have

$$C_2^*(L) = 0 \qquad (12.5.28)$$

We note that $C_{11}(L)$ is $(m - m^*) \times (m - m^*)$, $C_{22}(L)$ is $m^* \times m^*$, $C_1^*(L)$ is $(m - m^*) \times s$, $C_2^*(L)$ is $m^* \times s$, and the other matrices have easily established dimensions.

We thus see that we have the exact relation

$$y_{t\cdot}^{2'} = -Hy_{t\cdot}^{1'} \qquad (12.5.29)$$

From Chapter 10 we know that the spectral matrix of a (multivariate) stochastic process is the Fourier transform of the autocovariance matrix.

Since, by (12.5.29),

$$\text{Cov}(y_{t\cdot}^2) = H \, \text{Cov}(y_{t\cdot}^1)H' \qquad (12.5.30)$$

we conclude that the spectral matrices of $y_{t\cdot}^1$ and $y_{t\cdot}^2$—respectively $F_{y^1y^1}(\theta)$, $F_{y^2y^2}(\theta)$—are related by

$$F_{y^2y^2}(\theta) = HF_{y^1y^1}(\theta)H' \qquad (12.5.31)$$

We shall now show that the representation in (12.5.23) or (12.5.24) indeed reflects this relation.

Now, by definition,

$$\frac{A(\theta)}{b(\theta)} = [C(\theta)]^{-1}C^*(\theta) \qquad (12.5.32)$$

and, using the expression for a partitioned matrix, we obtain

$$[C(\theta)]^{-1} = \begin{bmatrix} C^{11} & -C_{11}^{-1}C_{12}C^{22} \\ -C_{22}^{-1}C_{21}C^{11} & C^{22} \end{bmatrix} \qquad (12.5.33)$$

where

$$C^{11} = (C_{11} - C_{12}C_{22}^{-1}C_{21})^{-1} \qquad C^{22} = (C_{22} - C_{21}C_{11}^{-1}C_{12})^{-1} \qquad (12.5.34)$$

For simplicity, we have suppressed the argument θ in the submatrices $C_{ij}(\theta)$, $i, j = 1, 2$. Thus, in terms of the relation in (12.5.23), we have

$$F_{y^1y^1}(\theta) = [C^{11}, -C_{11}^{-1}C_{12}C^{22}]C^*(\theta)F_\varepsilon(\theta)\bar{C}^{*'}(\theta)[\bar{C}^{11}, \bar{C}_{11}^{-1}\bar{C}_{12}\bar{C}^{22}]'$$
$$+ [C^{11}, -C_{11}^{-1}C_{12}C^{22}]F_u(\theta)[\bar{C}^{11}, -\bar{C}_{11}^{-1}\bar{C}_{12}\bar{C}^{22}]' \qquad (12.5.35)$$

and

$$F_{y^2y^2}(\theta) = [-C_{22}^{-1}C_{21}C^{11}, C^{22}]C^*(\theta)F_\varepsilon(\theta)\bar{C}^{*'}(\theta)[-\bar{C}_{22}^{-1}\bar{C}_{21}\bar{C}^{11}, \bar{C}^{22}]'$$
$$+ [-C_{22}^{-1}C_{21}C^{11}, C^{22}]F_u(\theta)[-\bar{C}_{22}^{-1}\bar{C}_{21}\bar{C}^{11}, \bar{C}^{22}]' \qquad (12.5.36)$$

If identities are present, then

$$F_u(\theta) = \frac{1}{2\pi}\begin{bmatrix} \Sigma_{11} & 0 \\ 0 & 0 \end{bmatrix} \quad C_{21}(\theta) = H \quad C_{22}(\theta) = I \tag{12.5.37}$$

where I now stands for the identity matrix.

Hence, in the presence of identities, the expression (12.5.35) simplifies to

$$F_{y^1y^1}(\theta) = C^{11}C_1^*(\theta)F_\varepsilon(\theta)\bar{C}_1^{*\prime}(\theta)\bar{C}^{11\prime} + \frac{1}{2\pi}C^{11}\Sigma_{11}\bar{C}^{11\prime} \tag{12.5.38}$$

while (12.5.36) simplifies to

$$F_{y^2y^2}(\theta) = HC^{11}C_1^*(\theta)F_\varepsilon(\theta)\bar{C}_1^{*\prime}(\theta)\bar{C}^{11\prime}H' + \frac{1}{2\pi}HC^{11}\Sigma_{11}\bar{C}^{11\prime}H'$$

$$= H[F_{y^1y^1}(\theta)]H' \tag{12.5.39}$$

Equations (12.5.38) and (12.5.39) quite clearly establish the conclusion that the representation in (12.5.23) or (12.5.24) remains valid even if the system contains (linear) identities.[8]

The preceding discussion may be summarized in

Theorem 1: Consider the (linear) dynamic general structural model

$$C(L)y_t'. = C^*(L)w_t'. + u_t'. \tag{12.5.40}$$

where $y_t.$ is the (row) vector of jointly dependent variables and $w_t.$ the (row) vector of the exogenous variables of the system. Suppose that the system is stable in the sense that the roots of

$$|C(\rho)| = 0 \tag{12.5.41}$$

lie outside the unit circle. Suppose, further, that the exogenous variables and error terms are mutually independent; that

$$u_t'. \sim N(0, \Sigma) \quad \text{Cov}(u_t'., u_{t'}'.) = \delta_{tt'}\Sigma \tag{12.5.42}$$

and

$$w_t'. = \omega(t) + \varepsilon_t. \tag{12.5.43}$$

where $\omega(t)$ is a purely deterministic function and $\varepsilon_t.$ is a (multivariate) covariance stationary process, admitting of a spectral matrix, say $F_\varepsilon(\theta)$.

Then

i. the final form of the system exists as

$$y_t'. = \frac{A(L)}{b(L)}w_t'. + \frac{G(L)}{b(L)}u_t'. \tag{12.5.44}$$

---

[8] Show that the stability conditions are unaffected by the presence of identities. (*Hint*: $|C(\rho)| = 0$ is equivalent to $|C_{11}(\rho) - C_{12}(\rho)H| = 0$, and the latter is related to the characteristic equation of the homogeneous part of the system resulting after identities have been substituted out.)

where

$$b(L) = |C(L)| \qquad A(L) = G(L)C^*(L) \tag{12.5.45}$$

and $G(L)$ is the adjoint of $C(L)$.

ii. the matrix of dynamic multipliers is given by $A(1)/b(1)$.

iii. the elements of $A(L)/b(L)$ are rational lag operators and admit of a power series representation.

iv. the spectral matrix of the dependent variables of the system is given by

$$F_y(\theta) = \frac{A(\theta)F_\varepsilon(\theta)\bar{A}'(\theta)}{|b(\theta)|^2} + \frac{1}{2\pi} \frac{G(\theta)\Sigma\bar{G}'(\theta)}{|b(\theta)|^2} \tag{12.5.46}$$

and (12.5.46) is valid whether or not the system contains (linear) identities.

The presentation in (12.5.46) is particularly useful; it allows us to obtain an estimator of the spectral matrix of the dependent variables of the system rather easily once the structural parameters have been estimated by one of the standard simultaneous equations methods developed in Chapters 4, 6, or 7. This will be greatly facilitated if the relation in (12.5.5) holds. In such a case, we need not estimate any spectral quantity from the data, for the matrix Ω can be estimated from the residuals of the trend-removal operation on the exogenous variables. The reader, however, is entitled to ask: If we are interested in the spectral matrix of the dependent variables, why not compute it directly from the data? Why go through the process in (12.5.46)?

There are several answers. First, when dealing with aggregative econometric models, it is not often that we have series of sufficient length to justify the use of spectral techniques directly. Second, the dependent variables will, generally, not have the property of (covariance) stationarity unless they have been sufficiently detrended, that is, unless they have been "purged" of their (systematic) mean function. However, the latter is essentially induced by the mean function of the *exogenous* variables through the complicated lag operator matrix $A(L)/b(L)$. Thus it would be simpler, and perhaps more effective, to operate on the *exogenous* variables for purposes of detrending. Third, we are typically interested in the structural parameters for their own sake, and it is thus pleasing that having obtained estimators for them we can, at relatively little additional computational cost, estimate the spectral matrix of the dependent variables, say

$$\hat{F}_y(\theta) = \frac{1}{2\pi} \frac{\hat{A}(\theta)\hat{\Omega}\bar{\hat{A}}'(\theta)}{|\hat{b}(\theta)|^2} + \frac{1}{2\pi} \frac{\hat{G}(\theta)\hat{\Sigma}\bar{\hat{G}}'(\theta)}{|\hat{b}(\theta)|^2} \tag{12.5.47}$$

where the caret over $A(\theta)$, $G(\theta)$, $b(\theta)$, Σ, and Ω indicates that a consistent estimator has been substituted for the structural parameters they contain.

A number of inferences may be made from (12.5.47). The most obvious one is that by studying the spectral densities [diagonal elements of $\hat{F}_y(\theta)$], we can deduce the cyclical characteristics of the dependent variables. The nature of the correlation among the dependent variables of the system can be studied more fully by considering their associated *coherencies*. Important lead-lag relations between variables may be discovered by examining their associated *phase* measures. Occasionally we may wish to consider simultaneously both the jointly dependent *and* exogenous variables of the system, that is the elements of the vector

$$z_{t\cdot} = (y_{t\cdot}, \, w_{t\cdot})$$ (12.5.48)

It is thus convenient, at this stage, to note that the spectral matrix of z is given by

$$F_z(\theta) = \frac{1}{2\pi} \begin{bmatrix} 2\pi F_y(\theta) & \dfrac{A(\theta)}{b(\theta)} \Omega \\ \Omega \dfrac{\bar{A}'(\theta)}{\bar{b}(\theta)} & \Omega \end{bmatrix}$$ (12.5.49)

12.6 AN EMPIRICAL APPLICATION

Consider the "structural" system

$$C_t = \alpha_0 + \alpha_1 Y_t + \alpha_2 C_{t-1} + u_{t1}$$
$$E_t = \beta_0 + \beta_1(Y_t - Y_{t-1}) + \beta_2 E_{t-1} + u_{t2}$$
$$Y_t = C_t + E_t + G_t$$ (12.6.1)

where C, E, Y, G are, respectively, aggregate consumption, investment, gross national product (GNP), and government expenditures.

The data of Table 12.1 have been used to obtain estimates for the parameters of the model by application of 2SLS techniques. The estimated equations are

$$C_t = 6.04 + 0.68 Y_t + 0.57 C_{t-1} \qquad\qquad R^2 = .98, \text{ D.W.} = 1.94$$
$$\quad\;\;(.38)\;\;(1.84)\quad\;(2.20)$$

$$E_t = 12.85 + 1.48(Y_t - Y_{t-1}) + 0.63 E_{t-1} \qquad R^2 = .77, \text{ D.W.} = 1.67$$
$$\quad\;(1.39)\;\;(3.16)\qquad\qquad\;\;(4.58)$$ (12.6.2)

In (12.6.2) the numbers in parentheses are the "t ratios" computed by analogy with the simple general linear model; similarly, R^2 and D.W. are the "coefficient of determination" and the Durbin-Watson statistic, the latter testing for the presence of serial correlation in the error terms. Although its use in the present case may be inappropriate, the results do not indicate strongly that the customary assumption of intertemporal uncorrelatedness of disturbances is violated. The estimated covariance matrix of the disturbances is

$$\hat{\Sigma} = \begin{bmatrix} 156.2 & 79.7 & 0 \\ & 53.3 & 0 \\ & & 0 \end{bmatrix}$$ (12.6.3)

The last column (and row) corresponds to the identity in (12.6.1), last equation.

TABLE 12.1. U.S. Series, Billions of 1958 dollars[a] (seasonally adjusted)

Year	G_t	E_t	C_t	Y_t
1948	46.3	66.5	210.8	323.7
1949	53.3	54.4	216.5	324.1
1950	52.8	72.0	230.5	355.3
1951	75.4	75.3	232.8	383.4
1952	92.1	63.5	239.4	395.1
1953	99.8	62.3	250.8	412.8
1954	88.9	62.4	255.7	407.0
1955	85.2	78.6	274.2	438.0
1956	85.3	79.3	281.4	446.1
1957	89.3	75.0	288.2	452.5
1958	94.2	63.1	290.1	447.3
1959	94.7	73.9	307.3	475.9
1960	94.9	76.7	316.1	487.7
1961	100.5	74.1	322.5	497.2
1962	107.5	83.9	338.4	529.8
1963	109.6	88.1	353.3	551.0
1964	111.2	96.1	373.7	581.1
1965	114.3	104.0	398.4	616.7
1966	124.5	110.0	418.0	652.6
1967	138.7	100.5	430.1	669.3

[a] Source: *Survey of Current Business*, vol. 48, no. 5, p. 4 and *Biennial Supplement*, 1967, p. 4.
G_t: Federal, state, and local expenditures on goods and services.
E_t: Gross domestic plus net foreign investment.
C_t: Personal consumption.
Y_t: Gross national product.

The matrix $C(L)$ of (12.3.9) was thus estimated as

$$C(L) = \begin{bmatrix} I - 0.57L & 0 & -0.68I \\ 0 & I - 0.63L & -1.48I + 1.48L \\ -I & -I & I \end{bmatrix} \tag{12.6.4}$$

Its associated determinantal equation [equation (12.3.12)], is

$$|C(\rho)| = -1.16 + 1.55\rho - 0.48\rho^2 = 0 \tag{12.6.5}$$

The roots of this equation are

$$\rho_1 = 2.05 \qquad \rho_2 = 1.18 \tag{12.6.6}$$

We see that we are dealing with a *stable* system.

Of course,

$$|C(L)| = b(L) = -1.16I + 1.55L - 0.48L^2 \qquad (12.6.7)$$

and the matrix $G(L)$—defined, say, after equation (12.5.2)—is

$$G(L) = \begin{bmatrix} -0.48I + 0.85L & 0.68I & 0.68I - 0.43L \\ 1.48I - 1.48L & 0.32I - 0.57L & 1.48I - 2.32L + 0.84L^2 \\ I - 0.63L & I - 0.57L & I - 1.20L + 0.36L^2 \end{bmatrix} \qquad (12.6.8)$$

The matrix $A(L)$ of equation (12.5.2) is

$$A(L) = \begin{bmatrix} 5.84I + 5.13L & 0.68I - 0.43L \\ 13.05I - 16.26L & 1.48I - 2.32L + 0.84L^2 \\ 18.89I - 11.13L & I - 1.20L + 0.36L^2 \end{bmatrix} \qquad (12.6.9)$$

Of course, in this model

$$C_0^* = \begin{bmatrix} 6.04 & 0 \\ 12.85 & 0 \\ 0 & 1 \end{bmatrix} \quad C_i^* = 0 \quad i = 1, 2, \dots, k \qquad (12.6.10)$$

Thus the estimated conditional expectation of the final form is [see equation (12.5.1)]:

$$C_t = -121.9 + \frac{0.68I - 0.43L}{--1.16I + 1.55L - 0.48L^2} G_t \qquad (12.6.11)$$

$$E_t = 35.6 + \frac{1.48I - 2.32L + 0.84L^2}{-1.16I + 1.55L - 0.48L^2} G_t \qquad (12.6.12)$$

$$Y_t = -86.3 + \frac{I - 1.20L + 0.36L^2}{-1.16I + 1.55L - 0.48L^2} G_t \qquad (12.6.13)$$

The reader should verify whether Y_t as expressed in (12.6.13) satisfies the identity of the model.

We see that all dependent variables have been expressed as infinite rational distributed lags in the *exogenous variable*, G_t.

The exogenous variable has been subjected to a detrending procedure, yielding

$$\hat{\omega}(t) = 92.36 + 3.97t \qquad R^2 = .93$$
$$(62.12) \quad (15.54) \qquad (12.6.14)$$

From this, the covariance matrix Ω of (12.5.5) has been obtained as

$$\hat{\Omega} = \begin{bmatrix} 0 & 0 \\ 0 & 39.7 \end{bmatrix} \qquad (12.6.15)$$

The zeros in (12.6.15) are due to the fictitious *exogenous* variable, unity, corresponding to the constant terms of the (structural) equations. The spectral matrix of this model is easily obtained from the expression in (12.5.47) and the relevant estimators. Thus in the present model we should have

$$F_y(\theta) = \frac{1}{2\pi} \frac{1}{|b(\theta)|^2} \{G(\theta)[C_0^* \Omega C_0^{*\prime} + \Sigma]\bar{G}'(\theta)\} \qquad (12.6.16)$$

Substituting the estimators in (12.6.3), (12.6.10), and (12.6.15), we find[9]

$$C_0^* \Omega C_0^{*\prime} + \Sigma = \begin{bmatrix} 156.2 & 79.7 & 0 \\ & 53.3 & 0 \\ & & 39.7 \end{bmatrix} \qquad (12.6.17)$$

From (12.6.8) we see that $G(\theta)$, in this model, is estimated as

$$G(\theta) = \begin{bmatrix} -0.48 + 0.85 \exp(-i\theta) & 0.68 \\ 1.48 - 1.48 \exp(-i\theta) & 0.32 - 0.57 \exp(-i\theta) \\ 1 - 0.63 \exp(-i\theta) & 1 - 0.57 \exp(-i\theta) \end{bmatrix}$$

$$\begin{bmatrix} 0.68 - 0.43 \exp(-i\theta) \\ 1.48 - 2.32 \exp(-i\theta) + 0.84 \exp(-i2\theta) \\ 1 - 1.20 \exp(-i\theta) + 0.36 \exp(-i2\theta) \end{bmatrix}$$

$$(12.6.18)$$

From (12.6.7) we find that

$$|b(\theta)|^2 = 3.98 - 5.08 \cos\theta + 1.11 \cos 2\theta \qquad (12.6.19)$$

Thus we determine the elements of the spectral matrix of the model as follows.
The spectrum of consumption is

$$f_{11}(\theta) = \frac{1}{2\pi} \frac{1}{|b(\theta)|^2} (147 - 58 \cos\theta) \qquad (12.6.20)$$

The cross spectrum of consumption and investment is

$$f_{12}(\theta) = \frac{1}{2\pi} \frac{1}{|b(\theta)|^2} [-187 + 148 \cos\theta + 23 \cos 2\theta - i(238 \sin\theta - 23 \sin 2\theta)] \qquad (12.6.21)$$

The cospectrum is

$$c_{12}(\theta) = \mathrm{Re}\,[f_{12}(\theta)] = \frac{1}{2\pi} \frac{1}{|b(\theta)|^2} (-187 + 148 \cos\theta + 23 \cos 2\theta) \qquad (12.6.22)$$

while the quadrature spectrum is

$$q_{12}(\theta) = \mathrm{Im}\,[f_{12}(\theta)] = \frac{1}{2\pi} \frac{1}{|b(\theta)|^2} (-238 \sin\theta + 23 \sin 2\theta) \qquad (12.6.23)$$

---

[9] For economy of notation, the caret over the relevant quantities—indicating that we are dealing with estimated quantities—will be omitted.

The cross spectrum between consumption and GNP is

$$f_{13}(\theta) = \frac{1}{2\pi} \frac{1}{|b(\theta)|^2} [-98 + 151 \cos \theta + 10 \cos 2\theta - i(207 \sin \theta + 10 \sin 2\theta)]$$

(12.6.24)

The relevant cospectrum and quadrature spectrum are

$$c_{13}(\theta) = \text{Re} \, [f_{13}(\theta)] = \frac{1}{2\pi} \frac{1}{|b(\theta)|^2} (-98 + 151 \cos \theta + 10 \cos 2\theta) \qquad (12.6.25)$$

$$q_{13}(\theta) = \text{Im} \, [f_{13}(\theta)] = \frac{1}{2\pi} \frac{1}{|b(\theta)|^2} (-207 \sin \theta - 10 \sin 2\theta) \qquad (12.6.26)$$

The spectrum of investment is

$$f_{22}(\theta) = \frac{1}{2\pi} \frac{1}{|(b\theta)|^2} (1246 - 1342 \cos \theta + 98 \cos 2\theta) \qquad (12.6.27)$$

The cross spectrum of investment and GNP is

$$f_{23}(\theta) = \frac{1}{2\pi} \frac{1}{|b(\theta)|^2} [832 - 899 \cos \theta + 54 \cos 2\theta + i(215 \sin \theta - 12 \sin 2\theta)]$$

(12.6.28)

The relevant cospectrum and quadrature spectrum are

$$c_{23}(\theta) = \text{Re} \, [f_{23}(\theta)] = \frac{1}{2\pi} \frac{1}{|b(\theta)|^2} (832 - 899 \cos \theta + 54 \cos 2\theta) \qquad (12.6.29)$$

$$q_{23}(\theta) = \text{Im} \, [f_{23}(\theta)] = \frac{1}{2\pi} \frac{1}{|b(\theta)|^2} (215 \sin \theta - 12 \sin 2\theta) \qquad (12.6.30)$$

The spectrum of GNP is

$$f_{33}(\theta) = \frac{1}{2\pi} \frac{1}{|b(\theta)|^2} (607 - 578 \cos \theta + 28 \cos 2\theta) \qquad (12.6.31)$$

In the previous section, we discussed the problem of identities and we demonstrated that treating them symmetrically with the behavioral equations of the model does not cause any difficulties. Let us verify this fact for the model under consideration.

Since, by definition,

$$Y_t = C_t + E_t + G_t \qquad (12.6.32)$$

It follows that

$$f_{33}(\theta) = f_{11}(\theta) + f_{22}(\theta) + f_{44}(\theta) + 2c_{12}(\theta) + 2c_{14}(\theta) + 2c_{24}(\theta) \qquad (12.6.33)$$

where $f_{44}(\theta)$ is the spectrum of government expenditures and $c_{14}(\theta)$, $c_{24}(\theta)$ are, respectively, the cospectra of consumption and government and of investment and government expenditures. To carry out this verification, we require the upper right-hand block of the matrix in (12.5.49). Thus we need

$$\frac{1}{2\pi} \frac{A(\theta)}{b(\theta)} \Omega = \frac{1}{2\pi} \frac{1}{|b(\theta)|^2} \left(\bar{b}(\theta) A(\theta) \begin{bmatrix} 0 & 0 \\ 0 & 39.7 \end{bmatrix} \right) \tag{12.6.34}$$

Utilizing the results in (12.6.9) and (12.6.19), we determine the cross spectrum of consumption and government as

$$f_{14}(\theta) = \frac{1}{2\pi} \frac{1}{|b(\theta)|^2}$$

$$\times [-58 + 69.9 \cos \theta - 13.1 \cos 2\theta + i(30.1 \sin \theta - 13.1 \sin 2\theta)] \tag{12.6.35}$$

The relevant cospectrum and quadrature spectrum are therefore

$$c_{14}(\theta) = \mathrm{Re}\,[f_{14}(\theta)] = \frac{1}{2\pi} \frac{1}{|b(\theta)|^2} (-58 + 69.9 \cos \theta - 13.1 \cos 2\theta) \tag{12.6.36}$$

$$q_{14}(\theta) = \mathrm{Im}\,[f_{14}(\theta)] = \frac{1}{2\pi} \frac{1}{|b(\theta)|^2} (30.1 \sin \theta - 13.1 \sin 2\theta) \tag{12.6.37}$$

The cross spectrum of investment and government expenditures is

$$f_{24}(\theta) = \frac{1}{2\pi} \frac{1}{|b(\theta)|^2}$$

$$\times [-227.1 + 293.4 \cos \theta - 66.7 \cos 2\theta - i(23.4 \sin \theta - 10.3 \sin 2\theta)] \tag{12.6.38}$$

Thus the relevant cospectrum and quadrature spectrum are

$$c_{24}(\theta) = \mathrm{Re}\,[f_{24}(\theta)] = \frac{1}{2\pi} \frac{1}{|b(\theta)|^2} (-227.1 + 293.4 \cos \theta - 66.7 \cos 2\theta) \tag{12.6.39}$$

$$q_{24}(\theta) = \mathrm{Im}\,[f_{24}(\theta)] = \frac{1}{2\pi} \frac{1}{|b(\theta)|^2} (-23.4 \sin \theta + 10.3 \sin 2\theta) \tag{12.6.40}$$

The cross spectrum between GNP and government expenditures is

$$f_{34}(\theta) = \frac{1}{2\pi} \frac{1}{|b(\theta)|^2} [-127 + 162 \cos \theta - 36 \cos 2\theta + i(7.2 \sin \theta - 2.5 \sin 2\theta)] \tag{12.6.41}$$

Hence the relevant cospectrum and quadrature spectrum are

$$c_{34}(\theta) = \text{Re}\,[f_{34}(\theta)] = \frac{1}{2\pi}\frac{1}{|b(\theta)|^2}(-127 + 162\cos\theta - 36\cos 2\theta) \qquad (12.6.42)$$

$$q_{34}(\theta) = \text{Im}\,[f_{34}(\theta)] = \frac{1}{2\pi}\frac{1}{|b(\theta)|^2}(7.2\sin\theta - 2.5\sin 2\theta) \qquad (12.6.43)$$

Finally, the spectrum of government expenditures is

$$f_{44}(\theta) = \frac{39.7}{2\pi} \qquad (12.6.44)$$

It should be pointed out that since the matrix $F_z(\theta)$ of (12.5.49) is Hermitian, equations (12.6.20), (12.6.21), (12.6.24), (12.6.27), (12.6.28), (12.6.31), (12.6.35), (12.6.38), (12.6.41), and (12.6.44) completely determine its elements.

Let us now verify that $f_{33}(\theta)$, as determined from (12.6.33), agrees with the expression given in (12.6.31). Carrying out the operations implied by (12.6.33), we find

$$f_{33}(\theta) = \frac{1}{2\pi}\frac{1}{|b(\theta)|^2}(606 - 579\cos\theta + 28\cos 2\theta) \qquad (12.6.45)$$

which is, of course, identical with (12.6.31) except for minor discrepancies due to rounding errors.

As an exercise, the reader should verify that, apart from discrepancies due to roundoff, $f_{34}(\theta)$ as given in (12.6.41) agrees with $f_{14}(\theta) + f_{24}(\theta) + f_{44}(\theta)$.

Consider now, what the spectral matrix implies about the behavior of the three jointly dependent variables of the system. Here we shall examine only the three spectral densities, $f_{11}(\theta), f_{22}(\theta), f_{33}(\theta)$. We shall evaluate these at the points $\theta = 0, \pi/6, \pi/5, \pi/4, \pi/3, \pi/2, \pi$. As the reader may easily verify, these points correspond respectively to components of period (in years) $\infty, 12, 10, 8, 6, 4, 2$.

We give in Table 12.2 on page 540, the ordinates of

$$2\pi|b(\theta)|^2 f_{ii}(\theta) = f_{ii}^*(\theta) \qquad i = 1, 2, 3 \qquad (12.6.46)$$

as well as the ordinates of the $f_{ii}(\theta)$.

Two features of the table are noteworthy. First, due to the fact that one of the roots of (12.6.5)—ρ_2—is rather close to one, the quantity $|b(0)|^2$ nearly vanishes at $\theta = 0$. Of course, this near singularity means that the general solution to the homogeneous part of the difference equation defining the final form vanishes rather slowly. In addition, this is also partly responsible for the high values assumed by the ordinates of the spectra of consumption and GNP at $\theta = 0$. From a spectral analytic point of view, as pointed out in Chapter 9, this may well mean that the detrending operation applied in this model has not been sufficient to remove the trend from consumption and GNP. Furthermore,

TABLE 12.2 **Ordinates of the spectral densities of consumption, investment, and** GNP

θ	Period	$\lvert b(\theta)\rvert^2$	$f_{11}^*(\theta)$	$f_{22}^*(\theta)$	$f_{33}^*(\theta)$	$f_{11}(\theta)$	$f_{22}(\theta)$	$f_{33}(\theta)$
0	∞	.01	89.0	2.00	57.00	1417	32	906
$\dfrac{\pi}{6}$	12	.16	97.12	132.82	120.45	97	132	120
$\dfrac{\pi}{5}$	10	.21	100.02	189.36	147.50	76	143	112
$\dfrac{\pi}{4}$	8	.38	105.82	297.18	196.62	45	125	84
$\dfrac{\pi}{3}$	6	.89	118.00	526.00	304.00	21	94	54
$\dfrac{\pi}{2}$	4	2.87	147.00	1148.00	579.00	8	64	32
π	2	10.17	205.00	2686.00	1213.00	3	42	19

one might argue that consumption and GNP contain trends of their own, in
addition to those induced by the trend in government expenditures—which presumably we have removed. This remark does not apply to the spectrum of
investment. Of course, we cannot claim very much from this simple model, which
is presented only for expository purposes.

Secondly, as is also made clear in Figure 12.1, investment appears to have a
substantial cyclical component of period 8–10 years, while the spectra of consumption and GNP are quite similar and disclose a shape that is akin to the
spectrum of a first-order Markov process as we obtained it in Chapter 10. This
shape, of course, may not be entirely surprising in view of the formulation of
the model.

Finally, the reader is invited to obtain the gain of consumption and income
and ask himself: What information, if any, does this convey regarding the
permanent income hypothesis?

Let us now ask a fundamental question: Is this model, as estimated, believable?
Well, this is a rather ambiguous question. Certainly the model is stable, which is
one of the properties we would require of a model of a real world economy. In
addition, however, we would want the long-run dynamic multipliers to be of
reasonable magnitude. From Section 12.4, we know that the matrix of dynamic
multipliers is given by $[C(1)]^{-1}C^*(1)$. In the present model, this matrix reduces

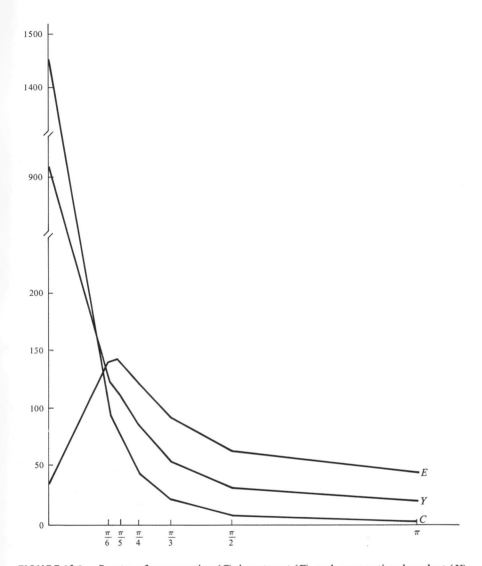

FIGURE 12.1. Spectra of consumption (C), investment (E), and gross national product (Y)

to the vector $1/b(L)$ times the second column of the matrix in (12.6.9). Evaluating, after substitution of 1 for L, we find that the elements of this vector are $-.25/.09$, 0, $-.16/.09$. Thus, although the estimated equations as given in (12.6.2) appear rather reasonable, the model has the undesirable property that if we imagine government expenditures to be fixed, at $\bar{G}$, the final form implies that GNP would tend to fluctuate about $-86.3-(.16/.09)\bar{G}$, investment about 35.6, and consumption about $-121.9-(.25/.09)\bar{G}$. Moreover, an increase in this fixed level $\bar{G}$ by a unit, this increase maintained forever, will have the ultimate impact of *reducing consumption* by .25/.09 and GNP by .16/.09. Of course, all these conclusions are based on the *point estimates* obtained for the parameters of our model. If their standard errors are taken into account, the conclusions might well be altered so that, conceivably, they may become more believable.[10]

Nonetheless, the reader should derive an important lesson from this, namely, *it is not enough to estimate the parameters of a model, casually inspect them, and pronounce them believable. If the model is dynamic, as most such econometric models are likely to be, one must carefully investigate its dynamic properties and verify that they are not absurd and inadmissible.* This may be done analytically for linear models—as we have done here. If the model is nonlinear, however, the techniques developed here are inadequate, although piecewise linear approximations may be used. But, failing this, one must resort to dynamic simulations. We shall not discuss this technique. The interested reader may consult [1], [7], [13].

Finally, for the estimated model to be useful, it must be capable of predicting sufficiently accurately beyond the sample on the basis of which its parameters have been estimated. Perhaps this is the definitive test of its usefulness, its worth; indeed, it might well be said to be its sole *raison d'être*.

REFERENCES

1. Adelman, I., and F. L. Adelman, "The Dynamic Properties of the Klein-Goldberger Model," *Econometrica*, vol. 28, 1959, pp. 596–625.
2. Chow, G. C., "Multiplier, Accelerator, and Liquidity Preference in the Determination of National Income in the United States," *The Review of Economics and Statistics*, vol. 49, 1967, pp. 1–15.
3. Chow, G. C., and R. E. Levitan, "Spectral Properties of Nonstationary Systems of Linear Stochastic Difference Equations," R. C. 2059, Yorktown Heights, New York, IBM Research Division, 1968.
4. Chow, G. C., and R. E. Levitan, "Nature of Business Cycles Implicit in a Linear Economic Model," R. C. 2085, Yorktown Heights, New York, IBM Research Division, 1969.
5. Dhrymes, P. J., *Distributed Lags*, San Francisco, Holden-Day, 1970.
6. Godfrey, M. D., "The Statistical Analysis of Stochastic Processes in Economics," *Kyklos*, vol. 20, 1967, pp. 373–386.
7. Goldberger, A. S., *Impact Multipliers and Dynamic Properties of the Klein-Goldberger Model*, Amsterdam, North-Holland Publishing Co., 1959.
8. Granger, C. W. J., "The Typical Spectral Shape of an Economic Variable," *Econometrica*, vol. 34, 1966, pp. 150–161.
9. Haavelmo, T., "The Inadequacy of Testing Dynamic Theory by Comparing Theoretical Solutions and Observed Cycles," *Econometrica*, vol. 13, 1940, pp. 312–321.
10. Howrey, P. E., "Dynamic Properties of Stochastic Linear Econometric Models," *Econometric Research Program, Research Memorandum No. 87*, Princeton, N.J., Princeton University, 1967.

---

[10] Having established that the estimated model yields inadmissible and absurd results, the reader should now take a look again at equation (12.6.2) and ask himself: Upon closer inspection, is there anything in the estimated coefficients that appears unreasonable? (*Hint*: What is the long-run marginal propensity to consume?)

11. Howrey, P. E., "Stochastic Properties of the Klein-Goldberger Model," *Econometric Research Program, Research Memorandum No 88*, Princeton, N.J., Princeton University, 1967.
12. Mann, H. B., and A. Wald, "On the Statistical Treatment of Linear Stochastic Difference Equations," *Econometrica*, vol. 11, 1943, pp. 173-220.
13. Nagar, A. L., "Stochastic Simulation of the Brookings Econometric Model," *The Brookings Model: Some Further Results*, J. Duesenberry, G. Fromm, L. R. Klein, and E. Kuh, (Eds.), Skokie, Ill. Rand McNally and Amsterdam, North-Holland Publishing Co., 1969.
14. Theil, H., and J. C. G. Boot, "The Final Form of Econometric Equation Systems," *Review of the International Statistical Institute*, vol. 30, 1962, pp. 136-152.

MATHEMATICAL
APPENDIX

In various chapters of this book, particularly Chapters 3, 9, and 10, the discussion presupposes a level of mathematical knowledge that may not have been attained by the typical student of econometrics.

Although it is not possible to provide a compendium of mathematical results to fill the needs of all possible readers, an attempt is being made, in the following sections, to make this book reasonably self-contained. The purpose of the appendix is not to impart rigorous mathematical training but rather to fill the gaps in the mathematical training of the typical reader.

Clearly our discussion will be, of necessity, somewhat superfluous for some and somewhat elliptic and obscure for others.

A.1 COMPLEX NUMBERS AND COMPLEX-VALUED FUNCTIONS

As the reader is well aware, the equation

$$x^2 + 1 = 0 \tag{A.1.1}$$

has no solution over the field of real numbers. To handle just such a situation, the mathematician Euler, in the eighteenth century, introduced the symbol i, having the property

$$i^2 = -1 \tag{A.1.2}$$

It is seen, then, that the solutions of (A.1.1) are $\pm i$. Occasionally i is referred to as the square root of -1 and indicated by $\sqrt{-1}$. A careless use of this notation, however, may lead to considerable confusion. Indeed, we have the following paradoxical (and contradictory) result:

$$i^2 = (\sqrt{-1})(\sqrt{-1}) = (\sqrt{-1})^2 = -1$$

$$i^2 = (\sqrt{-1})(\sqrt{-1}) = \sqrt{(-1)(-1)} = 1 \tag{A.1.3}$$

Equation (A.1.3) results from a careless use of the ambiguous definition of i as $\sqrt{-1}$, when it is not clear what meaning is to be ascribed to the symbol $\sqrt{-1}$. In this appendix, the only property defining the symbol i will be that in (A.1.2). It will thus possess *only* those properties that can be deduced therefrom. (The reader may ask himself: What is i^k for $k = 2r$? For $k = 2r + 1$?)

Definition 1: A complex number z is defined by

$$z = x + iy \tag{A.1.4}$$

where $x, y \in E.$[1] Thus a complex number is totally describable in terms of a *pair of real numbers*.

If the reader thoroughly assimilates this fact, he will quickly learn how to operate with complex numbers, for they do not involve very much beyond what he is already familiar with.

Definition 2: The *complex conjugate* of z, denoted by $\bar{z}$, is defined as

$$\bar{z} = x - iy \tag{A.1.5}$$

Definition 3: The *real part* of z, as in (A.1.4), is x, while y is said to be its *imaginary part*. Often one employs the notation

$$x = \text{Re}\,(z) \qquad y = \text{Im}\,(y) \tag{A.1.6}$$

Definition 4: The modulus of a complex number z, denoted by $|z|$, is defined by

$$|z| = (z\bar{z})^{\frac{1}{2}} \tag{A.1.7}$$

and one often uses the notation mod (z).

Remark 1: The terms *length, absolute value, magnitude* are frequently used synonymously with the term *modulus*.

---

[1] In the appendix, the symbol E^k will denote the k-dimensional Euclidean space. In the body of the book, the symbol R^k was used instead in order to avoid confusion with the expectation operator E.

In order to understand the meaning of (A.1.7), exactly, we need to define various algebraic operations on complex numbers. Such algebraic operations are solely derived from corresponding operations on their real and imaginary parts.

Addition and subtraction

Let

$$z_1 = x_1 + iy_1 \qquad z_2 = x_2 + iy_2 \tag{A.1.8}$$

Then

$$z_1 \pm z_2 = (x_1 \pm x_2) + i(y_1 \pm y_2) \tag{A.1.9}$$

Multiplication

Let z_1, z_2 be as in (A.1.8). Then

$$z_1 z_2 = x_1 x_2 + i x_1 y_2 + i y_1 x_2 + i^2 y_1 y_2 = (x_1 x_2 - y_1 y_2) + i(x_1 y_2 + y_1 x_2) \tag{A.1.10}$$

Notice that

$$z\bar{z} = (x + iy)(x - iy) = x^2 + y^2 \tag{A.1.11}$$

and thus the *modulus* of z is

$$|z| = (x^2 + y^2)^{\frac{1}{2}} \qquad |z|^2 = z\bar{z} = x^2 + y^2 \tag{A.1.12}$$

Division

Let z_1, z_2 be as in (A.1.8); then

$$\frac{z_1}{z_2} = \frac{z_1 \bar{z}_2}{|z_2|^2} = \frac{x_1 x_2 + y_1 y_2}{x_2^2 + y_2^2} + i\,\frac{y_1 x_2 - x_1 y_2}{x_2^2 + y_2^2} \tag{A.1.13}$$

Of course, (A.1.13) is valid *only* if $|z_2| \neq 0$.

Notice, however, that for any complex variable z

$$|z| = 0 \tag{A.1.14}$$

if and only if

$$z = 0 \tag{A.1.15}$$

We may represent any complex number by a point (or vector) in the two-dimensional Euclidean plane because, as we have seen, a complex number is expressible by a pair of real numbers (its real and imaginary parts). Thus if $z_1 = x_1 + iy_1$, z_1 can be represented by the point (or vector) as in Figure A.1. Here the position of z_1 in the plane is uniquely determined by its *distance* from

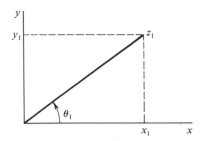

FIGURE A.1. Vector representation of a complex number

the origin, that is, the length of the line connecting the point to the origin, and the angle described by this line and denoted in the figure by θ_1. Conventionally, angles are measured in a counterclockwise fashion.

Now, the length, r_1, of the line is given by

$$r_1 = (x_1^2 + y_1^2)^{\frac{1}{2}} \tag{A.1.16}$$

and it is seen, by comparison with (A.1.11), to be exactly the *modulus* of z_1.

Notice that in terms of the diagram the real and imaginary parts of z_1 are given by

$$\cos \theta_1 = \frac{x_1}{r_1} \qquad \sin \theta_1 = \frac{y_1}{r_1} \tag{A.1.17}$$

Thus the complex number z_1 can also be written as

$$z_1 = r_1(\cos \theta_1 + i \sin \theta_1) \tag{A.1.18}$$

The quantity in parentheses will occur quite frequently, so that it is desirable to have a simpler notation for it. Thus *define* the symbol $\exp(i\theta)$ by

$$\exp(i\theta) = \cos \theta + i \sin \theta \tag{A.1.19}$$

Using (A.1.19), the complex number z_1 may be written as

$$z_1 = r_1 \exp(i\theta_1) \tag{A.1.20}$$

The representation of a complex number as in (A.1.20) is termed the *polar form* of the number.

The angle θ_1 is termed the *argument* of z_1 and the notation

$$\theta_1 = \arg(z_1) \tag{A.1.21}$$

is common.

The polar form is extremely convenient in that it can be shown that one can operate with $\exp(i\theta)$ as one does with a real exponential; for example, $\exp(i\theta_1)$ $\exp i\theta_2 = \exp[i(\theta_1 + \theta_2)]$, $[\exp(i\theta)]^k = \exp(ik\theta)$, and so on.

Notice that the complex conjugate of $\exp(i\theta)$ is given by

$$\overline{\exp(i\theta)} = \exp(-i\theta) \tag{A.1.22}$$

which can be easily verified from the definition in (A.1.19). Indeed, multiplication (and division) of complex numbers becomes particularly simple when the polar form is employed.

For instance, the reader may quickly verify that if

$$z_1 = r_1 \exp(i\theta_1) \qquad z_2 = r_2 \exp(i\theta_2) \tag{A.1.23}$$

then

$$z_1 z_2 = (r_1 r_2) \exp[i(\theta_1 + \theta_2)] \tag{A.1.24}$$

and

$$\frac{z_1}{z_2} = \left(\frac{r_1}{r_2}\right) \exp[i(\theta_1 - \theta_2)] \tag{A.1.25}$$

From (A.1.24) we see that

$$|z_1 z_2| = |z_1|\,|z_2| \tag{A.1.26}$$

and

$$\arg(z_1 z_2) = \theta_1 + \theta_2 \tag{A.1.27}$$

so that the modulus of a product (of two complex numbers) is the product of moduli and the argument of a product is the *sum* of arguments. Similarly, the modulus of a quotient (of two complex numbers) is the quotient of their moduli and the argument of a quotient is the difference of their arguments.

A function, $f(\cdot)$, of the complex variable z may be expressed in terms of a *pair* of *real-valued functions* of the real variables x and y. For instance, if

$$f(z) = z^2 \tag{A.1.28}$$

then we can write

$$f(z) = f_1(x, y) + if_2(x, y) \tag{A.1.29}$$

where, obviously,

$$f_1(x, y) = x^2 - y^2 \qquad f_2(x, y) = 2xy \tag{A.1.30}$$

Algebraic operations on functions of a complex variable are thus seen to be derivable from corresponding operations on their real and imaginary components. Similarly, the absolute value of the function $f(\cdot)$ can be obtained as

$$|f(z)| = \{[f_1(x, y)]^2 + [f_2(x, y)]^2\}^{\frac{1}{2}} \tag{A.1.31}$$

In the example above, we have

$$|f(z)| = |z|^2 = x^2 + y^2 \tag{A.1.32}$$

The derivative of a function $f(\cdot)$ (of the complex variable z) is defined by

$$\frac{df(z)}{dz} = f'(z) = \lim_{h \to 0} \frac{f(z+h) - f(z)}{h} \qquad \text{(A.1.33)}$$

where h is complex.

Consider again the function in (A.1.28) and note that

$$\frac{f(z+h) - f(z)}{h} = 2z + h \qquad \text{(A.1.34)}$$

and thus conclude

$$f'(z) = 2z \qquad \text{(A.1.35)}$$

The reader can easily show that

$$\frac{d}{dz} z^n = nz^{n-1} \qquad \text{(A.1.36)}$$

In general, the rules of differentiation for functions of real variables apply, more or less, to functions of a complex variable. Since we have little occasion to use such concepts in this book, the subject will not be pursued further. To test his understanding, the reader may obtain the derivative of

$$f(\theta) = \exp(i\theta) \qquad \text{(A.1.37)}$$

with respect to θ. Notice that θ is *real*.

Now, suppose that we wish to obtain the integral

$$g^*(\theta) = \int_{-\pi}^{\pi} \exp(i\theta x) g(x)\, dx \qquad \text{(A.1.38)}$$

where x is a *real variable*.[2] Well, if $g(\cdot)$ is complex valued then we have

$$g(x) = g_1(x) + ig_2(x) \qquad \text{(A.1.39)}$$

where $g_1(x)$ and $g_2(x)$ are *real valued*.

Thus

$$g(x) \exp(i\theta x) = [\cos \theta x g_1(x) - \sin \theta x g_2(x)] + i[\sin \theta x g_1(x) + \cos \theta x g_2(x)]$$
$$\text{(A.1.40)}$$

and we see that the integration above does not entail any knowledge other than what is pertinent for the integration of real-valued functions.

Indeed, if we write

$$g^*(\theta) = I_1(\theta) + iI_2(\theta) \qquad \text{(A.1.41)}$$

---

[2] Notice that this is exactly the problem involved in the spectral representation of the covariance stationary stochastic process, $X(t)$. Thus

$$X(t) = \int_{-\pi}^{\pi} \exp(it\lambda)\, dZ(\lambda)$$

then we have

$$I_1(\theta) = \int_{-\pi}^{\pi} [\cos \theta x g_1(x) - \sin \theta x g_2(x)] \, dx$$

$$I_2(\theta) = \int_{-\pi}^{\pi} [\sin \theta x g_1(x) + \cos \theta x g_2(x)] \, dx \tag{A.1.42}$$

A.2 THE RIEMANN-STIELTJES INTEGRAL

If $f(\cdot)$ is a real valued function defined on the (real) interval $[a, b]$, the reader is familiar with the definite integral

$$I(a, b) = \int_a^b f(x) \, dx \tag{A.2.1}$$

The meaning ascribed to (A.2.1) is as follows: Divide the interval by the points $a = x_0 < x_1 < x_2 \cdots < x_n = b$, and put

$$\Delta x_i = x_i - x_{i-1} \qquad i = 1, 2, \ldots, n \tag{A.2.2}$$

Let

$$x_i^* \in (x_{i-1}, x_i) \tag{A.2.3}$$

and consider the sum

$$S = \sum_{i=1}^{n} f(x_i^*) \, \Delta x_i \tag{A.2.4}$$

If the limit of S exists as $\max_i \Delta x_i$ approaches zero no matter what the subdivision is, then

$$\lim_{\Delta x_i \to 0} S = \int_a^b f(x) \, dx \tag{A.2.5}$$

and the function $f(\cdot)$ is said to be (Riemann) integrable.

A generalization of the above, due to the Dutch mathematician Stieltjes, is as follows: Let $f(\cdot)$, $g(\cdot)$ be two (real-valued) functions defined on the (real) interval $[a, b]$. Subdivide the interval by the points $a = a_0 < a_1 < a_2 < \cdots < a_n = b$; let

$$x_i \in (a_{i-1}, a_i) \qquad i = 1, 2, \ldots, n \tag{A.2.6}$$

and consider the sum

$$S = \sum_{i=1}^{n} f(x_i)[g(a_i) - g(a_{i-1})] \tag{A.2.7}$$

If, as $\max_i \Delta a_i$ tends to zero, S converges to the same limit no matter what the subdivision is, then $f(\cdot)$ is said to be (Riemann-Stieltjes) integrable relative to $g(\cdot)$ and the integral is denoted by

$$\lim_{\Delta a_i \to 0} S = \int_a^b f(x)\, dg(x) \tag{A.2.8}$$

Notice that if

$$f(x) = 1 \tag{A.2.9}$$

then the integral in (A.2.8) defines the Riemann-Stieltjes integral of $g(\cdot)$ over the interval $[a, b]$. If the derivative of $g(\cdot)$ exists on $[a, b]$, the Riemann and Riemann-Stieltjes definitions of integral coincide, as indicated by the following theorem, given without proof.

Theorem 1: Let $f(\cdot)$ and $g(\cdot)$ be defined on $[a, b]$. Suppose that the derivative $g'(x)$ exists on $[a, b]$ and that the functions $f(\cdot)$, $g(\cdot)$ and $g'(\cdot)$ are integrable there. Then

$$\int_a^b f(x)\, dg(x) = \int_a^b f(x) g'(x)\, dx \tag{A.2.10}$$

Remark 2: If we take

$$f(x) \equiv 1 \tag{A.2.11}$$

then the theorem shows that

$$\int_a^b dg(x) = \int_a^b g'(x)\, dx \tag{A.2.12}$$

A.3 MONOTONIC FUNCTIONS AND FUNCTIONS OF BOUNDED VARIATION

Definition 5: A real-valued function $f(\cdot)$ defined on the interval $[a, b]$ is said to be monotonic increasing if for any $x_1, x_2 \in [a, b]$ such that $x_1 < x_2$,

$$f(x_2) - f(x_1) > 0 \tag{A.3.1}$$

It is said to be monotonic *nondecreasing* if for x_1, x_2 as above,

$$f(x_2) - f(x_1) \geq 0 \tag{A.3.2}$$

Definition 6: A (real-valued) function $g(\cdot)$ defined on an interval $[a, b]$ is said to be monotonic decreasing (nonincreasing) if $-g(\cdot)$ is monotonic increasing (nondecreasing).

Remark 3: A function obeying the requirements of any of the two definitions above is said to be *monotonic*. A well-known example of a *monotonic nondecreasing* function is the *distribution function* of probability theory.

Monotonic functions have certain desirable properties, which we cite below without proof.

Proposition 1: Let $f(\cdot)$ be monotonic on $[a, b]$. Then

i. $f(\cdot)$ is continuous almost everywhere.
ii. $f(\cdot)$ is differentiable almost everywhere on $[a, b]$.

Frequently one may wish to add or subtract monotonic functions; the difference of two monotonic functions, however, will generally not be monotonic. It turns out that the class of sums and differences of monotonic functions is the class of *functions of bounded variation*, which we had found useful when dealing with spectral analysis.

Definition 7: Let $f(\cdot)$ be a function defined on the interval $[a, b]$. Subdivide this interval by the points $a = a_0 < a_1 < a_2 < \cdots < a_n = b$ and consider the sum

$$S = \sum_{i=1}^{n} |f(a_i) - f(a_{i-1})|$$ (A.3.3)

The least upper bound of this sum for all possible subdivisions of the interval is termed the total variation of $f(\cdot)$ over the interval $[a, b]$ and is denoted by $V_f[a, b]$. If $V_f[a, b]$ is *finite*, then $f(\cdot)$ is said to be a *function of bounded variation* over $[a, b]$. We have

Proposition 2: Any function $g(\cdot)$ defined *and* monotonic over the interval $[a, b]$ is of bounded variation.

PROOF: Without loss of relevance, let us suppose $g(\cdot)$ to be monotonic nondecreasing [if not, then $-g(\cdot)$ will be]. Thus for *any* subdivision we should have

$$\sum_{i=1}^{n} |g(a_i) - g(a_{i-1})| = g(b) - g(a)$$ Q.E.D.

(A.3.4)

Proposition 3: Let $f(\cdot)$ be a continuous function on $[a, b]$ having a *bounded* derivative on $[a, b]$. Then $f(\cdot)$ is a function of bounded variation on $[a, b]$.

PROOF: Let a_i, $i = 0, 1, 2, \ldots, n$, be any subdivision of the interval as in Definition 7. Let $x_i \in (a_{i-1}, a_i)$; then by the mean value theorem

$$f(a_i) = f(a_{i-1}) + f'(x_i)(a_i - a_{i-1})$$ (A.3.5)

Thus

$$S = \sum_{i=1}^{n} |f(a_i) - f(a_{i-1})| = \sum_{i=1}^{n} |f'(x_i)| (a_i - a_{i-1}) \tag{A.3.6}$$

Since $f'(\cdot)$ is bounded on $[a, b]$, for any $x \in (a, b)$, we have

$$|f'(x)| < M \tag{A.3.7}$$

for some constant M. Thus

$$S < M \sum_{i=1}^{n} (a_i - a_{i-1}) = M(b - a) \qquad \text{Q.E.D.}$$

$$\tag{A.3.8}$$

We shall now give a number of results without proof, for their proof is either obvious or not sufficiently enlightening to produce here.

Proposition 4: If $f(\cdot)$ and $g(\cdot)$ are functions of bounded variation on $[a, b]$, then so are $f(\cdot) \pm g(\cdot)$ and $f(\cdot)g(\cdot)$.

Proposition 5: If $f(\cdot)$ is of bounded variation on $[a, b]$ and if $[c, d]$ is *any* subinterval of $[a, b]$, then $f(\cdot)$ is of bounded variation on $[c, d]$.

Proposition 6: Let $g(\cdot)$ be a differentiable function on $[a, b]$ and suppose that its derivative, $g'(\cdot)$, is absolutely integrable there (i.e., $\int_a^b |g'(x)| dx$ exists and is finite). Then $g(\cdot)$ is of bounded variation and, moreover,

$$V_g[a, b] = \int_a^b |g'(x)| \, dx \tag{A.3.9}$$

We have given above a partial characterization of functions that are of bounded variation. The perceptive reader would have noticed that *continuity* of a function is *not* enough to ensure that it is of bounded variation.

We illustrate this by an example.

Example 1: Consider the function

$$f(x) = x \cos \left(\frac{\pi}{x} \right) \qquad 0 < x \le 1 \tag{A.3.10}$$

If $f(0)$ is defined to be zero, then the function is continuous on $[0, 1]$. Now choose the points of the subdivision as

$$a_0 = 0 \quad a_i = \frac{1}{n + 1 - i} \qquad i = 1, 2, \ldots, n \tag{A.3.11}$$

We observe that, for $i = 2, \ldots, n$,

$$|f(a_i) - f(a_{i-1})| = \left| \frac{\cos (n + 1 - i)\pi}{n + 1 - i} - \frac{\cos (n + 2 - i)\pi}{n + 2 - i} \right|$$

$$= \frac{1}{n + 1 - i} + \frac{1}{n + 2 - i} \qquad \text{(A.3.12)}$$

Thus

$$\sum_{i=1}^{n} |f(a_i) - f(a_{i-1})| = \frac{1}{n} + \sum_{i=2}^{n} \frac{1}{n + 1 - i} + \sum_{i=2}^{n} \frac{1}{n + 2 - i} = 2\sum_{k=2}^{n} \frac{1}{k} + 1$$

$$\text{(A.3.13)}$$

It may be easily verified, however, that as $n \to \infty$ this sum does not converge. Hence the function in (A.3.10), although continuous, is *not* of bounded variation.

The "trouble" is that the function changes very rapidly near the origin, and it can be shown to have as many maxima and minima as one wishes in an appropriately selected small neighborhood (near the origin).

Thus we see that bounded variation does not imply continuity, nor does the latter imply the former. On the other hand, it is interesting that if a function is *absolutely continuous* (a term to be defined below), then it is also of *bounded variation*.

Definition 8: A function $f(\cdot)$ defined on $[a, b]$ is said to be absolutely continuous if for any $\varepsilon > 0$ there exists $\delta > 0$ such that, if $\alpha_0 \leq \alpha_1 \leq \alpha_2 \leq \ldots \leq \alpha_n$, $\alpha_n - \alpha_1 < \delta$, and $\alpha_i \in [a, b]$, then

$$\sum_{i=1}^{n} |f(\alpha_i) - f(\alpha_{i-1})| < \varepsilon \qquad \text{(A.3.14)}$$

Remark 4: If $n = 1$, then the definition implies that, for $\alpha_1 - \alpha_0 < \delta$ we have

$$|f(\alpha_1) - f(\alpha_0)| < \varepsilon \qquad \text{(A.3.15)}$$

so that an absolutely continuous function is continuous, indeed uniformly continuous. Obviously, the converse is not correct.

Now, in order to give a characterization of the class of functions with bounded variation, we need a few additional terms.

Definition 9: Let $f(\cdot)$ be a function of bounded variation defined on $[a, b]$. Let $x \in [a, b]$. Then

$$v(x) = V_f[a, x] \qquad \text{(A.3.16)}$$

is termed the total variation function of $f(\cdot)$; and

$$p(x) = \tfrac{1}{2}[v(x) + f(x) - f(a)] \qquad \text{(A.3.17)}$$

$$n(x) = \tfrac{1}{2}[v(x) - f(x) + f(a)] \qquad \text{(A.3.18)}$$

are termed the positive and negative variation functions of $f(\cdot)$ respectively. We have

Proposition 7: The total, positive, and negative variation functions are nonnegative and monotonic nondecreasing.

PROOF: Consider any $x \in [a, b]$, $x > a$; choose points a_i, $i = 0, 1, 2, \ldots, n$ such that $a = a_0 < a_1 < a_2 < \cdots < a_n = x$. Then

$$|f(x) - f(a)| = \left| \sum_{i=1}^{n} f(a_i) - f(a_{i-1}) \right| \leq \sum_{i=1}^{n} |f(a_i) - f(a_{i-1})| \leq v(x) \qquad \text{(A.3.19)}$$

Now by construction $v(x)$ is nonnegative—indeed positive if $f(\cdot)$ is not constant over $[a, x]$. The nonnegativity of $p(x)$ and $n(x)$ is immediate from their definition and from (A.3.19). From the definition, it is clear that $v(x)$ is monotonic increasing, and it is apparent that the negative variation function of $f(\cdot)$ is the positive variation function of $-f(\cdot)$. Thus to complete the proof of the proposition, it is sufficient to show that $p(x)$ is nondecreasing.

Now, let $\alpha, \beta \in [a, b]$, $\beta > \alpha$. It is easily shown by the definition of the quantities that

$$V_f[a, \beta] = V_f[a, \alpha] + V_f[\alpha, \beta] \qquad \text{(A.3.20)}$$

Thus, since

$$\begin{aligned} p(\beta) - p(\alpha) &= \tfrac{1}{2}[V_f[a, \beta] - V_f[a, \alpha] + f(\beta) - f(\alpha)] \\ &= \tfrac{1}{2}[V_f[\alpha, \beta] + f(\beta) - f(\alpha)] \end{aligned} \qquad \text{(A.3.21)}$$

in view of (A.3.19) we conclude

$$p(\beta) - p(\alpha) \geq 0 \qquad \begin{array}{r} \text{Q.E.D.} \\ \text{(A.3.22)} \end{array}$$

Finally, we have

Proposition 8: Let $f(\cdot)$ be defined on $[a, b]$. Then $f(\cdot)$ is of bounded variation if and only if it can be expressed as the difference of two nonnegative, monotonic, nondecreasing functions.

PROOF: If $f(\cdot)$ is of bounded variation, consider the positive and negative variation functions defined in (A.3.17) and (A.3.18) respectively. Then it is obvious that

$$f(x) = [p(x) + f(a)] - n(x) \qquad \text{(A.3.23)}$$

Since $p(x) + f(a)$ is monotonic nondecreasing, necessity is proved. Sufficiency is obvious in view of Propositions 2 and 4.

Remark 5: Since a monotonic nondecreasing function over $[a, b]$ is certainly integrable there, we see that a function of bounded variation over $[a, b]$ is *absolutely* integrable there.

A.4 FOURIER SERIES

Definition 10: Let $f(\cdot)$ be a function defined on the real line. If, for any x

$$f(x + 2k\pi) = f(x) \qquad k = 0, \pm 1, \pm 2, \ldots \tag{A.4.1}$$

then $f(\cdot)$ is said to be periodic of period 2π.

Definition 11: Let $f(\cdot)$ be a function defined on the real line. Then if

$$f(x) = f(-x) \tag{A.4.2}$$

$f(\cdot)$ is said to be an *even* function. If

$$f(-x) = -f(x) \tag{A.4.3}$$

then $f(\cdot)$ is said to be an *odd* function.

Now, let $f(\cdot)$ be a complex-valued function of the real variable x and suppose that it can be written as

$$f(x) = \sum_{n=-\infty}^{\infty} c_n \exp(-inx) \tag{A.4.4}$$

where the c_n are complex constants.

Consider now the integral

$$\frac{1}{2\pi} \int_{-\pi}^{\pi} f(x) \exp(ikx)\, dx = \frac{1}{2\pi} \sum_{n=-\infty}^{\infty} c_n \int_{\pi}^{\pi} \exp[\; i(n-k)x]\, dx \tag{A.4.5}$$

Generally, we have, for $t \neq 0$,

$$\int_{-\pi}^{\pi} \exp(it\theta)\, d\theta = \frac{1}{it} \exp(it\theta)\Big|_{-\pi}^{\pi} = 0 \tag{A.4.6}$$

Hence in (A.4.5) we see that all integrals vanish except that corresponding to $n = k$. Thus we conclude

$$\frac{1}{2\pi} \int_{-\pi}^{\pi} f(x) \exp(ikx)\, dx = c_k \qquad k = 0, \pm 1, \pm 2, \ldots \tag{A.4.7}$$

Now, *even if $f(\cdot)$ is not given by (A.4.4) but it is integrable on $[-\pi, \pi]$, we can still compute the quantities in (A.4.7).*

We have

Definition 12: Let $f(\cdot)$ be an integrable function on $[-\pi, \pi]$; then the sequence

$$c = \{c_k : k = 0, \pm 1, \pm 2, \ldots\} \tag{A.4.8}$$

defined by

$$c_k = \frac{1}{2\pi} \int_{-\pi}^{\pi} f(x) \exp(ikx)\, dx \tag{A.4.9}$$

is said to be the sequence of *Fourier coefficients* of $f(\cdot)$ and the quantity in (A.4.9) is termed the kth (complex) *Fourier coefficient* of $f(\cdot)$.

Remark 6: Notice that if $f(\cdot)$ is written as

$$f(x) = f_1(x) + if_2(x) \tag{A.4.10}$$

then the integral in (A.4.7) can be expressed as

$$c_k = \frac{1}{2\pi} \int_{-\pi}^{\pi} (f_1(x) \cos kx - f_2(x) \sin kx) \, dx$$
$$+ i \int_{-\pi}^{\pi} (f_1(x) \sin kx + f_2(x) \cos kx) \, dx \tag{A.4.11}$$

If $f(\cdot)$ is *real valued*, then

$$f_2(x) \equiv 0 \tag{A.4.12}$$

and (A.4.11) reduces to

$$c_k = \frac{1}{2\pi} \int_{-\pi}^{\pi} f_1(x) \cos kx \, dx + i \frac{1}{2\pi} \int_{-\pi}^{\pi} f_1(x) \sin kx \, dx \tag{A.4.13}$$

If we write the Fourier coefficients of $f(\cdot)$ as

$$c_k = \alpha_k + i\beta_k \qquad k = 0, \pm 1, \pm 2, \ldots \tag{A.4.14}$$

then we see that when $f(\cdot)$ is real valued

$$\alpha_k = \frac{1}{2\pi} \int_{-\pi}^{\pi} f(x) \cos kx \, dx \qquad \beta_k = \frac{1}{2\pi} \int_{-\pi}^{\pi} f(x) \sin kx \, dx \tag{A.4.15}$$

and, furthermore,

$$\alpha_k = \alpha_{-k} \qquad \beta_{-k} = -\beta_k \qquad k = 0, \pm 1, \pm 2, \ldots \tag{A.4.16}$$

Of course, (A.4.16) implies that $\beta_0 = 0$. From (A.4.14) we then see that for real-valued $f(\cdot)$ its Fourier coefficients have the property

$$\bar{c}_k = c_{-k} \tag{A.4.17}$$

If $f(\cdot)$ is real valued and *even*, then it is easily seen from (A.4.15) that

$$\beta_k = 0 \qquad \text{all } k \tag{A.4.18}$$

On the other hand, if $f(\cdot)$ is *odd*, then

$$\alpha_k = 0 \qquad \text{all } k. \tag{A.4.19}$$

Definition 13: Let $f(\cdot)$ be a complex-valued function and consider its associated sequence of Fourier coefficients. The series

$$S(x) = \sum_{n=-\infty}^{\infty} c_n \exp(-inx) \tag{A.4.20}$$

is said to be the Fourier series associated with $f(\cdot)$.

The question now arises as to whether it is possible to represent $f(\cdot)$ as in (A.4.20) and, if so, under what circumstances.

More precisely, let us define the nth partial sum of the Fourier series

$$S_n(x) = \sum_{k=-n}^{n} c_k \exp(-ikx) \tag{A.4.21}$$

What we ask is this: Is there any class of functions $f(\cdot)$ such that

$$\lim_{n\to\infty} S_n(x) = f(x) \tag{A.4.22}$$

It is apparent that since $S_n(\cdot)$ is periodic of period 2π, for $f(\cdot)$ to be representable as in (A.4.22) it, too, must be periodic of period 2π. Before we give an answer to the question above, let us prove the following useful property of Fourier coefficients.

Theorem 2 (Bessel Inequality): Let $f(\cdot)$ be an absolutely (square) integrable function on $[-\pi, \pi]$ and let c_k, $k = 0, \pm 1, \pm 2, \ldots$ be the sequence of its Fourier coefficients. Then

$$\frac{1}{2\pi} \int_{-\pi}^{\pi} |f(x)|^2 \, dx \geq \sum_{k=-\infty}^{\infty} |c_k|^2 \tag{A.4.23}$$

PROOF: For *any* n, observe that

$$0 \leq r(x) = [f(x) - S_n(x)][\overline{f(x) - S_n(x)}] = |f(x)|^2 - S_n(x)\overline{f(x)}$$
$$- \overline{S_n(x)}f(x) + S_n(x)\overline{S_n(x)} \tag{A.4.24}$$

where $S_n(x)$ was defined in (A.4.21).

Since $r(x) \geq 0$, we conclude that

$$\frac{1}{2\pi} \int_{-\pi}^{\pi} r(x) \, dx \geq 0 \tag{A.4.25}$$

Now

$$\frac{1}{2\pi} \int_{-\pi}^{\pi} f(x)\overline{S_n(x)} \, dx = \sum_{k=-n}^{n} \bar{c}_k \left[\frac{1}{2\pi} \int_{-\pi}^{\pi} f(x) \exp(ikx) \, dx \right] = \sum_{k=-n}^{n} \bar{c}_k c_k = \sum_{k=-n}^{n} |c_k|^2$$
$$\tag{A.4.26}$$

Similarly,

$$\frac{1}{2\pi} \int_{-\pi}^{\pi} S_n(x)\overline{S_n(x)} \, dx = \sum_{k=-n}^{n} \sum_{k'=-n}^{n} c_k \bar{c}_{k'} \left[\frac{1}{2\pi} \int_{-\pi}^{\pi} \exp[i(k-k')x] \, dx \right] = \sum_{k=-n}^{n} |c_k|^2$$
$$\tag{A.4.27}$$

Since $\bar{f}(x)S_n(x) = \overline{f(x)\bar{S}_n(x)}$, in view of (A.4.24), (A.4.25), (A.4.26) and (A.4.27), we conclude

$$\frac{1}{2\pi} \int_{-\pi}^{\pi} |f(x)|^2 \, dx \geq \sum_{k=-n}^{n} |c_k|^2 \tag{A.4.28}$$

Since (A.4.28) holds for any n, the theorem is proved.

Corollary 1: If $f(\cdot)$ is absolutely (square) integrable on $[-\pi, \pi]$ then

$$\lim_{n \to \infty} \frac{1}{2\pi} \int_{-\pi}^{\pi} f(x) \exp (inx) \, dx = 0 \tag{A.4.29}$$

PROOF: We observe that

$$c_n = \frac{1}{2\pi} \int_{-\pi}^{\pi} f(x) \exp (inx) \, dx \tag{A.4.30}$$

Since

$$\sum_{k=-\infty}^{\infty} |c_k|^2 < \infty \tag{A.4.31}$$

we must have

$$\lim_{n \to \infty} |c_n| = 0 \tag{A.4.32}$$

In view of (A.4.30), the corollary is proved.

Notice that an alternative form of (A.4.29) is

$$\lim_{n \to \infty} \frac{1}{2\pi} \int_{-\pi}^{\pi} f(x) \cos nx \, dx = \lim_{n \to \infty} \frac{1}{2\pi} \int_{-\pi}^{\pi} f(x) \sin nx \, dx = 0 \tag{A.4.33}$$

This is a weak form of a result known as the *Riemann-Lebesgue Lemma*, which states that if $|f|$ is integrable on $(-\infty, \infty)$ then

$$\lim_{t \to \infty} \int_{-\infty}^{\infty} f(x) \exp (itx) \, dx = 0 \tag{A.4.34}$$

Here t need not be an integer.

Now, let us return to the question raised earlier concerning the class of functions for which (A.4.22) is valid. We have

Theorem 3: Let $f(\cdot)$ be a function of a real variable; suppose that it is periodic of period 2π and of bounded variation on $[-\pi, \pi]$.[3] Then for any $x \in [-\pi, \pi]$

$$\lim_{n \to \infty} S_n(x) = \tfrac{1}{2}[f(x + 0) + f(x - 0)] \tag{A.4.35}$$

---

[3] The reader may best view $f(\cdot)$ as real valued. Certain modifications of the proof will be required if it is complex valued, although in no way is the validity of the theorem affected.

where $S_n(x)$ is the partial sum of the Fourier series of $f(\cdot)$ as defined in (A.4.21), and $f(x + 0)$, $f(x - 0)$ are, respectively, the right- and left-hand limits of $f(\cdot)$ at the point x.[4]

PROOF: Since

$$S_n(x) = \sum_{k=-n}^{n} c_k \exp\,(-ikx) \tag{A.4.36}$$

substituting therein the definition of the Fourier coefficients, we obtain

$$S_n(x) = \frac{1}{2\pi} \int_{-\pi}^{\pi} f(\xi) \left\{ \sum_{k=-n}^{n} \exp\,[ik(\xi - x)] \right\} d\xi \tag{A.4.37}$$

Now

$$\sum_{k=-n}^{n} \exp\,[ik(\xi - x)] = 1 + \sum_{k=1}^{n} \{\exp\,[ik(\xi - x)] + \exp\,[-ik(\xi - x)]\}$$

$$= 1 + 2 \sum_{k=1}^{n} \cos k(\xi - x) \tag{A.4.38}$$

It will be shown below that

$$1 + 2 \sum_{k=1}^{n} \cos k(\xi - x) = \frac{\sin\,(n + \tfrac{1}{2})(\xi - x)}{\sin\,\tfrac{1}{2}(\xi - x)} \tag{A.4.39}$$

and, furthermore, that

$$\frac{1}{2\pi} \int_{-\pi}^{\pi} \frac{\sin\,(n + \tfrac{1}{2})u}{\sin\,\tfrac{1}{2}u}\,du = 1 \tag{A.4.40}$$

Thus (A.4.37) can also be written as

$$S_n(x) = \frac{1}{2\pi} \int_{-\pi}^{\pi} f(\xi)\,\frac{\sin\,(n + \tfrac{1}{2})(\xi - x)}{\sin\,\tfrac{1}{2}(\xi - x)}\,d\xi \tag{A.4.41}$$

Making the change in variable $\xi - x = \phi$ and noting that the integrand in (A.4.41) is periodic of period 2π, we can write

$$S_n(x) = \frac{1}{2\pi} \int_{-\pi}^{\pi} f(x + \phi)\,\frac{\sin\,(n + \tfrac{1}{2})\phi}{\sin\,\tfrac{1}{2}\phi}\,d\phi \tag{A.4.42}$$

If we put $-\phi$ for ϕ in (A.4.42), we note that $S_n(x)$ can also be written as

$$S_n(x) = \frac{1}{2\pi} \int_{-\pi}^{\pi} f(x - \phi)\,\frac{\sin\,(n + \tfrac{1}{2})\phi}{\sin\,\tfrac{1}{2}\phi}\,d\phi \tag{A.4.43}$$

---

[4] The left-hand limit of $f(\cdot)$ at the point ξ is defined by $\lim_{x \uparrow \xi} f(x)$, that is, it is the limit as x approaches ξ through values lower than ξ. Similarly, the right-hand limit [of $f(\cdot)$ at ξ] is the limit as x approaches ξ through values greater than ξ.

Define

$$g(\phi) = f(x + \phi) + f(x - \phi) - 2f(x) \tag{A.4.44}$$

and note that

 i. $g(\phi)$ is a function of bounded variation.
 ii. $g(-\phi) = g(\phi)$.

Thus to prove the theorem, we need to demonstrate, in view of (A.4.40), that

$$\lim_{n \to \infty} \frac{1}{2\pi} \int_{-\pi}^{\pi} g(\phi) \frac{\sin (n + \frac{1}{2})\phi}{\sin \frac{1}{2}\phi} \, d\phi = 0 \tag{A.4.45}$$

We first observe that the integrand in (A.4.45) is even and thus the integral over $(-\pi, \pi)$ is simply twice the integral over $(0, \pi)$.

Now write

$$\int_0^{\pi} g(\phi) \frac{\sin (n + \frac{1}{2})\phi}{2 \sin \frac{1}{2}\phi} \, d\phi = \int_0^{\delta} g(\phi) \frac{\sin (n + \frac{1}{2})\phi}{2 \sin \frac{1}{2}\phi} \, d\phi + \int_{\delta}^{\pi} g(\phi) \frac{\sin (n + \frac{1}{2})\phi}{2 \sin \frac{1}{2}\phi} \, d\phi \tag{A.4.46}$$

where $\delta \in (0, \pi)$.

We shall now show that if we let $n \to \infty$ and $\delta \to 0$, both integrals in the right member of (A.4.46) vanish, thus proving the theorem. But it is clear from Corollary 1 and the ensuing discussion that the second integral vanishes as $n \to \infty$. Consider now the first integral and notice that

$$\frac{\sin (n + \frac{1}{2})\phi}{2 \sin \frac{1}{2}\phi} = \frac{\sin (n + \frac{1}{2})\phi}{\phi} + \sin (n + \frac{1}{2})\phi \left(\frac{1}{2 \sin \frac{1}{2}\phi} - \frac{1}{\phi} \right) \tag{A.4.47}$$

We observe that if we define

$$\frac{1}{2 \sin \frac{1}{2}\phi} - \frac{1}{\phi}$$

to be zero for $\phi = 0$, then this is a continuous function on $[0, \delta]$, and thus by the Riemann-Lebesgue Lemma referred to above

$$\lim_{n \to \infty} \int_0^{\delta} \left(\frac{1}{2 \sin \frac{1}{2}\phi} - \frac{1}{\phi} \right) g(\phi) \sin (n + \frac{1}{2})\phi \, d\phi = 0 \tag{A.4.48}$$

Thus to complete the proof of our theorem, we need only show that

$$\int_0^{\delta} \frac{\sin (n + \frac{1}{2})\phi}{\phi} g(\phi) \, d\phi$$

vanishes as $n \to \infty$ and then $\delta \to 0$.

Now, $g(\phi)$ is a function of bounded variation that assumes the value zero for $\phi = 0$. Thus we can express it as the difference between two (nonnegative) monotonic nondecreasing functions, which may be assumed to vanish at the origin. Hence

$$g(\phi) = \alpha(\phi) - \beta(\phi) \tag{A.4.49}$$

such that $\alpha(\cdot)$, $\beta(\cdot)$ are monotonic nondecreasing and

$$\alpha(0) = \beta(0) = 0 \tag{A.4.50}$$

Thus to prove the theorem, it will be sufficient to show that

$$\lim_{\substack{n \to \infty \\ \delta \to 0}} \int_0^\delta \alpha(\phi) \frac{\sin(n + \frac{1}{2})\phi}{\phi} \, d\phi = 0 \tag{A.4.51}$$

Now, it can be shown that since $\alpha(\phi) \geq 0$ and is monotonic nondecreasing, there exists a point, $\gamma \in (0, \delta)$ such that

$$\int_0^\delta \alpha(\phi) \frac{\sin(n + \frac{1}{2})\phi}{\phi} \, d\phi = \alpha(\delta) \int_\gamma^\delta \frac{\sin(n + \frac{1}{2})}{\phi} \, d\phi \tag{A.4.52}$$

Make the change in variable

$$u = (n + \tfrac{1}{2})\phi \tag{A.4.53}$$

and notice that

$$\int_\gamma^\delta \frac{\sin(n + \frac{1}{2})\phi}{\phi} \, d\phi = \int_{\gamma(n+\frac{1}{2})}^{\delta(n+\frac{1}{2})} \frac{\sin u}{u} \, du \tag{A.4.54}$$

The integral in the right member of (A.4.54) is certainly bounded, say, by the constant C, independently of n. Thus we see that for any n,

$$\left| \int_0^\delta \alpha(\phi) \frac{\sin(n + \frac{1}{2})\phi}{\phi} \, d\phi \right| \leq \alpha(\delta)C \tag{A.4.55}$$

Since $\alpha(\delta)$ is monotonic nondecreasing and assumes the value zero at $\delta = 0$, we see that

$$\lim_{\substack{n \to \infty \\ \delta \to 0}} \int_0^\delta \alpha(\phi) \frac{\sin(n + \frac{1}{2})\phi}{\phi} \, d\phi = 0 \qquad \text{Q.E.D.} \tag{A.4.56}$$

Let us prove the validity of (A.4.39) and (A.4.40). Notice that

$$2 \sin \tfrac{1}{2}x \cos kx = \sin(\tfrac{1}{2} + k)x + \sin(\tfrac{1}{2} - k)x \tag{A.4.57}$$

Summing for $k = 1, 2, \ldots n$, the right-hand side becomes

$$\sin \tfrac{3}{2}x + \sin(-\tfrac{1}{2})x + \sin \tfrac{5}{2}x + \sin(-\tfrac{3}{2})x + \cdots + \sin(n + \tfrac{1}{2})x + \sin(-n + \tfrac{1}{2})x$$

Since $\sin (-b)x = -\sin bx$, we see that all terms of the sum cancel except for

$$\sin (n + \tfrac{1}{2})x + \sin (-\tfrac{1}{2})x = \sin (n + \tfrac{1}{2})x - \sin \tfrac{1}{2}x \qquad \text{(A.4.58)}$$

Now to prove (A.4.40), notice that if we integrate both sides of (A.4.39) over $[-\pi, \pi]$, all cosine integrals in the left member vanish and we are left only with the integral of the first term, which is 2π. Dividing through by 2π, we have (A.4.40).

Concerning the continuity of $1/2 \sin \tfrac{1}{2}\phi - 1/\phi$ over $[0, \delta]$, we observe that for any x we have the expansion

$$\sin x = x - \frac{x^3}{3!} + \frac{x^5}{5!} - \frac{x^7}{7!} + \cdots \qquad \text{(A.4.59)}$$

Proceeding somewhat heuristically, we note

$$\frac{1}{2 \sin \tfrac{1}{2}\phi} - \frac{1}{\phi} = \frac{\phi - 2 \sin \tfrac{1}{2}\phi}{2\phi \sin \tfrac{1}{2}\phi} \qquad \text{(A.4.60)}$$

Letting

$$\tfrac{1}{2}\phi = r \qquad \text{(A.4.61·)}$$

and using the expansion in (A.4.59), we find (after cancelling a factor r^2 from both numerator and denominator),

$$\frac{\phi - 2 \sin \tfrac{1}{2}\phi}{2\phi \sin \tfrac{1}{2}\phi} = \frac{\dfrac{r}{3!} - \dfrac{r^3}{5!} + \dfrac{r^5}{7!} \cdots}{2\left(1 - \dfrac{r^2}{3!} + \dfrac{r^4}{5!} \cdots\right)} \qquad \text{(A.4.62)}$$

and we see that as $\phi \to 0$ the fraction in (A.4.62) approaches zero. Since the fraction is continuous on $(0, \delta]$, it will be continuous on $[0, \delta]$ as well if defined at the origin by its limit.

Finally, the reader may show, using similar arguments, that

$$\lim_{u \to 0} \frac{\sin u}{u} = 1 \qquad \text{(A.4.63)}$$

Or he may use L'Hôspital's rule.

Remark 7: Since $f(\cdot)$ is of bounded variation, it is continuous almost everywhere. Thus Theorem 3 states that at a point of continuity the Fourier series converges to the function (since there the left- and right-hand limits are equal). If there is a discontinuity at x, then the Fourier series converges to the average of the function's left and right limits at x.

We shall now deal, somewhat informally, with the problems of *Fourier transform pairs.*

If $f(\cdot)$ is an integrable function on $(-\infty, \infty)$, then the integral

$$F(t) = \int_{-\infty}^{\infty} \exp{(itx)} f(x)\, dx \qquad\qquad\qquad (A.4.64)$$

exists. Indeed, the Riemann-Lebesgue lemma above indicates that if $|f(\cdot)|$ is integrable over $(-\infty, \infty)$, then

$$\lim_{t\to\infty} F(t) = 0 \qquad\qquad\qquad (A.4.65)$$

Moreover, the integral defining $F(\cdot)$ is uniformly convergent for all t.

We have

Definition 14: If $f(\cdot)$ is absolutely integrable on $(-\infty, \infty)$, the function $F(\cdot)$ defined in (A.4.64) is said to be the *Fourier transform* of $f(\cdot)$.

Suppose we now define in analogy with (A.4.64)

$$\omega(x) = \frac{1}{2\pi} \int_{-\infty}^{\infty} F(t) \exp{(-itx)}\, dt \qquad\qquad\qquad (A.4.66)$$

Since the integral defining $F(t)$ is uniformly convergent, we can also express (A.4.66) as

$$\omega(x) = \lim_{R\to\infty} \frac{1}{2\pi} \int_{-R}^{R} F(t) \exp{(-itx)}\, dt \qquad\qquad\qquad (A.4.67)$$

Let

$$S_R(x) = \frac{1}{2\pi} \int_{-R}^{R} F(t) \exp{(-itx)}\, dt \qquad\qquad\qquad (A.4.68)$$

and substitute in (A.4.68) the expression of $F(t)$ from (A.4.64) to obtain

$$S_R(x) = \frac{1}{2\pi} \int_{-R}^{R} \int_{-\infty}^{\infty} f(\xi) \exp{(it\xi)} \exp{(-itx)}\, d\xi\, dt \qquad\qquad\qquad (A.4.69)$$

Changing the order of integration, which we can do since the integral defining $F(t)$ is uniformly convergent in t, we find

$$S_R(x) = \frac{1}{2\pi} \int_{-\infty}^{\infty} f(\xi) \left[\int_{-R}^{R} \exp{[it(\xi - x)]}\, dt \right] d\xi \qquad\qquad\qquad (A.4.70)$$

But

$$\int_{-R}^{R} \exp{[it(\xi - x)]}\, dt = \frac{\exp{[it(\xi - x)]}}{i(\xi - x)} \Big|_{-R}^{R} = \frac{2 \sin R(\xi - x)}{\xi - x} \qquad\qquad\qquad (A.4.71)$$

so that

$$S_R(x) = \frac{2}{2\pi} \int_{-\infty}^{\infty} f(\xi) \frac{\sin R(\xi - x)}{\xi - x}\, d\xi \qquad\qquad\qquad (A.4.72)$$

Make in (A.4.72), the change of variable $\phi = \xi - x$ to obtain

$$S_R(x) = \frac{2}{2\pi} \int_{-\infty}^{\infty} f(x + \phi) \frac{\sin R\phi}{\phi} \, d\phi = \frac{2}{2\pi} \int_{0}^{\infty} [f(x + \phi) + f(x - \phi)] \frac{\sin R\phi}{\phi} \, d\phi$$

(A.4.73)

Now, for $R > 0$, one easily establishes that

$$\int_{0}^{\infty} \frac{\sin R\phi}{\phi} \, d\phi = \frac{\pi}{2}$$

(A.4.74)

Thus

$$\frac{1}{\pi} \int_{0}^{\infty} 2f(x) \frac{\sin R\phi}{\phi} \, d\phi = f(x)$$

(A.4.75)

It follows that

$$S_R(x) - f(x) = \frac{1}{\pi} \int_{0}^{\infty} g(\phi) \frac{\sin R\phi}{\phi} \, d\phi$$

(A.4.76)

where

$$g(\phi) = f(x + \phi) + f(x - \phi) - 2f(x)$$

(A.4.77)

We can write

$$\frac{1}{\pi} \int_{0}^{\infty} g(\phi) \frac{\sin R\phi}{\phi} \, d\phi = \frac{1}{\pi} \int_{0}^{\delta} g(\phi) \frac{\sin R\phi}{\phi} \, d\phi + \frac{1}{\pi} \int_{\delta}^{\infty} g(\phi) \frac{\sin R\phi}{\phi} \, d\phi$$

(A.4.78)

By the Riemann-Lebesgue lemma, the second integral in the right member of (A.4.78) will vanish as $R \to \infty$. The first integral there, however, is essentially the integral considered in the proof of Theorem 3. Thus we see that the *same conditions* on $f(\cdot)$ which will guarantee its representation by its Fourier series will also guarantee that

$$\lim_{R \to \infty} S_R(x) = f(x)$$

(A.4.79)

or that

$$f(x) = \frac{1}{2\pi} \int_{-\infty}^{\infty} F(t) \exp(-itx) \, dt$$

(A.4.80)

where $F(\cdot)$ is the Fourier transform of $f(\cdot)$.

Therefore we have shown that the following relations hold for an absolutely integrable function of bounded variation:

$$F(t) = \int_{-\infty}^{\infty} f(x) \exp(itx) \, dx \qquad f(x) = \frac{1}{2\pi} \int_{-\infty}^{\infty} F(t) \exp(-itx) \, dt$$

(A.4.81)

This is the so-called *Fourier transform pair*.

If $f(\cdot)$ is periodic of period 2π, we also have the discrete analog of (A.4.81):

$$F(t) = \int_{-\pi}^{\pi} f(x) \exp(itx)\, dx \qquad f(x) = \frac{1}{2\pi} \sum_{t=-\infty}^{\infty} F(t) \exp(-itx) \qquad \text{(A.4.82)}$$

Notice that the relation between the autocovariance functions and spectral (or cross-spectral) densities of Chapters 9 and 10 is of the form (A.4.82).

A.5 SYSTEMS OF DIFFERENCE EQUATIONS WITH CONSTANT COEFFICIENTS

The second-order difference equation

$$\alpha_0 y_t + \alpha_1 y_{t+1} + \alpha_2 y_{t+2} = g(t) \qquad \text{(A.5.1)}$$

with "forcing" function $g(\cdot)$ is solved as follows:
    We consider its homogeneous part

$$\alpha_0 y_t + \alpha_1 y_{t+1} + \alpha_2 y_{t+2} = 0 \qquad \text{(A.5.2)}$$

and try a solution of the form

$$y_t = x^t \qquad \text{(A.5.3)}$$

where x is to be determined.
    Substituting in (A.5.2) and cancelling the factor x^t, we obtain

$$\alpha_2 x^2 + \alpha_1 x + \alpha_0 = 0 \qquad \text{(A.5.4)}$$

This is called the *characteristic equation* [associated with the homogeneous part of the difference equation in (A.5.2)].
    Let x_1, x_2 be the roots of (A.5.4). Then the *general solution to the homogeneous part* is obtained as

$$y_t^H = C_1 x_1^t + C_2 x_2^t \qquad \text{(A.5.5)}$$

where the C_i, $i = 1, 2$, are arbitrary constants to be determined by *initial conditions*. If y_t^P is *any* solution to the equation in (A.5.1)—called the *particular solution*—then the general solution of the difference equation in (A.5.1) is determined as

$$y_t = y_t^H + y_t^P \qquad \text{(A.5.6)}$$

The equation in (A.5.1) is said to be *stable* if

$$|x_i| < 1 \qquad i = 1, 2 \qquad \text{(A.5.7)}$$

    The intuitive explanation of stability is that as t becomes large, the behavior of y_t depends less and less on initial conditions until it is ultimately determined solely by the forcing function. Notice that this implies

$$\lim_{t \to \infty} y_t^H = 0 \tag{A.5.8}$$

The reader is assumed to be familiar with the development above.

Now suppose that $y_t = (y_{t1}, y_{t2}, \ldots, y_{tm})'$ and suppose that we are confronted with the *system* of difference equations

$$A_0 y_t + A_1 y_{t+1} + \cdots + A_r y_{t+r} = g(t) \tag{A.5.9}$$

where the A_i, $i = 0, 1, 2, \ldots, r$ are *square* matrices of order m, and

$$g(t) = (g_1(t), g_2(t), \ldots g_m(t))' \tag{A.5.10}$$

is the *vector* of "forcing functions."

The reader will recall that (A.5.9) is the form of the standard (linear) dynamic structural econometric model. To solve this system, we proceed in exactly the same fashion as we did with the simple difference equation in (A.5.1). Thus consider the homogeneous part

$$A_0 y_t + A_1 y_{t+1} + A_2 y_{t+2} \cdots A_r y_{t+r} = 0 \tag{A.5.11}$$

and try a solution of the form

$$y_t = c\rho^t \tag{A.5.12}$$

where c is now a *vector* of m elements and ρ is a scalar.

Substituting in (A.5.11) and cancelling the factor ρ^t—since we are not interested in the trivial solution $y_t \equiv 0$—we find

$$(A_0 + A_1 \rho + A_2 \rho^2 + \cdots + A_r \rho^r)c = 0 \tag{A.5.13}$$

But this system of equations has a nontrivial solution in c if and only if the matrix in parentheses is singular.

Thus we must have

$$|A_0 + A_1 \rho + A_2 \rho^2 + \cdots + A_r \rho^r| = 0 \tag{A.5.14}$$

We note that (A.5.14) is a polynomial of degree mr at most. Indeed, if $|A_0| \neq 0$, $\rho = 0$ is not one of its roots.[5] Let such roots, for the moment, be distinct and be numbered by increasing magnitude. To each root ρ_i, $i = 1, 2, \ldots, mr$, there corresponds a solution $c_{\cdot i}$ of (A.5.13). It is then quickly verified that

$$y_t^i = c_{\cdot i} \rho_i^t \tag{A.5.15}$$

---

[5] The reader should note that $y_t \equiv 0$, referred to as the *trivial solution*, is *always* a solution to the homogeneous difference equation. We shall not be concerned with such solutions here.

is *a* solution to the system in (A.5.11). Thus, substituting in the latter the expression in (A.5.15), we find

$$(A_0 c_{.i} + A_1 c_{.i} \rho_i + A_2 c_{.i} \rho_i^2 + \cdots + A_r c_{.i} \rho_i^r)\rho_i^t = \phi(\rho_i, c_{.i}) \qquad \text{(A.5.16)}$$

Since $|\rho_i| \neq 0$, we notice that $\phi(\rho_i, c_{.i})$ will vanish *only* if the expression in parentheses vanishes. But the $c_{.i}$ and ρ_t are chosen so that they are *solutions* of (A.5.13). Thus, indeed, for any t we have identically

$$\phi(\rho_i, c_{.i}) = 0 \qquad \text{(A.5.17)}$$

which shows that y_t^i is *a* solution to the system.

We also notice that the $c_{.i}$ are arbitrary within multiplication by a scalar. Thus, having adopted some convention—for example, that the vectors $c_{.i}$ have unit length—we observe that the *general* solution to the homogeneous part can be written as

$$y_t^H = \sum_{i=1}^{mr} d_i c_{.i} \rho_i^t \qquad \text{(A.5.18)}$$

the d_i being arbitrary constants to be determined by initial conditions. As an example of how this may be done, suppose that we wish to determine the time path of the system with *initial conditions* $y_0, y_1, y_2, \ldots, y_{r-1}$. Thus we would have

$$y_0 = \sum_{i=1}^{mr} d_i c_{.i}$$

$$y_1 = \sum_{i=1}^{mr} d_i c_{.i} \rho_i$$

$$y_2 = \sum_{i=1}^{mr} d_i c_{.i} \rho_i^2$$

$$\vdots$$

$$y_{r-1} = \sum_{i=1}^{mr} d_i c_{.i} \rho_i^{r-1} \qquad \text{(A.5.19)}$$

Define a matrix C by

$$C = \begin{bmatrix} c_{.1} & c_{.2} & \cdots & c_{.mr} \\ c_{.1}\rho_1 & c_{.2}\rho_2 & \cdots & c_{.mr}\rho_{mr} \\ \vdots & \vdots & & \vdots \\ c_{.1}\rho_1^{r-1} & c_{.2}\rho_2^{r-1} & \cdots & c_{.mr}\rho_{mr}^{r-1} \end{bmatrix} \qquad \text{(A.5.20)}$$

Then the system in (A.5.19) can be written compactly as

$$y = Cd \qquad \text{(A.5.21)}$$

where

$$y = \begin{bmatrix} y_0 \\ y_1 \\ \vdots \\ y_{r-1} \end{bmatrix} \qquad d = (d_1, d_2, \ldots, d_{mr})' \qquad (A.5.22)$$

Then if C is nonsingular, d is *uniquely* determined in terms of the vector of initial conditions, y. If (A.5.14) has a root of multiplicity k, say ρ^*, and if the vector associated with ρ^* is c^*, then the solutions corresponding to ρ^* are $c^* \rho^{*t}$, $c^* t \rho^{*t}$, $\ldots$, $c^* t^{k-1} \rho^{*t}$. If now y_t^P is a *particular* solution to the (non-homogeneous) system in (A.5.9), then the *general* solution of that system is

$$y_t = y_t^H + y_t^P \qquad (A.5.23)$$

As before, stability of the system is defined as the *asymptotic vanishing of the general solution to the homogeneous part*; that is,

$$\lim_{t \to \infty} y_t^H = 0 \qquad (A.5.24)$$

irrespective of initial conditions.

This, of course, requires that

$$|\rho_i| < 1 \qquad i = 1, 2, \ldots, mr \qquad (A.5.25)$$

A.6 MATRIX ALGEBRA

It is assumed that the reader is thoroughly acquainted with the basic operations of matrix algebra. Here we shall merely provide a convenient collection of results cited without proof in our earlier discussions. The aim is not to be exhaustive relative to the topics covered but rather to aid the reader in following the development in Chapters 1 through 8.

PARTITIONED MATRICES

If A is $n \times n$, D is $m \times m$, B is $n \times m$, C is $m \times n$ and

$$E = \begin{bmatrix} A & B \\ C & D \end{bmatrix} \qquad (A.6.1)$$

then

$$|E| = |D| \, |A - BD^{-1}C| \qquad (A.6.2)$$

provided $|D| \neq 0$.

The proof of this is as follows: Consider

$$\begin{bmatrix} I & -BD^{-1} \\ 0 & I \end{bmatrix} \begin{bmatrix} A & B \\ C & D \end{bmatrix} = \begin{bmatrix} A - BD^{-1}C & 0 \\ C & D \end{bmatrix} \qquad (A.6.3)$$

Since the determinant of a triangular matrix is the product of its diagonal elements,[6] the validity of (A.6.2) follows immediately from (A.6.3). As an exercise, the reader may show that if $|A| \neq 0$, then we can also write

$$|E| = |A| \, |D - CA^{-1}B| \qquad \text{(A.6.4)}$$

If A is a nonsingular matrix of order n and α is $n \times 1$, then

$$|A + \alpha\alpha'| = |A|(1 + \alpha'A^{-1}\alpha) \qquad \text{(A.6.5)}$$

To prove (A.6.5), notice that, applying (A.6.4), we find

$$|A + \alpha\alpha'| = \begin{vmatrix} 1 & -\alpha' \\ \alpha & A \end{vmatrix} \qquad \text{(A.6.6)}$$

Then, by (A.6.2), we have

$$\begin{vmatrix} 1 & -\alpha' \\ \alpha & A \end{vmatrix} = |A|(1 + \alpha'A^{-1}\alpha) \qquad \text{(A.6.7)}$$

The validity of (A.6.5) is then obtained from (A.6.6) and (A.6.7).

PROPERTIES OF THE TRACE

We recall that if A is a *square* matrix of order n, then its *trace* is defined by

$$\text{tr } A = \sum_{i=1}^{n} a_{ii} \qquad \text{(A.6.8)}$$

If A is $m \times n$ and B is $n \times m$, then

$$\text{tr } (AB) = \text{tr } (BA)$$

The proof of this is as follows: $\qquad \text{(A.6.9)}$

$$\text{tr } (AB) = \sum_{i=1}^{m} \sum_{j=1}^{n} a_{ij} b_{ji} \qquad \text{(A.6.10)}$$

$$\text{tr } (BA) = \sum_{j=1}^{n} \sum_{i=1}^{m} b_{ji} a_{ij} \qquad \text{(A.6.11)}$$

The conclusion is evident from (A.6.10) and (A.6.11).

If A, B are two square matrices of order n, then

$$\text{tr } (A + B) = \text{tr } A + \text{tr } B. \qquad \text{(A.6.12)}$$

The proof of this is left as an exercise for the reader.

---

[6] Similarly, the determinant of a *block* triangular matrix, such as the one in the last member of (A.6.3), is the *product* of the determinants of its diagonal blocks.

CHARACTERISTIC ROOTS AND VECTORS

If A is a square matrix of order n, we recall that its characteristic roots and their associated characteristic vectors satisfy

$$Ax = \lambda x \tag{A.6.13}$$

where x is a *characteristic vector* and λ its associated *characteristic root*.

We see that (A.6.13) can also be written as

$$(\lambda I - A)x = 0 \tag{A.6.14}$$

For (A.6.14) to have a *nontrivial* solution in x, we must have

$$|\lambda I - A| = 0 \tag{A.6.15}$$

But this is a polynomial equation of degree n and as such it has n roots, say $\lambda_1, \lambda_2, \ldots, \lambda_n$. For each λ_i we can find a nonzero solution $x_{.i}$, to (A.6.14). It is clear that if $x_{.i}$ is a solution, then so is $cx_{.i}$ for any scalar $c \neq 0$. Thus the $x_{.i}$ are not unique. We may, however, make them unique by insisting on some convention, for example, that they obey

$$x'_{.i} x_{.i} = 1 \tag{A.6.16}$$

Thus characteristic roots and vectors satisfy

$$Ax_{.i} = \lambda_i x_{.i} \qquad i = 1, 2, \ldots, n \tag{A.6.17}$$

or

$$AX = X\Lambda \tag{A.6.18}$$

where

$$X = (x_{.1}, x_{.2}, \ldots, x_{.n}) \qquad \Lambda = \text{diag}(\lambda_1, \lambda_2, \ldots, \lambda_n) \tag{A.6.19}$$

It is interesting to note that *if* the λ_i are *distinct*, then the vectors $x_{.i}$ are linearly independent and thus the matrix X is *nonsingular*. To see this, we proceed as follows: Suppose that there exist constants c_i, $i = 1, 2, \ldots, n$, such that

$$\sum_{i=1}^{n} c_i x_{.i} = 0 \tag{A.6.20}$$

We shall show that (A.6.20) implies

$$c_i = 0 \qquad i = 1, 2, \ldots, n \tag{A.6.21}$$

which will demonstrate the linear independence of the $x_{.i}$.

Multiply both sides of (A.6.20) by $(\lambda_1 I - A)$ to obtain

$$\sum_{i=1}^{n} c_i(\lambda_1 I - A)x_{.i} = \sum_{i=2}^{n} c_i(\lambda_1 - \lambda_i)x_{.i} = 0 \tag{A.6.22}$$

since the λ_i and $x._i$ obey (A.6.17). Apply $(\lambda_2 I - A)$ to (A.6.22) to obtain

$$\sum_{i=2}^{n} c_i(\lambda_1 - \lambda_i)(\lambda_2 I - A)x._i = \sum_{i=3}^{n} c_i(\lambda_1 - \lambda_i)(\lambda_2 - \lambda_i)x._i = 0 \qquad \text{(A.6.23)}$$

Proceed in this fashion, applying sequentially $(\lambda_3 I - A), \ldots, (\lambda_{n-1}I - A)$ to obtain

$$c_n(\lambda_1 - \lambda_n)(\lambda_2 - \lambda_n) \ldots (\lambda_{n-1} - \lambda_n)x._n = 0 \qquad \text{(A.6.24)}$$

Because the roots are distinct and $x._n$ is nonnull, we conclude from (A.6.24) that

$$c_n = 0 \qquad \text{(A.6.25)}$$

Since we could have omitted any factor, and not merely $(\lambda_n I - A)$, we conclude

$$c_i = 0 \qquad i = 1, 2, \ldots, n \qquad \text{(A.6.26)}$$

A consequence of the above is that A can also be represented as

$$A = X\Lambda X^{-1} \qquad \text{(A.6.27)}$$

Notice that a *sufficient* condition for the representation in (A.6.27) is *that the roots be distinct*; however, this is not a *necessary* condition. On the other hand, *the reader should bear in mind that not every square matrix can be represented as in* (A.6.27).

A further consequence of (A.6.27) is that when A can be so represented, its determinant is the product of its roots and the sum of its roots is equal to its trace. As an exercise, the reader should prove these assertions. It should also be noted that even if the roots of a (square) matrix are not distinct, it is still true that the product of the roots is equal to its determinant and the sum of the roots is equal to its trace. The proof of this more general assertion is rather cumbersome and will not be given here.

An interesting and useful result is the following: Let A, B be, respectively, $m \times n$, $n \times m$ matrices, and suppose that $m < n$. Then the roots of AB (an $m \times m$ matrix) are a subset of the roots of BA (an $n \times n$ matrix).

We proceed somewhat heuristically. Consider the matrix

$$C = \begin{bmatrix} I & -\dfrac{1}{\lambda} A \\ -B & I \end{bmatrix} \qquad \text{(A.6.28)}$$

and observe that the characteristic equation of AB is of the form

$$\lambda^m |C| = 0 \qquad \text{(A.6.29)}$$

To see this, consider

$$\begin{bmatrix} \lambda I & A \\ 0 & I \end{bmatrix} \begin{bmatrix} I & -\dfrac{1}{\lambda} A \\ -B & I \end{bmatrix} = \begin{bmatrix} \lambda I - AB & 0 \\ -B & I \end{bmatrix} \qquad \text{(A.6.30)}$$

The determinant of the left member of (A.6.30) is the left member of (A.6.29), while the determinant of the right member set to zero yields

$$\lambda^m|C| = |\lambda I - AB| = 0 \tag{A.6.31}$$

which is the characteristic equation of the matrix AB.

Now consider the relation

$$\begin{bmatrix} I & -\dfrac{1}{\lambda}A \\ -B & I \end{bmatrix} \begin{bmatrix} I & A \\ 0 & \lambda I \end{bmatrix} = \begin{bmatrix} I & 0 \\ -B & \lambda I - BA \end{bmatrix} \tag{A.6.32}$$

Taking determinants and equating to zero, we find

$$\lambda^n|C| = |\lambda I - BA| = 0 \tag{A.6.33}$$

Comparing (A.6.31) and (A.6.33), we see that the roots AB and BA differ only to the extent of the *multiplicity* of their zero root. Their nonzero roots, however, are identical. Thus observe that (A.6.31) and (A.6.33) imply

$$\lambda^{n-m}|\lambda I - AB| = |\lambda I - BA| = 0 \tag{A.6.34}$$

ORTHOGONAL, SYMMETRIC, IDEMPOTENT, AND DEFINITE MATRICES

In this section se shall be somewhat more formal than previously.

Definition 15: Let $x_{.i}$, $x_{.j}$ be two n-dimensional vectors. If

$$x'_{.i}x_{.j} = 0 \tag{A.6.35}$$

the vectors are said to be (mutually) orthogonal. If, in addition to (A.6.35),

$$x'_{.i}x_{.i} = x'_{.j}x_{.j} = 1 \tag{A.6.36}$$

the vectors are said to be *orthonormal*.

Definition 16: Let X be the matrix

$$X = (x_{.1}, x_{.2}, \ldots, x_{.n}) \tag{A.6.37}$$

the $x_{.i}$, $i = 1, 2, \ldots n$ being orthonormal vectors. Then X is said to be an *orthogonal* matrix.

Proposition 9: Every orthogonal matrix X is nonsingular and, moreover,

$$X^{-1} = X' \tag{A.6.38}$$

PROOF: Let X be defined as in (A.6.37). Then

$$X'X = (x'_{.i}x_{.j}) \qquad i, j = 1, 2, \ldots, n \tag{A.6.39}$$

Now, since the vectors $x._i$ are orthonormal, the typical (i, j) element of $X'X$ obeys

$$x'._i x._j = 1 \quad \text{if } i = j$$
$$= 0 \quad \text{otherwise} \tag{A.6.40}$$

Hence

$$X'X = I \tag{A.6.41}$$

which shows that X' is the *inverse* of X.   Q.E.D.

    Another useful result is the following

Proposition 10: Let $x._1$ be an n-element vector such that

$$x'._1 x._1 = 1 \tag{A.6.42}$$

Then there exists an *orthogonal* matrix X having $x._1$ as one of its columns.

    PROOF: Let $x._2, x._3, \ldots, x._n$ be *any* set of vectors that, together with $x._1$, constitute a linearly independent set. Then define

$$x^*._2 = x._2 - \frac{x^*._1 (x^{*\prime}._1 x._2)}{x^{*\prime}._1 x^*._1} \tag{A.6.43}$$

where we have put

$$x^*._1 = x._1 \tag{A.6.44}$$

We observe that

$$x^{*\prime}._1 x^*._2 = x^{*\prime}._1 x._2 - x^{*\prime}._1 x._2 = 0 \tag{A.6.45}$$

Generally define

$$x^*._j = x._j - \sum_{i=1}^{j-1} \left[\frac{x^*._i (x^{*\prime}._i x._j)}{x^{*\prime}._i x^*._i} \right] \quad j = 2, 3, \ldots, n \tag{A.6.46}$$

and observe that the set $\{x^*._1, x^*._2, \ldots, x^*._n\}$ constitutes a set of mutually orthogonal vectors. (As an exercise, the reader should obtain the length of these vectors and verify that the starred vectors constitute a linearly independent set.)

    If we normalize the vectors so that

$$x^{*\prime}._i x^*._i = 1 \quad i = 1, 2, \ldots, n \tag{A.6.47}$$

then

$$X = (x^*._1, x^*._2, \ldots, x^*._n) \tag{A.6.48}$$

is the desired matrix.

    Remark 8: The procedure given in (A.6.46) for constructing the orthogonal vectors is known as *Gram-Schmidt orthogonalization*.

Definition 17: If A is a square matrix of order n

$$A = (a_{ij}) \qquad\qquad\qquad \text{(A.6.49)}$$

such that

$$a_{ij} = a_{ji} \qquad\qquad\qquad \text{(A.6.50)}$$

then A is said to be a symmetric matrix.

If A is symmetric, it is apparent from the definition that A is *equal* to its transpose, that is,

$$A = A' \qquad\qquad\qquad \text{(A.6.51)}$$

The following are two useful properties of symmetric matrices.

Proposition 11: Let A be a symmetric matrix of order n and suppose that its characteristic roots are distinct. Then the matrix of their associated characteristic vectors is orthogonal.

PROOF: Let λ_i, λ_j be any two roots and $x_{.i}$, $x_{.j}$ their associated (normalized) characteristic vectors. Note that

$$Ax_{.i} = \lambda_i x_{.i} \qquad Ax_{.j} = \lambda_j x_{.j} \qquad\qquad \text{(A.6.52)}$$

Premultiply the first equation by $x'_{.j}$ and the second by $x'_{.i}$ to obtain

$$x'_{.j} Ax_{.i} = \lambda_i x'_{.j} x_{.i} \qquad x'_{.i} Ax_{.j} = \lambda_j x'_{.i} x_{.j} \qquad\qquad \text{(A.6.53)}$$

Since A is symmetric, we have

$$x'_{.j} Ax_{.i} = x'_{.i} Ax_{.j} \qquad\qquad\qquad \text{(A.6.54)}$$

But (A.6.53) and (A.6.54) imply

$$(\lambda_i - \lambda_j)x'_{.i} x_{.j} = 0 \qquad\qquad\qquad \text{(A.6.55)}$$

Since $\lambda_i \neq \lambda_j$, we conclude

$$x'_{.i} x_{.j} = 0 \qquad i \neq j \qquad\qquad \text{(A.6.56)}$$

The vectors are normalized, that is,

$$x'_{.i} x_{.i} = 1 \qquad\qquad\qquad \text{(A.6.57)}$$

Thus the matrix

$$X = (x_{.1}, x_{.2}, \ldots, x_{.n}) \qquad\qquad\qquad \text{(A.6.58)}$$

is orthogonal.   Q.E.D.

The matrix of characteristic vectors of a real symmetric matrix could still be chosen orthogonal, even if the roots are not distinct. The proof of this assertion is, however, too complicated to produce here.

Proposition 12: Let A be a symmetric matrix of order n; then its characteristic roots are real.

PROOF: Let λ be any characteristic root and x its associated (normalized) characteristic vector. Write λ, x in complex form

$$\lambda = \alpha + i\beta \qquad x = u + iv \tag{A.6.59}$$

We shall show that $\beta = 0$, thus establishing that λ is real. Now since x is normalized,

$$x'\bar{x} = u'u + v'v = 1 \tag{A.6.60}$$

We also have

$$Ax = Au + iAv = (\alpha u - \beta v) + i(\alpha v + \beta u) \tag{A.6.61}$$

which implies

$$Au = \alpha u - \beta v$$
$$Av = \alpha v + \beta u \tag{A.6.62}$$

Premultiply the first equation by v', the second by u', and subtract to obtain

$$u'Av - v'Au = \beta(u'u + v'v) \tag{A.6.63}$$

Since A is symmetric, the left member of (A.6.63) vanishes. In view of (A.6.60), we conclude

$$\beta = 0 \qquad\qquad\qquad\qquad \text{Q.E.D.} \tag{A.6.64}$$

Definition 18: If A is a square matrix of order n such that

$$AA = A \tag{A.6.65}$$

then A is said to be an *idempotent* matrix.

We have

Proposition 13: Let A be an indempotent matrix of order n. Then its characteristic roots are either zero or one; moreover,

$$\text{rank } (A) = \text{tr } A \tag{A.6.66}$$

PROOF: Let λ be any root and x is associated characteristic vector. Then we have the relation

$$Ax = \lambda x \tag{A.6.67}$$

Premultiply both sides by A to obtain

$$AAx = \lambda Ax = \lambda^2 x \tag{A.6.68}$$

Since A is idempotent,

$$AAx = Ax \tag{A.6.69}$$

Thus the above implies

$$(\lambda^2 - \lambda)x = 0 \tag{A.6.70}$$

Since x is a nonnull vector, we conclude from (A.6.60) that

$$\lambda^2 = \lambda \tag{A.6.71}$$

which implies that

$$\lambda = 1 \quad \text{or} \quad \lambda = 0 \tag{A.6.72}$$

Thus

$$\text{tr } A = \text{sum of its roots} = \text{number of its nonzero roots} \tag{A.6.73}$$

But the rank of a matrix is the number of its nonzero roots. In view of (A.6.73), we conclude

$$\text{rank } (A) = \text{tr } A \qquad\qquad \text{Q.E.D.} \tag{A.6.74}$$

Definition 19: Let A be a real symmetric matrix of order n. Then A is said to be *positive semidefinite* if

$$x'Ax \geq 0 \tag{A.6.75}$$

for *any* (real) vector x. If for *nonnull x*

$$x'Ax > 0 \tag{A.6.76}$$

then A is said to be *positive definite*.

Definition 20: A real symmetric matrix A is said to be negative (semi-) definite if $-A$ is positive (semi-) definite.

As a result of these definitions, we need only deal with positive (semi-) definite matrices. The following are immediate consequences of Definition 19.

Proposition 14: If A is a positive definite matrix, then

$$a_{ii} > 0 \qquad i = 1, 2, \ldots, n \tag{A.6.77}$$

If A is positive semidefinite (but *not* positive definite), then

$$a_{ii} \geq 0 \qquad i = 1, 2, \ldots, n \tag{A.6.78}$$

PROOF: Let x be the vector

$$x = (0, 0, \ldots, 1, 0, \ldots, 0)' \tag{A.6.79}$$

that is, all its elements are zero save the ith, which is unity. Then

$$x'Ax = a_{ii} \tag{A.6.80}$$

The conclusions of the proposition then follow from (A.6.76) and (A.6.75).

An interesting property of definite matrices is as follows.

Proposition 15: Let A be a positive definite matrix of order n. Then there exists a lower triangular matrix T such that

$$A = TT' \tag{A.6.81}$$

PROOF: Let

$$T = \begin{bmatrix} t_{11} & 0 & 0 & \cdots & 0 \\ t_{21} & t_{22} & 0 & \cdots & 0 \\ \vdots & & & & \vdots \\ t_{n1} & & & & t_{nn} \end{bmatrix} \tag{A.6.82}$$

For T to exist, we should be able to solve the equations implied by equation (A.6.81). These, in turn, are

$$t_{11}^2 = a_{11}, t_{11}t_{21} = a_{22}, t_{11}t_{31} = a_{13} \cdots t_{11}t_{n1} = a_{1n}$$

$$t_{21}t_{11} = a_{21}, t_{21}^2 + t_{22}^2 = a_{22}, t_{21}t_{31} + t_{22}t_{32} = a_{23} \cdots t_{21}t_{n1} + t_{22}t_{n2} = a_{2n}$$

$$\vdots$$

$$t_{n1}t_{11} = a_{n1}, t_{n1}t_{21} + t_{n2}t_{22} = a_{n2} \cdots \sum_{i=1}^{n} t_{ni}^2 = a_{nn} \tag{A.6.83}$$

This is seen to be a recursive set of equations. Proceeding line by line, we notice that the first line yields

$$_{11} = \pm\sqrt{a_{11}} \quad t_{i1} = \frac{a_{1i}}{t_{11}} \quad i = 2, \ldots, n \tag{A.6.84}$$

Similarly, from the second line we obtain

$$t_{21} = \frac{a_{21}}{t_{11}} \quad t_{22} = \pm\sqrt{a_{22} - t_{21}^2} \quad t_{i2} = \frac{a_{21} - t_{21}t_{i1}}{t_{22}} \quad i = 3, \ldots, n \tag{A.6.85}$$

and so on.

Thus the matrix T is definable in terms of the elements of A.   Q.E.D.

Remark 9: As a test of his understanding of the argument in the proof, the reader should obtain a formula for the (i, j) element of T, in terms of the of the elements of A. He should also verify that the matrix T, of (A.6.81), could be chosen as *upper triangular*.

Remark 10: The matrix T is obviously nonunique. Indeed, from (A.6.84) and (A.6.85) we see that we have two choices for the *diagonal* elements t_{11},

t_{22}. If the argument of the proof is further developed, the same will be noticed for *all* the diagonal elements. If we specify, however, that *all* diagonal elements of T be *positive*, then T is unique.

Proposition 16: Let A be a positive definite (semidefinite) matrix of order n. Then the roots of A are positive (nonnegative).

PROOF: Let A be positive (semi-) definite and λ be *any* root. Let x be its associated normalized characteristic vector. Then

$$x'Ax = \lambda x'x = \lambda \tag{A.6.86}$$

If A is positive definite, we conclude

$$\lambda > 0 \tag{A.6.87}$$

If A is positive semidefinite, we conclude

$$\lambda \geq 0 \qquad\qquad\qquad\qquad \text{Q.E.D.} \tag{A.6.88}$$

Corollary 2: If A is positive definite, then A is *nonsingular*. If A is positive semidefinite (but *not* positive definite), then A is singular.

The proof of this is left as an exercise for the reader.

Corollary 3: If A is a positive definite matrix, then there exists a nonsingular matrix W such that

$$A = WW' \tag{A.6.89}$$

PROOF: From Proposition 15 there exists a triangular matrix T, obeying (A.6.81) and thus satisfying (A.6.89). In addition, let Γ be an *orthogonal* matrix, and consider

$$W = T\Gamma \tag{A.6.90}$$

Thus

$$WW' = T\Gamma\Gamma'T' = TT' = A \tag{A.6.91}$$

Corollary 4: Let A be a positive definite matrix of order n and let

$$\Lambda = \text{diag}\,(\lambda_1, \lambda_2, \ldots, \lambda_n) \tag{A.6.92}$$

be the matrix of its characteristic roots. Then there exists a nonsingular matrix W such that

$$A = W\Lambda W' \tag{A.6.93}$$

PROOF: Let

$$D = \text{diag}\,(\lambda_1^{-\frac{1}{2}}, \lambda_2^{-\frac{1}{2}}, \ldots, \lambda_n^{-\frac{1}{2}}) \tag{A.6.94}$$

This exists because the λ_i are all positive. Let T be the triangular matrix of Proposition 15 and define

$$W = TD \tag{A.6.95}$$

Then

$$A = TT' = TD\Lambda DT' = W\Lambda W' \tag{A.6.96}$$

Q.E.D.

Remark 11: Notice that the matrix W of Corollary 3 and that of Corollary 4 is *not* unique.

The results above relate to the *decomposition* of a positive definite matrix. Occasionally we may wish to decompose *simultaneously* two matrices. To this effect, we have

Definition 21: Let A, B be two matrices of order n. The roots of the equation

$$|\lambda A - B| = 0 \tag{A.6.97}$$

are said to be the *characteristic roots of B in the metric of A*.

Remark 12: It is seen that the characteristic roots of a matrix as defined in, say, equation (A.6.15) form a special case in which the roots are taken in the *metric of the identity matrix.*

We have the following useful

Proposition 17: Let A be positive definite and B be positive semidefinite. Then the roots of B in the metric of A are nonnegative. If B is also positive definite, then such roots are positive.

PROOF: Consider the equation

$$|\lambda A - B| = 0 \tag{A.6.98}$$

Since A is positive definite, there exists a nonsingular matrix W such that

$$A = WW' \tag{A.6.99}$$

Thus (A.6.98) can be written as

$$0 = |\lambda A - B| = |\lambda WW' - B| = |W|^2 |\lambda I - W^{-1}BW'^{-1}| \tag{A.6.100}$$

Since W is nonsingular, we see that the roots of (A.6.98) are exactly those of

$$|\lambda I - W^{-1}BW'^{-1}| = 0 \tag{A.6.101}$$

We shall now show that if B is positive (semi-) definite, then so is $W^{-1}BW'^{-1}$, thus concluding the proof. Let x be any vector and consider

$$y = W'^{-1}x \tag{A.6.102}$$

Since W is nonsingular, x is the null vector if and only if y is the null vector. We have

$$x'W^{-1}BW'^{-1}x = y'By \qquad \text{(A.6.103)}$$

which establishes that if B is positive (semi-) definite, then so is $W^{-1}BW'^{-1}$. The conclusion of this proposition is then obvious from Proposition 16.

Corollary 5: Let A be positive definite and B positive (semi-) definite. Then there exists a nonsingular matrix W^* such that

$$A = W^*W^{*\prime} \qquad B = W^*\Lambda W^{*\prime} \qquad \text{(A.6.104)}$$

where

$$\Lambda = \text{diag}\,(\lambda_1, \lambda_2, \ldots, \lambda_n) \qquad \text{(A.6.105)}$$

and the λ_i are the roots of B in the metric of A.

PROOF: Using equation (A.6.100), let $x_{\cdot i}$ be the characteristic vector associated with the root λ_i, and define the (orthogonal) matrix

$$X = (x_{\cdot 1}, x_{\cdot 2}, \ldots, x_{\cdot n}) \qquad \text{(A.6.106)}$$

We may then write

$$W^{-1}BW'^{-1}X = X\Lambda \qquad \text{(A.6.107)}$$

Postmultiply by X' $(=X^{-1})$ to obtain

$$W^{-1}BW'^{-1} = X\Lambda X' \qquad \text{(A.6.108)}$$

which implies

$$B = WX\Lambda X'W' \qquad \text{(A.6.109)}$$

Defining

$$W^* = WX \qquad \text{(A.6.110)}$$

we see that W^* obeys

$$A = W^*W^{*\prime} \qquad B = W^*\Lambda W^{*\prime} \qquad \qquad \text{Q.E.D.} \\ \text{(A.6.111)}$$

Frequently we deal with differences of positive definite (or semidefinite) matrices. The following propositions are useful in this connection.

Proposition 18: Let A be positive definite and B positive definite (or semidefinite). Then $A - B$ is positive definite if and only if the roots of B in the metric of A, λ_i, $i = 1, 2, \ldots, n$ obey

$$\lambda_i < 1 \qquad \text{(A.6.112)}$$

and is semidefinite if the roots obey

$$\lambda_i \leq 1 \tag{A.6.113}$$

PROOF: By the previous corollary, we may write

$$A - B = WW' - W\Lambda W' \tag{A.6.114}$$

where W is nonsingular and Λ is the diagonal matrix containing the roots of B in the metric of A.

Let x be given by

$$x = W'^{-1}y \tag{A.6.115}$$

and observe

$$x'(A - B)x = y'(I - \Lambda)y = \sum_{i=1}^{n} (1 - \lambda_i)y_i^2 \tag{A.6.116}$$

Since W is nonsingular, we can certainly choose x so that all elements of y are zero, save the kth, which is unity. Hence if $A - B$ is positive definite, (A.6.116) shows that

$$\lambda_k < 1 \tag{A.6.117}$$

for any k. On the other hand, if (A.6.117) holds, then (A.6.116) shows that $A - B$ is positive definite.

If the weaker condition (A.6.113) is examined, similar arguments will show that $A - B$ is positive semidefinite. We leave the details as an exercise for the reader.

Corollary 6: Let A, B be positive definite matrices. If $A - B$ is positive definite, then so is $B^{-1} - A^{-1}$.

PROOF: Consider again the simultaneous decomposition

$$WW' = A \qquad W\Lambda W' = B \tag{A.6.118}$$

as above. Then

$$B^{-1} - A^{-1} = B^{-1}(A - B)A^{-1} = W'^{-1}\Lambda^{-1}W^{-1}(WW' - W\Lambda W')W'^{-1}W^{-1}$$
$$= W'^{-1}(\Lambda^{-1} - I)W^{-1} \tag{A.6.119}$$

Let x be any vector such that

$$y = W^{-1}x \tag{A.6.120}$$

Then

$$x'(B^{-1} - A^{-1})x = y'(\Lambda^{-1} - I)y = \sum_{i=1}^{n} \left(\frac{1}{\lambda_i} - 1\right)y_i^2 \tag{A.6.121}$$

Since $A - B$ is positive definite, the proposition just proved implies

$$\frac{1}{\lambda_i} > 1 \qquad i = 1, 2, \ldots, n \tag{A.6.122}$$

which concludes the proof of the corollary.

Corollary 7: If $A - B$ is positive definite, then

$$|A| > |B| \tag{A.6.123}$$

If $A - B$ is positive semidefinite, then

$$|A| \geq |B| \tag{A.6.124}$$

PROOF: Consider again the decomposition in (A.6.118). Taking determinants, we find

$$|A| = |W|^2 \qquad |B| = |W|^2 |\Lambda| \tag{A.6.125}$$

If $A - B$ is positive definite, then equation (A.6.117) is valid, so that

$$|\Lambda| < 1 \tag{A.6.126}$$

which implies

$$|A| > |B| \tag{A.6.127}$$

On the other hand, if $A - B$ is positive semidefinite, then equation (A.6.113) is valid, which implies

$$|\Lambda| \leq 1 \tag{A.6.128}$$

so that now we can only assert

$$|A| \geq |B| \qquad \text{Q.E.D.} \tag{A.6.129}$$

Remark 13: We should caution the reader that the converse of Corollary 7 is false, as he may convince himself by means of a counterexample.

INDEX

Expectation (mean) (*Continued*)
  of random vector, 2; estimation of, 25–27
Explanatory variables, 145
External finance, dividend, and investment policies of firms, simultaneous estimation of, 236–240

Factor analysis, 77–82
Factor loadings, 78
Factors, 78
Feasible Aitken estimators, 152
Filters, 445–450
  and cross spectra, 471–474
  effect on spectra, 450–456
FIML (full information maximum likelihood) estimation, 316–328
  relation to 3SLS, 367–372
Final form (of general structural model), 509
  autoregressive, 519 n.
  dynamic multipliers and, 521–525
  operator representation of, 517–521
  spectral properties of, 525–533
Fisher-Neyman criterion, 131–133
Forcing function, 567
Fourier coefficients, 557–558
Fourier series, 557–567
Fourier transform pair, 566
Fourier transforms, 565–566
  in cross-spectral analysis, 448–450
  in study of covariance stationary processes, 403–404
Fourier-Stiltjes integral, 405–406
Frequency, angular, 447
  Nyquist, 486
  true (fundamental), 447
Frequency domain, representation of random variable in, 383
Frequency response function, 449
Full information estimators, relationships among, 367–372
Full information maximum likelihood (FIML) estimation, 316–328
Function(s), absolutely continuous, 555
  of bounded variation, 553–556
  of complex variable, 549–550
  even, 385 n., 557
  monotonic, 552–553
  odd, 385 n., 557
  periodic, 557
  square integrable, 431 n.
  total variation, 555–556
Fundamental frequency, of sinusoid, 447

Gain, *see* Transfer function
General *k*-class estimator, 200–208

General linear (regression) models, efficient estimation of, 234–236
  measure of goodness of fit in, 240–244
  parameter estimation in, 153–161
Generalized variance, 56–57
Goodness of fit, measures of, in econometric systems, 261–263
  in general linear model, 240–244
  in multiple equations systems, 244–261
  in reduced form model, 246–263
Gram-Schmidt orthogonalization, 575

h-class estimator, 201–202
Harmonics, 447
  See also Sinusoids
Harmonic analysis, 422, 424 n.
  See also Periodogram
Helly-Bray lemma, 93
Hermitian matrices, 459–460

Idempotent matrices, 150 n., 577–578
Identifiability, of structural parameters, 280–295
Identities, in structural system, 171
Identity operator, 509
ILS (indirect least squares) estimators, 279–289
  relation to double *k*-class estimators, 364–365
Imaginary part, of complex number, 546
Impact (instantaneous) multipliers, matrix of, 508, 518
Inconsistency, 176
  of periodogram, 422–430
  specification, 277–278
Independence, mutual (statistical), 9
  test for, 18
Independent increments, of stochastic processes, 404
Indirect least squares (ILS) estimators, 279–289
  relation to double *k*-class estimators, 364–365
Instantaneous (impact) multipliers, matrix of, 508, 518
Instrument (instrumental variable), 296–299
Instrumental variables (I.V.) estimation, 296–303
  relation to double *k*-class estimation, 364–365
Investment, dividend, and external finance policies of firms, simultaneous estimation of, 236–240
Investment model, as example of efficient estimation, 234–236
I.V. (instrumental variables) estimation, 296–303

I.V. (*Continued*)
relation to double *k*-class estimation, 364–365

Jacobian, of transformation, 10
Joint density function, 6
Joint (cumulative) distribution, 5–6
Jointly covariance stationary stochastic processes, 457–459
Jointly dependent (endogenous) variables, 169, 172
Just identification, and relations among limited information estimators, 365–366
Just identified equations, 188, 287

k-class estimator, double, 202
general, 200–208
Kernel, of filter, 446, 509
of stochastic process, *see* Covariance kernel; Cross-covariance kernel
Keynesian model of economy, as example of S.E. systems estimation, 167–176
as example of asymptotic distribution of 2SLS, 193–200
Khinchine's lemma, 101
Koopman-Pittman lemma, 131
Kronecker product, 155

Lag operators, 509–515
Lag window generators, 432
Lagged endogenous variables, 171–172
effect on dynamic behavior of system, 507–509
Large numbers, law of, 100–103
Leakage (distortion of spectral estimator), 490–492
Least squares bias, 176
Least variance ratio estimator, *see* Limited information maximum likelihood (LIML) estimation
Liapunov condition, 104–106
Likelihood function, 115–116
concentrated, 324–325
use in obtaining estimators, 25–27
Likelihood ratio, 34
Limited information estimators, relations among, 365–366
Limited information maximum likelihood (LIML) estimation, 316–324, 328–356
Lindeberg-Feller theorem, 106
Linear set, 383
Linear time invariant filter, 446

Markov theorem, 147–148
Marginal density, 6–7
Marginal expectation, 8

Marginal mean, 8
Markov process, first-order, as output of filter, 453–456
Matrices, covariance, 2; estimators of, 25–27
definite, 578–584
of dynamic multipliers, 522; Hermitian, 459–460
idempotent, 577–578
of impact (instantaneous) multipliers, 508
Kronecker product of, 155
with operator elements, 515–517
orthogonal, 27 n., 574–575
partitioned, 570–571
positive, 578–584
random, 2
of reduced-form coefficients, 508
of regression coefficients, 22 n.
spectral, 463; of final form, 525–533
Matrix algebra, 570–584
Maximum likelihood (ML) estimators, 84–90, 114–130
and sufficiency, 133–136
Maximum likelihood methods, 25–27, 314–356
Mean, *see* Expectation
Mean function, of complex stochastic process, 398
of stochastic process, 383
Mean vector, estimator of, 25–27
Meat consumption and meat prices, canonical correlation theory applied to, 51–52
Metric, 120 n.
Metric space, 120 n.
Minimax solution, 72 n.
Minimum variance (MV) estimators, 128
Minimum variance bound (MVB) estimators, 127
Minkowski inequality, 97
ML (maximum likelihood) estimators, 84–90, 114–130
and sufficiency, 133–136
Modified cross periodogram, 474–476
Modulus, of complex number, 546
Moment-generating function, 95
Monotonic functions, 552–553
Monte Carlo methods, 372–380
Moving average processes, 393–394
Multiple correlation coefficient, 21–23
Multiple equations systems, measures of goodness of fit in, 244–261
parameter estimation in, 153–161
See also Simultaneous equations systems
Multiple regression, coefficient of determination of, 240
Multiplication, of complex numbers, 547

Stochastic production function, 224
Strong convergence, 93
Strong law of large numbers, 102–103
Structural systems of equations, 171, 173–174
    maximum likelihood methods of estimating, 314–356
      See also Econometric systems
Subtraction, of complex numbers, 547
Sufficiency (sufficient statistics), 130–136
    and maximum likelihood estimation, 133–136
    and minimum variance estimation, 136–142
Supply and demand model, identification of structural parameters in, 289–295
Symmetric matrices, 576–577

Technical (institutional) equations, in structural system, 171
Three-stage least squares (3SLS) estimation, 209–219
    example of, 238–240
    relation to FIML estimation, 367–372
Time domain, analysis in, 382
Time series, 383
    inference in, 386–390
    related, cross-spectral analysis of, 444–483
      See also Stochastic processes
Total variation function, 555–556
Trace, of matrix, 571
Trace correlation, 263
Traffic data, spectral analysis of, 436–442
Transfer function, 449
Transformation, Jacobian of, 10
True (fundamental) frequency, of sinusoid, 447
Tukey-Hanning spectral window, 492
Two-stage least squares (2SLS) estimation, 167–200
    asymptotic tests of significance for, 272–277
    relation to k-class estimation, 359–364

Unbiased estimator, 87
    of spectral density, 431–432
Uncertainty principles (UP), 501

Underidentified equations, 189, 287
Unemployment series, analysis in frequency domain, 408
" Units " transformation, in canonical correlation theory, 49–50
    in principal component theory, 58–59
Univariate central limit theorem, 103–107
Univariate normal distribution, estimator of parameters of, 85

Variability, 57
Variables, canonical, 43–44; estimation of, 50–52
    current endogenous, 172–174
    dependent, 145
    endogenous (jointly dependent), 169
    exogenous, 169
    explanatory, 145
    lagged endogenous, 171
    predetermined, 172
    random, *see* Random variables
    standardized, 103
Variance, 9
    of complex random variable, 397
    generalized, 56–57
    of spectral window, 497
Vector, orthogonal, 574
    orthonormal, 54
    of principal components, 56
    of regression coefficients, 22 n.
Vector representation, of complex number, 547–548
Vector random variables, correlations between, *see* Canonical correlations
    in econometric models, 1–2

Weak convergence, 93
Weak law of large numbers, 100–102
Weight (lag window generator), 432
Wharton School econometric model, 264
    variables in, 260 n.
Wicksell function, *see* Cobb-Douglas function
Window generators, 432
Windows, spectral, *see* Spectral windows
Wishart distribution, 31–34